OIL! TITAN
OF THE SOUTHWEST

OIL! TITAN
OF THE SOUTHWEST

By CARL COKE RISTER

NORMAN
UNIVERSITY OF OKLAHOMA PRESS
1949

By CARL COKE RISTER
Published by the University of Oklahoma Press
Norman, Oklahoma

Southern Plainsmen, 1938
Border Captives, 1940
Land Hunger, 1942
Border Command, 1944
Robert E. Lee in Texas, 1946
No Man's Land, 1948
Oil! Titan of the Southwest, 1949

and

The Southwestern Frontier, 1865–1881
    Cleveland, 1928
The Greater Southwest
    (with R. N. Richardson)
    Glendale, 1934
Western America
    (with LeRoy R. Hafen)
    New York, 1941

To the early-day oilman
America's greatest industrial pioneer

Foreword

THE OIL INDUSTRY approaches maturity. It has begun recently to show increased interest in its early history. One of the first fine fruits of this interest is Professor Rister's *Oil! Titan of the Southwest,* a study made possible by the disinterested generosity of Standard Oil Company (New Jersey), the co-operation of the University of Oklahoma, and a lot of hard work by Professor Rister.

We are accustomed to reckon the beginning of our domestic industry from the completion of the Drake well, Oil Creek, Pennsylvania, in August, 1859. We date the modern industry, likewise, from the completion of the Lucas gusher, Spindletop, Texas, January, 1901. Qualitatively the early period was important. It was during this period that the pattern of the industry was set. It was during this period that its technology began to be developed. It was during this period particularly and for a long time afterward that the industry struggled with a constantly recurring rhythm of over- and underproduction—that it lived in feast or famine. Quantitatively the early period—the lamp and lubricating oil period—was almost insignificant. The Drake well, 69.5 feet deep, pumped ten to twenty barrels daily. It was a whole year after its completion before the first flowing well was discovered. Total production in the United States for the first forty-one years of production amounted to approximately one billion barrels of oil, almost all of which came from the Eastern fields. The state of Texas alone produced almost as much and the nation produced twice as much oil during the past year. The United States has produced thirty-six billion barrels of oil since the completion of the Lucas gusher.

During the year which closed as Spindletop was discovered, our national production had averaged approximately 175,000 barrels daily. Almost half of this oil, 48.2 per cent, or 84,000 barrels daily, had come from the Appalachian region—the old fields of New York, Pennsylvania, and West Virginia. Another 42.7 per cent, or almost 75,000 barrels daily, had come from the newer Ohio-Indiana fields with a driblet from Kentucky. The Eastern fields thus accounted for 91 per cent of our production. California, with a little less than 12,000 barrels daily, had produced 6.8 per cent of the total. A little less than 1,000 barrels daily had come from the Florence field, Colorado, and a little more than 2,000 barrels daily from the newly discovered Corsicana field, Texas. That was all.

But a new era in oil had begun, and the spectacular rise of the great Mid-Continent and Gulf oil-producing region, all of which is covered in Professor Rister's field of study, was approaching. This region includes the states of Kansas, Oklahoma, Texas, Arkansas, Louisiana, and New Mexico. The area is vitally important. From it has come almost two-thirds of our total oil production, and its wells are producing approximately three-quarters of our current supply of oil.

The history of oil, particularly of its prospecting effort, can be exciting—even thrilling. The search for new fields, commonly called "wildcatting," is a part of the daily business of the industry to an extent not approached by any other mineral industry. At present we have proven reserves of about twenty-four or twenty-five billion barrels of oil, and we produce two billion barrels annually. In order to continue producing at this rate, we must discover each year new reserves approximately equal to the amount taken from the underground reservoirs. This is a big job.

Professor Rister, I suspect, regards our success in this important wildcatting function with all of the disinterested amusement of an amiable bystander who has just seen a stranger hit the jack pot. If this suspicion is well founded, I hasten to agree that he is partly right. Success in exploration depends upon luck and skill. What the proper proportion of each may be, I do not know. Success can be due, as it has been due many times, to luck alone, but I doubt whether it ever can be due solely to skill. The most perfect of prospects, selected by the most refined and exact of techniques, may be a failure. On the other hand, a prospect drilled at random for mistaken reasons or no reason at all may result in the discovery of a new and important oil field. The mammoth East Texas field was such a discovery.

One must recognize luck but not overemphasize it. The word "luck" itself is merely a convenient catchall. By using it, we ascribe to chance the favorable outcome of a complex of conditions, all of which we have not yet been able to analyze, much less understand. Some of these elements of the unknown may be and probably are controlling. All wildcatting thus becomes a considered risk and a matter of odds. Dr. Frederic Lahee has studied the results of prospecting in our country for the years 1938–47 inclusive. He finds that 20.33 per cent of all exploratory wells located on technical advice were successful as against 6.07 per cent of those drilled without such advice. Technically located wells were thus 3.34 times as successful as those not so located. It behooves us therefore to follow the advice given by a mineral prospector of the sixteenth century and "place more faith in art and good practice than in chance."

The United States oil industry has been able to produce almost two-thirds of the world's oil because of its success in prospecting for new fields. It is able to maintain its position of leadership because of continued success, although the burden of discovery sufficient to maintain adequate reserves and so make necessary production possible has increased tremendously. To my mind the basic and fundamental reason for such success is multiple individual effort. Of all human enterprises, prospecting for oil seems to prosper most under a relatively free economy. It is the thousands of American wildcatters—thousands of independent venture-minded managements, corporate and individual—who have made possible discovery at the rate required. Multiple effort and many minds are as essential to finding oil as they are to solving the problems of science.

Perfect history would recount not only men's deeds but the thinking which compelled their actions. Deeds are material and can be dated, measured, and otherwise specifically described. The thinking which impels action, however, is less tangible. John Doe drilled a wildcat well in the early days. It was drilled at a certain place and time to a specific depth and gave definite results, good, bad, or indifferent. All of these facts generally can be ascertained. Why did he drill the well? How did he select its location? What reasons enabled him to secure necessary financial aid? These are matters of historical importance upon which Doe himself may not be too clear, especially if questioned years after the event. Indeed, if his well was a spectacular success and the reasons for drilling somewhat vague or mistaken, he is likely to rationalize his motives. He is likely either to conform to reasons which fit with then current methods of prospecting or to insist mysteriously on a superior knowledge which he does not reveal. In either case he honestly believes his revised and entirely fictitious reasoning.

This is one of the real problems of the trained historian. He can search out the landmarks of fact. When he comes to motives beyond those expressed in old letters and reports written at the time, however, he is left to inference and must weigh and check even the recollections of participants in the event. History thus becomes a matter of interpretation.

We are grateful to Professor Rister for the fine job he has done in this, his first report. Let us hope that his subject has caught his interest to such a degree that he will pursue it further. We are appreciative, likewise, of the grant by Standard Oil Company (New Jersey) and the action of the University of Oklahoma Foundation which have made possible Professor Rister's work. Let us hope that this grant and this action will inspire other grants by the companies and co-operation by the schools, and so make possible similar unbiased and unprejudiced studies of the history of the oil industry.

E. DeGolyer

Dallas, Texas
February 1, 1949

Preface

THE TIME in which we live has been variously designated: as the age of science, of technology, of steel, and much else. We are assured that it is the Modern Age, as every generation has been since the first when the recorded history of the next preceding one was accessible to men who could read. The era since the Civil War, or, more accurately, since 1859, when the Drake and Ross wells were brought in, is, however, undeniably different from all the rest. It is the age of hydrocarbons—a designation which I purposely leave uncapitalized as much for emphasis as out of deference to other, competing, claimants.

This is not the place for panegyrics. The role of oil in our economy and in the human cultures that have developed throughout the world under its benefits is simple and unassailable. The moving parts of all the machinery of industry, commerce, and transportation are bathed in oil. The force which moves most of it is oil. Individual transportation rests largely upon oil—rationing during the late war made that fact entirely obvious. The further ramifications and by-products are enormous in number and vast in their influence.

Without prejudice to the works in history which have attempted (some of them with brilliant success) to interpret our political, economic, and social life since the Civil War, it can be said that the significance of petroleum, its constant, pervasive influence, is so thoroughly neglected as to constitute a major flaw in historical writing. It is as if the Industrial Revolution of the late eighteenth century could be estimated without reference to steam or steel.

The fault is not an unusual one in the historian's craft. It comes in large part from the temptation to rely upon the work of others who have plowed ground earlier. In short, and as has been said before, historians have rewritten each other. In this instance, however, the failure of historical scholarship to orient itself with reference to a development of signal importance not only leaves the task of history unfulfilled, but continues a perspective which, however valid thirty-five or forty years ago, is now obviously well past its prime.

The stuff of which the history of this period is made is not the single fact of the early trustification of the oil industry, or the dissolution of the Standard Oil Company in 1911, important though these events admittedly are. At least two of the facts which seem to me worthy of a historian's interests are the search for and the development of oil resources and the rise of a vast industrial civilization largely as a consequence of that search and development. I have chosen the former for the purposes of this book. I have, moreover, confined my efforts to the Southwest, partly because the area is the special field of my historical interest, partly because 70 per cent of the nation's oil production is presently drawn from the Southwest.

An undertaking of such proportions as the present one obviously has required a considerable expenditure of both time and money. In these I have had most generous aid. Three years ago (in September, 1945), the Standard Oil Company of New Jersey made a research grant (subsequently to be increased) to the University of Oklahoma Foundation. President George L. Cross of the University of Oklahoma, who is also chairman of the Foundation, and his colleagues on the Board of Trustees invited me to undertake the necessary research for and the writing of a history of Southwestern oil under grants from this research fund. The Board of Regents of the University generously offered me the necessary leave of absence from my teaching duties. Both the invitation and the offer were made with the clear understanding that I should be free to write such a historical account and interpretation as the facts, in my opinion, warranted. These terms, offering a handsome opportunity for an objective history of oil within the area of its greatest development in the United States, were, of course, entirely acceptable to me.

I immediately began my travels and research to assemble the materials for this book, a task far greater than anyone could foresee

Preface

when the grant was made. Before this task was finished, I had sought data in twenty-seven libraries, archives, and collections, had traveled by automobile and train more than thirty-five thousand miles, visiting major oil-producing areas of Arkansas, Kansas, Louisiana, Oklahoma, New Mexico, and Texas. I had interviewed indulgent oilmen (from roustabouts to company executives), studied refineries and oil-field installations, and conferred with federal and state officials, directors and secretaries of chambers of commerce and of oil and gas associations, and oil editors—examining miscellaneous materials in their "morgues" or retired files, and digging into trade-journal files. As a result, I finally assembled upward of ten thousand copied pages of information, hundreds of oil-field, town, and refinery photographs, microfilms, photostats, maps, charts, and out-of-print publications. From all of these, I have found the necessary information for this account.

I am deeply grateful to the Standard Oil Company of New Jersey for its generosity in making possible this study. I am grateful for the many services and time given me by numbers of oilmen and other persons in every part of the Southwest, whose names and contributions are too numerous to mention here. Major-company officials and independent oilmen alike have rendered unstinted support. And I offer my sincere thanks to officials of the federal and state governments, chambers of commerce, and oil and gas associations, and to Southwestern men and women not connected with the oil industry who have supplied me with oil materials or helped in other ways.

Directors and staff members of the following libraries, archives and collections have rendered every possible courtesy: Library of Congress, National Archives, and the United States Geological Survey Library, Washington, D. C.; The American Petroleum Institute Library, New York City; Kansas State Historical Library, Topeka; Oklahoma Historical Library (including the Indian Archives) and Interstate Oil Compact Commission Collection, Oklahoma City; University of Oklahoma Library (including the Geological library, Engineering library, and Phillips Collection), Norman; Texas State Archives and the University of Texas Library (including the Newspaper Division), Austin; E. DeGolyer's petroleum library, the Magnolia Company library, the Dallas *News* library,

xiii

and William E. Howard's collection, Dallas; *Oil and Gas Journal* library and the Oklahoma-Kansas Mid-Continent Oil and Gas Association collection, Tulsa; the *World Oil* library, Lou Kemp's collection, Houston; the Hardin-Simmons University Library, Abilene; the El Dorado Public Library, El Dorado, Arkansas; the Galveston Carnegie Library; and the public libraries of Beaumont, Corsicana, and Wichita Falls, Texas, and Shreveport, Louisiana.

A number of persons read the manuscript either in part or in entirety. For their advice, criticism, and suggestions, I am grateful to each of these: E. DeGolyer and Walace Hawkins, Dallas, Texas; the late H. C. Weiss, Richard Gonzalez, Ray Dudley, Warren Baker, and Lou Kemp, Houston, Texas; David Donoghue and R. E. Hardwicke, Fort Worth, Texas; Fred Sehmann and L. C. Heydrick, Wichita Falls, Texas; Clarel B. Mapes, Tulsa, Oklahoma; Claude V. Barrow, Miss Muriel Wright, Earl Foster, and E. G. Dahlgren, Oklahoma City; E. Vandale, Amarillo, Texas; E. O. Thompson, Austin, Texas; W. B. Cotten, Jr., Baton Rouge, Louisiana; and V. E. Monnett, Norman, Oklahoma.

Oscar C. Schorp and C. D. Watson of Tulsa, E. DeGolyer of Dallas, and Dean W. H. Carson and Professor V. E. Monnett of Norman, have given me professional advice and rendered many services related to this study during the last three years, for which I am deeply grateful. To my wife, Mattie May Rister, my faithful assistant, I am especially grateful. She has accompanied me on my travels, delved into libraries, copied items from out-of-print publications, newspapers, and manuscripts and assisted me in many other ways under difficult circumstances. And to my secretary, Mrs. Gwendolyne Harris, I am also indebted for supervising the work of copyists, assembling data in local libraries, typing, and cataloguing the materials assembled. I alone am responsible for any mistake which inadvertently may appear in this book.

C. C. R.

Norman, Oklahoma
February 5, 1949

Contents

Contents

ing oil to the war front; Cushing's producing sands; the Palmer well at Healdton; early Healdton leases; Healdton's development, 1913; Magnolia *vs.* local producers; rising power of the Corporation Commission; influence of motor cars on the price of oil; Kansas and Oklahoma refineries; major companies enter Oklahoma; oil at Garber, 1917; at Yale, 1914–17; elsewhere in Oklahoma; Augusta, Eldorado, and Towanda, Kansas, 1916–17.

Contents

Illustrations

Oil! Titan of the Southwest

Illustrations

Graphs and Maps

OIL! TITAN
OF THE SOUTHWEST

I

Texas' Oil-Spring Era

HE USE OF PETROLEUM is frequently mentioned in the writings of the ancients, but the earliest documentary account of its use in North America dates from a blustery July day in 1543, when storm-tossed Spanish ships—bearing the survivors of the ill-fated De Soto expedition on their way back to Mexico—sought shelter on the Gulf coast of Texas near Sabine Pass.

The record of this expedition, published at Evora, Portugal, fourteen years later, tells how "The vessels came together in a creek, where lay the two brigantines that preceded them." On the water, floating about the ships, was a dark scum, which the Spaniards called "*copé.*" Since it was like the pitch which they had used in Spain to calk their ships, they "payed the bottoms of their vessels with it."[1]

This was the white man's first use of a petroleum product in what is now the United States—sixty-four years before the first English colonists stepped ashore at Jamestown. Texas Gulf Coast oilmen of today confirm this Spanish narrative, for oil springs are yet found near Sabine Pass, and "*copé*" is occasionally seen upon the water.

Indians had used petroleum before the white explorers came. Their traditions include stories of their visits to oil springs in times of affliction; and both early Spanish and Anglo narratives mention similar incidents. The Indians bathed in oil springs to drive away rheumatic pains, applied the oil as an ointment to cuts, burns, and sores, and drank it as medicine. No doubt East Texans found more interest in their oil springs in 1846, when Samuel M. Kier, of Pittsburgh, Pennsylvania, publicized not only oil's commercial value,

[1] Edward Gaylord Bourne (ed.), *Narratives of the Career of Hernando de Soto,* I, 290.

but also its "wonderful curative powers"—a "natural remedy," he said, that came from "four hundred feet below the earth's surface."

According to local tradition, French and Spanish explorers occasionally visited Indian springs. Later, Anglo-American settlers found oil seeps in "the counties of Sabine, Shelby, Nacogdoches, San Augustine, Anderson, Griner, Travis, Bexar, and others."[2] To record each of these and to locate all the East and South Texas springs during this era would serve little purpose here. Those should be mentioned, however, that relate directly to the beginning of the Texas oil industry, the best known of which was in Angelina County, Texas, near the place where Jack Graham dug a pit into which seeped a heavy oil. This encouraged him and others, early in 1859, to sink a well by a spring pole rig, but little oil was found.

Early records reveal that in 1866 Lynis T. Barrett drilled the first Texas producer. The Barretts had moved from Virginia to Texas thirty-four years earlier, settling near Melrose. As a boy, Lynis often visited a near-by oil spring and learned of the commercial possibilities of oil. He believed that the spring was fed by a hidden oil reservoir. Why could he not find it by boring a well? To answer this question, he presently leased the Skillern tract and started to drill, but the outbreak of the Civil War disrupted his plans, for he entered the Confederate Army.

Following the Civil War, the Pennsylvania oil boom was infectious. Far-away Texas felt its influence. In a letter to George W. O'Brien of Beaumont, a former comrade in arms, writing from Liberty, Texas, discussed what was seemingly the popular subject of conversation in his town. "The great excitement of this age is oil," he said. "It promises to lay in the shade the great 'South Sea Bubble' or any other bubble of any age. This region of Texas will be wild upon the subject within a few months. A company has been organized and a cash capital of $25,000 paid in to experiment at Sour Lake in Hardin County, and a man and the money has already gone north to buy the necessary machinery to search the bowels of the earth for *oil*. Millions of dollars are now ready to be invested so soon as the results in Hardin County are known. None doubt but what oil will be found and the excitement will not wait the slow process of experiments, and if we are prepared for the excitement,

2 E. T. Dumble, *Second Annual Report of the Geological Survey of Texas*, xliv.

we will make our fortune. What is the use of toiling and struggling with aching brains and weary hands for bread, when gold so temptingly invites you to reach out and clutch it?"[3] He urged his friend to acquire extensive leases about town, but there is no record to show whether his advice was heeded.

Eighteen hundred and sixty-four was the year of great oil-stock promotion and excitement, which helped to create this Texas boom. Soon Barrett joined Benjamin P. Hollingsworth, Charles A. Hamilton, and John B. Early in promoting a new oil enterprise. On October 9, 1865, they secured a renewal of the lease on the Skillern tract, promising the heirs an immediate payment of one hundred dollars, two hundred dollars more within thirty days, and a royalty of one-twelfth "of minerals or oils" found on the land. C. A. Warner, the Texas petroleum historian, states that Barrett employed the rotary principle in "boring" for oil.[4] He used an auger eight feet long and eight inches in diameter fastened by clamps to a pipe and powered by a cogwheel that was connected by a drive shaft to a steam engine. The drill stem was mounted under a pole-tripod.

While boring at a depth of one hundred feet, according to the *South-Western* (Shreveport, Louisiana) of September 12, 1866, the drillers noticed that "the auger suddenly dropped about 6 inches." They drew it up and found "earth adhering to the auger... perfectly saturated with oil," and ten minutes later "pure oil several inches deep came to the surface." The discovery promised lucrative returns for Barrett and his associates, who composed the Melrose Petroleum Company.[5]

The *Oil Investors' Journal* of November 18, 1906, later carried Barrett's own story of his next move. "I then went to the oil fields of Pennsylvania," he said, "and carried with me specimens of oil and other indications and presented them to John F. Carll,[6] who, after

---

[3] This letter is in possession of Mr. Chilton O'Brien, Beaumont, Texas, grandson of George W. O'Brien to whom it was addressed. The Sour Lake mentioned had been known as a health resort for several years prior to the Civil War, and afterward became an important oil field.

[4] *Texas Oil and Gas Since 1543*, 6.

[5] During 1866 the Texas legislature passed many acts creating oil companies. See H. P. N. Gammel, *Laws of Texas*, V, 1250, 1299, 1378, 1457, 1495, 1642, 1645. See also Wallace Hawkins *El Sal Del Rey*, 58–59.

[6] Carll was born in Bushwick, New York (now a part of Brooklyn). He acquired a liberal education at Union Hill Academy, Jamaica, Long Island, and afterwards

examining the same, entered into a contract, as the representative of Messrs. Brown Bros. of Titusville, Pennsylvania, with me, to come to our field in Texas with about $5,000 worth of machinery suitable to the development of oil, all of which was accomplished in the early part of 1866 and in the early spring of 1867, but unfortunately for me on the day that the test of my well with the use of the machinery was made, Carll received instructions from the company he represented that on account of the low price of oil and the unsettled condition of the country (political reconstruction then existing), it would be inadvisable to prosecute the work further."[7]

After the failure of the Melrose Petroleum Company, Barrett vainly sought financial assistance elsewhere, and the Nacogdoches field remained dormant for about two decades.

In 1868, according to one authority, Emory Starr and Peyton F. Edwards, two hunters, visited Oil Springs on the "first authentic prospecting for oil" in that region. Using spades, they dug some pits in the sandy soil and left them for the night. Next morning they found the pits filled with water and oil. Then they skimmed the oil from the water and took a quantity of it to Nacogdoches, where it was tested on leather and harness and for domestic purposes. But this seemed to be as far as they went to exploit their discovery.

In 1887, B. F. Hitchcock revived the interest of East Texans by going to New Orleans for capital to drill another well near Nacogdoches. In the Crescent City, E. H. Farrar helped him to organize the Petroleum Prospecting Company, capitalized at $100,000; and in keeping with the plans of the company's officials, J. E. Prince and a crew of Pennsylvania drillers set up a cable-tool rig near Oil Springs and began operations, putting down an eight-inch casing. At about seventy feet the well blew in, and between 250 and 300 barrels of a heavy brown-colored oil flowed on the ground, for they had not prepared tanks or a reservoir to care for it. But after the first day the well ceased to flow and was put on a pump.

---

studied civil engineering. During his youth he spent some time on a farm, then as a civil engineer in the East for several years, and later as editor of the *Morning Eagle* at Newark, New Jersey. Finally, in November, 1864, he moved to the Pennsylvania oil region and engaged in oil producing near Pleasantville. There he gained widespread recognition.

[7] Quoting from *Oil, Paint and Drug Reporter.*

Texas' Oil-Spring Era

Thus began Texas' first oil boom. East Texans came to Nacogdoches, thronging the streets and the oil field, to see this "wonder of wonders." The Petroleum Prospecting Company officials were also impressed with their discovery and started other wells. They "continued drilling, with some intermission," says Dumble,[8] "until the spring of 1889"—indeed until forty wells had been sunk, each to a depth of about one hundred feet. The holdings of the company consisted of an office in the spring lot; a storage house containing four wooden tanks of 250 barrels each; four wooden tanks of the same kind not set up; two iron tanks of 1,000-barrel capacity each, full of oil; an engine house, with stationary engine; fourteen and one-half miles of a three-inch pipe line, leading from the well to a 2,000-barrel iron shipping tank on Aaron's Hill, west of Nacogdoches; and several derricks and portable field engines.

Four other companies had entered the field by 1890, bringing the total of wells drilled to about ninety. Among these, the Lubricating Oil Company in the valley of the Bayou Visitador, three or four miles northeast of the first well, was the most important. Its holdings consisted of a receiving or "dump" tank; five storage tanks; an iron evaporating pan, three by twenty feet, with a steam chest underneath; a steam filter pump; a boiler house, with portable boiler and engine; an iron shipping tank; iron drums for shipping; portable derricks and engines; a manager's office and dwelling; stables and outhouses; and a storehouse, with piping, fittings, and tools of all description.

Dumble describes Texas' first, although quite primitive, oil refinery operated by this company.[9] It was served, he said, by "bailing the water and the oil semi-weekly from each oil-bearing well by means of a cylindrical galvanized iron bored into a separating barrel

---

[8] *Op. cit.*

[9] Samuel M. Kier is generally conceded to have built the first refinery, at Pittsburgh, Pennsylvania, in 1850. He had sought to use petroleum as an illuminant, but smoke and an offensive odor from his lamp filled the room. To help solve this problem, he sent a quantity of oil to a Philadelphia chemist to have it analyzed and learned that if he could perfect a lamp to burn it, it would make an excellent illuminant. Then he set to work in earnest, trying to improve his lamp and to refine the oil so that he would eliminate its offensive smoke and smell. He succeeded with his lamp by using the "Vienna Burner" and the crude oil by refining it. His refining still had a capacity of five barrels. It was four feet, eight inches in height, three feet, seven and one-half inches in diameter, and eleven feet, two inches in circumference.—*The Derrick's Hand-Book of Petroleum, from 1859 to 1898*, I, 947–53.

7

Oil! Titan of the Southwest

... for oil. From the separating barrel the oil is drawn into carrying barrels in a wagon, which conveys it to the receiving or dump tank, into which it is emptied. This tank is located on a hillside. From the storage tanks the oil is fed by iron pipes into the oil evaporating pan, provided with a steam chest below, which heats the oil and drives off the remaining water and the small amount of naphtha. While still hot, the oil is forced by steam through a specially woven filter cloth to remove any particles of grit, and the oil is discharged through a pipe into the iron shipping drum provided with wrought iron tires for rolling. The capacity of each drum is about 100 gallons. They are conveyed by wagon to the town of Nacogdoches for shipment by railway."

Meanwhile, petroleum discoveries were reported elsewhere in Texas. As early as September 13, 1847, Andrew Briscoe wrote from Houston that "about 74 or 75 miles east of this . . . in the low coast prairie, there is a shallow pond," from the bottom of which rose "sulphurous gas bubbles . . . and British oil or something very like it. . . . This place is called Sour Lake."[10] Here, in 1865, G. W. Cochran secured a lease to bore a well, but he was unsuccessful in his quest for oil.

Dick Dowling, known in Confederate history for his heroic defense of Sabine Pass, was active in oil operations near Houston about the same time. In partnership with John M. Fennerty he acquired a considerable oil lease near the town, as well as leases in other counties; but the two men met with no great success.

Gas wells were also found in Texas. At Graham, in Young County, R. G. Graham struck gas while drilling a salt-water well, in 1871; and about the same time gas wells were found in Palo Pinto County, one near Gordon and another five miles north of Palo Pinto. Local citizens regarded them as phenomena rather than as of commercial value. Yet, undoubtedly Central Texas oil reports encouraged the

[10] Earlier, Captain Briscoe had commanded a company in the Texas Army at San Jacinto and afterwards became the first chief justice of Harris County.—A. Briscoe to "Dear Father," September 13, 1847, MS in Looscan Papers, San Jacinto Museum of History, a copy of which was furnished the author by Lou Kemp of Houston, Texas.

Frederick Law Olmsted visited Sour Lake a decade later. For his description of it, see *A Journey Through Texas*, 375–76. The Houston *Tri-Weekly News* of October 2, 1862, states that "The waters from the lake [Sour Lake] and springs are now being regularly received daily, and for sale by the barrel, demijohn or gallon."

8

Early-day spring-pole drilling

Early New Mexico refinery, homemade plant on Rattle-
snake lease, making fifty barrels of high-grade gasoline
daily

Early oil well in Washington County, Oklahoma, completed April 15, 1897, and alleged to be the first commercial well in the state

Bartlesville, Oklahoma, 1906

Oil and Gas Journal

Standard Oil Company to drill two test wells in Bell County in 1881, without satisfactory results. Other gas wells were found at Greenwine in Washington County during the period, 1879–89, starting with William Seidell's striking gas while boring for water.

A Brown County oil well, however, caused the widest interest among Central Texas settlers seeking petroleum. In 1878, Martin Meinsinger, a Brownwood wagon-yard keeper, dug by hand a well three and one-half feet in diameter to a depth of 102 feet and found an oil-bearing sand, from which he drew about five gallons of 38-gravity, dark green oil a day. His discovery caused much excitement in this border town, and settlers came from far and near to buy the oil to grease their wagons, buggies, harness, and saddles, and to use it as a medicine to treat "blood boils" and skin diseases.

As a lubricant, the Brownwood oil sold at fifty cents a gallon, and as a medicine, at twenty-five cents for a four-ounce bottle.[11] Contemporary records do not reveal that other wells were drilled there at that time. But fourteen years later N. F. Drake reported that oil from the Meinsinger well was still sold as a lubricant, and that two companies (the Sunset Oil Company and the Colorado Company) had drilled other near-by wells to a depth of 1,500 feet but had found only a "sipe of oil."[12]

Eight years after Meinsinger encountered oil instead of water in his Brownwood well, George Dullnig, a rancher living six miles southeast of San Antonio had a similar experience. At a depth of 235 feet he struck a vein of reddish-brown oil, which local citizens found to be an excellent lubricant. They bought it at prices ranging from twenty cents to thirty-five cents a gallon, depending on the quantity bought. A short time later Dullnig drilled a second well fifteen feet from the first one, and at a depth of 300 feet he again struck oil. Then he drilled still a third well to a depth of 900 feet, but he found no oil below the horizons of the other wells. Since there was only a limited local market, his wells were of passing interest.

[11] Mrs. J. D. Sandefer, Sr., of Abilene, Texas, furnished the author a copy of an affidavit sworn to by Brooke Smith and C. V. Harriss, dated June 13, 1935, titled "First Crude Oil Found in Texas," relating to the Martin Meinsinger (spelled "Meichinger") discovery well. See also "Brownwood, Site of First Oil Well in Texas, Was Found in 1878 in Drilling for Water," in *The Galveston News*, September 14, 1935.

[12] "Report on the Colorado Coal Field of Texas," in *Fourth Annual Report of the Geological Survey of Texas*, 1892, 436–37.

Oil! Titan of the Southwest

Yet in 1889, for the first time, federal statistics classified Texas as a gas- and oil-producing state, with forty-eight barrels of oil, and natural gas valued at $1,728,[13] both representing the output of the Dullnig wells. Later, other oil wells were drilled about San Antonio —on the Dashiell farm, on the F. T. Walsh ranch, at Sutherland Springs in Wilson County, and south of Dunlay, in Medina County[14] —but they were small producers and of minor importance.

Reports from various parts of Texas during the eighteen eighties and eighteen nineties continued to make good copy for the press. For example, the Corpus Christi *Caller* of November 12, 1887, under the headline "Struck Oil Near Palestine," carried the exciting news that seven days earlier stockholders of a Palestine oil company had been highly elated over an "oil showing" in a near-by well, which a few hours later was "overflowing with a fair quality of oil, and in paying quantities." But no subsequent report confirmed this single optimistic account.

Thus runs the history of the Texas oil-spring era. Reports about the foregoing and many other mid-nineteenth-century seeps, springs, and wells, coming from Bexar, Clay, Cooke, Liberty, McLennan, Polk, Tyler, and other counties, constitute the folklore mosaic, partly obscured and also partly elaborated by oral tradition. Indeed, some pre–Civil War Texan may have dug an oil "pit" or well long before Edwin L. Drake made his Pennsylvania discovery on August 28, 1859. Southwestern oil lacked efficient press agents. Certainly oil springs and seeps in Texas were known and used as early as those east of the Mississippi River.

Truly, the Texas oil-spring era introduced several of the Southwestern petroleum industry's firsts—the auger principle later employed in the rotary rig[15] and the first, although primitive, cable-

---

[13] C. A. Warner, *op. cit.*, 17.

[14] *Ibid.*

[15] No doubt the techniques of more than one early-day driller were combined to perfect the modern rotary drilling system. Late nineteenth-century oil-field operators knew of three men who employed certain features of this system. Among these were M. C. and C. E. Baker, of Yankton, Dakota Territory, who came to Corsicana soon after the discovery of oil there. They were successful in forcing water through a drill stem by connecting a pump with a near-by windmill, which, in turn, brought the mud out of the casing. The two Bakers were later employed by the American Well and Prospecting Company, which, by the beginning of the twentieth century, marketed rotary equipment. Another driller named Chapman by the early eighteen-

tool rig, the first lease, the first oil pipe line, the first wooden and iron storage tanks, the first iron drums for transporting crude oil, and the first refinery—all in the Nacogdoches oil field. But it is equally true that all these innovations were greatly improved and given wider use during the boom days to follow.

eighties employed a water-jet-cable tool system and developed a flat rotary table, rotating with a vertical axis. The drill passed through a hole in the middle of the rotary table where grip rings held the drill stem for turning it and letting the pipe slip through as the hole was deepened.—"Rotary Drilling," in *Oil Weekly*, February 11, 1935; Benjamin Andrews to Chester W. Washburn, February 18, 1922, MS in DeGolyer papers, Dallas, Texas.

II

The Red Man's Hidden Wealth

B Y THE CLOSE of the second quarter of the nineteenth century, land-hungry pioneers, who could not find free lands along the eastern seaboard, had broken across the Appalachian barrier and had moved westward to occupy the lush wilderness beyond. Rapidly they overran both the Old Northwest and the Old Southwest and settled the bottom lands beyond the Mississippi River. This westward surge forced the Indians to abandon 77,000,000 acres of land east of the Mississippi, the land of their fathers, and to accept greatly restricted reservations beyond the first tier of states carved from the Louisiana Purchase.

The Southern Indians (Cherokees, Creeks, Choctaws, Chickasaws, and Seminoles) joined this westward trek over many a "trail of tears," to wrestle with unknown hardships and problems, bitterly complaining that the federal government was sending them to a wasteland to starve. They little realized that beneath Indian Territory's or Oklahoma's red earth were vast sand and lime horizons of oil, far richer than all the gold in the Georgia hills. Nor did the white men know of these riches, although tradition has it that for many years the native Indians had known and visited Oklahoma's oil springs.

Just when the immigrant Indians first discovered an Oklahoma oil spring is not a matter of record. Certainly, they were visiting such springs long before the Drake well was drilled in Pennsylvania. In 1846, Agent A. M. Upshaw of the Chickasaws mentioned Indian "medicine springs" in his report to the Commissioner of Indian Affairs,[1] and two years later he again referred to them, saying that

[1] *Annual Report, Commissioner of Indian Affairs*, 1846-49, 275.

one of them was an oil spring, the oil from which both Indians and Texans used for medicine.[2] In 1853, Agent A. J. Smith, who had succeeded Upshaw, informed Commissioner G. W. Manypenny that "the oil springs at the foot of the Wichita Mountains on the Washita River" were visited by "a great many Texans . . . and some from Arkansas," and that the oil served as a remedy for all chronic diseases, including rheumatism and dropsy. "The fact is that it cures anything that has been tried," he confidently wrote.[3]

The value of these oil showings caused the Indians to seek others—and they found them. One, New Spring Place (now Oaks) in Delaware County, was north of Tahlequah, in the Cherokee country; another, Boyd Springs, was northeast of Ardmore, on Oil Creek, twelve miles west of Tishomingo; a third, a Pontotoc water (oil) well was southwest of present-day Ada, in the Fitts oil field; and a fourth, on Peter Maytubby's place, was six miles northwest of Caddo, in Bryan County. The Indian who dug the Pontotoc well found in it green oil, and water also, and being a practical man, he used the oil for greasing a grass-cutting machine which he had recently bought.[4]

Lewis Ross, brother of the principal chief of the Cherokees, John Ross, made the most sensational discovery in the summer of 1859, the exact date of which is not a matter of record. He was engaged in salt mining at the Grand Saline, on the Grand River, and decided to sink a deep well for greater production. About seven hundred feet down he "struck a vein of oil that flowed by estimate,

[2]*Ibid.*

[3] *Ibid.*, 1850–53, 401–402. Twenty years later, Asa Toyett, a Comanche chief, went with Thomas C. Battey to Medicine Creek near the foot of the Wichitas, "where there was a 'heap of medicine—good black medicine,'" a spring, upon the water of which was floating petroleum, oozing from a small hole in the ground. "There are other places in the vicinity where petroleum is found," said Battey. "I know of two within ten miles of Fort Sill; but there being no cheap means of transportation, it is here valueless, except as an application to the sore backs of mules and ponies."— Thomas C. Battey, *A Quaker Among the Indians*, 189–90.

[4] Muriel H. Wright, "First Oklahoma Oil Was Produced in 1859," in *Chronicles of Oklahoma*, Vol. IV, No. 4 (December, 1926), 323. Subsequently a health resort was located on Peter Maytubby's place. New Spring Place may have been the "Oil Spring" from which Superintendent James M. Payne of the Cherokee schools wrote a letter to Agent James McKissick, on September 7, 1847. Grant Foreman of Muskogee, Oklahoma, furnished the author with a photostatic copy of the letter.

about ten barrels per day for nearly a year, until the pressure of gas became exhausted and failed to support the volume of water."[5]

The same early-day document that mentions Ross's discovery well also speaks of many other "outcroppings" of a fine green oil on water springs and streams that the Indians subsequently found. It revealed that near Boyd Springs was a favorite camping site to which the Indians came "in great number to light their camps with the gas, by inserting a tube or gun barrel in the ground."

Following the outbreak of the Civil War, demoralization overtook Indian Territory. Confederate and Union armies marched and countermarched across the land, and all semblance of law and order vanished. Pillagers from both armies burned homes, stole livestock, and laid waste fields and allowed them to grow in weeds and grass. Noncombatant, terror-stricken Indians, the aged, and women and children sought protection by "forting-up" or by establishing temporary camps outside the devastated area. It was not until after the war clouds had passed that they could return to their homes to resume their old way of life. But, as before the war, they visited their favorite springs to heal their sick and to use the oil as a lubricant; and shortly, too, the lame and the sick from Arkansas, Missouri, and Texas also came.

News of Oklahoma oil springs caused great excitement in Kansas and Texas. Pennsylvania oil, following the Drake discovery, was becoming increasingly important in the economy of that state, and discoveries in these two Western states brought a similar opportunity to their poverty-stricken and war-weary settlers.

By 1871, Robert M. Darden, a Missourian, appeared in the Choctaw-Chickasaw country to organize an oil company. He was faced by almost insurmountable difficulties in that capital was hard to secure, the Indians were suspicious of his intentions, and the Department of the Interior had launched a white-man exclusion policy. Undaunted by these handicaps, he went about his work. He convinced Choctaw and Chickasaw leaders, including Winchester Colbert, Allen Wright, and others, that they and their people might find untold riches if they entered into a company agreement with

[5] A pamphlet, *The National Oil Trust Company*, not dated, but about 1886; S. W. Ross to C. C. Rister, March 26, 1947; Robert L. Owen to Rister, March 17, 1947. The late Mr. Owen said, "I am sure this was previous to the Drake well."

The Red Man's Hidden Wealth

him. So, early in February, 1872, they organized the Chickasaw Oil Company, under the laws of Missouri, perhaps because Darden, the prime mover of the enterprise, was from Missouri. This was Oklahoma's first oil company.

According to the Choctaw and Chickasaw constitutions, land was held in common by all the Indians, but individual citizens were permitted to develop the natural resources. Consequently, under Darden's encouragement, representatives of the two tribes met at the home of former Governor Colbert, in old Pontotoc County, Chickasaw Nation, to organize the company.

Manuscripts now in the National Archives and others in the possession of Miss Muriel Wright of the Oklahoma Historical Society tell the story of this interesting compact. The draft of the resolution of agreement was signed by nineteen men and women representing prominent Choctaw and Chickasaw families and headed by former Governor Colbert.[6] Among other things, the signers agreed "to stand by said contract and protect said oil company" in all its rights and privileges; to solicit the co-operation of other Indians in the enterprise; and to grant "the said Oil Company" one-half of all oil produced on every quarter-section under contract, although the company was to bear all the expenses in "boring and barreling" the oil at each well, to be divided between the company and the lessors. In addition, according to Commissioner F. A. Walker, after a "term of years," the lessors ("certain persons") were to receive the sum of $48,000.[7]

The Indian stockholders knew little about anticlines and geology; but they delegated two of their number, Colbert and Buckner Burns, at five dollars a day, to be paid from their oil royalties, to secure other leases about an "Oil Ridge" near Colbert's home. Although they were confident of success, Darden knew that he must have Washington's blessing, and this was not easy. Already other similar requests were pending before Commissioner Walker, who, a short time previously, had told Secretary Delano that designing whites were trying to "open up" the Indian country and that he

[6] Miss Wright permitted the author to use this manuscript, dated February 1, 1872, as well as a certificate of one-fourth stock grant to Allen Wright. Other manuscripts taken from her files are hereafter cited as "Wright Col."

[7] Walker to Secretary of Interior, February 1, 1872, Office of Indian Affairs, Interior Department Archives, National Archives.

was opposed to it.[8] Secretary Delano supported this exclusion policy,[9] and thus the fate of the Chickasaw Oil Company, as well as other similar organizations, was sealed.

This temporarily stopped ambitious oil promoters in Indian Territory. But a decade later, perhaps because of oil and gas discoveries near Paola, Kansas, oilmen's interest was renewed in Indian Territory possibilities. The most prominent of these promoters was Dr. H. W. Faucett of New York, who was backed by R. Lenox Belknap, treasurer of the Northern Pacific Railroad.[10] On July 9, 1883, he made a proposal in writing to Allen Wright. He suggested that Wright and other Choctaws form a company and secure a lease to a large acreage from the Choctaw Council. Then the company could sublease to Faucett, who would pay 15 per cent of the entire production from the wells drilled. Of this, Wright could pay the Council 5 per cent, his company retaining the other 10 per cent, "and that without any capital whatever invested."[11]

Five months later he inquired whether Wright had succeeded in getting a bill for the lease through the Choctaw Council, and if so, whether the Chickasaw Council had also taken action. He was interested not only in "boring" for oil but in securing "exclusive . . . pipe-line privilege for transporting oil."[12] He thought that it would be impossible to interest capital in the enterprise unless "there was some agreement as to the extent of the territory that could be had and the specified royalty."

The Choctaw Council needed little encouragement. On October 3, 1884, it approved an act creating the Choctaw Oil and Refining Company, for the purpose of finding petroleum or rock oil and

---

[8] Walker to Delano, February 1, 1872, Office of Indian Affairs records, National Archives.

[9] Delano to Walker, February 4, 1872, in Letters, December 6, 1875 to March 18, 1872 (Choctaw, W. 1213), *ibid.* Darden had evidently made a request of Congress to recognize his lease to produce oil and to transport it out of Indian Territory much earlier. See Erastus Wells to Walker, January 20, 1872, *ibid.* Delano's successor, Acting Secretary B. R. Cowan, wrote to Commissioner Frederick Watts of Agriculture, on January 23, 1873, that two promoters, Cuthbertson and Irvine, were trying to secure mineral-land leases in the country of the Peorias, Kaskaskias, Piankeshaws, and Weas. See Interior Department Records, Press Copies, Letters Sent, Vol. 21, 4–5, National Archives.

[10] Faucett to Allen Wright, Esq., July 9, 1883, Wright Col.

[11] *Ibid.*

[12] Faucett to Wright, Wright Col.

increasing the revenue of the Choctaw Nation. Chief Edmund Mc-Curtain signed the measure and joined E. N. Wright, A. R. Durant, and Allen Wright, former governor, as an incorporator.

This was an ambitious beginning, but it was not all. The enterprising Faucett succeeded in having the Cherokee Council enact the same kind of law, creating the Cherokee Oil Company, on December 13. It was signed by Principal Chief D. W. Bushyhead, and the charter of the company was granted to Robert L. Owen and James S. Stapler. Owen and E. N. Wright, the two immediate promoters, had already agreed upon a trust compact "to equalize" their composite royalties.[13]

Thus, assignments of the two grants were made to Faucett covering the exclusive privilege "to produce, to transport by pipeline and to refine petroleum within the boundaries of these Nations," including the entire Cherokee Nation east of the ninety-sixth meridian and that part of the Choctaw Nation from the Arkansas and Canadian rivers to the Red River, making a total of nearly "20,000 square miles of about 13,000,000 acres," the nation's largest lease up to that time.

Among the members of the new Choctaw company were Samson Holson, McKee James, E. N. Wright, Alexander R. Durant, Allen Wright, Charles Winston, Robert Benton, James King, G. W. McCurtain, J. F. McCurtain, J. R. James, Jos. W. Everidge, Thomas E. Oakes, Isaac Burass, Edmund McCurtain, C. W. Frazier, Thomas Byington, and G. C. Dukes.[14] The incorporators elected Dr. E. N. Wright president, McKee James, treasurer, and Allen Wright, secretary.

A short time later the members of the company met to sign a contract with Dr. Faucett; but they adjourned to meet again at Sherman, Texas, to complete the business.[15] Here the agreement was concluded on November 25, 1884, in the presence of the county

[13] Owen-Wright Agreement, July 25, 1884, Wright Col.

[14] Minutes of the Choctaw Oil and Refining Company, October 24, 1884, Wright Col.

[15] To comply with law, Faucett, a United States citizen, met the members of the Choctaw Oil Company at Sherman, Texas, to sign the contract. Each member signed his name in the presence of the Grayson County judge, E. P. Gregg.—Minutes of the Choctaw Oil Company, November 25, 1884, Wright Col.

judge, E. P. Gregg; and they decided to meet next at Tuskahoma, during the first week of the general council, in October, 1885.[16]

Meanwhile, the United States Senate had enacted a resolution inquiring about the legality of such a lease.[17] The Secretary of the Interior assured the Senate that the Cherokee and Choctaw councils had acted quite within their rights. Cherokee rights were defined under Article 5 of the Cherokee treaty of 1835 and Article 16 of the treaty of 1866. Choctaw treaty rights were substantially the same.

Then the Indians became uneasy. By the summer of 1885, members of both companies complained that Dr. Faucett was moving slowly with drilling preparations. However, on August 8 he wrote to Allen Wright: "I shall go to Fort Smith the beginning of the coming week if nothing prevents, and then down into the Nation to make a selection of locality and arrange for lumber, mills, etc., for the rig so as to commence drilling."[18] He added that he would reassure Governor McCurtain while he was in the Choctaw country and that he had no intention of allowing the agreement to expire by limitation, for he had "spent too much money and time to allow it to go by default."

True to his promise, Faucett soon had an oil rig up on Clear Boggy, seven miles south of Lehigh and fourteen miles west of Atoka; and workmen started assembling another rig at Alum Bluff, on the Illinois River, Going Snake District, Cherokee Nation. But since Faucett had failed to file a notice with the Cherokee Council concerning his intentions, this body, two days before its adjournment, repealed the lease act of 1884.

This was a stunning blow. The New York financiers became alarmed and withdrew from the enterprise. In the following year, Robert L. Owen induced the Council to renew the charter. The resourceful Faucett would not acknowledge defeat. He turned to St. Louis capitalists, who furnished him with enough money to resume operations. Under Illinois law, the company was reorganized as the National Oil Trust Company with a capital stock of $10,-000,000. Its officers were William A. Adams, president, Joseph W. Buel, vice-president, and George A. Hynes, secretary-treasurer.

[16] Wright, *loc. cit.*, 325
[17] *The National Oil Trust Company* (pamphlet), Wright Col.
[18] Faucett to Wright, August 8, 1885, Wright Col.

The Red Man's Hidden Wealth

Faucett was one of three directors, the other two being F. G. Flanagan and E. H. Smith.[19]

Meanwhile, at the annual meeting of the Choctaw Company in the fall of 1886, the members voted to drop Dr. Faucett from their organization if he did not start drilling immediately. The harassed promoter had other worries, also. It was hard to secure supplies, since those sent from St. Louis came by way of the Katy (Missouri, Kansas and Texas) Railroad to Atoka, and from there were hauled by ox-wagon to the well. Company funds, too, were not always available, but Faucett's generous friend, Dr. E. N. Wright, helped him to feed his drill crew and to keep the work going. Thus, drilling was continued until the well reached a depth of 1,400 feet, where it struck a showing of both gas and oil.

Then, in 1888, Faucett became ill with typhoid fever[20] and returned to his home at Neosho, Missouri, where he died a short time later. As there was no one else to carry on his work, the well was abandoned.

One day in 1882, while Edward Byrd, an intermarried Cherokee citizen, was looking for strayed livestock on Spencer Creek (Oil Branch), about four miles from Chelsea, he noticed "something glittering" on the water of the creek. Upon closer inspection he found it to be oil. He had heard of Pennsylvania and East Texas oil and decided that if the Cherokee Council ever approved oil leases, he would secure one for this area. Not long afterward approval was granted, and in 1886 he secured a lease to a one-half-section tract. Oil promoters, however, could not be induced to invest in so small a body of land; therefore, he went to Robert Ross, treasurer of the Cherokee Nation, and asked for a larger tract. When this request was granted, Byrd selected a tract of 94,000 acres commencing on the east side of Chelsea and running northwest via Pat Henry's farm to Coody's Bluff; thence southwest to Yellow Leaf Crossing on the Verdigris River and down this river to the Clem V. Rogers Crossing; and thence east, via Sageeyah Switch, on the Frisco Railroad, to the point of beginning.[21]

[19] *Ibid.*   [20] Hon. Robert L. Owen to C. C. Rister, March 8, 1947.
[21] Edward Byrd's own story, titled "History and Discovery of Oil and Gas West of the Mississippi River." A copy of this narrative was presented the author by Dr. Charles N. Gould, Norman, Oklahoma. For the size and location of the lease see map in Oklahoma Geological Survey *Bull. No. 40, Oil and Gas in Oklahoma*, III.

Oil! Titan of the Southwest

Having his lease, Byrd next came to an agreement with a Pennsylvanian, William Linn, who had associated with him Martin Hellar, Finley Ross, William Woodman, and Oak Daeson, all of Wichita, Kansas. These men organized the United States Oil and Gas Company, capitalized at $1,000,000, with shares at $1.00 each.

Sam Francis and a crew were employed to drill the first well, the site of which Byrd selected about fifty feet from the spot where he had first seen the oil seep, on the west bank of Oil Branch. He started drilling with a horse-powered outfit, and in August, 1889, completed the well at a depth of thirty-six feet. The well produced about one-half barrel a day of 32-gravity light green oil. A small pump and tank were installed, and the oil was sold as a dip for tick-infested cattle to Bill Hallsall of Vinita and to other cattlemen, who, of course, constituted a limited market.

Byrd also selected other sites for drilling: one two hundred yards west of the first well; another, one mile northwest of the second; a fourth, fifty yards from the third; and a fifth, farther down Oil Branch. The best of these was the last, which produced fifteen barrels a day.

In all, by 1891 the United States Oil Company had drilled eleven wells on the Cochran place, centering around Section 30.[22] But the company failed because of the limited market and production, and in 1895 sold out at twenty-five cents on the dollar to John Phillips of Butler, Pennsylvania, and others. The new organization, known as the Cherokee Oil and Gas Company, completed fourteen more wells, but found the same handicaps as its predecessor and abandoned its holdings long before the Chelsea and Nowata districts attained commercial importance.

The next oil development in eastern Oklahoma came when Michael Cudahy of Omaha, Nebraska, secured a blanket lease for oil and gas on more than 200,000 acres in the Creek Nation, and employed McBride and Bloom of Independence, Kansas, to drill the wells. The first well was sunk in 1894 on what is now the townsite of Muskogee and reached an oil sand at 1,120 feet, but at 1,800

---

[22] Tom Galey, "Historical Outline of the Petroleum Industry in Oklahoma and Kansas," MS in files of Gulf Oil Corporation, Gypsy Division, Tulsa, Oklahoma, and loaned the author by Mr. Rush Greenslade; *Bull. No. 40*, III, 282–85.

The survey location was T24N-R17E of the Indian Meridian.

feet the hole was lost. The second, 900 feet southwest of the first, found a high-grade oil at 645 feet; but at 1,300 feet, after the well had been "shot," it was abandoned.[23] Nothing further was done here until 1904, when it was possible to get title to the land.

On March 16, 1896, Edwin B. Foster signed a lease agreement with Chief James Bigheart and the Osage Council, which was approved by the Secretary of the Interior, providing for the development of the entire reservation. Foster's lease for the "mining" of oil and gas was to last ten years. It provided a royalty of one-tenth of the oil produced and fifty dollars a year for each gas well utilized.

When Foster died a short time later, his brother Henry organized the Phoenix Oil Company, after the lease had been assigned to him on May 8, 1896. On June 20, the Phoenix Oil Company started its first well about the center northeast quarter, Section 13, T29N-R10E of the Indian meridian, approximately one-fourth mile south of the Kansas line and about nine and one-half miles west of the northeast corner of the Osage reservation.[24] It was completed in July with only a show of oil and gas and was plugged. A second well was completed in September, nearly six miles farther west, but also as a dry hole. Then a third was drilled on Lot 32, of the southwest quarter, Section 34, T27N-R12E, and came in as a small producer. This well was drilled to a depth of 1,349 feet, where it reached an oil formation, to be known presently as the prolific "Bartlesville sand."

However, later developments on the Osage lease were slow, since the Phoenix Oil Company had to transport supplies by wagon from Independence, Kansas. In addition, there were no railroads or pipe lines to transport the oil. Indeed, it was not until 1899 that the Atchison, Topeka, and Santa Fe Railroad was built into Bartlesville.

According to one authority, this Osage well narrowly missed the distinction of being Oklahoma's "first commercial well." This honor came to a well brought in on April 15, 1897, by the Cudahy Oil Company, located on the south bank of the Caney River at Bartlesville and described as No. 1 Nellie Johnstone, northeast corner, Sec-

[23] From memorandum titled, "Outline of the Early History of the Indian Territory Illuminating Oil Company and the Beginning of the Oil Industry in Oklahoma," in the files of the Mid-Continent Oil and Gas Association, Tulsa, Oklahoma.

[24] *Ibid.* A photostat of the Foster lease was furnished the author by the Osage Indian Agency, Pawhuska, Oklahoma.

tion 12, T26N-R12E.[25] George B. Keeler had found an oil seep here as early as 1875. He had reported his discovery to William Johnstone, owner of the land, and the two men then sought to arouse the interest of others in a well. They went for advice to John F. Overfield, a traveling salesman from Chicago; and he in turn tried to induce Guffey and Galey, two Pennsylvania oilmen interested in properties at Chanute and Neodesha, Kansas, to sink a well at Bartlesville. The Pennsylvanians were interested but required that the promoters secure an extensive lease about the proposed well site. The well promoters secured their lease from the Cherokee Council, after a considerable delay, but in the meantime Guffey and Galey had lost interest.

They had better success with Michael Cudahy, who had been watching the Osage development closely. In 1896 he had taken over and deepened a well between Red Fork and Sapulpa from 1,300 to 1,750 feet but had found no oil. Then his drillers, A. P. McBride and C. L. Bloom, tore down his rig, and Keeler hauled it by wagon about seventy miles to Bartlesville in January, 1897, to start the well there.

The well reached the Oswego lime at 880 to 942 feet, the Layton sand at 975 to 987 feet, a gas sand at 1,252 to 1,267 feet, and the Bartlesville sand at 1,252 feet, when it was drilled fifteen feet deeper and then shot with nitroglycerin.[26] It was a producer, making from fifty to seventy-five barrels of oil a day. Then Cudahy met the same stalemate as Foster had on the Osage lease. Since there was no pipe line in the territory and no railroad near, the well was capped for several years. A new Congressional enactment, the Curtis law, also caused trouble; Cudahy was required to release all "unproved land," so he selected the section on which the discovery well had been drilled and in which was Bartlesville, in whose streets he drilled his wells. Later, however, it was possible to secure Indian allottee leases, and developments continued.

Bartlesville, which sprang up in the heart of the new oil field,

[25] Glenn W. Patchett, "Oklahoma's First Commercial Oil Well," in Mid-Continent Oil and Gas Association *September Bulletin* (September 29, 1937). Patchett says George B. Keeler, William Johnstone, and Frank Overlees deserve much credit for the drilling of this well.

[26] A. P. McBride, "History of the Mid-Continent Oil and Gas Field," MS summary in Kansas State Historical Library, Topeka.

was Indian Territory's first oil-boom town. Yet its roots grew deep into the past. In 1868, Nelson F. Carr had established a trading post at Silver Lake, five miles south of present-day Bartlesville. For two years he did a thriving business with the neighborhood Cherokee and Delaware Indians. Then a visiting Osage band who had been on a buffalo hunt came along and promptly put him into "involuntary bankruptcy."

Six years later, Jacob Bartles, an adopted Delaware citizen, built a trading post on the north side of the Big Caney, opposite the site of future Bartlesville. In those days this was a wild and sparsely settled region, and several families located near "Bartles Store" for mutual protection. A short time later the inevitable blacksmith shop, a grist mill, and a hotel also appeared, and a village had been formed.

But the foundation for present-day Bartlesville was not yet laid. In 1882, William Johnstone and George Keeler, the same two young men who were to bring in the first commercial well and who had formerly worked for Bartles, set up a store of their own on the west bank of the Caney. Here they did a good business. It was not long until other people from the Bartles community moved over the river to share in their prosperity. A hotel, a blacksmith shop, a drugstore, a livery stable, and, later, furniture and hardware stores were built. By 1896 the settlers had incorporated the new village of about two hundred population, with Dr. T. A. Stewart as mayor and Professor Albert Rupard as the first principal of the public school.

The Santa Fe Railroad, building south from Kansas, missed the town on the west by half a mile. But the bustling citizens moved to a new site on the railroad when Johnstone donated eighty acres for a townsite. Thus, when the first passenger train crossed the Big Caney from the north, it stopped in a brand new town. "The architectural makeshifts, the shacks and lean-tos had mostly been torn down to make room for substantial brick and stone business blocks and for commodious, modern dwellings," wrote the editor of the Bartlesville *Weekly Examiner* on December 26, 1903.

The town's real growth came with the revival of oil development. While the assessor's returns in the spring of 1902 had shown a population of only a few short of one thousand, a special enumeration made in August of the next year listed over two thousand. Bartlesville had doubled its population in twelve months. The news of oil had brought hundreds of people—oil prospectors, investors, merchants, freighters, drillers, and many others seeking adventure and opportunity. The streets of the town were muddy in rainy weather and dusty in the hot summer season. Yet they were crowded with boisterous but good-natured men, fashionably gowned women, and mules, horses, buggies, carriages, and heavily laden oil-supply wagons.

The local editor was impressed by all he saw. About the people, he said that "here the representatives of nearly every civilized nation on the globe are to be found—the sturdy Norseman from the 'Land of the Midnight Sun,' the industrious German, the Englishman who has had his eye-teeth cut, the excitable Frenchman, the 'Wild Irishman,' the carefree son of Italy, the polite scion of the Montezumas, and the patient laborer from the Isles of Greece. All are here animated by a common desire—to capture and sequester the Great American Dollar."

Important business enterprises promised greater stability. There was a glass works employing one hundred or more hands, the American Well and Prospecting Company factory, the National Supply Company, the Oil Well Supply Company, machine shops, and other businesses. The prosperity of the town was also emphasized by three banks: the First National, the Bartlesville National, and the American National, representing an aggregate capital of $100,000.

As might be expected under such circumstances, complete democracy prevailed. "The Eastern capitalist thinks nothing of lighting his fifteen-cent Havana from the stump of the cowboy's proffered 'two-fer,'" declared the editor of the *Examiner*. As he saw Bartlesville society, "All sorts and conditions of humanity are to be found here, but in spite of this heterogeneous mass the people get along well together and in the main are peaceable and law-abiding."

III

From Paola to Neodesha, Kansas

EARLY OIL DISCOVERIES in southeastern Kansas, the northern-
most segment of the eastern border of the Mid-Continent oil
district, likewise date back to the pre–Civil War period. Indeed, Kansas tradition and journals of Santa Fé traders have it that
at a very early date one of Johnson County's squatters dug a well beside the Santa Fé Trail and found in it both oil and water. He skimmed the oil from the water and sold it to lubricate the wheels of the
big freighters on the trail.

The first press notice of Kansas petroleum appeared in the
Herald of Freedom (Lawrence, Kansas) on March 31, 1855, in a
report of an Osawatomie "pure mineral oil" spring. The town sur-
veyor, a Mr. Sear, had brought a specimen of it to Editor G. W.
Brown, who proclaimed it "equally pure with the celebrated medicinal agent known as 'petroleum,' found in the vicinity of Allegheny
City, Pennsylvania." And Brown was a former Pennsylvanian.

Two years later, on July 25, R. S. Stevens also came to Brown
reporting that he had found a valuable oil spring, "or rock oil," eight
miles northeast of Paola, Kansas, and that it could be collected to
the amount of several gallons daily. He had brought a bottle of it
with him. Brown examined it and was duly impressed; and, being a
scientist, he decided to explore its possibilities.

The *Kansas State Record* (Topeka) of June 16, 1860, referred to
the same "tar springs," stating that they had been known for many
years for their curative value in treating "rheumatism and chronic
diseases, owing their origin to the diseased liver and kidneys."
Whole families of Shawnee, Sac, Fox, and Kaw Indians had camped
about them for weeks, "anointing themselves with the oil and drinking it." The editor of the *Record* believed that if this oil were in-

25

troduced into medical practice, "it would dispense with the so general use of calomel and quicksilver"; and also that the new illuminant, kerosene, extracted from "Barbadoes tar, rock oil, and Seneca oil," would soon supplant whale oil. Only recently New Bedford whalers, seeing that whale oil had declined in price from "eighty cents and one dollar a gallon to forty cents," had complained that petroleum was ruining their industry.

A short time prior to this, Brown had visited Conneautville, Pennsylvania, where the Drake well had caused a boom in oil properties, to study its oil industry. Naturally, he reasoned, Kansas would also profit if only he could drill oil wells near the Paola springs. Then, having learned all he could about Pennsylvania oil, he returned to Lawrence and persuaded a member of the territorial legislature to accompany him to the springs. The two men came to a small rivulet emptying into the Wea, a tributary to Bull Creek, east of Paola. There they found a shale bluff about ten feet in height, at the base of which springs of oil were feeding into the creek and giving the water rainbow colors.

Greatly excited, the men returned to Lawrence to study available maps of the region about the springs. Then they organized an oil company,[1] the first of its kind in Kansas, and leased 40,000 acres of land covering the district, taking the precaution of including in their contract the right of mining "for gold, silver, copper, iron, zinc, lead, tin, rock oil, or any other valuable mineral." This provision would make their stock more attractive to buyers.

After this, Brown secured a drill crew and machinery and began on Wea well No. 1 (Section 15-T17-R23) in June, 1860, continuing meanwhile, to study the surrounding terrain. Concerning this well, the federal census enumerator of 1880 said, "It is supposed that it would yield about one barrel a day." A few miles south of his first discovery, Brown found another "outcropping of oil" on a prairie rivulet, flowing over a rocky bed, and there started the company's second well. Still a few miles south, he came to a ravine filled with a waxy substance, even denser than maltha but not as hard and brittle as asphalt. It was clearly the product of the oil springs farther

[1] *The Emporia News,* of June 2, 1860, explained that Brown's lease was for thirty years and that this company had sufficient capital to carry on extensive operations.

north, he thought, which had flowed for countless ages and had hardened by evaporation and oxidation.[2]

Oil seeped into each of the company's wells when they reached a depth of about one hundred feet. Each morning, before the drillers started to work, they lifted from the wells with sand pumps the oil that had accumulated during the night.

About the same time, Dr. David Lykins found a showing of oil in a well he was digging on the mission farm (Section 15-T17-R24), about a mile southeast of Paola. He induced Brown, Solomon and Company, Brown's organization, to commence its well No. 3 in the bottom of this well, and they ultimately drilled to a total depth of about 275 feet. But when they had drilled sixty feet, about ninety feet from the surface, the drillers found a "gold bearing rock some two feet in thickness," according to Brown. Each day he subjected the "borings" to a mercury test and found that with each spoonful of the dust and chippings, globules of gold from the size of a pinhead to that of duck shot were extracted. Other officials of the company now wanted to sink a shaft to this formation and to start mining for gold, not knowing, as Brown had suspected from the first, that one of their number had deliberately tampered with the well to create interest. And it was only with great difficulty that the excitement was allayed and drilling resumed.

From the waxy substance that Brown had found in the rivulet, those members of his company who were "somewhat posted in geology" thought that nature's erosion through countless millions of years might have caused the oil formation to disappear and to leave behind only maltha. "Is it not possible that we are below the oil-bearing sand?" they inquired. Brown thought not and persuaded them to continue drilling; but with the approach of winter (1860–61) drilling was discontinued.

Then, said Brown, "To satisfy ourselves the oil was still below us we procured tubing, a steam engine, and with these in place, and a seed bag at the bottom to cut off drippings from above, we commenced pumping. The salt water, which with seventy-two hours of

[2] Dr. G. W. Brown, "First Well In Kansas," in the Independence (Kansas) *Daily Reporter*, Vol. XXV (December, 1905), 5–6, Kansas Historical Library, Topeka. Also Brown to "State Geologist of Kansas," October 28, 1903, in *The University Geological Survey of Kansas*, Special Report on Oil and Gas, IX, 22.

continuous pumping we could not exhaust, was continuously covered with oil."

While they were making this experiment, the Civil War began. With raiding by Jayhawkers on the one hand and by Bushwackers on the other, it was thought best to suspend operations until after the war. However, when that time came, two of the company officials were dead, one had suffered financial ruin from Quantrill's raid on Lawrence, and one had fled from Kansas because of his Southern sympathies; consequently, operations were not resumed.

Brown's own story of this early Kansas oil venture reveals that during the winter of 1860–61, he had visited Pennsylvania to gather facts about "drilling, tubing, storing of oil, and refining," preparatory to a full-scale oil business in Kansas. He made the naïve confession that he had consulted a local lady clairvoyant, whose advice and forecast were "furnished gratuitously." She said that "the whole country where you are proposing to explore for oil, at a considerable depth, appears filled with oil. It is not only on the Wea, but the south and west is saturated with oil. . . I see it in the sand, in the rocks, and there are vast pools of it."

Popular interest in the Paola wells revived in 1865. As early as February 23 of this year the *Kansas Weekly Tribune* (Lawrence) carried a report from Topeka of "Coal oil wells" in Miami County, no doubt referring to the renewal of work on the Lykins well by a local company. Three months later the *Tribune* stated that Paola oil discoveries were attracting considerable attention, that a great quantity of land had been leased, and that machinery was being shipped in so that boring could begin.

Then came a report on the Miami County development from another quarter. J. G. Reaser wrote the editor of the Leavenworth *Conservative* that he had seen a bottle of Miami petroleum, "the simon pure article," and that a sample of it had been sent to a competent Philadelphia chemist for analysis. Paola luxuriated in an oil boom. "Gentlemen from Ohio, Indiana, Illinois, and Pennsylvania" were there, the enthusiastic Reaser said. They were "looking around" but keeping quiet. He hoped that this boom would bring thousands of prospectors and promoters; but there is no record of the fulfillment of his wishes.

Paola was crowded out of the news column by Fort Scott on

From Paola to Neodesha, Kansas

July 22, when the *Tribune* published a letter from B. P. McDonald to John W. Wright. "We struck oil on the evening of the 20th at a depth of 280 feet in oil-bearing sand stone," was McDonald's exciting announcement. "We had bored about eighteen feet in sand stone when we struck the oil first—expect a large supply when we get through that rock. Gas is so strong that a bucket will not pass through without weighting." Nevertheless, the Fort Scott well proved to be little more than a gasser.

In fact, there were many other similar discoveries during these postwar days. The Kansas state geologist, Professor G. C. Swallow, added immeasurably to oilmen's interest by reporting in November, 1865, that scarcely a well had been dug in Miami County without "finding petroleum in some of its forms." He said that "four sandstone formations are in many places perfectly saturated with it," that it was found in all other rock cavities, and that it had been flowing in considerable quantities from a "score of springs from time immemorial."[3]

Within the next two decades there were several small gas wells drilled near southeastern Kansas towns. In 1870 one of these, at Wyandotte, struck a strong flow of gas at 737 feet.[4] Another was drilled at Guilford in the spring of 1874. The roar of the escaping gas could be heard for more than a mile. An inquisitive well driller tested its burning quality by applying a match to the well's mouth. "A solid column of flame shot up from the well," singeing his whiskers, eyebrows, and hair, and throwing him some distance from the well, evidently leaving him meditating upon the peculiarity of gas.[5] The Fort Scott *Monitor* of January 1, 1887, mentioned similar discoveries, and reported that the Economy Gas and Fuel Company was engaged in drilling other wells and piping the gas into town.

J. J. Werner, a Pennsylvanian who had come from the Pennsylvania oil region to Texas, kept a hotel at Belleville. On a table in the waiting room was a book, *History of Pennsylvania,* in which a visit-

[3] Swallow's report was quoted in part in the *Kansas Tribune* (Lawrence), November 23, 1865.

[4] Account of this well is found in the Newton *Weekly Republican*, October 5, 1888.

[5] *The Wilson County Citizen* (Fredonia, Kansas), June 12, 1874. Later, in the eighteen-nineties other gas wells were drilled at Iola in Allen County, and Cherryville, Coffeyville, and Independence in Montgomery County.

ing roomer, H. J. Foote, read about oil. He told Werner that he knew where there were fine oil showings in Kansas and Indian Territory. Werner, with a show of great interest, suggested that if he could go with him to these sites, they would organize a company, lease the necessary lands, and drill. Foote accepted his offer, and a short time later the two men were traveling northward. They stopped in Indian Territory to secure leases, but they found the federal government's restrictive policy too much of a handicap. Then they moved on to Kansas, leased properties about Paola, and organized an oil and gas company composed of Foote, Werner, Charles Kitchen, James Briggs, A. Buck, E. M. Wickersham, and H. M. Lauchlin, all except the first two of Paola and Olathe, Kansas, and W. C. McCartney of New York.[6]

The two ambitious promoters lost no time. While Foote was busy acquiring leases, Werner went east to purchase drilling equipment, which he shipped to Paola, and they commenced work on their first well.

The interest of local citizens was intense. Day after day they thronged the well, watching operations. One night someone poured enough oil into the well to make an excellent showing the next morning. This increased spectator excitement. Then several barrels of oil were shipped in, and it was suggested to Werner that he pour it into the well so that they could sell their rights to an unsuspecting public. Werner indignantly refused. And presently his honesty was rewarded, for on July 25, 1882, the drillers encountered a considerable showing of gas. Paolans now came in even greater numbers, all curious to see this phenomenon. To accommodate them, enterprising merchants built soft-drink stands and a dancing platform in the vicinity of the well.

The first oil well, good for about ten barrels a day, was found at Paola, in June, 1888, on the Russell farm six miles east of town, after more than a dozen others had been bored for gas. "Lubricating oil is thrown out in considerable quantity and the sand in which the gas was struck is more like the sand of the gas deposits in Ohio and Pennsylvania," wrote the Paola editor of the *Western Spirit* on May 10, 1889.

Here for the first time in Kansas a nitroglycerin shot was tried to

[6] *University Geological Survey of Kansas*, IX, 28.

increase production. In one or two other instances dynamite had been fired but without great success. In this case, when ten quarts of nitroglycerin were used in the bottom of the well, "a stream of oil went to the top of the derrick," and "the casing was blown up 15 feet or 20 feet and a joint or two of it bursted." A Standard Oil Company official pronounced the black oil which came from the well a superior lubricant, and the Smithsonian Institution at Washington classified it as superior to the West Virginia oil and the best oil yet found.

Later, the *Western Spirit* amplified its first announcement. The promoters were importing barrels and tanks to hold the oil, which found a friendly market at twenty cents a gallon. This, thought the editor, would net the oil company $800 a month, or $9,600 a year. Other chemical analyses had also been made, in New York, Cincinnati, and Rochester, which confirmed the previous finding.[7] Only the product of Mecca, Ohio, was thought to be superior.

News of the Russell farm well brought other drillers and promoters to Paola. McBride and Bloom drilled a second well on the Rathwell farm east of town,[8] and others quickly followed. Most of the drilling at this time was for gas, although some oil was found. The Paola Oil, Gas and Mining Company erected a small twenty-five-barrel refinery. Then a declining market caused officials to turn the plant over to a receiver, Henry C. Jones, who five years later sold it to the Standard Oil Company. The refinery parts were then removed to Neodesha, Kansas, and subsequently used there.

Neither Paola's oil wells nor its refinery became commercially important. Kansas properly dates the beginning of its commercial production from 1892. W. M. Mills, a former Pennsylvanian, drilled the first truly commercial well. Earlier, he had put down gas wells about Paola and had installed gas-distribution systems there and at Osawatomie and Spring Hill. In 1891 he came to Neodesha, in Wilson County, advancing the belief that both gas and oil could be found in paying quantities there, and backed his judgment by securing leases on 10,000 acres of land. The well-known driller, C. L. Bloom, aided Mills in securing the support of Neodesha business-

[7] *Western Enterprise*, May 24, 1889.

[8] A. P. McBride, "A History of the Mid-Continent Oil and Gas Field," MS in the Kansas State Historical Library, Topeka, Kansas.

men—Dr. Thomas Blakeslee, William Hill, banker, and two drug-gists, Pierce and Eson. These men promised support for Mills' pro-posal to provide the town with a natural-gas supply.

A local blacksmith, T. J. Norman, played a more important part; he donated a four-acre tract in the eastern part of the town for a drilling site. Here Mills drilled his first well, which reached an oil sand at 832 feet on November 28, 1892, with an initial production of twelve barrels of 32-gravity oil. He started another well on an eight-acre tract a short time later but abandoned it because of drilling difficulties. Then he began a third well, but exhausted his funds and was forced to suspend operations.[9]

Mills made several trips to New York and Pennsylvania to se-cure funds for the development of his Neodesha leases, but Eastern oilmen had little faith in Kansas as an oil country. Next, he visited Pittsburgh, taking with him a two-ounce bottle of oil from the Nor-man well, and applied for a loan to John H. Galey, of the firm of Guffey and Galey.[10] Galey made no loan but, instead, offered to take over Mills' interests in the name of his firm, carrying him for a one-quarter interest. Mills accepted, although a short time later he sold his share to his two partners for $4,000 and returned to Osawatomie to resume his natural-gas operations.

Galey came to Neodesha in 1893 to appraise his company's holdings and to secure other leases. He employed William G. Bry-son, an Ohio drilling contractor, as field superintendent, and he and Guffey were thus able to ship supplies and materials to Neodesha without having it become known that they were backing the local development.

A Pittsburgh stranger, representing the Mellon interests, also entered the field in quest of leases. He warned landowners against trading with Guffey and Galey, because of their sharp dealing.

9 Galey MS, as cited.

10 John H. Galey had been associated with William Hartley in bringing in the Maple Shade well, at Pleasantville, Pennsylvania. He had also been identified with the firm of McKinney Brothers, of Titusville, Pennsylvania. And he was credited with achieving perhaps the greatest success in the oil industry up to that time by his early development of the world-famous McDonald field, in 1891. In this field was the Mathew well which had a record production of 850 barrels of oil an hour when it was nearly sixty days old. It was during this period that Galey became as-sociated with James M. Guffey, with whom he later operated in the Southwest.— *Derrick's Hand-Book of Petroleum, from 1859 to 1898*, I, 670.

From Paola to Neodesha, Kansas

When Bryson relayed this information to his employers, Colonel James M. Guffey immediately came to Neodesha. On the streets of this western town he was a striking figure, with long hair, flowing tie, shining boots and a wide-brimmed soft hat.[11] Bryson drove him in a buckboard to various parts of the field to counteract his competitor's representations, and success crowned his efforts, for he secured leases on upward of 1,000,000 acres of land in Wilson, Allen, Neosho, Elk, Montgomery, Linn, and Chautauqua counties.

These leases gave the company the privilege of drilling on the land for ten years; they provided for a royalty of twenty-five cents an acre each year, to be paid if the drilling was not begun within two years; and provided further that landowners should receive one-tenth of the oil stored in tanks. If gas were found, the landowner was to receive free light and fuel for domestic use and fifty dollars a year for every well utilized by the lessees.

Guffey and Galey first drilled a gas well on the J. J. Haag farm three miles northwest of Neodesha in June, 1893. Their next was a fair oil producer on the Pierce farm a short distance southwest of town. They drilled fifteen wells that summer, all of them near Neodesha, and all but two were oil producers. Then they were ready to move. In fact, they were typical wildcatters, searching always for new oil territory and for "gushers." They drilled as far northeast as Pleasanton and Mound City and as far west as western Chautauqua County. They also moved into Indian Territory, pioneering at Bartlesville, Chelsea, Muskogee, Tulsa, and Red Fork.[12] Crude production from their wells had presently filled their storage, consisting of earthern reservoirs and two 36,000-barrel steel tanks. And there was no immediate prospect for a market.

They did have a slender revenue from the sale of gas which they piped into Neodesha. Other pipes were also laid from oil wells,

[11] James M. Guffey's experience in the oil industry began in 1872 while he was general agent for the Gibbs and Sterrett Manufacturing Company, at that time the largest manufacturers of oil-well machinery and supplies in Pennsylvania. For the next twenty-five years he operated in nearly every new oil field in Pennsylvania and West Virginia, and as early as 1883 he became interested in the possibilities of natural gas, to which interest the cities and towns of western Pennsylvania, Ohio, and Indiana owed him a great debt for the development of their gas lands. Then in 1893 he came to Kansas as a partner of John H. Galey.

[12] Frank C. Schrader and Erasmus Haworth, *Economic Geology of the Independence Quadrangle, Kansas*, 21.

so that Guffey and Galey may well be credited with beginning the north Mid-Continent area's oil pipe lines.

The fact that Guffey and Galey had no great market outlet did not halt them. Their drilling activities expanded widely and rapidly, resulting in the discovery of pool after pool, all the way from Peru to Pleasanton. This only added to their storage problem, for by 1895 they had on hand 150,000 barrels of oil, a daily output of 800 barrels in the Neodesha pool and 1,000 more in widely scattered wells. Yet it was essential that they dispose of their oil. They had invested a half-million dollars in their Kansas venture and had only an inconsiderable income from their gas wells.

The two operators had attempted to secure favorable railroad rates to Kansas City and Omaha without success; they could ship neither crude nor refined oil from Neodesha without a loss. With this difficulty confronting them, Galey went to New York and laid his company's problem before Henry M. Flagler and John D. Archbold of the Standard Oil Company. The result was that on October 30, 1895, the Forest Oil Company, a producing branch of the Standard Oil Company, bought Guffey and Galey's holdings and properties for $225,000.

In recounting the history of these early days, Thomas F. Smiley states that the Forest Oil Company then employed at a handsome salary John Fertig as Kansas manager.[13] Fertig was making gas engines in Pittsburgh, but accepted the Forest Oil Company's offer and started for the new field at once. Neodeshans were so jubilant that a big company was entering the field that they built Fertig a substantial two-story house in the best part of town. Now, they thought, their town would grow, and refineries, steel plants, factories, and other businesses would follow.

In Kansas, Fertig reported that Guffey and Galey had left their records and leases in confusion. He said that he had unearthed some of the leases from barrels, and some from "other queer receptacles," of which only one thousand of perhaps a total of nine thousand leases were yet alive. But others were acquired, and the business was reorganized.

Fertig energetically started to work. He extended to Chanute

[13] "The Mid-Continent's Discovery Oil Well," a MS supplied the author, along with others, by President E. A. Warren of the First National Bank, Neodesha, Kansas.

the pipe line which Guffey and Galey had built. He ordered carloads of casing, boilers, engines, rig irons, and other equipment, and also asked an Eastern representative of the firm to send along forty oil-field workers, such as drillers, tool dressers, and roustabouts. When they arrived, they appeared to Neodeshans as a sorry lot. "After an uproarious journey," says Smiley, "the men marched in swaying lines through the main street vociferously inquiring of the world at large 'What the hell did you bring us here for?' The coaches in which they had ridden had to undergo repairs. Mr. Fertig paid the railroad for the damage done and was reimbursed by Mr. Archbold."

"It is practically impossible for anyone to learn accurately the results of the operations of the Forest Oil Company," complained the *Kansas City Star* on April 30, 1896. The company's policy was to keep its affairs to itself, warning that "the man who talks walks." Its officers were "smooth, courteous and silent, yet willing to give information that was unimportant." But the *Star* also admitted progress. From Humbolt on the north to the southern boundary of Chautauqua County, the Forest Company had drilled 34 wells, owned 136, of which 40 were oil wells, and 10 gas; it had built four great iron storage tanks, each with a capacity of from 30,000 to 35,000 barrels and was building another. Three of these tanks were at Neodesha, two of which stored 70,000 barrels of oil; two were at Thayer, in Neosho County, about twelve miles from Neodesha. The company owned 500,000 acres of leases and had a force of experienced oilmen, including drillers, rig builders, pumpers, and office men, with a pay roll of $3,000 a month. The average depth of its wells was 850 feet, and drilling cost ranged from $1,800 to $2,800 a well.

For pumping oil from wells to storage tanks in the field, the Forest Oil Company used a "shackle-rod system," a device so arranged that a dozen or more rods extended from all sides of the power house and were supported on posts to operate as many wells, thus requiring only one man to care for the gas-burning engine and to watch all the wells within his district.

In January, 1897, O. A. Evans became manager of the Forest Oil Company at Neodesha, and a month later the first stakes of a 500-barrel refinery were driven. The work was pushed, so that on May

11, 1897, the first batch of crude oil was run to the stills.[14] At this time the plant consisted of two crude stills, one steam still, one agitator, one pump house, one boiler house, a small loading rack, seventeen tanks, and other miscellaneous installations, all on about eight and one-half acres of land. Thomas Black was the refinery's first superintendent, coming to Neodesha from Whiting, Indiana, in April, 1897. He was an experienced refiner, having begun his career with the Atlantic Refining Company at Franklin, Pennsylvania, in 1882.

Black explained to occasional visitors his refining process. Crude oil was first placed into a shell still[15] and put through a distillation process to take out the black color. It thus went to the steam still where it received a flash test to determine its safety burning point, after which it passed on to the agitator.[16] There it was treated with sulphuric acid to remove the color remaining after distillation. Thousands of water-sprays were shot into the oil while it was in the agitator. The water passed from the tank bottom, carrying with it dirt and discoloration and leaving the refined oil.

The refinery did a thriving business and attracted other industries to Neodesha. In fact, petroleum's impact on Kansas towns and society within the oil belt was marked. The *Kansas City Star* of January 18, 1903, boasted that "Kansas, struggling a few years ago to pay off a heart-breaking load of indebtedness, is alive today with the hum of factory wheels, the flare of furnaces in foundry and glass plants, brick yard and smelters, flour mills, sorghum mills, cotton mills"—all as a result of the coming of oil. Iola had no fewer than one hundred gas wells, with manufacturing industries, cement works, smelters, brick plants, and other businesses. At Neodesha, Cherryvale, Coffeyville, and Chanute, there were other similar enterprises.

[14] On January 1, 1901, the Forest Oil Company was taken over by the Prairie Oil and Gas Company, with a capital stock of $2,500,000, under the presidency of W. J. Young of Pittsburgh, Pennsylvania.—E. A. Metcalf, "Data on Early History of the Standard Oil Company [Kansas]," MS furnished the author by Mr. Metcalf, superintendent of the Neodesha refinery. Mr. Metcalf also supplied the author with other valuable materials on Neodesha's early oil history.

[15] A cylindrical container for heating oil so that the resulting vapors could be produced for condensing.

[16] An "agitator" was a tower or chamber for mixing and agitating the crude oil being treated.

From Paola to Neodesha, Kansas

But an overindulgence in optimism sometimes brought fatal results, as in the case of Radical City, a few miles northeast of Independence. It sprang up and grew as a result of oil- and gas-field prosperity and the approach of the Missouri Pacific Railroad. A city hall, a church, and a schoolhouse were built, and attractive homes surrounded the business center. Streets were laid out and a park platted, with fountains, driveways, shade trees, and flowers. Then the railroad surveyors came, and planted their stakes nearly two miles southeast of town, and Radical City went the way of many another boom town.

Everywhere in the Kansas oil country fortunes were made from small investments. The drillers A. C. McBride and C. L. Bloom furnish an interesting example. At first they were tool dressers, earning a meager wage by the sweat of their brows and the strength of their brawny arms. One day, according to a contemporary observer, McBride astonished his partner by saying, "Bloom, this won't do. We must break into something. Let's buy a string of tools and get a lease."

"But how?" Bloom queried. "I haven't the price, and you know better than to tell me that you have."

"That's all right," Mac grinned. "We'll buy the tools just the same."

They did, on credit; and by 1902, under the name of the Independence Gas Company, they had several good gas and oil wells near by, and controlled other favorable drilling sites in Montgomery County, amounting to more than 75,000 acres.

Kansas also remembers the experiences of three railroad men. One of them, Samuel Warner, general passenger agent of the Kansas City Southern Railway, invested $500 in Chanute property, and by 1902 his holdings were quoted at $30,000. Another, Hugh Hale, a former railroad conductor who had saved his wages made on a Santa Fe passenger train, purchased a Neodesha lease, which in a short time became a valuable oil property. And the third, N. N. Pauline, also a Santa Fe Railroad conductor, grew rich from a small investment made at Moline, in Elk County. Like Hale, he had saved his money; and, after trying to make a lucky strike in the Iola gas field, he arranged with a Kansas City friend to drill a well for him at Moline. At a shallow depth the well struck a strong flow of gas, which Pauline piped into town to consumers and thus ended his ticket-punching days.

J. H. Brown surprised his friends by selling his Beaumont, Texas, property after the first Spindletop well was drilled and buying acreage on a low-lying ridge north of Cherryvale, Kansas. But his faith was justified; his first well opened an important gas field.

Then there were Chanute quick-rich oilmen. Alderman Rosenthal would not drill for gas and oil but reaped a rich harvest from his land in leases and royalties; and Dr. Barker, his neighbor, who owned a large tract of land in the near-by oil field, sold 240 acres of it to a company for $25,000 and, in addition, received one-eighth royalty and one-eighth interest in the company. George Z. Work, a Chicago dry-goods merchant accepted 400 acres of Chanute land on an overdue account, and, when oil was found on it a short time later, refused an offer of $50,000 for it.

The spread of gas- and oil-field discoveries in southeastern Kansas during the late eighteen nineties was rapid. A federal report of 1901 listed oil and gas fields at Paola, Osawatomie, Fort Scott, Wyandotte, Rosedale, Greeley, Iola, and La Harpe, Chanute, Peru, Cherryvale, Coffeyville, Humbolt, and Neodesha. In addition, it gave the Kansas yearly oil production from 1889 to 1900.

PRODUCTION OF PETROLEUM IN KANSAS FROM 1889 TO 1900[17]

Year	Amount (Barrels)	Year	Amount (Barrels)
1889	500	1896	113,571
1890	1,200	1897	81,098
1891	1,400	1898	71,980
1892	-----	1899	69,700
1893	18,000	1900	74,714
1894	40,000	Total	516,593
1895	44,430		

I. N. Knapp opened the Chanute oil field, and by the next year he had drilled more than one hundred wells and had begun shipping

[17] Geological Survey, No. 184 (49,120), MS, Series A, Economic Geology, 13, Department of the Interior, National Archives, Washington, D. C.

crude oil to Kansas City and Omaha. Other discoveries were made in adjoining counties, so that by 1905 leases covered much of Neosho, Wilson, Montgomery, Chautauqua, Franklin, and Miami counties, and production exceeded 3,000,000 barrels. This went quite beyond Kansas' "lamp and lubricant" needs, and only the state railroads and Standard Oil Company's pipe line could furnish the producers a market outlet.

Although Independence was primarily noted for its gas field, its citizens in 1903 became excited over an oil field near the little town of Bolton, five miles southwest of Independence on the Atchison, Topeka and Santa Fe Railroad. Almost the entire area of the field—three and one-half square miles—was productive of oil. McBride and Bloom drilled the first well on Jeff Bolt's land[18] during the fall and winter of 1902–1903, then a larger producer on J. L. Bank's farm made 1,000 barrels at better than 1,100 feet. The drillers of the Bolt well were hunting gas and found oil at a depth of 1,180 feet. Derricks were built rapidly and other 1,000-barrel producers came in. By the middle of 1904 the Bolton area had about two hundred producing wells, and the field had been extended northward to and around Walker Mound and to another productive pool between Wayside and Havana, southwest of Bolton.[19]

For four years, from 1899 to 1902, the crude-oil market was fairly stable, the price ranging from 75 to 90 cents a barrel, but by the end of the next year it had increased to $1.38. Then it began a rapid decline from which it did not recover. On February 12, 1904, it was quoted at $1.31 and by January 31 of the next year it had sunk to 70 cents.[20]

When the Standard Oil Company first started buying Kansas oil, it divided the region into two divisions, called North Neodesha and South Neodesha. It set its bigger price on the South Neodesha (south of the town) oil, paying 20 cents more than for oil from the North Neodesha division. Early in the summer of 1903, South Neodesha oil sold for as high as $1.38 a barrel. Late in the next year the Standard Oil Company revised its system of classifying oil, buying by gravity tests, with the highest price on 32 degrees Baumé

[18] Southeast quarter, S18-T33-R15E.
[19] *University Geological Survey of Kansas*, IX, 38.
[20] Schrader and Haworth, *op. cit.*, 25–26.

(0.8641), which it still called South Neodesha oil, and oil heavier than this, e.g. 28 degrees (0.8860), was priced at 40 cents a barrel below that testing 32 degrees. Oil from the Bolton field graded about 34 degrees, and in that from the eastern part of Montgomery County, around Cherryvale and Coffeyville, the grade was variable.

Oilmen anxiously watched this price trend. The fortunes of four hundred companies, six thousand farmers whose lands were under lease, and about twenty-five thousand persons interested directly or indirectly in the oil business were affected. Clearly the market was glutted. The small Neodesha refinery could not buy all the oil offered for sale. The Prairie Oil and Gas Company frantically built tanks, laid pipe lines, and bought all the oil it could market or store; but this was not enough. Seven million barrels of crude oil were in Kansas storage tanks, and wells were still producing at a rapid rate. Then, to handle a probable increase of oil in the future, the Standard Oil Company in the fall of 1904 began to lay a pipe line from the Kansas field to its large refinery, at Whiting, Indiana (near Chicago), thereby connecting with its eastern system of pipe lines and making a composite line of 1,800 miles reaching from Kansas to the Atlantic seaboard.

Corporation activities that in former years would have passed unnoticed were now watched suspiciously by persons caught in this oil-transportation tie-up. The fact that the Standard Oil Company had in 1905 acquired holdings in Indian Territory caused the Kansans to believe that their petroleum was being refused and that this company was seeking the better quality Indian Territory oil.[21]

[21] John D. Rockefeller was the guiding genius of Standard Oil's early development. In 1862 he entered a partnership with Maurice B. Clark and Samuel Andrews to operate a small Cleveland, Ohio, refinery, a venture that was successful. Then, ten years later, he organized the Standard Oil Company, the country's foremost shipper of petroleum products; and soon thereafter Standard broadened its base to engage in producing, refining, and marketing oil. Like other corporations of this period, Standard engaged in exclusive contracts (particularly with railroads) and increased public suspicion, from which it could not escape in later years, when it employed more circumspect business ethics. In 1882, Rockefeller and his associates organized the Standard Oil Trust, which was shortly dissolved because of an adverse court decision in a case brought against the company by the state of Ohio.

Standard then incorporated under the New Jersey law as a $100,000,000 corporation, but it continued to meet with unfriendly court action. Subsequently, in 1911, it was forced to relinquish control of its subsidiaries and two years later was ousted from Texas, as will be seen in Chapter XIV.

But the mother company, Standard Oil Company (N. J.), yet burdened by a

OSAWATOMIE.

The old historic town of Osawatomie is beautifully situated between the Osage and Potawatomie rivers, about one-half mile above their junction. Holy memories cluster around this spot. Here John Brown struck the first blows of the contest that caused the shackles to drop from the limbs of 4,000,000 slaves. Here Horace Greely made his famous speech at the organization of the Republican Party. Here were fought those desperate battles between the Free Soilers and and Border Ruffians. Here happened many of the events that are preserved in song and story.

But all these things has passed away. We wish to speak now of the Osawatomie of to-day. One by one the old "war horses" have passed away and their places filled with younger men, bent upon developing the natural resources of the the country.

The Pennsylvania Mining and Gas Co. have leased 100,000 acres of land, and are now engaged in drilling wells. The view given on the other side is "Well No. 1." This well is 700 feet deep and furnishes the strongest flow of natural gas of any well west of the Penn. gas region. At a depth of 500 feet they passsed through a vein of superior coal seven feet in thickness. They also found a superior quality of lubricating oil containing so little refuse matter that no refining is necessary before using. They are now (Apr. 22,) at work on well No. 2 and will put several wells down.

Large manufacturers from the east are inquiring daily about our resources with a view to locating here. Other companies have been organized who will put down wells at once, and will guarantee a supply of cheap fuel to all comers.

Jay Gould has decided to locate the machine and repair shops of his whole S. W. system here. These shops will employ over 2000 men.

Osawatomie is the eastern terminus of the C. G., O, C. & O. R. R. that is completed to Great Bend, Kas., a distance of 250 miles, and is being built to Denver Colorado. This city is also the Northern terminus of the V. V. & I. R. R. that is now completed to Independence and will soon pass through the Indian Territory. We extend an invitation to all to come. Manufactures, investors, home seekers.

Well improved farms near Osawatomie are selling for less money than poorer land farther west.

Ours is no spasmodic "Boom" but is a Boom that has a solid basis. A Boom that will live long after other so called "Booms" have passed to the "Long ago."

Letters addressed to any of the following will receive prompt attention: Smith & Campbell, Real Estate Agents. Roberts & Giller, Real Etate Agents Chas. S. Bixby, Editor of "The GASLIGHT."

Presented by *Chas S. Bixby*

Osawatomie Kas

E. A. Warren

John H. Galey at a southeastern Kansas oil well

American Petroleum Institute

From Paola to Neodesha, Kansas

Now, they said, the Standard Oil Company had a direct pipe-line connection between its Indian Territory field and its new Sugar Creek refinery near Kansas City, Missouri. Unhappily, too, the Santa Fe Railroad raised its freight rates unreasonably high, as though to tie in with "the conspiracy." To the Kansans this seemed plausible since there were other rumors of Standard's "sharp dealings." It had made a differential of twenty cents a barrel in favor of oil from fields south of Neodesha and had imposed a mileage charge of 3 per cent against oil impurities, which the independents declared did not exist, and another of from one-half to 1 per cent for "steaming" the oil, to move it more easily through the pipe lines.

The Prairie Company explained to the independents that neither its pipe-line system nor its refinery had been built to care for the total amount of Kansas oil production, and that beyond purchasing what it could handle locally, it had as a favor to them filled its storage space with oil it could not then refine.

Governor Edward W. Hock called the attention of his legislature to the southeastern Kansas oil problem and asked for remedial legislation. Meanwhile, the independent lease jobbers, producers, and royalty-holders went into action. They held a mass meeting in H. E. West's office at Peru, and made tentative plans for a second meeting at Topeka, in late January, 1905.

At this second meeting, held in the Commercial Club, W. E. Connelley, a Chanute oil promoter, proposed a series of five laws, which, a short time later, the legislature approved.[22] One established maximum freight rates on oil; another prohibited rebates; a third declared against discrimination by any person or corporation in the price of oil in one place from that in another; a fourth made

handicap of official distrust because of Standard's early corporate and trust practices, has grown into one of America's biggest industrial enterprises, now under the presidency of Eugene Holman. By 1940 it had become a two-billion-dollar holding company, with such powerful regional subsidiaries or affiliates as the Standard Oil Company of Louisiana (with its big refinery at Baton Rouge), the Humble Oil and Refining Company (an affiliate), and the Carter Oil Company. It produced in 1940 about 10 per cent of the world's crude oil, refined over 14 per cent of it, operated 12.5 per cent of the world's total tanker tonnage, and held 36,000,000 barrels of the world gross proven reserves.

[22] For Connelley's narrative of this period, see "The Kansas Oil Producers Against the Standard Oil Company," in Kansas Historical *Collections, 1905–1906,* IX, 94–101. Kansas Session Laws of 1905, chap. 315, p. 526; *ibid.,* chap. 2, p. 2; and *ibid.,* chap. 315, secs. 3, 4, p. 536.

pipe lines common carriers for all oil producers; and a fifth provided for a state-owned, 1,000-barrel refinery. But the state supreme court a short time later declared the last, the refinery measure, unconstitutional.

In fact, a state refinery was hardly needed, for by 1905 independent refineries began to spring up—the Paola Refinery Company of 250-barrel capacity; the Uncle Sam Refining Company at Cherryvale; the Superior Refinery at Longston; and the Sunflower Refining Company at Niotaze, in Chautauqua County. In 1906, six more refineries were built, and within the next three years, one in every town of the district.

IV

Corsicana, the Curtain Raiser

PETROLEUM DERIVATIVES, such as those used in medicine, kerosene, fuel, and lubricants, had come into general use in the United States by the late eighteen nineties and the early nineteen hundreds. But producers and refiners were hardly prepared to handle the deluge of oil dumped on the market with the turn of the century.

The Corsicana oil field served as a curtain raiser to a new era, the oil age, a period during which radically increased production, volume transportation, better refining, and improved marketing gave truth to the old adage that "necessity is the mother of invention." Obviously, these four problems were not entirely solved; but progress made in this direction, as in the building of pipe lines, tank cars, sea-going tankers, and refineries, and in the finding of new markets, focused the attention of ambitious and thoughtful businessmen and financiers on this new industry.

The discovery of oil at Corsicana was accidental. The city fathers had given a contract to the American Well and Prospecting Company, headed by H. G. Johnson, Elmer Akins, and Charles Rittersbacher, to bore three water wells. On June 9, 1894, while drilling at a depth of 1,027 feet,[1] the drillers were annoyed to find oil—annoyed since they had to case it off to keep it from contaminating warm artesian water, which they finally reached at 2,470 feet. But still oil permeated the soil on the outside of the casing. News of this oil strike was heralded throughout the community, and people came daily to see the well.

[1] J. S. Cullinan stated that the oil sand was reached at 1,035 feet. See Cullinan to Z. T. Fullmore, May 19, 1899, in Lou Kemp Papers, Houston. C. A. Warner gives 1,027, in *Texas Oil and Gas*, 24. *Derrick's Hand-Book of Petroleum, 1898 and 1899*, II, 172.

Oil! Titan of the Southwest

Texas was far removed from the Eastern oil fields, where petroleum had already found a ready market, but there were Corsicana businessmen willing to invest in it, although three derricks over the first well had been burned down by the carelessness of curious spectators, and the drilling contractors had become almost bankrupt. Earlier oil finds in Jefferson, Hardin, and Bexar counties had proved that oil could be produced and sold at profit in Texas.

There might be even major possibilities at Corsicana, reasoned Major Alexander Beaton and H. G. Damon, two local promoters, who organized the Corsicana Oil Development Company to prove their theory. John Davidson, an experienced Pennsylvania oilman, joined their firm. On September 6, 1894, they secured, from A. Bunert and his wife, a lease, carrying with it the provision "to dig, bore and mine for and gather all oil, gasses, coal or other minerals," and promising the lessors one-tenth of their proceeds. They also procured other leases and granted J. M. Guffey and John H. Galey a one-half interest in their Corsicana holdings if they would bore and equip five wells.

The two Pennsylvanians accepted the proposal. The site chosen for the first well was on a lot two hundred feet south of the city's new artesian well. At a depth of 1,030 feet the drill reached a "shale sand" and in it secured both oil and gas, the oil output being by natural flow two and one-half barrels a day. Afterwards the drillers used a nitroglycerin shot to increase the flow of oil, and finally worked it with compressed air, but it never paid well.

Galey selected the site of his second well on South Eleventh Street, about a block north of the Cotton Belt Railroad, on January 15, 1896, but he found no oil. In the following May, he drilled the third well at Fourth and Collins streets, and it came in as a twenty-two-barrel producer. On July 1 and August 5 of the same year, the fourth and fifth wells were finished producing twenty and twenty-five barrels of oil a day. This completed the contract of Guffey and Galey, and by the end of the year their Corsicana output increased the total production of oil in Texas to 1,450 barrels.

These successful wells caused local men to organize the Texas Petroleum Oil Company. Still other companies sprang up like mushrooms. Leading Corsicana businessmen bought stock in these concerns, and by 1897 development work on a large scale had be-

44

gun. For several months operations were confined to the city limits. Town lots were leased all over the eastern part of the city, a royalty of 8 and 10 per cent being given the owner.

Presently an oil craze struck the town and the inrush of oil seekers grew day by day. Derricks sprang up as if by magic all over the east side of Corsicana and then beyond the city limits. "It was frequently the case," said an eyewitness, "that wells on different lots of 50x150 feet would be drilled within a few feet of each other."[2] Property owners consented to wells being drilled in their front or back yards, in their gardens and horse lots.

When news regarding the Corsicana oil field first reached the East, people from the oil regions of Pennsylvania, Ohio, Indiana, and other states flocked into the quiet little Texas town, which speedily grew into a crowded, hustling, and boisterous young city, with overcrowded hotels and boardinghouses. Houses that had been vacant for years were rented at fancy prices, and everyone had employment. The boom was on. Every available lot in town and farm property well beyond town were plastered with oil leases.

The boom went beyond Corsicana to other Texas oil-producing areas. During 1897, fifty-seven wells were completed at Corsicana, fifty of which were producers. The state's yearly output had reached 65,975 barrels of oil, with a daily production at the close of the year of 500 barrels.[3] During the next year the Corsicana well completions reached 316—287 as oil producers, 25 as dry, and 4 as gas wells, with the daily production climbing to 2,300 barrels of oil.

The Corsicana field embraced an area about five miles by two miles, in which area the driller was almost sure to strike oil. But the best producing wells were just outside the eastern limit of town on a tract of land owned by W. H. Booth and leased to Hardy and Halbert, who had wells with a daily oil output of forty-five barrels each.

Wildcatting was common. Wells were drilled in territory far beyond the proven field, but without appreciable results, although natural gas "in great volume" was found seven miles from Corsicana, on Colonel W. J. McKie's farm which had been leased by W.

[2] *Ibid.,* 173.

[3] Beaton reported on October 16, 1897, that his company had already laid four miles of pipe line and had storage capacity for 5,000 barrels of oil.—Dallas *Morning News,* October 17, 1897.

H. Staley. This well also yielded about two barrels of oil a day, an oil that was heavier than the Corsicana oil and considered excellent as a lubricant. Local oilmen believed that a bigger oil pay sand was yet to be found. "There has been no big or paying strikes outside the field marked out by the limits [of the city]," said a local prospector, "but there is a strong faith among oil producers that there will yet be struck in this vicinity another pool that will prove just as valuable as the one that is at present vomiting up over 3,000 barrels of oil per day."[4] This statement was indeed prophetic, for by 1900 the Powell shallow field had been found.

Corsicana's oil production soon outran demand. The local need was for fuel, the demand for which was small compared with the output. Tanks built to receive the oil ran over, the oil saturating the ground for a considerable distance on every side. Local citizens talked of building a refinery but did nothing. Still the number of producing wells increased, and oil as good as that sold in Pennsylvania at one dollar a barrel went begging in Corsicana at fifty cents.

At this critical point Mayor James E. Whitesell invited J. S. Cullinan, a Pennsylvania refiner, to come to Corsicana.[5] Cullinan, who was then in Washington, Pennsylvania, had planned a trip to California, but he changed his plans and started for Texas, since he had already received favorable reports on the Corsicana field. He arrived in Dallas on October 17, 1897, and from there was escorted to Corsicana by Mayor Whitesell and others. He was greatly impressed by what he found in the Corsicana field. "The average cost of wells fitted ready for operation is approximately $1,500," he wrote later. "Taking this average the 445 completed wells would cost $669,000. Adding the cost of leases and other incidentals, there has no doubt been [since] $700,000 to $800,000 invested in the oil producing business in Corsicana."[6] These favorable circumstances caused him to close deals with the leading oil producers for the delivery to him at the wells of 100,000 barrels of oil. Then he built pipe lines connecting the wells with iron tanks having a capacity

[4] *Hand-Book,* II, 173.

[5] Dallas *Morning News,* October 17, 1897. The *News* reported that the oil sample presented Cullinan by Whitesell produced "kerosine and naphtha," and that "the kerosine is pure white, resembling very closely the best grade of lamp oil sold in the Texas market."

[6] Cullinan to Fullmore, May 19, 1899, as cited.

of from 16,000 to 36,000 barrels of oil, and presently he began work on a refinery, but not before he had closed contracts with other producers for large amounts of oil. This he continued to do and to build storage tanks for the oil until he had secured practically the entire output of the field. He also entered a contract with the Waters-Pierce Oil Company[7] to distribute refined oil to the various cities and towns.

Then, to secure support in his enterprise, Cullinan went to St. Louis, where he met and entered into contract with still another Pennsylvanian, Calvin N. Payne, and a financier, Henry C. Folger, of New York City, the latter supplying $150,000 to build the refinery. Thus began the J. S. Cullinan and Company, the predecessor of the Magnolia Petroleum Company. After this agreement was concluded, Cullinan returned to Corsicana and immediately began work on a refinery. He acquired one hundred acres of land on the southwestern outskirts of the city, lying between the Houston and Texas Central and the Cotton Belt railroads, to which he built spur tracks. Here he built a small refinery of six or eight 200-barrel batch stills.

While his plant was nearing completion, Cullinan fired his stills for the first time on Christmas Day, 1898, although the first run to stills was not until six days later,[8] and on January 3 he had completed his refinery. His products were illuminating oil and gasoline, the paraffin in the crude oil not being of sufficient quantity to justify its manufacture. It was left in the residuum that was sold as fuel and used at the refinery. The refinery was an imposing Corsicana business enterprise—of 1,000-barrel capacity, with storage tanks to accommodate 1,000,000 barrels of oil.

Cullinan's refinery and new market for oil caused the crude-oil price to take an upward swing. While the plant was under construction, the price had dipped as low as fifty cents a barrel, but by the close of the year 1898 it had climbed back to ninety-eight cents. This encouraged other producers (Garrity-Mills; W. H. Staley; Navarro Oil Company; Home Oil Company; Staley, Halbert and Barth; Staley and Halbert; and N. J. Mills and Company) to enter the field.

[7] A Standard Oil Company subsidiary.
[8] Dallas *Morning News*, January 1, 1899.

Oil! Titan of the Southwest

Corsicana champions claim three important oil industry "firsts" for their town. The Cullinan refinery, comparable to Standard Oil's refinery at Neodesha, Kansas, was the first Texas refinery to operate extensively and continuously. The town's oil field supplied the first oil-burning locomotive. In 1898, J. S. Cullinan and his brother, Dr. M. P. Cullinan, devised and equipped an oil-burning mechanism for a Cotton Belt passenger engine running between Corsicana and Hillsboro, the success of which caused the Houston and Texas Central Railroad Company, in 1901, to convert its engine No. 1 into an oil burner. Cullinan also experimented with oiling streets and roads to prevent dust from blowing, and Corsicana was the first Texas town to boast of dustless streets, although native asphalt had been used prior to 1898 in Palestine and St. Jo, Texas.

But none of these innovations was more important than a Texas legislative enactment, House Bill No. 542, "An Act to Regulate Drilling, Operation, and Abandonment of Petroleum Oil, Natural Gas and Mineral Water Wells, and to Prevent Certain Abuses Connected Therewith," approved on March 29, 1899, and growing out of Corsicana oil-field experience. This law prohibited drilling into a second oil-bearing sand without first "incasing" the well passing through the first, plugging an abandoned well, and burning gas for illumination between 8 A.M. and 5 P.M., and required the closing in of a wild gas well within a period of ten days. County courts could impose a fine of as much as one hundred dollars for the violation of any one of these provisions.

The *Oil Investors' Journal* of October 15, 1904, announced that the "Corsicana District" had maintained an annual production of 500,000 barrels of petroleum from 1897 to 1901, probably including the whole of Texas within its "District" and even then an average yearly production.[9]

At best, however, the Corsicana field served only as the curtain raiser for major commercial production starting with the famous Lucas gusher at Beaumont on January 10, 1901. Indeed, for many months following this momentous discovery, Spindletop, one mile

---

[9] The exact amount was 65,975 in 1897; 546,070 in 1898; 669,813 in 1899; and 836,039 in 1900. Charles A. Whiteshot stated in 1905 that Corsicana was still producing annually over 500,000 barrels of "a superior grade of crude petroleum." See *Oil-Well Driller . . .* (Mannington, West Virginia, 1905), 825.

Type of rotary table, as used at Corsicana

Keeling Studio

J. S. Cullinan's refinery at Corsicana in 1898

Magnolia Petroleum Company

Nick Parrish of Corsicana in-
spects the old casing of the
town's first oil well

*Texas Mid-Continent Oil and Gas
Association*

J. S. Cullinan, with his associates and employees, in front
of the office of the J. S. Cullinan Pipe Line Company,
Corsicana, at the turn of the century. Left to right: J. S.
Cullinan, Craig Cullinan (child), F. T. Whitehill, Dr.
M. P. Cullinan, Willis C. Collier, W. H. Page, John
Cullinan (child), W. C. Proctor, E. R. Brown, Dannie
Burk, W. T. Cushing (builder of the pipe line), Frank
Cullinan, Ed Wright, Frank Perfield

American Petroleum Institute

Corsicana, the Curtain Raiser

south of Beaumont and two hundred miles southeast of Corsicana, held the nation's spotlight. No other event in the history of petroleum was more important. Within two years the state's oil output increased approximately twenty-fold.

V

Queen of the Neches

BEAUMONT IN 1900 was said to be like the old part of Boston, or
New York around Cherry Street, or New Orleans at the head
of Elysian Field Street. Its streets had been built along old
paths from store to store, from blacksmith shop to saloon, or railway
station to tavern. "A man will lose his way three times every day
looking for his favorite restaurant, and the way from the Crosby
House to the post office is a labyrinthine journey more baffling than
a mirror maze," said a resident. Railway tracks, as if lost in their
direction, cut through the heart of the town; and banks, business
houses, stores, saloons, and confectionaries of substantial brick
and pine lined the sand streets. Yet Beaumont was a rice-market
town, going about the even tenor of its way, not suspecting the
hectic, mad swirl soon to come.

Nor did Texas. Its population in 1900 was only 2,235,527, less
than half its present status. In fact, the present six Southwestern
oil-producing states could boast of but 8,200,000 persons, including
liberal estimates for Indians on and off reservations. The combined
population of Indian Territory and New Mexico was less than
1,000,000.

Improved or paved interstate roads did not exist, and, indeed,
very few improved roads of any kind stretched continuously across
two or more adjoining counties, since horse-drawn buggies, hacks,
and wagons did not require them. Ordinarily, the operating radius
of these vehicles was about twenty miles. At this early date, motor-
driven vehicles had hardly made their appearance in the Southwest, for the adaptation of internal-combustion engines to vehicle
propulsion was yet in its experimental stage.

Neither manufacturing nor mining was of great importance in

Queen of the Neches

Texas. There were flour mills in Kansas, Oklahoma, and northern Texas; a few sugar refineries and rice mills in southern Louisiana; sawmills in eastern Texas and Louisiana; and coal mining in Arkansas, Oklahoma, and Kansas. None of these, however, was of major importance. Texas featured cattle raising and agriculture, with cotton as its money crop. Railroad mileage was limited but adequate to take care of the state's industrial needs, and some of the railroads operated wood-burning locomotives.[1] So Texas was ready for a new industrial era; indeed, it urgently needed a change.

As has been pointed out, the earliest commercial oil fields were at Neodesha and Corsicana. By the end of 1900 these two fields had produced an accumulated total of only 2,647,000 barrels of crude oil, "a relatively insignificant amount considering the fact that during 1945 oil fields in the Southwest produced a slightly larger quantity each nineteen hours, or nearly five hundred times as much during the entire year."[2]

The Lucas gusher at Spindletop, on January 10, 1901, marked the dawn of a new era in the Southwest. The history of petroleum falls within (1) the lamp and lubrication period, 1859 to 1900; (2) the fuel-oil period, 1900 to about 1910; and (3) the gasoline or motor-fuel age, since 1910.[3] Thus, in 1900, Texas stood on the threshold of the fuel-oil period.

Today there are Beaumonters who declare that the word "Spindletop" was first applied locally to an inverted cone-shaped tree standing on a bluff near the present turning basin of the Neches River, just east of town; and that it was so named by upriver voyagers of rice and lumber boats. What today is known as "Spindletop Hill," they say, was then "Sour Spring Mound" because of oil seeps, known to exist from earliest times of settlement, although little use was made of them.

The Gladys City Oil, Gas and Manufacturing Company first sought to exploit these oil prospects. On August 24, 1892, this com-

---

[1] This summary of Texas in 1900 is based on a "Memorandum by B. E. Hull of The Texas Company, Houston, Texas, in an interview with C. C. Rister, February, 1946."

[2] *Ibid.*

[3] Manuscripts: H. C. Wiess, Humble Oil and Refining Company, "Interpretation of Petroleum Developments," September 30, 1946; E. DeGolyer, "Seventy-Five Years of Progress in Petroleum, 1871–1946."

pany was organized with G. W. Carroll, G. W. O'Brien, Patillo Higgins, J. F. Lanier, and Emma E. John as its first board of directors. Carroll, a local philanthropist who had recently given Baylor University $50,000 for a new building, was president (268 shares); O'Brien, a well-known local attorney, vice-president (201 shares); and Chenault O'Brien, secretary-treasurer (1 share).[4] Other stockholders were Mrs. Minnie S. Starke, as guardian of the estate of Emma E. John and Alfred E. John (68 shares), and Miss Gladys Bingham, after whom Gladys City was named by her father and trustee, Ike Bingham (2 shares).

Lanier soon disposed of his interest in the company, and on September 12, 1892, Higgins transferred the most of his stock to Carroll, retaining not more than two shares in the company. Yet he still had faith in "Sour Spring Mound."

In the meantime, the Gladys City Oil, Gas and Manufacturing Company entered into a contract with M. B. Looney, a former Dallas councilman, on February 17, 1893; and he, in turn, subleased to Walter B. Sharp, who used a "70-foot derrick, a light rotary rig, a 25 horse-power boiler, and a 16 horse-power engine" to drill an experimental well.[5] But the well was abandoned after it had reached a depth of 418 feet.

On May 27, 1895, Savage and Company of West Virginia agreed to sink a second test well, but they also failed to find oil. Then on June 4, 1896, the Gladys City company entered into a third contract with the Texas Oil and Mineral Company, of which W. A. Savage served as manager, but this effort was also unsuccessful. "They had all failed to pass through the immense thickness (500 feet) of quicksand which underlies the surface soil," said Lucas.[6]

[4] Higgins served as treasurer and general manager for a short time. See minutes, September 1, 1892, in "Minute Book," Gladys City Oil, Gas and Manufacturing Company, p. 1. This early record was made available to the author by Chilton O'Brien of the Gladys City Company, Beaumont, Texas. The company had been formed when by resolution the entire interests of its first board of directors "in and to the J. A. Veatch survey of land in Jefferson County" were purchased, payable in stock of the company at twenty dollars an acre. The Gladys City Company is still a Spindletop operator.

[5] Warner, *Texas Oil and Gas*, 20.

[6] "The Great Oil Well Near Beaumont, Texas," an address given at Richmond, February, 1901, a reprint from the American Institute of Mining Engineers *Transactions*, 1.

Queen of the Neches

Finally, a lease and option-sale contract was given to A. F. Lucas,[7] a mining engineer of Washington, D. C. and a former salt-dome prospector in Louisiana, on June 20, 1899. When this agreement expired on September 18 of the next year, he was given another lease. The firm's minutes of September 18 give the terms of this agreement. "The stockholders of the Gladys City Oil, Gas and Manufacturing Company met on this date," the entry ran, "and after due consideration approved and ratified the written oil and mineral lease, as drafted by Captain George W. O'Brien, by and between this company and A. F. Lucas."[8] This was a fortunate move for the Gladys City company. There was no other man in the United States at that time who knew as much about salt domes as Captain Lucas.

Lucas now became the soul of Spindletop operations. He rewarded Higgins for his efforts in securing the lease with a one-tenth interest in the "said option or lease."[9] Then Lucas sank a test well to a depth of 575 feet and bailed a little oil. But his money ran out, and he had to abandon the well.

Lucas could not secure local financial aid. Oil experts told him that there was no oil in that vicinity and that he had better return to salt mining. However, William Battle Phillips of the Texas Geological Survey had faith in his enterprise and suggested that he go for aid to Guffey and Galey, the former operators at Corsicana, who knew of Gulf Coast prospects. Lucas accepted Phillips' advice, went to Pittsburgh, and laid the matter before Guffey and Galey, who agreed to assume the financial obligations of the Gladys City company for a considerable interest in its holdings, and secured from this firm a new twenty-year lease, on September 18, 1900.

A short time later Galey informed the Hamill brothers, who had drilled wells for him at Corsicana, that Lucas would ask them to

[7] Lucas was an Austrian, trained as an engineer at the Polytechnic Institute at Graz. He later served in the Austrian navy. But dissatisfied with this service, in 1879 he took a six months' leave of absence to visit his father's brother in Saginaw, Michigan. He never returned to Austria. In 1885 he became a naturalized United States citizen. Subsequently, he prospected for gold in the San Juan Mountains of Colorado and for salt in Louisiana salt domes, at Avery Island, Cote Caroline, Belle Isle, Grand Cote, and Anse la Butte.

[8] Entry in "Minute Book" of the Gladys City Oil Company.

[9] Lucas-Higgins "Agreement," Deed Records of Jefferson County, Beaumont, Texas, Vol. 30, p. 136.

drill a test well south of Beaumont, under the new agreement by which Guffey and Galey would assume full financial responsibility. Hence, Lucas had no difficulty in securing the services of these men. J. G. Hamill, the drilling firm's business manager, went to Beaumont to look over the field and to sign a final agreement with Lucas, who agreed to pay two dollars a foot for drilling a 1,200-foot test, with Guffey and Galey furnishing all necessary pipe.

Early in October the Hamills loaded their rotary drilling outfit for shipment to the proposed well site. "At first," said Lucas, "I employed the system of boring which I had previously used in the Louisiana salt deposits. But I soon found this method was inadequate, without modification, to deal with the quicksand. Accordingly, I adopted the use of large and heavy castings, and pipes of 12, 10, 8, 6, and 4 inches in diameter, successively telescoped one into the other."[10]

Al Hamill accompanied the rig to Beaumont to make arrangements for derrick lumber, teaming, fuel, and other necessary equipment and services; and when all was in readiness, he wired his brothers, J. G. and Curt, to join him. Curt, Henry McLeod, Peck Byrd, and Al became the drill crew.

They first turned to the task of building the derrick, by laying the lumber on the ground in the shape of a derrick and cutting it out from this pattern. When finally set up, their drilling equipment consisted of one 25-horse power boiler, two 5x8x10 Smith-Valle circulating pumps, an American Well Works rotary rig, a two-post draw works, and a 9x12 F and T engine, with necessary chain tongs and tools. Peck Byrd, the fireman, had to burn in the furnace water-soaked logs cut by the Beaumont Lumber Company mill and had a hard time keeping up steam.

Al Hamill, in charge of drilling, at this point tells an interesting story of their progress on the well. After he had started drilling, he set about twenty feet of ten-inch surface pipe. Drilling progressed nicely until the well reached a depth of about 160 feet, when circulation was lost. Al sought repeatedly to overcome this situation, but failed. He then decided to retake and wash in all the eight-inch pipe that he could. After that, he put in the four-inch drill pipe for wash pipe and rigged up a heavy drive block to work around the

10 Lucas, *loc. cit.*, 1.

drill pipe, with a heavy drivehead for the eight-inch pipe. The drillers used the drive block on the order of a pile driver, giving it a quick slip from the cathead to deliver the hardest blow possible. They took turn-about on this man-killing job, working the cat-line, and every little while they would start the circulating pump to wash out the sand from below the bottom of the eight-inch pipe. In this manner they made headway every day, some days only a few feet, and at times the sand would wash out better, allowing that around the eight-inch pipe to settle more freely and to assist their driving. This method was continued until the Gumbo formation was reached at 445 feet, making 285 feet that the workers had mauled down with cathead and drive block.

From these experiences it was apparent why the Sharp brothers and others had failed to get through this thick formation of "heaving" quicksand. This was the fifth attempt to drill for sulphur or oil at what came to be known as "Spindletop."

From the Gumbo seat of the eight-inch casing, drilling progressed satisfactorily for about two hundred feet. At that depth the drillers noticed the circulating mud boiling and flowing up through the rotary table, which presently was displaced by muddy water and gas spewing halfway up the derrick. This did not last long, and they concluded that they had struck a gas pocket. But it caused them to change their drilling procedure. Formerly they had worked only during the day. Now, they decided to drill during the day and to keep their circulating pumps going at night. Meanwhile, McLeod had found the work too hard and had quit, thus handicapping progress. The new drilling procedure imposed an additional burden on the three remaining workmen—Al and Curt Hamill and Peck Byrd—which made necessary an eighteen-hour schedule. That is, one would work eighteen hours every third shift, but all would work during the day. At night it was necessary only for the lone driller to keep the pumps in motion and the drill pipe rotating slowly. This would help prevent gas blowouts and keep the pipe from sticking.

"On December 9," wrote Al later in a memorandum, "it was my turn to get up at midnight for my 18-hour shift. As usual, while I was on duty, I tried to make all the hole I could. At this time we had put up the evening before an additional joint of drill pipe. I do

55

not recall which one of the boys I relieved, but he had not been able to make much hole. He left almost the full length of drill pipe above the rotary table. At about three o'clock in the morning, I noticed the pump working more freely and the rotary turning very easily, so I began to let the pipe down. Still both pump and rotary worked freely. I kept it going and soon had down all the length of pipe, but our lights were very poor.

"As daylight began to appear, I could detect oil on the ditch and slush pit. When Curt and Byrd came with my little bit of break-fast, the slush pit had a big showing of oil on it. We at once sent Byrd for Captain Lucas, who at that time lived within one and one-half miles of where we were drilling. On his arrival, he showed some excitement and asked how much of a well I thought it would make. The only experience any of us had was at drilling in small wells in the Corsicana field, but I thought it would easily make 50 barrels per day.

"After Captain Lucas watched the circulating ditch for a while, he asked us to put up another joint of drill pipe in order to see how much oil formation there was. After making about 35 feet through the soft sand, we struck hard going. The depth at this point was about 880 feet. We spent the morning watching the oil showing, and deciding what was the most logical and practical procedure to follow. Captain Lucas decided to wire Mr. Galey and have us set our 4-inch drill pipe as a test string. We did this, and on the arrival of Mr. Galey, started bailing out with a small flow resulting. In running the bailer again, we found that the soft sand had heaved up in the pipe more than 300 feet. It was then decided to wash out the well with 2-inch pipe, but without great success. The washing and bailing was attempted several times, with no definite results.[11] After Mr. Galey had spent a week with us, he decided we would try to pull the 4-inch pipe, if possible. We were then to set the string of 6-inch pipe that we had on hand through this heaving sand and see if we would get any more showing in the next 300 feet. Fortune favored us in pulling the 4-inch pipe and in a short time we had the

[11] Clear water had been used for drilling in the Corsicana field, but it was not successful at Beaumont. Deciding that a mud fluid would serve his purpose better in getting through this heaving sand, Curt Hamill plowed up the bottom of his water pit, drove some cows through it, and muddied the water, which he then pumped down the drill stem.

The Lucas gusher at Spindletop

Spindletop at the height of its development in 1902

Texas Mid-Continent Oil and Gas Association

After forty-seven years, Spindletop is still producing

6-inch pipe landed at the 880 feet on the hard formation below the oil sand."

On December 24, Galey saw that the drillers were exhausted. He suggested, therefore, that they shut down for Christmas, and gave them some money on their contract account. After Al and Curt had spent the Christmas season in Corsicana, they were back on the job by January 1. Within a week they had made "140 feet of hole," making a total of 1,020 feet, at which depth the drill "seemed to hit a crevice," driving it off center.

On January 9, Al wired his brother Jim in Corsicana to send him a fishtail bit, with the hope of better results. The next day after it arrived it was fastened on the drill pipe and put again in the well to the depth of seven hundred feet, when the rotary mud began once more to flow through the rotary table. It increased rapidly in power and force so that Curt, who was on the rig's double boards, was drenched with mud and water before he could climb down. And hardly was he down before the drill pipe catapulted up through the derrick, knocking off the crown block and breaking off in several joints at a time as it shot upward.

All this happened in a matter of moments. Gas followed the eruption of mud, water, and drill pipe; then the well was quiet and the men returned to the derrick to find "things in a terrible mess," with mud covering the derrick floor. They started shoveling this away, when again, without warning, a large volume of heavy mud shot out of the well with the sound of a cannon shot, followed by a sustained deafening roar. First came a strong flow of gas, then oil by head flows. The flow increased in force so that within a short time rocks shot upward for hundreds of feet. Then black oil in a powerful stream, increasing in volume, gushed skyward for more than twice the height of the derrick, crested, and settled back to earth in a greasy shower.

Al sent Byrd on the run to tell Lucas, but he was in town. Then, he notified Mrs. Lucas, who finally located her husband at Louis Myers' store. It was not long until Lucas could be seen in a buggy approaching swiftly, belaboring his team. As the vehicle came near, Lucas jumped out and was sent rolling. Picking himself up, he ran to Al, wild with excitement.

"Al! Al! What is it!" he shouted, embracing the grinning driller.

"When I told him 'Oil,' " said Al later, "he exclaimed, 'Thank God.' "

In a short time spectators began to arrive by horseback, in buggies, hacks, and wagons, and some on foot. Near-by farmers had heard the roar of the escaping gas and had seen the oil cascading. Before nightfall several hundred people were on the ground, standing transfixed and awe-inspired, watching the wild gusher, heedless of danger.

Figuratively, the roar of that gusher was heard around the world. By nightfall, the news had traveled far. An oil gusher flowing at the unbelievable rate of from 75,000 to 100,000 barrels of oil daily had been found on the Texas Gulf Coast! The oil flow "was estimated," said Lucas, "by officials and engineers of the Standard Oil Company, who were naturally the most experienced judges, to be at least 3,000 42-gallon barrels of oil per hour or about 75,000 barrels in 24 hours."[12]

"Now that we have got her, boys, how are we going to close her up?" Lucas is said to have asked the drillers. He received many telegrams and letters from men proposing to close the well—for large rewards. Some of them required cash down payments ranging from $30,000 to $100,000. But this problem, too, was solved by the Hamill brothers a few days later. They devised an apparatus consisting of a carriage, anchoring an eight-inch gate valve against upward movement, and below the valve a short nipple, with an eight-inch tee attached. Then the Hamills launched the whole apparatus against the column of solid oil, met its terrific impact, and successfully placed the carriage over the well with the aid of bolts until the tee could be screwed into the eight-inch casing.

There was no time for speculation. The well was pouring its black oil on the ground by thousands of barrels hourly, and every pond and gulley was filled with it. Lucas organized a corps of fifty men to keep back the spectators during the day and forty men during the night, both under Perry Wiess, who was instructed to guard the well. Then he employed men with forty four-horse teams and gang plows from the McFaddin, Wiess,[13] and Kyle farm to build a dyke about an earthen reservoir and to plow under the

[12] *Loc. cit.*, 2.

[13] Father of Harry Wiess, late chairman of the Board of Directors, Humble Oil and Refining Company, Houston, Texas.

grass which the gusher had soaked with oil. This would help prevent fire. But it didn't. On the third day a careless spectator set fire to the grass, and Lucas's fireguards saved the well. The reservoir soon filled, and other reservoirs had to be built, so that within a few weeks hundreds of thousands of barrels of oil covered many acres of storage.

Dr. A. R. Ledoux, in his New York City laboratory, tested a sample of the Beaumont oil that Dr. R. W. Raymond had sent him on January 22, 1901. He pronounced its gravity as 21.5 degrees Baumé, higher than other oils that had yielded notable quantities of illuminants.

The January 10 evening edition of the Beaumont *Daily Enterprise* represented the Lucas gusher as a spectacular wonder of nature that would bring many people to Beaumont. "About 10 o'clock this morning while the men employed by Mr. A. F. Lucas were boring for oil," it related, "an explosion occurred that forced the tubing into the air like it was a mere plaything, and then immediately followed a stream of black petroleum. The news was the cause of great excitement, every available livery team being pressed into service to carry people to the well." Then the writer seemed to add as an afterthought: "This discovery will no doubt induce capitalists to prospect on the lands which are not leased, and the result will be very beneficial to Beaumont."

He was right in two particulars. First, Beaumont was benefited. An avalanche of oil experts, prospectors, speculators, and oil-company executives from the East and from Colorado, California, and even Europe descended on Beaumont. The wildest of booms, a California gold rush concentrated in time and space, was launched.

Texas railroads advertised, "In Beaumont, You'll See a Gusher Gushing!" Within a matter of hours, crowded trains left Dallas, San Antonio, Corsicana, and Houston, bound for Beaumont. The first Corsicana train brought Mayor "Golden Rule" (Samuel M.) Jones, of Toledo, Ohio, who was in Texas at that time and who was accompanied by J. S. Cullinan, T. J. Wood, and others. Jones pronounced the Lucas gusher one of the "oil wonders of the world" that had launched a fuel-oil era.

Other oilmen came from the East because the Standard Oil Company marked down the price it paid for Pennsylvania and other

Oil! Titan of the Southwest

Eastern oil as a result of the Lucas gusher. Among the Easterners to come were some of the old Standard Oil operators. "Uncle" John Galloway was the first; then Senator Lockwood, J. W. Grandon, J. H. Schiede, W. S. Watson, J. A. Quay, J. L. O'Donnell, John Gruver, John M. Murphy, M. Eagan, W. C. McBride, and J. J. Liedecker came from Pennsylvania; and J. L. Caldwell, J. C. McManus, E. Stiner, F. H. Park, Clell Nichols, T. M. Kiser, and J. M. Kelly from West Virginia. Ohio was represented by C. F. Lufkin, Senator Shaw, N. S. Meadows, D. A. Herring, C. C. Conroy, V. Ceville and Harry Decker; and California by Scott Heywood, C. L. Hanson, Chancellor and Canfield, E. W. Hayward, and many others.

R. L. Blaffer of New Orleans sought to purchase fuel oil for the Southern Pacific Railroad, but he was convinced of oil possibilities at Spindletop and became an oil prospector. W. S. Farish, just out of a Mississippi law school, also joined the quest for oil. And still others—Ed Prather, Hollis Reavis,[14] T. J. Donoghue, Colonel Rupert John, Judge Freeman, George Neely, Bill Cushing, George Hamon, R. R. Hobson, Blaine Johnston, R. E. Josey, F. A. Leovy, John W. ("Bet-a-Million") Gates, James Roche, James S. Hogg, Jim Swayne, and many more—swamped the list of notables. Up to the summer of 1901, those men oldest in oil experiences had made the least at Spindletop, with the exception of Guffey and Galey. These two Pennsylvanians, as has already been seen, were first in the new fields of Neodesha and Corsicana.

Beaumont mushroomed into a boisterous, oil-crazed metropolis, increasing its population from 10,000 to 30,000 in three months, claiming to be the "Queen of the Neches." Tents, one-room shacks, lean-tos, saloons, and gambling houses appeared overnight. And still people came. An enterprising hackman charged passengers from eighteen to twenty dollars for a ride from the excursion trains to the oil field.

Wild speculation followed. At the Cordova Hotel, "Madame la Monte" did a thriving business foretelling many who sought her service where rich oil lands and gushers were to be found. Land

14 Reavis was the son of an editor of the old *Saint Louis Republic* and was sent as a reporter to cover early-day Spindletop operations. But he became convinced that his future success was with the oil business and remained. He founded the *Oil Investors' Journal* which, after Volume VIII, became the *Oil and Gas Journal*, which has continued without a break down to the present time.

lease and sale transactions were made at all hours of the day and night; and prospectors sought for other salt domes near the coast, hoping that each mound might become another Spindletop.

Daily, Beaumont heard of fabulous land deals. A woman garbage collector sold her pig pasture for $35,000. . . . Blocks of real estate, 25x34 feet, brought $6,000 each. . . . Land farther removed from the gusher that had sold in previous years for $40 an acre was now divided into lots and brought as high as $40,000. . . . One tract that was previously offered at $8.00 an acre now sold for $35,000.

A year after the Lucas gusher blew in, R. T. Hill wrote: "Thousands of acres of this land 150 miles from Beaumont have sold for as much as $1,000 per acre. Land within the proved field has sold for nearly $1,000,000 an acre; $900,000 having recently been paid for one acre. No sales were made for less than $200,000 per acre. Spindletop today may be justly assessed at a valuation of $500,000 an acre, or $100,000,000. Two years ago it could have been bought for less than $10 an acre."[15]

This was not all. At Spindletop, many wells were spudded in and hundreds of companies were organized. Within five months there were fourteen producers, three wells abandoned, fifteen being drilled, and eighteen rigs being built over drilling sites—all on an eighty-acre tract. Hill said a few months later that there were 214 wells at Spindletop owned by about one hundred companies, 120 of which were drilled upon fifteen of the two hundred producing acres. At that time the development of the field had cost $7,-000,000, of which $1,250,000 had been paid for labor, with "tubing and well-rigs" costing another $1,000,000. Including those companies within the whole Beaumont area, the grand capitalization reached $200,000,000.

Among these early companies were a number that grew into powerful present-day organizations, such as the Guffey Petroleum Company[16] (later the Gulf Oil Corporation backed by Andrew

[15] "The Beaumont Oil Field, with Notes on Other Oil Fields of the Texas Region," reprinted from the *Journal of the Franklin Institute*, August-October, 1902, 27.

[16] The business enterprise now comprising the Gulf Oil Corporation and its domestic and foreign subsidiaries, had its beginnings at Spindletop, in 1901. Gulf operated through predecessor and subsidiary companies, e.g., J. M. Guffey Petroleum Company, Gulf Refining Company of Louisiana, and Gypsy Oil Company. The present Gulf Oil Corporation, a Pennsylvania company, was chartered in 1922. By

Oil! Titan of the Southwest

Mellon, R. A. Greer, E. L. Nall, J. A. Reed, and others), and the Texas Fuel Company (now The Texas Company, launched by J. S. Cullinan, president, T. J. Donoghue, treasurer, and Fred W. Freeman, secretary).

Within a few weeks derricks stood so close together on Spindletop that in some instances plank runways were built from one to the other, so that the workmen could escape in case of fire; and in many places from one to four wells were drilled under one floor. The Hogg-Swayne Syndicate[17] did a thriving business selling drilling sites just large enough for a derrick.

Wild wells constituted an ever present threat, often providing fuel for costly fires and causing death. In this connection, another step was taken in oil-field control. On August 30, 1901, sixty-one oilmen met in Beaumont, adopted measures for their own protection, and named a committee consisting of George A. Hill, Sr. (chairman), A. D. Lipscomb (secretary), F. M. Brown, George Carroll, W. B. Dunlap, W. E. Griffith, O. W. Heywood, C. K. McFaddin, John McVey, James Sharp, D. S. Speer, W. P. Strum, James Swayne, John C. Ward, and William Wiess. In general, the regulations adopted were to guard against fire hazards, make proper drainage, and prevent saloons from being established within one thousand feet of any oil well.

The Lucas gusher brought still other problems, among which storage space, pipe lines and tank cars, refineries, and new markets were foremost. First, the rapidly accumulating oil in the temporary ground reservoirs made urgent the securing of permanent iron-tank sites and of pipe lines from wells to sites, the erection of the tankage, and access to shipping and loading facilities. Even having

---

1945, Gulf was operating in all the major Southwestern oil-producing areas. Its first pipe line was built from Spindletop to Port Arthur, Texas, in 1901. Six years later it was extended to Glenn Pool, Oklahoma, a distance of 440 miles, and as new fields were opened, extended still more. At present its pipe-line system consists of a main line from Tulsa to Port Arthur, Texas, and from Tulsa to Dublin, Indiana, with various gathering branches tapping oil fields at Hobbs, New Mexico, and West Texas, in southern Oklahoma and North Texas, and at El Dorado and Smackover, Arkansas. In addition to its huge Port Arthur refinery, Gulf also has extensive refining facilities near Philadelphia, Pittsburgh, Toledo, Cincinnati, and New York.

[17] Release of a part of the Veatch Survey lease by J. M. Guffey Company to James W. Swayne, July 5, 1901, in Deed Records of Jefferson County, Beaumont, Texas, Vol. 53, p. 140.

a well, a tank site, tankage, pipe-line connection, a loading rack, and all other facilities, the producer was still confronted with his most difficult problem of the sale of his oil when the market was already many times oversupplied. For example, by midsummer of 1901, oil was actually cheaper than drinking water. Oil sold for as low as three cents a barrel;[18] and water was five cents a cup!

Dr. A. W. Burrell and other chemists had favorably analyzed the Beaumont oil within a few months after the first well was drilled. These analyses gave the local promoters and producers tangible advantages in offering their oil to a hesitant market. *The Daily Enterprise* of August 20, 1901, explained that by one process of refining, 35 per cent of standard white export burning oil (kerosene) of 150 degrees Fahrenheit fire test, a considerable quantity of lubricants, and from 6 to 10 per cent of asphalt resulted. And another produced 2 to 3 per cent of benzine or gasoline, 15 per cent of A-1 white burning oil of 150 degrees Fahrenheit fire test, 20 per cent gas or fuel oil according to the method, 10 per cent of asphalt and about 50 per cent of lubricants. But these analyses met a sales resistance coming as the result of an early report that Beaumont oil had an "asphalt base" and was worth little.

Still, Beaumont would not accept defeat. During the latter part of January, a six-inch pipe line was started from the field to El Vista, which was finished by February 4 of the next year. And two days later, the J. M. Guffey company, a Galey-Guffey-Lucas concern, bound itself to sell and deliver to the Gulf Company, "doing business in and about Morgan City in the State of Louisiana," 2,500 barrels (forty-two gallons each) of oil a day by tank cars and barges at twenty-five cents a barrel. If the price of oil should be less after March 1, 1902, then the price of the oil delivered would be reduced proportionately.

Still other preparations were made to handle the greatly increased production. By January, 1902, three pipe lines had been finished, two to Port Arthur, nineteen miles from the oil field, and one to Sabine, twenty-four miles away. Other pipe lines, from Beaumont to New Orleans and from Beaumont to Galveston, Houston, and other Texas towns, were contemplated.

[18] See contract of the Texas Fuel Company with the Georgetown-Waco Oil Company, *ibid.*, Vol. 61, p. 323. In these records are many other similar contracts.

Oil! Titan of the Southwest

The storage problem was ever present. By March 1, 1902, tank storage exceeded 5,000,000 barrels. Among those tanks of 37,000-barrel capacity and over, there were twenty-two at El Vista, twenty-eight at Gladys City adjacent to the field, and thirty-three at Port Arthur. But these were hardly sufficient to accommodate the producers' needs. Yet a partial solution of the problem was found by making available better transportation facilities. In February, 1902, the railroads had added 500 tank cars, increasing the total to 1,500. And within the next few weeks the Southern Pacific Railroad purchased 250 tank cars of 12,850-gallon capacity each, many of which were kept at Beaumont loading racks. Many companies had provided their own shipping. They owned between 800 and 1,000 tank cars in addition to those of the railroads. Moreover, a tank-car factory was constructed at Beaumont.

"Tank-steamers" had also been put in service. The Guffey company started construction on five tankers, one of which was to carry 60,000 barrels of oil. This last tanker was reported to be the largest ever made in the United States up to that time and equal to any in the world.

Local refining, too, helped to solve the petroleum supply problem. By 1902 the Guffey company had built two refineries at Port Arthur and had under construction another of 2,500-barrel daily capacity. These refineries made it possible for the firm to reduce the tanker's hazards in handling crude oil, by bringing the flash point up from 120 degrees to 145 and 150 degrees and by taking out naphtha and kerosene.

The shipments for 1901 were 1,750,000 barrels of crude oil; and by April of the next year the total shipments of the previous year had been exceeded, those of March alone being more than 800,000 barrels and the shipment of upward of 20,000,000 being possible by the end of the year.

"Within a year from its discovery [Spindletop]," wrote R. T. Hill, "Beaumont oil is burning in Germany, England, Cuba, Mexico, New York and Philadelphia. By its energy steamers are being propelled across the ocean, trains are hastening across the continent, electricity generated and artificial ice frozen in New York, ores ground and stamped in Mexico, Portland cement manufactured in Havana and Texas, and gas enriched in Philadelphia; and this,

Queen of the Neches

too, while half the world is either unaware or incredulous of the value of this fuel."[19]

Within a year after the Lucas well was discovered, Beaumont truly became "Queen of the Neches," with a population of 30,000. It could boast of the largest iron works in the South (in which cars and engines and heavy machinery were built and sold over the South), three sawmills and three planers, two shingle mills, three rice mills, one woodworking plant, one army and pin factory, one creosoting plant, two brickyards, six oil-tank factories, one boiler works, one box factory, one shipyard, one lath mill, one stave mill, an ice plant, four bottling works, a marble works, and smaller enterprises. Paved streets, an adequate water supply and sewage system, and electric lights completed the town's transformation. "We are independent of everybody and everything," boomed the *Enterprise* editor. "We are wealthy beyond our calculations."

The financial statements of local banks proved that Beaumont was indeed wealthy. The *Enterprise* of August 20, 1901, announced that local banks enjoyed "the greatest increases in deposits in the history of the south." At the close of business on December 13, 1900, the combined deposits of the two banks, the First National and Beaumont National, were $661,818. By July 24 two other banks had been added and the total deposits reached $3,369,587.40, a gain of $2,249,385.80.

Water transportation promised even greater things for this "Queen of the Neches." Tankers could take Beaumont oil on a privately built short channel connecting Port Arthur with Sabine Pass, through which more than 689,000 tons of oil passed from Spindletop through the Sabine jetties in 1902. During 1904 this waterway accommodated 553 ships carrying 1,734,934 dead-weight tons, including 423,926,992 gallons of crude and refined oil. Meanwhile, Congressman Samuel Bronson Cooper urged Congress to appropriate funds for a public ship canal that would give Beaumont an outlet to the Gulf, a need that was finally met.

[19] Hill, *loc. cit.*, 26.

VI

Exploiting Other Salt Domes

S PINDLETOP'S INDUSTRIAL SIGNIFICANCE can hardly be overestimated. Petroleum poured from dozens of its gushers as if from so many faucets during 1901, filling all storage tanks and earthen reservoirs, outmoding small-capacity refineries, making pipe-line facilities entirely inadequate, and swamping the market. And for a time three-cent oil went begging.

"Golden Rule" Jones had said that the Lucas gusher would launch a fuel-oil era. Indeed, it made one necessary. Beaumont promoters, representing 585 oil and leasing companies, were desperate, for every day saw a rapid accumulation of oil. And in their haste to get quick returns on their investments, they drilled well after well, knowing that their transportation and storage facilities were taxed to the limit and that the market was glutted.

Profligate waste violated every present-day conservation measure. Gas was allowed to escape, and no one thought of repressuring it back into the earth. Designing promoters allowed "gushers to gush" for gaping visitors and possible investors. *The Oil Investors' Journal* of May 24, 1902, estimated that ten million barrels of oil at Spindletop had been wasted since the Lucas gusher. Giant fires, destroying many derricks, much equipment, and hundreds of thousands of barrels of petroleum, raged because of a lack of simple safeguards. On April 15, 1903, a fire broke out on the Hogg-Swayne Blocks 36, 37, and 38 and destroyed 152 derricks. An "eat-drink-and-be-merry" attitude possessed these get-rich-quick speculators.

But industrial leaders of sound judgment and business acumen were also present, who hastened the fulfillment of Jones' prophecy. "Oil drummers" said to manufacturers and industrial leaders that fuel oil was more economical than coal. Magazine and newspaper editors preached the same doctrine, and oil companies employed chemists to analyze Beaumont oil to prove that it was equal, if not superior, to Pennsylvania oil. When the price of oil was only a little more than ten cents a barrel, one experimenter demonstrated that even at fifty cents a barrel, it was a cheaper fuel than coal.[1]

These efforts brought quick results; industrialists were convinced. The American Brewery Company of Houston was among the first of the industrial concerns to change from coal to petroleum. Its plant had a battery of five boilers, two of 200-horsepower and three of 350-horsepower. It tested the steam power of the two fuels and found that the two 200-horsepower boilers using refinery residuum made as much steam as two 350-horsepower boilers using coal.[2]

The Star Flour Milling Company of Galveston also installed an oil-burning apparatus early in 1901, using about five barrels of oil a day for a 50-horsepower engine. The Sunset Brick and Tile Company's kiln of Gonzales; the ice-factory and electric-light-plant boilers and an oil mill at Brenham, Texas; the Hutchins Hotel at Houston, with two 100-horsepower boilers; the Magnolia Brewery and the Houston Electric Street Railway Company; and the City Brewery of San Antonio—all installed oil-burning equipment in that same year.

Railroads also turned to fuel oil as fast as engines could be converted. Following the Spindletop discovery, the first locomotive equipped with oil burners was sold to the Gulf, Beaumont and Kansas City Railroad, in June, 1901, and was the property of the Gulf, Colorado and Santa Fe Railroad. In reaching Beaumont, it traveled 450 miles, consuming forty-two barrels of oil on the trip, or the equivalent of twelve tons of coal. At the close of 1905, the Santa Fe Railroad had a total of 227 oil-burning engines, and oil was used generally in its shops, the company consuming during the year 1,592,000 barrels of petroleum, or the equivalent of 454,857 tons of coal.[3] This change from one oil-burning engine in 1901 to 227 oil burners in 1905 represents a growth of fifty-seven engines a year for almost five years.

[1] *The American Review of Reviews,* Vol. XXIX, No. 1 (January–June, 1904), 56ff.

[2] *Oil Investors' Journal,* Vol. IV, No. 21 (April 3, 1906), 12–13.

[3] *Ibid.*

Oil! Titan of the Southwest

On July 31, 1901, a Southern Pacific Railroad official announced that his company had placed an order for five hundred tank cars and fifty storage tanks for immediate delivery as the first step toward changing from coal to petroleum on its Atlantic division and that locomotive oil burners had also been ordered. The Southern Pacific also built storage tanks at Beaumont, Houston, Lake Charles, Lafayette, and Algiers. The Houston and Texas Central, and eastern and western Texas railroads, controlled by the Southern Pacific, installed oil burners in many of their locomotives. For example, the Galveston, Harrisburg and San Antonio Railroad equipped 204 of its engines with oil burners, and the Texas and New Orleans Railroad, 38. The total fuel-oil consumption of all the Southern Pacific lines in Texas and Louisiana was approximately 2,640,000 barrels a year. As though to explain this revolutionary change, the company's home office announced that 915 pounds of oil would generate as much boiler steam power as 2,000 pounds of Indian Territory coal, a barrel of crude oil weighing 311 pounds.

The International and Great Northern was among the other railroads changing from coal to oil. On August 7, it began a test with engines No. 206 and 215, one burning oil and the other coal. Both ran between Palestine and Houston, and both ended with petroleum showing an advantage. The Kansas City Southern, whose southern terminus was in Port Arthur, had thirty-eight engines equipped with oil-burners, which, by 1905, consumed 227,111 barrels of oil, or the equivalent of 64,889 tons of coal. This company also provided storage for 77,954 barrels of oil at various points on its line from Shreveport southward, and placed in service ninety-eight tank cars having a gross capacity of 98,926 barrels of oil.

On May 11, 1901, a Guffey and Galey barge arrived at Port Arthur to receive its first consignment of Spindletop oil, for the use of pumping stations on Taylor's Bayou; and the *Nellie of Beaumont*, a seagoing ship belonging to the same firm, put in at the same port the next day for a cargo of oil for the Port Arthur Irrigation Company's pumping plant on the Neches River.[4]

Steamship companies were making similar changes. On February 20, 1902, the Shell Trading and Transport Company's tanker, the *Strombus*, of about 60,000-barrels capacity, docked at Port

[4] Dallas *Morning News*, May 11, 1901.

Exploiting Other Salt Domes

Arthur, and Captain N. Hocken and Engineer Dunlop landed to "take in the sights" of Spindletop. The *Strombus* was a sister ship of the *Cardium*, which had put in at Port Arthur on other occasions to take on cargoes of "desulphurized petroleum" and distillates. Both vessels used oil for fuel. Captain Hocken told Beaumonters that still a third tanker, the *Pennsylvania*, would visit Port Arthur shortly to share in this oil traffic.

Undoubtedly, these early steamship experiments attracted the attention of other steamship officials. On May 1, 1902, the Galveston *Semi-Weekly News* stated that the *Breakwater* of the United Fruit Company's fleet, the first of its kind to go to sea with oil under her boilers, had returned to New Orleans after a record-breaking trip to Belise of two days and nineteen hours, "demonstrating the unequivocal success of the Texas fuel oil under steamship boilers." A United Fruit Company official announced that his company would also equip its steamships *Anselm*, *Olympia*, and *Beverly* with oil burners and would erect a large storage oil tank at Puerto Cortez, Hondurus.

This and other steamship company changes from coal to oil only added to a rapidly expanding fuel-oil-market. "The sale of oil-burning machinery has become so extensive in Louisiana and Texas," wrote D. A. Willey, "that this section is now one of the principal markets of the world for such equipment. . . . The permanent demand for domestic consumption from the sources indicated has increased so rapidly that a strong incentive is given to continue the development of the old fields and to open up new ones."[5]

Much of the promotional work for fuel oil was done by major oil companies, two of which had their inception at Beaumont. In 1901, James Roche, a shrewd English adventurer, penniless and without friends, came to Beaumont. Immediately, he plunged into a series of breath-taking business deals by which he obtained options on a large part of Spindletop's three-cent oil and a sixty-day, tentative lease on a forty-acre refinery site. Then he sold out to the Hogg-Swayne Syndicate at a large profit, although he had not invested a penny. From these transactions came the Producers Oil Company, having as its directors such distinguished men as George

[5] *American Review of Reviews*, Vol. XXIX, No. 1 (January–June, 1904), 60.

Oil! Titan of the Southwest

M. Craig, J. S. Cullinan, and John W. ("Bet-a-Million") Gates. This company had acquired thirteen acres of land on Spindletop, 49,000 acres of leases in Texas and Louisiana, and now Roche's contracts for 1,000,000 barrels of oil. In 1915, the Producers Oil Company was absorbed by The Texas Company.[6]

The Gulf Refining Company had also made its appearance, on November 27, 1901. Both companies organized refining divisions with refineries at Port Arthur, where their major plants are today.

Then by February 15, 1903, the *Oil Investors' Journal* announced that J. E. Pew, representing the Sun Oil Company,[7] was in Beaumont. This firm held nearly 1,000,000 barrels of oil in storage there.

Spindletop's amazing oil production caused prospectors to seek out other Gulf Coast salt domes—peculiar salt masses, or plugs, that had pushed through the country rock toward the earth's surface

[6] The Texas Company was founded by J. S. Cullinan. He had organized the Texas Fuel Company with an authorized capital of $50,000. In April, 1902, he closed a deal with J. S. Hogg and J. W. Swayne, whereby, among assorted belongings, he came into possession of a site for a water terminal at Port Arthur and a partially completed oil pipe line and right-of-way from Beaumont to Port Arthur. Hogg and Swayne were given half interest in the little company, which was then incorporated as The Texas Company. John W. Gates was also brought into the company about the same time, and operations were started at Sour Lake. In 1903 two small stills of 1,000-barrel capacity each were built at Port Arthur. These were the beginning of the present refinery covering thousands of acres, with a capacity of more than 100,000 barrels daily. Today The Texas Company is a major operator in all the Southwestern states.

[7] About 1878 a gas well was drilled at Murrysville, Pennsylvania, known as the Haymaker well. Joseph N. Pew and E. O. Emerson formed a partnership to develop this and other wells in that area and to build a five and five-eighths–inch pipe line from Murrysville to Pittsburgh, the first pipe line installed for natural-gas service to a large city. Later, the partners expanded their operations to include Pennsylvania, Ohio, Indiana, West Virginia, and Illinois, which formed the basis for what is now the Sun Oil Company. In 1889 the name "Sun" was first used with the organization of the Sun Oil Line Company; and five years later a refinery was acquired from the Crystal Oil Company, at Toledo.

In the late nineties, Sun interests passed under the control of the Pews—J. N., J. Howard, Robert C., and J. Edgar—when Emerson sold his interest. Then the Sun Oil Company moved into the Southwest. Robert C. and J. Edgar Pew came to Beaumont, Texas, soon after the Spindletop gusher blew in; but after a short time Robert C. returned to Toledo to direct Sun's interests there. J. Edgar remained in Texas. Indeed, over a period of thirty years he was one of the Southwest's most conspicuously successful oil operators. Sun entered Oklahoma in 1909 through the Twin State Oil Company and later acquired desirable leases at Healdton and other fields. Still later, its interests were expanded to include all the Southwestern states; and its newly acquired Marcus Hook refinery processed much of this region's oil.

70

and had in some instances trapped gas and oil. In April, 1893, a German homesteader had come to Tom Mahaffey, of Jennings, Louisiana, about ninety miles east of Beaumont, with a report that he had found a gas-emitting spring. Tom was from the Pennsylvania oil country and had been told that gas was commonly found with oil; so he had asked the homesteader to sink two two-inch holes to an underlying sand formation to see if he could find a stronger flow. The German had done this and had returned the next day, saying that he had found gas and had proved it by applying a match. Gas coming from the two holes was still burning.

Next, Tom had written to an experienced oil operator in Finley, Ohio, telling him about the German's discovery and had received the reply, "Tom, you've got marsh gas." Satisfied with this opinion, Tom had let the matter drop.

Then came the Spindletop discovery and the search for other salt domes. Might not this Jennings gas spring be evidence of one? Tom interested other local men, including Dr. A. C. Wilkins, S. A. Spencer, Frank Jaenke, and I. D. L. Williams, in an oil exploration co-partnership, and they secured Louisiana's first oil leases, acquiring drilling rights to two thousand acres of land about the old gas spring. At a company meeting a committee was selected to confer with W. Scott Heywood, a successful Spindletop oil operator.

Heywood[8] was a former California operator, who had come to Beaumont early in 1901; and he with his four brothers, Alba, O. W., Dewey, and Clint, had drilled, on a fifteen-acre lease near the discovery well, the field's greatest gusher, the 148,000-barrel Spindletop No. 2. Their other operations there were also successful.

The Jennings promoters, Williams and Spencer, visited Beaumont and outlined their proposal to Scott, who tentatively accepted. Later, on April 29, 1901, he signed a contract with them (S.

[8] Heywood was born in Cleveland, Ohio, May 21, 1872, the son of a Hiram College professor. As a youth, he first turned to music for a living, studying the cornet under a teacher at Grand Rapids. Then he and his brothers (also musicians) formed a troupe that played to audiences over the nation. He became a cornet soloist with the Iowa state band that played at the Chicago World's Fair through the season of 1893. A short time later he joined in the Alaska gold rush but found little gold. Stranded in this far-away country, he again resorted to music to replenish his depleted funds, playing before crowds of miners. While thus engaged, he heard of the new oil strike at Coalinga, California. He promptly sought his fortune there, organized a California company, and became a successful promoter.

A. Spencer and Company), out of which came the Jennings Oil Company. The S. A. Spencer and Company deeded to the new firm any forty acres of its holdings that Heywood might designate. The Jennings Oil Company was capitalized at $60,000 or 60,000 shares at $1.00 a share, of which the Spencer Company would receive 30,-000 shares, and the Heywoods 15,000 shares, the remaining 15,000 to be sold to the public. Then, after the Heywoods completed their contract, they were given one-half of all acreage leases by checkerboard selections. For this interest in their mineral leases, they agreed to put down two wells, each to a depth of one thousand feet.[9]

Scott selected the Jennings Oil Company's forty acres on the Jules Clement farm, six miles northeast of Jennings, Acadia Parish, to which site he hauled a draw works, a small gripping rotary, two swivels, two Smith-Vale pumps, fish-tail bits, a forty-horsepower boiler, timbers for a sixty-four-foot derrick, piping, and other essentials. And he lost no time in drilling. When he and his drillers, Elmer Dobbins, C. O. Noble, and Sank Hendricks, had reached 250 feet, they found a slight showing of oil, but they drilled the required 1,000 feet without finding any other.

Since Scott believed that oil could be found in a deeper formation, the Heywoods asked for the right of starting the second well at the bottom of the first, an unusual proposal that the Jennings associates reluctantly accepted. Finally, on September 21, 1901, when the bit struck the sand at 1,800 feet, oil came spouting twenty-five feet above the derrick. Thus was begun Louisiana's first major oil field (sometimes called the Evangeline Oil Field).

Scott's trials had only started. The oil was in a heaving sand formation, and to keep sand from filling the hole, he employed a California technique of "washing, bailing, and flushing," which showed that his well was about a 7,000-barrel producer. In spite of his precautions, however, the well "sanded," and he was forced to abandon it.

Meanwhile, he started a second well near the first. He also built a pipe line from the field to the Southern Pacific Railroad near Jennings, a 50,000-barrel steel storage tank at the field and another

[9] For Heywood's own narrative of these events, see his "Autobiography of an Oil Man," In *Oil*, Vol. I, No. 4 (June, 1941), 31–34, and No. 6, 21–24. See also *The Sunday Item-Tribune*, New Orleans, March 14, 1937, p. 6 ff.

Gulf Refining Company, Port Arthur, Texas, in 1901

Gulf Oil Corporation

First refinery of The Texas Company, near Port Arthur, 1901

Oil Weekly

Sour Lake, Texas, oil field

of 37,500-barrel capacity and a loading rack at the railroad, with other loading facilities for barges at the Bayou Nezpique. To save his second well from "sanding," Scott purchased some copper-wire gauze of sixty mesh and perforated the well piping with three-eighth-inch holes, about which he soldered the wire gauze to form a screen.[10] This proved to be effective in solving his heaving-sand problem and saved his second well, which was a good producer.

The Jennings associates organized the Southern Oil Company, to which the Heywoods sold six acres of land near their No. 1 well for $12,000; and the new concern drilled a well in August, 1901, which produced 200,000 barrels of oil before its gushing ceased.[11] After this it drilled others. *The Oil Investors' Journal* of June 7, 1902, announced that Scott was the happiest man in Jennings when the Southern No. 3 blew in at an estimated 70,000 barrels of oil a day. "Small wonder Scott Heywood took off his hat and shouted when the oil from the gusher . . . took its skyward flight," commented the editor. His company's holdings at Jennings were now quoted at $5,000,000.

The Galveston *Semi-Weekly News* of June 2, 1902, noticed that Beaumont's boom days were being repeated at Jennings, previously a small rice-market town of 1,500 people. Now its streets were crowded with excited prospectors and speculators trying "to get in on the ground floor" of opportunity. Land in the McDaniel tract, near the Southern No. 3 well, was held for $10,000 an acre, and a tract a quarter of a mile away brought $800 an acre. Within the same month, the *Oil Investors' Journal* stated that Jennings had grown into a town of thrifty, well-to-do people, whose homes would do credit to those in cities of 5,000 to 10,000. Another evidence of the town's growth was the Citizens' National Bank Building, a "beautiful specimen of graceful architecture."[12] By August 14, the recently organized Commercial Club had promised that car shops were to be established, new brick buildings were under construction, and "enterprises of various natures" headed that way.

10 *Oil Weekly*, Vol. XV, No. 3 (October 18, 1919), 89–90, stated that Heywood's screen "led to the development of one of the most important oil field's inventions—the screen."

11 N. M. Fenneman, "Oil Fields of the Texas Louisiana Gulf Coastal Plain," in U.S.G.S. *Bull. No. 282*, 94–95.

12 Vol. I, No. 2 (June 7, 1902), 1–3.

Oil! Titan of the Southwest

The Jennings oil field grew astonishingly fast after the drilling of these first few wells. By 1902 its production reached 548,617 barrels of oil. And Beaumont could offer no competition, since a freight rate of twenty-four cents a barrel was imposed on oil shipped from Beaumont to Jennings. By midsummer of 1904, bigger production came when the Producers Oil Company brought in the field's greatest gusher on the Latreille tract, on the east side of the field, increasing the output to over 50,000 barrels a day; and the Bass-Benckenstein well added greatly to the field's output,[13] yielding from September 8, 1904, to January 31, 1905, 1,500,000 barrels of oil. The field produced over 6,000,000 barrels of oil during the last five months of 1905.

Before the Jennings oil field was many months old, the Heywoods were receiving letters about other Louisiana prospects of gas seepages. Scott decided to examine some of them. One prospect was at Anse la Butte, between Lafayette and Breau Bridge. He found the site a likely one and leased a few thousand acres of land. Then he sent a driller to start a well, and moved a second rig to Bayou Boullion. By this time the Heywoods had purchased all the tugs and barges possible on the Mermentau River and had shipped oil to Morgan City. They also hauled all their drilling equipment seventy miles up the Atchafalaya River and on up to Bayou Boullion. But Bayou Boullion was disappointing.

The drill at the first Anse la Butte well struck gas at about 1,700 feet and "sanded up." Heywood plugged back to 1,170 feet, put in a screen and brought in a 100-barrel well. Later, he drilled other small producers.

The Lake Oil Company, headed by Senator Robert Martin of St. Martinville and Walter Burke of New Iberia, then drilled near Heywood's first well and found a 7,000-barrel producer. After this, the Gulf Refining Company pooled with the Heywoods and leased over five thousand acres but found no well comparable to the Lake Oil Company well. Heywood later sold out to the Gulf company.[14] Other Louisiana petroleum and gas during this period were found

[13] *Oil Investors' Journal*, Vol. III, No. 67 (January 1, 1905), 5; Gerald Forbes, "Jennings, First Louisiana Salt-dome Pool," in *Louisiana Historical Quarterly*, Vol. XXIX, No. 2 (April, 1946), 500.

[14] Heywood, *loc. cit.*, No. 6, 23.

at Welsh, Lake Charles, Crowley, Lafayette, and Sulphur, but none of these early fields measured up to Jennings.

Saratoga and Sour Lake were two other Texas salt domes that attracted the attention of prospectors soon after the development of Spindletop. The No. 1 Hooks, a small producer, was drilled at Saratoga in the fall of 1901; but it was not until March 13 of the next year that the No. 2 Hooks definitely launched this field's modern era. A Kountze, Hardin County, report of this date carried in the Galveston *Semi-Weekly News* proclaimed the good tidings. "This little city is in a fever of excitement today," ran the report. "About ten o'clock this morning a telephone message from Saratoga brought information that the Hooks well No. 2 was performing in a way that would equal any of the freaks on Spindle Top . . . a roaring sound like an approaching tornado." The ground trembled and a shower of mud, water, and rocks belched from the pipe and shot high into the air. The well settled down to a daily yield of 500 barrels of oil.

On May 1, 1903, the No. 1 Teel accented still more Saratoga's possibilities, so much so that fourteen other locations were immediately made in the field. Both the Gulf and Texas companies built pipe lines from the field to Beaumont.

At Sour Lake, development was much the same. In 1901, the J. M. Guffey company had struck a strong flow of gas and some oil at 900 feet. This stimulated renewed interest in a field long known for its "sour springs." In November following, the Great Western Oil Company drilled another well to a depth of 1,500 feet and found four oil sands. Then on March 7, 1902, the Atlantic and Pacific Company struck an oil sand at 646 feet, went through thirty-six feet of it, "and when they commenced to draw the drill pipe the well bailed itself." It "gushed pure high grade oil to the top of the derrick." On the next day, the Galveston *Semi-Weekly News* announced the oil flow as "simply enormous . . . the largest gusher of lubricating and illuminating oil in the United States—if not in the world." Its daily output was estimated above 30,000 barrels.

During 1902, several other Sour Lake wells were completed with daily outputs from 500 to 10,000 barrels of oil; and during August or September of the next year, production climbed to more than 50,000 barrels of oil daily.

Oil! Titan of the Southwest

W. B. Sharp's clever work for The Texas Company is now a part of Sour Lake tradition. In the fall of 1902 he began drilling three wells on The Texas Company's Roche option of 815 acres at Sour Lake Spring. The first well was just outside and to the southeast of the Sour Lake hotel; and to the northwest, the second, which had a good showing of oil. But Sharp kept both wells "under wraps." Then a third was drilled northeast of the hotel, and at 780 feet it showed "every indication of developing into a gusher." But it was not tested until a stormy January night. It roared in as a gusher, throwing oil over the near-by trees, but the torrential rain washed away all traces of oil, and on the following day visitors did not know what had happened. The Texas Company officials knew enough to take up their option and to contract their oil output at sixty cents a barrel. "In thirty days after their well came in," averred the *Oil Investors' Journal,* "it had earned $150,000, and while they [The Texas Company] were getting sixty cents a barrel on their contract, the spot price at Sour Lake had dropped to ten and twelve cents."[15]

But, as at Spindletop, wells at Sour Lake were drilled too close, as on the "shoestring tract"; and the gas pressure declined rapidly, which, with reservoir depletion, caused the abandonment of 75 of the 150 wells by 1903. The enormous output of the field had fairly adequate pipe-line facilities. The J. M. Guffey Petroleum Company built a pipe line to Beaumont in 1902; and by the close of 1903, an eight-inch line and four six-inch lines to Beaumont, a six-inch line to Saratoga, and a four-inch line to Raymond, met the field's immediate needs.[16]

Prior to 1901, a small Sour Lake output of dark, heavy oil came from depths of less than 400 feet, but in subsequent drilling more abundant sources of oil were found in horizons at 750, 850, and 1,050 feet. The Sharp well was among the field's best producers, yielding 325,000 barrels of oil in twenty days.[17]

Three other Gulf Coast salt domes added greatly to Texas's oil production from 1901 to 1905. At Batson, about forty miles northwest of Beaumont, in 1901 the Libby Oil Company found small production at 1,000 feet. But it launched no leasing craze as at other

15 Vol. IV, No. 15 (January 3, 1906), 9.
16 Warner, *Texas Oil and Gas,* 191.
17 *Ibid.,* 192.

76

salt domes. It was not until the Paraffin Oil Company's No. 3 strike, a 15,000-barrel-a-day producer, that Batson had its leasing frenzy. After this, other developments came quickly, and within four months this field had a daily output of 151,000 barrels of oil.

Humble, a short distance northeast of Houston, in Harris County, experienced much the same cycle of oil play. Its gas seeps had been known for many decades. Then, during 1904, C. E. Barrett drilled several shallow wells on a hilltop. But he found only small producers. In October and December of this year the Higgins Oil and Fuel Company drilled two large gas wells. This accelerated the tempo of prospecting, and on January 7, 1905, the No. 2 Beaty rewarded its owners with an initial daily yield of 8,500 barrels of oil. Within three months the field's output had climbed to 2,000,000 barrels of oil.

By 1905, the salt-dome oil yield reached 130,000 barrels daily. On June 18, the *Oil Investors' Journal's* estimates of production per month for the various fields ran: Humble, 2,900,000; Batson, 410,000; Saratoga, 300,000; Sour Lake, 305,000; Spindletop, 145,000; and Jennings, 979,000. The Gulf Coast's tremendous production over a four-year period, however, may best be seen by a tabulation. During 1901, 1902, and 1903, the coastal salt domes produced 38,514,000 barrels of low gravity oil, classified as fuel oil, for which the producers received an average of eighteen cents in 1901; twenty-one cents in 1902; and forty-one cents in 1903.

THE GULF COAST SALT DOME OIL OUTPUT, 1902–1905[18]

Year	Texas		Louisiana		Total	
	Quantity (Barrels)	Value	Quantity (Barrels)	Value	Quantity (Barrels)	Value
1902	18,083,658	$3,998,097	548,617	$ 188,985	18,632,275	$4,187,082
1903	17,955,572	7,517,479	917,771	416,228	18,873,343	7,933,707
1904	22,241,413	8,156,220	2,958,958	1,073,594	25,200,371	9,229,814
1905	28,136,189	7,552,262	8,910,416	1,601,325	37,046,605	9,153,587

Louisiana producers did even better. They received $605,000 for 1,467,000 barrels of crude in 1902 and 1903, or an average of

[18] *Mineral Resources of the United States, 1905, Part II, Nonmetals,* 859.

forty-one cents a barrel. In 1902, the Gulf salt domes produced 20 per cent of the country's crude oil.

The building of pipe lines and refineries kept pace with this increase of oil production. The J. M. Guffey company had a six-inch line running from Batson to Saratoga and Sour Lake, where it joined an eight-inch line from Sour Lake to Port Arthur. On November 30, 1906, the Gulf Pipe Line Company was organized under the laws of Texas to connect with the Oklahoma oil fields. In the next year, an eight-inch line was completed from Sour Lake to Watkins, Oklahoma, to tap the Glenn Pool oil.

The Texas Company had matched the Gulf company's strides. It had started by laying a six-inch line from Spindletop to Port Arthur, a distance of twenty miles. And as new oil fields were found, its lines were extended—from Spindletop to Sour Lake, about twenty miles; from Sour Lake to Saratoga, about ten miles; from Sour Lake to Humble, about fifty miles; and from Humble to Houston, about twenty miles. Late in 1907, it also began construction on an eight-inch pipe line from Humble, then its line terminus, to the Oklahoma oil fields, a distance of about 470 miles.

The Sun company was another competitor. This company had been a Spindletop oil operator since 1901, buying large quantities of oil and sending it to Port Arthur through the pipe lines of other companies. From this port the Sun company shipped to Philadelphia. But on May 30, 1904, a United States Circuit Court forced the Lone Star and Crescent Oil Company to sell its holdings. The Sun company bought for $100,000 all its holdings, consisting of seven and one-half acres in the proven Spindletop field, with oil wells and pumping equipment thereon, steel tanks at Spindletop, Gladys City, and Sabine Pass, pumping stations, and twenty-seven miles of a six-inch pipe line from Gladys City to the Sabine Pass docks. This raised the Sun company to the position of a major operator.

As has been seen, The Texas Company and Gulf refineries at Port Arthur helped to solve the problem of Spindletop's rapidly accumulating oil supply. Their builders now expanded them as fast as equipment could be had. The Gulf plant had a battery of stills capable of running 24,000 barrels of crude oil daily, exceeded only by the Standard Oil's Whiting refinery of 30,000 barrels capacity.

Exploiting Other Salt Domes

Cheap oil made possible rapid expansion, and in June, 1902, with this in mind, Guffey sold $5,000,000 of bonds to Eastern bankers.

The Texas Company announced in May, 1902, the erection of ten steel tanks of 37,500-barrel capacity each to store crude oil for processing in a refinery to be built at Port Arthur, for which a part of the company's $3,000,000 capital was furnished by Gates' financial arrangements.

But the Spindletop oil field was also serviced by near-by refineries—the United Oil and Refining Company; the Central Asphalt and Refining Company at Port Neches; and the Burt Refinery, later owned by the Magnolia Petroleum Company. Those starting the Burt plant had built in secrecy by putting up "a solid fence 25 feet high," enclosing the 400- or 800-acre site. But Jefferson County deed records later revealed its importance. The deed was to "Samuel G. Bayne, president of the Seaboard National Bank of New York, for a consideration of $5,000,000."[19] In May, 1903, the refinery was operated by the Security Oil Company, which immediately started to store Spindletop oil. In June, this company let a contract for eight wood-lined earthen tanks, each of 130,000-barrel capacity to bring its total storage to 2,280,000 barrels. At that time Spindletop oil was selling at seventy to eighty cents a barrel, and oil companies were declaring monthly dividends as high as 19 per cent.

Considerable as was the Gulf Coast oil output, the eyes of wildcatters and prospectors were shortly fixed on fields farther north. In a short time records of Mid-Continent oil fields were hardly less spectacular.

[19] *Oil and Gas Journal—Oil City Derrick* (Diamond Jubilee edition), August 27, 1934, p. 146.

VII

Red Fork, Cleveland, and Glenn Pool

FROM 1897 TO 1901 there was little oil prospecting in Indian Territory, except for limited activity in the Osage and Cherokee country. Lease men and wildcatters twiddled their thumbs and idled, waiting for the federal government to give them liberal leasing terms.

All the while John and Michael Cudahy had been unable to sell the oil from their Muskogee wells, since they had neither market nor pipe-line outlet. In their plight, they sent their trusted general manager, W. H. Isom, to London to ask the assistance of a British-Dutch firm of financiers. At first, these financiers seemed uninterested. Then when Isom explained the possibility of developing a large Indian Territory oil field and offered them half-interest in the Cudahy Company's holdings there for $5,000,000, they finally decided to send a committee to the Muskogee area to investigate.

In due time the British delegation arrived at Muskogee aboard a special car. In spite of a raw, wintry day a large throng of curious residents was at the railroad station to greet them. But the Adams Hotel, the only lodging house in town, had recently burned, and the visitors were forced to remain on their private car. They were joined a short time later by a distinguished Englishman, Sir Boverton Redwood, who took the lead in inspecting the surrounding country and in negotiations. They were favorably impressed by what they saw and so reported to their home office. Redwood advised that they could build a refinery and a pipe line and could pipe the refined product from Muskogee to Webbers Falls for shipment by boat down the Arkansas River to New Orleans for sale. Promptly the British-Dutch financiers prepared to move in, but Congress blasted their plans by passing the Curtis Act, on June 28, 1898.

80

Red Fork, Cleveland, and Glenn Pool

For ten years, little by little the federal government had encroached on Indian treaty rights. The Chickasaws and Choctaws had accepted this federal policy by the Atoka agreement of April 23, 1897, providing departmental rules and regulations to govern the leasing of asphalt, coal, oil, and other mineral lands; but not so, the Cherokees and the Creeks. They, too, waited. Then the Curtis Act staggered them, abolishing their tribal courts and laws, and putting their lands at the disposal of the Dawes Commission for allotment. Mineral lands were set aside to be leased for the benefit of each tribe.

In April, 1899, a land office was opened at Muskogee to receive land filings, but still the prospectors hesitated. Then in May, 1901, drilling was resumed in the Creek country without the sanction of Secretary E. A. Hitchcock of the Department of the Interior, an action that was regarded "as a brazen, presumptuous and unwarranted proceeding."[1]

Federal officials and Indians alike believed that there was oil in Oklahoma. The Muskogee *Weekly Phoenix*, of November 2, 1899, had said that there were great deposits of oil in Indian Territory. There were producing wells at Muskogee, Chelsea, and Bartlesville, and vast potential oil fields stretched across the Cherokee and Creek country.

And while these fields lay unexploited, the Texas Spindletop discovery startled the petroleum world and galvanized into action Oklahoma landholders and prospectors.

John S. Wick, a "sanguine and poverty-stricken" Oklahoma operator, was one of these. One authority says that after meeting with indifferent success in Indian Territory, he still dreamed of the day when his oil wealth would eclipse that of John D. Rockfeller. But his dreaming also carried practical sales value, for he interested Jesse A. Heydrick, an experienced Butler, Pennsylvania, oil operator, in an Indian Territory lease. Lease men were stymied by Indian Office regulations. Notwithstanding this, acting solely as individual Creek citizens, Thomas J., Wash, and Lewis Adams, James and William A. Sapulpa, Samuel C. Davis, John I. Yargee, former Chief L. C. Perryman, D. L. Berryhill, and Lilah D. Lindsey,

[1] The John W. Flenner MS, in the files of the Mid-Continent Oil and Gas Association, Kansas-Oklahoma Division, Tulsa.

on November 9, 1899, leased 410,000 acres of Red Fork land, presumably on an assignment of the original lessors, the Adams Coal and Mining Company, to the John S. Wick Company (Jesse A. Heydrick for the most part being the company). The bounds of the lease were the Arkansas River on the north; the Frisco Railroad on the east and south; and Oklahoma Territory on the west, just across the river from and south of the small town of Tulsa.[2] The lease was to run for ten years, or as long as oil, gas, or minerals were found in paying quantities.

Although the Creek members of the agreement were eager to start operations immediately, Heydrick moved with caution. First, he had Wick and J. M. Dunn, an experienced operator, examine the lease. Shortly these two men reported favorably, and Heydrick came from Pennsylvania, with John Q. A. Kennedy, a Butler miner and oil producer, to inspect and approve the lease for prospective Pennsylvania stock-buyers, and select a drilling site. According to Wick, Heydrick's selection of a site "led to the drilling a year later of the discovery well."[3]

Before the two Pennsylvanians were ready to start drilling, however, the lease lapsed. (They had been required to drill their first well within six months.) Then Wick persuaded the Indians to renew the lease. This new agreement (but with the old terms), on July 16, 1900, carried the names of Sue A. Bland, the half-blood Creek wife of the Red Fork physician, Dr. John C. W. Bland; Timmie Fife; Eli E. Hardridge; J. H. Land; E. L. Simley; Albert P. Owen; and others—all Creek citizens.[4] Fifty shares of stock, of which the par value was $100, were sold to provide a working capital, and the well was started.

[2] A charter grant to much of this same territory had been given in 1896 by the Creek Council to the Red Fork Mining Company, consisting of T. E. Smiley, J. C. W. Bland, Butler R. Brassfield, H. F. Smith, Charley W. Brown, and J. S. Benson. But it should "not be so construed as to include *Coal, Oil and Gas.*" See Doc. No. 32333, Creek Nation, Indian Archives Division, Historical Building, Oklahoma City.

[3] *Ibid.*

[4] J. S. Wick's affidavit, December 21, 1901, a similar affidavit signed by W. A. Sapulpa, Timmie Fife, James Sapulpa, and J. H. Land, stating that the Indians owned their land in fee simple, and that the "Creek or Muscogee Indians have not as yet accepted the Curtis Law [August 6, 1900]; and the lease agreement of July 16, 1900." These papers were furnished the author by Mr. L. C. Heydrick, Wichita Falls, Texas, and are hereafter referred to as Heydrick papers.

Red Fork, Cleveland, and Glenn Pool

Heydrick and Wick employed the Crossman brothers[5] (Perry L. Crossman of Joplin, Missouri, being in charge) to drill a well on a location tentatively fixed about two miles southeast of Sapulpa; and late in the spring of 1901, he moved his cable-tool rig to Red Fork. But when it arrived, the Frisco station agent refused to accept Heydrick's New York draft to pay for the freight charges, whereupon Bland and his young friend, Dr. Fred S. Clinton, a prominent Tulsa physician, cashed it. It has been said that Heydrick was grateful for this service and gave to each of them a share of his company's stock. It was after this that Bland persuaded the Pennsylvanians to drill the first well on his forty-acre tract at Red Fork. Then, with all his preliminary work finished, Heydrick spudded in the company's first well on May 10, 1901, on the site previously chosen.[6]

Meanwhile, five days later, when the well had reached a depth of 150 feet, Eastern stockholders questioned the lease and refused to pay for their shares, and Heydrick returned to Pennsylvania to reassure them.

It was while Heydrick was on this trip, that the drillers of the Red Fork well hit a gas pocket and the well blew in as a producer, shortly before midnight on Monday, June 24, 1901. Crossman had reached a "stray gritty lime"[7] (probably the Oswego limestone) at 534 feet, and when his bit dug into it, "oil shot thirty feet over the top of the derrick."

Here was a dilemma: Heydrick was in Butler, Pennsylvania; Crossman, having gone to Joplin for the week end, was in bed; Wick was sleeping near the rig; and Crossman's son, Luther, was in charge of the drilling. Heydrick had previously warned Wick to close down the well and keep quiet if oil were struck in his absence. But now, unduly elated, Wick wired the elder Crossman, "Send packer, oil is spouting over the top of the derrick."[8] He might just as well have wired all metropolitan newspapers announcing the discovery, for his message, picked up by listening operators, was

[5] See "Well Record," Heydrick papers.

[6] NW¼ S22-T19N-R12E.

[7] Defined in the well log as "Grit and Lime," and first reached at 527 feet. See "Well Record," *ibid.*

[8] Flenner MS.

broadcast, electrifying the whole region and starting a stampede for Red Fork.

Early next morning Red Fork seethed with excitement. The report that had gone out was that the well was good for from sixty to three hundred barrels a day; and fickle rumor had enlarged it to a well potentially equal to, if not better than, the Lucas gusher. Within a few hours the roads leading into Red Fork, a village of two or three stores and a dozen dwellings, were choked with traffic. By midafternoon there was not a livery rig to be had at near-by Tulsa and Sapulpa.

Ambitious lawyers were on the ground to examine land titles; speculators and designing promoters worked with them, to launch hastily organized, and some fraudulently organized, oil companies to take advantage of unwary buyers; and adventurers, gamblers, hucksters, and fortunetellers appeared to pick up "the small change."

By June 25, Oklahoma City was excited over "the striking of the big oil gusher at Red Fork." And ambitious townsmen, Charles F. Colcord, Robert Galbreath, Usher Thomas, Boston Wilson, Lee Van Winkle, afterwards mayor of Oklahoma City, William Pettee, and Dr. Beard (and Dr. Childs and Dorsett Carter of Purcell) had boarded a special train bound for Red Fork. The town was described as "one of the vilest spots in the Territory . . . the Mecca of men and women dreaming of future oil millions. On every train, in all manner of conveyances, afoot and on horseback, a steady stream of humanity had come pouring in, and not a geologist in the lot."

Crossman returned to Red Fork on the first train. "I found a special car from Oklahoma City loaded with gamesters," he later wrote, "as soon as July 4th, over 1,000 men of oil firms were there, especially from Beaumont."[9]

Red Fork changed into a carnival town. It could not feed the tired, hungry, and thirsty army of invaders, milling about aimlessly. But like magic, tents and hastily constructed eating places and lemonade stands appeared where the tired throng might seek rest and refreshment. Speculation was rampant, fake oil-stock promoters and rival town-lot salesmen added to the general uproar. "Everything went, the sky being the limit, for the boom was on and the

[9] P. L. Crossman to J. C. Heydrick, September 3, 1931, in Heydrick papers.

restless humans hot in pursuit of the elusive goddess of chance were fairly tumbling over one another in their undignified but eager scramble for anticipated wealth." And strange to say, within four days, while this maelstrom of activity and excitement steadily mounted, the total oil recovered from the well was stored in two barrels.

Doubtless never before, and certainly never since, had so undignified a rush and wild scramble for leases struck. Far better oil prospects had been found at Bartlesville, Chelsea, and Muskogee. But the Red Fork discovery marked the beginning of a new epoch in Oklahoma oil development.

By June 26, 1901, the Red Fork news had reached Kansas City and the *Times* had headlined, "OIL WELL GUSHER FIFTEEN FEET HIGH," and stated that "two lucky Pennsylvanians, Heydrick and Kennedy [Wick],"[10] had taken up all the leases about the discovery well. This report was picked up also by the Eastern press and started a rush of Pennsylvania and Ohio oilmen for Red Fork.

Major Clifton R. Breckenridge of the Dawes Commission notified the Secretary of the Interior of the Red Fork oil strike, and the Secretary in turn wired George P. Wright at Muskogee "to investigate the report promptly regarding Red Fork, Creek Nation." Inspector Guy P. Cobb, who was in the Red Fork vicinity, was asked to investigate, and his findings, in turn, appeared in Wright's report to the Secretary. It was to the effect that "P. L. Crossman, formerly of Joplin, Missouri, and two Pennsylvanians, Hiderick [Heydrick] and Wicks [Wick]" were the promoters and controllers of the well. "I arrived at the well Thursday, June 27, about 3 P.M.," said Cobb, "and about that time there was a considerable flow of gas issuing from the top of the casing pipe, accompanied by a bubbling, rumbling sound, and at intervals of perhaps from 15 to 30 minutes each, a small quantity of oil was forced up by the gas to a distance of perhaps two feet above the top of the pipe, part of the oil falling back in and part slopping over the sides of the pipe."[11]

[10] Oklahoma City report, carried in the *Kansas City Times*, June 26, 1901.

[11] Flenner MS, 320. Credit for the discovery of the Red Fork well was later given to Bland and Clinton, but the Heydrick-Wick lease agreements, well log, and other contemporary evidence prove beyond reasonable doubt that Heydrick and Wick should have that dubious honor.

Cobb also reported that the "bailer or cleaner" caused the well to gush for prospective buyers by an ingenious method. "A canvas bag large enough to completely fill the drill hole was fastened at the top of the bailer and lowered slowly to the bottom of the well and permitted to remain there for a sufficient length of time to confine the gas and to permit the accumulation of oil; then the engine was started up at full speed, and the bailer and canvas sack drawn up as rapidly as possible, causing the sudden discharge of gas and oil to be thrown up to a distance of 3 to 10 feet above the top of the pipe."[12] Photographers were there to make pictures of these spasmodic gushings for the benefit of Oklahoma newspapers and to impress the outside world.

But no artificial stimulus would impress Heydrick, when he stepped from a Frisco passenger train on Saturday, June 29. He had scarcely set foot on Red Fork soil before he was beseiged with offers to buy the well and forty acres surrounding it, there being a speculator rivalry to obtain this coveted property. After he had hastily visited the well, he came away greatly disappointed. It had not reached a horizon of prolific production.

That night Heydrick wrote his son, James A. Heydrick, from the Gladstone Hotel in Sapulpa, probably because no accommodations could be found at Red Fork. "The wild stories set afloat," he confided, "has brot hundreds here. When let loose it [the well] flows high into the air but soon blows out. In the present state it is not more than 10 bbls. per day, all things considered—depth 537 feet, of quality of oil, etc. It looks like an oil field. . . . I have an offer of $20,000 for well and 40 acres around the well if they, the Eastern associates, think best and I will hold the drill until closed."[13]

But the Eastern associates did not think best. They had read the press reports and discounted Heydrick's opinion. Secretary Hitchcock had also read newspaper accounts, as well as the reports of Wright and Cobb; and he became alarmed. Revenue Inspector Cobb had sought the opinion of Chief Porter of the Creeks on the many leases that had followed the discovery well. Porter had said that he thought they were all void. Hitchcock thought so, too, and

[12] *Ibid.*, 319.

[13] In Heydrick papers. The original well, as well as other wells there, yet produces about one barrel of oil a day.

despite every effort made by Heydrick to validate his claim, the Secretary withheld his approval and the lease was voided.

Within less than four months after the Heydrick-Wick well came in, John Davidson, a pioneer Pennsylvania oilman, drilled another, under the direction of C. H. Donohue, general superintendent for Charles F. Colcord and associates. Other developments came later, but the Red Fork pool was never a large one.

While oilmen were crowding into Red Fork, another oil strike, 175 miles southwest of the Heydrick-Wick well, north of the Granite Mountain and about three miles north of the town of Granite on Watt Armstrong's farm, was reported. W. M. Stephenson, a Waco, Texas, citizen and "an experienced oil man," gave the Dallas *Morning News* an account of this discovery on June 25, 1901.[14] "The oil and gas structures paralleling the Wichita Mountain range," he said, "will produce giant gushers that will rival the famous Spindletop gushers in Texas. . . . The crude oil is good as any crude. I tested it by greasing the wheels of my buggy." The well produced about eight or ten barrels of oil a day, according to Joe D. Morse, one of the well's sponsors.[15]

Almost a month later, A. J. Greiner, secretary-treasurer of the Oklahoma Natural Gas, Light and Heat Company,[16] promoter of the well, gave the Guthrie *State Capital* (Tuesday Morning, July 18, 1901) a similar story, adding that Granite oil was worth fifty to sixty cents a gallon. He furnished a list of his company officers—E. R. Suppe, president; J. D. Morse, vice-president; A. J. Greiner, secretary-treasurer; and W. H. Suppe, superintendent. The company was capitalized at $100,000.

Dr. Charles N. Gould drove from Norman out to the well, the No. 1 Armstrong, accompanied by Bailey Willis of the United States Geological Survey. When the two men arrived at the well, they found the producer employing a novel method to get the oil. "The oil was secured from the well by rope which ran over a pulley and was attached to a sheet-iron bucket. . . . A horse was hitched to the end of the rope and started across the prairie and the oil brought

[14] The *News* story was recopied by the Guthrie *State Capital*.

[15] Joe D. Morse to C. C. Rister, June 24, 1948.

[16] On July 18, 1901. The company charter is on file in the Secretary of State's Office, Oklahoma City.

to the surface and dumped in a small metal tank. The farmers from the vicinity bought the oil for greasing livestock, mowing machines, and other farm machinery."[17]

At near-by Gotebo was a small refinery and a distributing system taking natural gas from the shallow wells, but the supply of both oil and gas was soon of little consequence.

Meanwhile, back at Red Fork excitement was high. The oil field drew many prospectors who drilled other small-producing wells. But it had other important but indirect results. Increasing pressure brought by Oklahoma oilmen on the Department of the Interior, finally, in 1902, caused the Secretary to approve the first lease of Indian lands.

The boom also started Tulsa on a period of growth, to become the Mid-Continent oil capital. The Osage development, too, moved toward Tulsa. Brennan and Frost, Bob Rodd, Colonel Bilkey, and a few others purchased Lot 63, several miles below J. S. Glenn's Lot 49 property; and Senator Matson leased Lot 62. Both tests were started about the same time; and that on Lot 62 came in on June 23, 1904, as a 500-barrel well from the Bartlesville sand and that on Lot 63 as a slightly larger producer. In addition, the Red Fork craze, when coupled with oil development at Allowe and Chelsea, also caused oil exploration at Guthrie, Oklahoma City, McCloud, Shawnee, Blackwell, Chandler, and Cushing, but no major pool was found at this time.

Cleveland, Indian Territory, claimed the next important discovery, in July, 1904, with what its citizens erroneously called "the first commercially productive well in Oklahoma." The well was drilled jointly by W. J. Fellows and John Shell, just south of the local townsite on the Bill Lowery farm, and produced about fifty barrels of oil per day from what was then thought to be the Bartlesville sand (1,615 feet), but later proved to be several hundred feet above this sand. The Cleveland and Kelso sands were the two productive horizons. Other wells came quickly, the field spreading out south and west, on sections 16 and 17, although sections 18, 20, and 29 were in proven territory; and oil was also found in several near-by

[17] Interview with Dr. C. N. Gould, April 17, 1947. Other data regarding this well furnished the author by Howard A. Tucker and Claude Barrow, of the *Daily Oklahoman*, Oklahoma City.

but seperate pools. But close well-spacing and open production soon exhausted the gas pressure, resulting in great waste to the operators.

Cleveland ran much the same cycle of experience as had Red Fork. Speculators, "law-shysters," prospectors, and "fly-by-nighters" appeared, some from outside states, and helped to accelerate a land boom. "Deposits in local banks have increased seventy-five per cent," wrote a local enthusiast on September 7.[18] Within six months the town had a building boom, with twenty-five new residences and several two-story business buildings. "Hotels are badly overcrowded and it is almost impossible to secure accommodations," complained a new arrival.

Within a year, the Cleveland oil field, with 255 wells, had grown astonishingly fast. Of this number, 28 wells were dry, 7 were gas wells with an aggregate daily production of 50,000,000 feet, and 220 were oil wells with a daily production of 11,000 barrels. The Prairie Oil and Gas Company pipe line furnished the principal outlet to market.

But Glenn Pool capped all early-day Oklahoma fields. Bob Galbreath, a Red Fork and West Tulsa operator, had discovered a sandstone outcrop on the Ida Glenn farm about ten miles south of Tulsa. He induced Frank Chesley to join him in a lease of the farm[19] and they completed their first well on November 22, 1905. The well made 85 barrels of oil per day at a depth of 1,481 feet; and a second well, a short distance south of the first, 700 barrels a day, and a nearby third, 2,000 barrels. The initial production came from what was then called the Glenn sand but later, the Bartlesville sand.

Shortly before Galbreath and Chesley had drilled their first well, they took in as partners C. F. Colcord of Oklahoma City and J. O. Mitchell of Tulsa, to give them operating funds. By the late summer they had a daily output of 2,000 barrels of oil. Meanwhile, other operators had swarmed into the field and leased large tracts about the Galbreath-Chesley discovery well. At this time the field was yielding 500 to 1,000 barrels of oil daily. The biggest operator,

[18] Clippings from unidentified newspapers, volume listed, "August 1, 1904–February 1, 1905," p. 25, col. 1, in Barde Collection, Oklahoma Historical Library, Oklahoma City.

[19] SE¼ S4-T17N-R12E.

the Prairie Oil and Gas Company, succeeded in getting several leases in advance of the pool and secured some leases on the post-oak hill on the west side of the valley, beyond the railroad. Leases brought up to $16,000 a tract, one company paying $12,000 for a 160-acre farm.

By the opening of 1907, there were 125 wells at Glenn Pool, 102 of which were producing oil, 12 gas wells, and 11 dry. But no dry holes had been found in the producing area proper. Galbreath and Company had 24 producing wells (with 14,000 barrels of oil a day), three gassers, two wells drilling, and five rigs. Then there were twenty-four other companies claiming an output of more than 55,000 barrels of oil.

In late January, W. E. Campbell, a Tulsa lease and real-estate dealer, "got a rig and drove over" to Glenn Pool. He then wrote his son, R. B., that it was "simply wonderful" to see what was being done there. A Standard Oil subsidiary "had mamouth wells and quite a number of steel tanks filled with oil and others in the course of construction, and more wells going down." On the Galbreath and Chesley lease, he saw "some wonderful wells . . . one earthern tank or lake of oil . . . containing 100,000 barrels and three two-inch pipes flowing full under pressure into another great steel tank."

"A large force of men and teams are also busy making excavations in the earth with plows and scrapers to hold the oil that cannot now be received by the pipe lines for lack of capacity. If the development continues," Campbell predicted, "the two big eight-inch pipe lines from the Glenn to the Gulf and the Standard line now to the north will have all they can handle."

Campbell also wrote of important Glenn Pool real-estate deals. One group of lease-holders was offered $2,500,000 for a choice tract, but some of the associates would not sell. Campbell thought their decision unwise. They could "have gone out with $1,000,000 clear cash," he believed. Then there was G. W. Barnes, Jr., who had "bought a piece of land last spring near Keiffer for $13 per acre. He now has a daily production of 3,000 barrels on the property." As for his own and his associates' property, Campbell said: "A number of exceedingly large oil wells and immense oil tanks are on three tracts of 160 acres, each adjoining this 320 acres of ours, and drilling is now going on on another 160 adjoining, and one well, their

first one, is said to be a 1,000-barrel well. Some of these wells have flowed 2,500 to 3,000 barrels in 24 hours."[20]

The Glenn Pool discovery brought the growth of such towns as Tulsa, Sapulpa, and Red Fork. In addition, Kiefer, known as a hell hole, about four miles below Sapulpa and eighteen miles from Tulsa on the Frisco Railroad, sprang up. It had appeared since the Gulf Pipe Line people began unloading supplies for their pipe line, stations, and tankage in the Glenn field, in late November, 1906. In three months the town's freight business had grown from practically nothing to $15,000 a month, with a prospect of $45,000 before summer. The Gulf Production Company put in a loading rack just above town and the Frisco an extra siding at the station, making room for about forty cars. Real-estate promoters platted a town site, and the businessmen erected mercantile houses, bank buildings, and residences. This brought lumber dealers; the Vertress tank shops worked overtime; and restaurants were overcrowded.

In one respect, the Glenn Pool producers were fortunate. High grade crude oil was in great demand, and crude from the Glenn Pool rated 32–38 degrees gravity, with a paraffin base. But the new field's transportation problem was its bottleneck, and within a few months its output overflowed all hastily built earthen reservoirs and wooden and steel tanks and deflated the oil price to thirty cents a barrel. Loading racks were installed at Jenks on the Midland Valley Railroad and at Kiefer on the Frisco soon after the drilling of the discovery well; but railroad facilities were entirely inadequate.

The Standard Oil's subsidiary, the Prairie Oil and Gas Company, was the first major firm to reach Glenn Pool with its pipe line. In August, 1906, this occasion was celebrated by a participant's breaking a bottle of wine over the last pipe-line connection and by dubbing the spot "Southwestern Terminus."[21] A short time later Glenn Pool oil was turned into the new line, bound for points north. But the Prairie Oil and Gas Company could handle only 20,000 barrels of oil a day, hardly more than Galbreath and associates could furnish.

[20] MS, W. E. Campbell to R. B. Campbell, February 2, 1907. R. B. Campbell of Colorado Springs, Colorado, permitted the author to use this letter and an accompanying diagram of the producing properties at Glenn Pool, now in University of Oklahoma Manuscript Division.

[21] The Frederick (Oklahoma Territory) *Enterprise*, August 16, 1906, p 6, col. 4.

Oil! Titan of the Southwest

By February of the next year, as Campbell said, there was much pipe-line building. The Gulf Production and Texas companies' eight-inch cast-iron pipes were approaching Oklahoma from the south; and a sixteen-inch gas line was reaching out from the Tulsa country toward Oklahoma City and intermediate points. The Gulf refinery received its first Glenn Pool crude at Port Arthur, Texas, in October, 1907, and The Texas Company completed its testing between Bobbin and Humble, Texas, in January, and announced its line ready for business.[22] The anticipated annual use of 7,000,000 barrels of Glenn Pool crude oil by these two Port Arthur refineries depressed the market for salt-dome crude oil, which was not to be devoted to asphalt, lubricants, and products for which heavy oil was desirable. The consequent decline in the refineries' purchase of salt-dome oil was from 7,300,000 barrels in 1906 to 4,600,000 barrels in 1907. Gulf and Texas operators felt that Glenn Pool crude would better enable them to compete with the oil markets of the South, the Atlantic coast, and Europe. To meet this competition, they expanded their plants. The Gulf Production Company built thirty-five or forty distributing stations in the South, some of which represented investments of $25,000 to $40,000.[23]

This Glenn Pool outlet to refineries only stimulated the Texas market for a short time. The Prairie Oil and Gas Company's price seldom went below forty cents, but local brokers and smaller purchasers bought millions of barrels of Glenn Pool crude below this price. With thousands of barrels of oil going down Pole Cat Creek each day, some producers offered their current output at twenty-seven and twenty-eight cents.

Glenn Pool was the oilman's dream field. Its depth was reason-

[22] During this period there was no law on the statute books to restrain a major company if it chose to oppress the individual operator. Amos Beaty, a former president of The Texas Company, testified before the Cole Committee in 1934 that the major companies having pipe lines at Glenn Pool "ran largely their own oil," thus causing the small operator "a very hard time . . . taking out their own oil and leaving him to find a market as best he could." (Hearings, Part I, p. 200.) Judge James A. Veasey added that a large company owning a pipe line and refinery had a very small lease of ten acres. There were large leases on either side. The company ran its own production from the ten acres, running none whatever from its neighbors, and the ten-acre lease naturally drained not only its own oil but that of its neighbor's land as well. (Hearings, Part 3, 1934, p. 1704.)

[23] *Oil Investors' Journal*, Vol. VI, No. 16 (January 19, 1908), 28.

ably shallow, the cost of drilling moderate, the oil output by gas pressure, and the quality of oil excellent. Yet major oil companies entered the field gingerly. Tide Water,[24] as the Associated Producers Company, led the way, paying $17,500 for 160 acres near the Galbreath-Chesley No. 1 well. David P. Connelly, Tide Water's representative in Oklahoma, had bought the leases and was scolded for doing so by his New York office. But his faith was rewarded when his first well produced 1,500 barrels of oil daily; and within two years he had stored 1,100,000 barrels of Glenn Pool crude beyond that which he had sold to the Prairie Oil and Gas Company.

W. H. Milliken had the adjoining lease, for which he paid $20,-000 and from which he produced over 3,000,000 barrels of oil before his least expired. The Prairie Oil and Gas Company was another large dealer, acquiring a large lease for which it paid $3,-000,000 and about which it later built up a large and profitable production. But no one fared better in ratio production than Galbreath and his associates. From an 870-acre lease they got in excess of 16,000 barrels at the peak of their output. They had many offers for their holdings, at one time $1,500,000, but they refused them. Later, after the field had begun to decline, their holdings were sold for $490,000.[25]

The *Daily Oklahoman* (Oklahoma City) of March 28, 1907, paid tribute to the remarkable development of Glenn Pool, which had grown from an eighty-acre tract to almost eight thousand acres of proven territory in little more than a year. And well it might, for on September 24, of this year, Glenn Pool had broken all records in the history of crude-oil production. Up to September 1, the takings

[24] Tide Water first acquired its leases in Oklahoma in Tulsa and Creek counties through its Pennsylvania producing subsidiary, the Associated Producers. In 1907 it organized the Oklahoma Oil Company to substitute for the Associated Producers, which, in turn, in 1916, was changed to the Tidal Oil Company. In 1916, Tide Water purchased producing properties in the Drumright-Cushing field and ten years later, in Greater Seminole. In Texas, it held several prolific leases in the Powell field in 1923; and then expanded rapidly into other major Southwestern fields. Since 1936 it has had substantial production in the Louisiana Gulf Coast area, on the Venice Salt Dome and elsewhere. Much of Tide Water's Southwestern crude oil is shipped by tanker to its Bayonne, New Jersey, refinery.

In 1932 the name "Tidal Oil Company" was changed to Tide Water Oil Company of Delaware, and four years later it was merged with and into Tide Water Associated Oil Company.

[25] Galey MS, as cited, p. 29.

of Standard, the Gulf, and the Texas pipe lines were 27,050,100 barrels of Glenn Pool oil, or an average of 3,381, 263 barrels a month. At this rate the yearly production would total 40,575,144 barrels, more than was ever produced by any field outside the famous Baku district of Russia.

While Glenn Pool excitement was high, oil discoveries in Okmulgee County, starting with that near the town of Okmulgee, in 1906, created a temporary diversion for oil operators.[26] Other discoveries at Bald Hill by Joe Burns and Lou Caton in the spring of 1908, and by Bob Galbreath a short time later, made Okmulgee an active lease-trading center. "The Okmulgee influence," writes Claude Barrow, "was felt in Oklahoma until after the discovery of the Oklahoma City field." These traders were "fast-moving, fast-trading, and good gamblers." It was often said that "if you can't trade a lease anywhere else, go to Okmulgee."[27]

[26] The shallow sands of the Beggs oil field were developed in 1911–12; and the deeper zones, in 1919–20. Also in 1920, Homer F. Wilcox opened another oil field in Okmulgee County, about six miles west of Beggs. The "deep sand," as this oil horizon into which he drilled was called, was later known as the Wilcox sand.

[27] Claude Barrow to C. C. Rister, June 10, 1948.

VIII

Louisiana in the News

P ROSPECTORS AND WILDCATTERS began a widespread search for other Spindletops following the Lucas oil discovery in 1901. Hundreds of dry holes were drilled and millions of dollars were spent during this ever expanding and, to a great degree, indiscriminate movement, covering an area larger than the whole of New England. Still, there were a few important discoveries along the Texas and Louisiana coastal belt, where oil was found on the tops or flanks of salt domes. By 1921 there were forty-four known coastal domes—twenty-eight in Texas and sixteen in Louisiana. Hardly one-third of these were productive.[1]

Five years after its discovery, the Spindletop oil field had passed its production peak and had settled down to declining returns. South Texas oilmen still hoped for bigger production than had yet been found; but for the decade to follow, the output of the Texas coast's five oil fields went down, with the exception of Saratoga, which maintained flush production longer than her four sister fields because of wider well spacing, the result mainly of large lease units.

Although the oil output of some of its fields declined, the Gulf Coast produced 900,000 barrels more in 1908 than in 1907, but the market slumped. This drop was primarily the result of a decrease in consumption, and, in addition, the completion of the Gulf Oil Corporation and The Texas Company pipe lines from Oklahoma to the Texas coast, thereby opening the Mid-Continent oil fields to Gulf Coast purchasers, undoubtedly influenced the market. For Oklahoma crude oil, particularly that from Glenn Pool and Cleve-

[1] Sidney Powers, "Occurrence of Petroleum in North America," in *Technical Publication, No. 377,* American Institute of Mining and Metallurgical Engineers, 24–26.

land, was of finer quality and commanded top price. Louisiana also felt this Oklahoma competition, for in 1909 its production fell off 47.15 per cent.[2]

Caddo was Louisiana's surprise gas and oil field of this ten-year period, opening as an oil field in 1906 without fanfare and growing in importance during the next ten years. It was northern Louisiana's oldest and largest field, lying near the northwest corner of the Sabine Uplift. Gas seepages in Caddo Lake and near-by water pools led to its discovery. When the region was developed, both oil and gas were found in the Nacatoch sand (generally called the "gas rock"); in the "Chalk rock"; in the Buckrange sand; and in the so-called "Woodbine" sand, later thought to be of Tokio age.[3]

In 1902, Ellison M. Adger of Belcher, Louisiana, sought to drill a water well near Dixie, on Cottonwood Bayou, in the reclaimed Soda Lake region. At 425 feet he abandoned the well without encountering anything but salt water. Still believing that water could be found here, he sent some samples of the soil to A. C. Veatch of the United States Geological Survey, asking if there was a possibility of finding artesian water at this location. Veatch, who had previously studied the area and knew its structure, replied that there was no water where Adger had drilled but that if he would sink his well to a depth of 1,000 feet he felt sure that he would get gas or oil there.[4]

"This sounded like a fairy tale," Adger wrote later. Since at that time he was not interested in testing Veatch's theory, he abandoned the well.

Other prospectors, however, had more faith in Caddo's oil possibilities. In 1904 oil was discovered in the Savage-Morrical test, but it did not flow and the well was abandoned. Next year the Latex Oil and Pipe Line Company reached two producing sands;

[2] But from 1908 to 1910 crude oil advanced from twenty-eight to forty-two cents. This price advance also stimulated exploration and development in the entire Mid-Continent area, the oil output of which increased 4,000,000 barrels. In Kansas, drilling was particularly active in Allen, Chautauqua, Neosho, Montgomery, and Wilson counties.

[3] Generally, northwestern Louisiana oil was obtained from the Upper Cretaceous formation of the Sabine Uplift (in the Caddo, Elm Grove, Crichton, Bull Bayou, and Bellevue fields).—Powers, *op. cit.*, 33; George Charlton Matson, *The Caddo Oil and Gas Field, Louisiana and Texas*, U.S.G.S. *Bull. No. 619*, 13 ff.

[4] *Oil Investors' Journal*, Vol. VIII, No. 12 (November 20, 1908), 18.

The first Heydrick-Wick well at Red Fork, Oklahoma,
still pumping in 1946

photograph by the author

Robert Galbreath near his discovery site at Glenn Pool,
1946

photograph by the author

First smokestack, Baton Rouge refinery, 1906

Esso Standard Oil Company (La.)

The three catalytic crackers of the Baton Rouge refinery today

Esso Standard Oil Company (La.)

but, in both, gas was so strong that the well was plugged. Then in May, 1905, the Producers No. 2 well was drilled into a strong gas flow, which blew a huge crater in the well and forced its abandonment;[5] and Producers No. 3, completed a short time later, was equally wild.[6]

Although these wells were abandoned, the finding of gas caused oilmen to believe that a major oil pool was somewhere near by, so they moved into the region, leased extensive acreage of the Caddo Lake land, and started drilling. The Savage brothers discovered the first Caddo oil well, a small producer, their No. 1 Auffenhauser, on March 28, 1906.[7]

Belcher and Dixie citizens were among the persons who now started other operations. Early in 1907 they organized the Dixie Oil, Gas and Pipe Line Company and sank their first well near the old Adger site. At 825 feet the drill struck a strong gas flow, estimated at over 1,000,000 cubic feet each twenty-four hours; drilling was resumed, and at 2,167 feet an oil sand was struck, but without much oil, and the well was abandoned. Then the driller moved his rig about one mile from the first well. Here, too, he encountered gas; and, indeed, for several weeks the well ran wild before it could be capped, after which it supplied gas for the towns of Dixie, Uni, and Belcher.

By 1908 eleven gas wells had been drilled in the Caddo field, a six-inch pipe line was laid from Dixie to Shreveport, and later gas was furnished 28 industrial firms and 2,700 domestic consumers at Mooringsport, Blanchard, and Caddo.

As in other fields where major oil strikes were made, operators at Caddo drilled rapidly, trying for a rich oil pay which they believed was indicated by so much gas. They did not try to conserve the enormous gas flow, the roar of which could be heard at Caddo and neighboring towns. Several burning wells near Oil City shot flames high in the air, lighting the landscape brilliantly at night, and one of these burned uncontrolled for five years. Other wells in

[5] Gerald Forbes, "History of Caddo Oil and Gas Field," in *Louisiana Historical Quarterly,* Vol. XXIX, No. 1 (January, 1946), 60.

[6] G. D. Harris, *Oil and Gas in Louisiana,* U.S.G.S. Bull. No. 429, 136.

[7] The site of this well was S1-T20N-R16W. Information furnished the author by Mr. A. R. Carmody, Louisiana-Arkansas Division, Mid-Continent Oil and Gas Association, Shreveport, Louisiana.

the field vented millions of feet of gas into the air for month after month.

Such profligate waste made good newspaper copy, and Caddo oil reports were read over the nation. Louisiana citizens, greatly aroused, demanded that the state legislature take some action to halt this reckless waste of gas. Thus encouraged, in 1906 the General Assembly enacted the first of its conservation laws, making it a criminal offense to allow a gas well to remain out of control or to burn or blow wastefully into the air.[8]

But the development of the field went on. J. B. McCann, of the J. M. Guffey Petroleum Company, traced a gas seepage across the lake by setting fire to its vapors rising from the water. In a boat, he followed the fire to the opposite shore line, where later he leased 1,000 acres of the land. Here he drilled on the Hostetter farm. Luck was with him. At 800 feet he found a gas flow measured at 15,000,-000 cubic feet; and a second well drilled near by became a wild gasser and was abandoned.

During 1907, twenty-three wells dotted the Caddo field, eight of which were oil producers and eleven gassers. The oil output climbed to 50,000 barrels and the gas from 35,000,000 to 50,000,000 cubic feet. A short time later a Caddo observer reported that 70,-000,000 cubic feet of gas were wasted daily, and at night Shreveport residents, twenty-five miles away, could see the field's giant "blow" torches.

David T. Day of the United States Geological Survey denounced the Caddo oil operators for their profligate waste of gas, saying that it was the "most flagrant abuse of natural wealth yet recorded in the industry."[9] Nor did he stop there. In 1908, Day, accompanied by C. W. Hayes, the Survey's chief geologist, visited the Caddo field, saw the burning No. 1 Trustee well, and noticed on every hand the "popping" of gas. The two officials were appalled. Upon their return to Washington, they reported that Caddo's gas wastage equalled one-twentieth of the total gas consumption in the country.

This charge brought corrective measures. First, the Secretary of the Interior, with President Theodore Roosevelt's approval, di-

[8] Conservation Commission's Report, 1908–10, 903–904; *The Link*, Vol. X, No. 3 (March, 1910), 4.

[9] *Mineral Resources of the United States, 1907, Part II, Nonmetals*, 323.

rected the withdrawal from settlement, entry, or appropriation of all public lands in townships 15 to 23 north, of ranges 10 to 16 west, affecting about 6,500 acres of oil and gas lands. The Louisiana Land Office also helped by annulling certain applications for lands, by fixing land prices, and by empowering the Caddo Levee Board to hold land sales.

Meanwhile, Caddo's development was spectacular. In 1908, 56 wells were completed; the oil output reached 499,937 barrels and was valued at $214,048; and in the next year, the field had 183 wells and a production of 1,028,818 barrels of oil, valued at $549,081. Then in 1910 its yield spurted to 5,090,793 barrels of oil, valued at $2,292,349.

A new oil pay zone had been discovered. At the end of 1909, the J. C. Trees No. 4 well was drilled past 2,300 feet and found an initial production of over 2,000 barrels of crude oil daily before the drill bit could be removed. This well was in the Stiles tract, on the west side of the Jeems Bayou, or the western edge of the Caddo field.[10]

Within a month the Trees No. 4 well had declined in output, then gradually increased its flow again until it reached 3,000 barrels of oil daily. On a large tract two and one-half miles southwest of the Trees well, the Gulf Refining Company drilled its No. 1 Burr well, which, in April, roared in at a depth of 2,225 feet, flowing 2,000 barrels of oil a day. Then the Producers Oil Company developed the area between the Burr and Stiles tracts, thus linking the two areas. Late in June the sensational Producers No. 6 well[11] yielded over 12,000 barrels a day. On June 19, lightning set this well on fire before it was finished, but it was brought under control after a two-day fight.

Also in 1910 the Levee Board advertised for bids on the 8,000-acre bed of Caddo Lake, which was bought by the Gulf Refining Company for $30,000. In addition, the Gulf company agreed to pay $70,000 in royalties and to drill eight wells, a contract that was soon met by gusher after gusher which paid many times over the cost of the lease.

[10] In S17-T21N-R16W.
[11] In S33-T21N-R16W.

Oil! Titan of the Southwest

The following table shows that by 1910 Caddo had become the biggest oil field in Louisiana:

LOUISIANA OIL PRODUCTION AND VALUE, 1909–10[12]

District	1909			1910		
	Quantity	Value	Price Per Barrel	Quantity	Value	Price Per Barrel
Jennings	1,966,614	$1,421,806	$0.723	1,625,159	$1,187,312	$0.731
Welsh	26,169	19,882	.760	54,724	46,047	.841
Anse la But'e	37,930	31,680	.835	44,018	35,010	.795
Caddo	1,028,818	549,081	.533	5,090,793	2,292,349	.500
Totals	3,059,531	$2,022,449	---	6,841,395	$3,594,069	---

The Gulf Refining Company was fully prepared to drill the lake bed. It maintained a fleet of three tugboats, ten barges, a floating pile driver, and thirty-six small boats. The rigs were hauled on barges, while the derricks were built on piling; and fifty-barrel tanks, mounted on posts, served as slush pits.[13] This was Louisiana's spectacular beginning of marine drilling, which was to assume great importance in later years when oil was discovered near the Gulf shore.

For the most part, producers ignored Roosevelt's withdrawal order, believing that it was illegal. In time, federal legal advisers thought so, too, and recommended a new measure. Therefore, on June 2, 1910, President William Howard Taft established the Petroleum Reserve No. 4, embracing 414,720 acres near the producing area. The fact that oilmen had already drilled on some of the restricted lands, however, led to prolonged litigation, which kept the gas-waste problem before the public and ultimately brought the enactment of state conservation laws.

Caddo continued to attract attention. In 1911 its Producers No. 7 Harral blew in with an estimated flush production of 40,000 barrels a day;[14] and in the same year the field was extended by successful drilling at Naborton and near Mansfield, in the De Soto Parish. Substantial gushers were also found in its old proven areas. The

12 *Mineral Resources of the United States, 1910, Part II, Nonmetals,* 410.

13 Forbes, *loc. cit.,* 68–69.

14 D. H. Brancroft, "Sketch of the History of Oil and Gas in Caddo Parish," in *Chronicles of Shreveport and Caddo Parish,* 108.

Louisiana in the News

Texas company completed an eight-inch pipe line from Port Arthur to Caddo, making possible greater marketing facilities, and the Standard Oil Company's pipe line furnished a short carriage to the Baton Rouge refinery.

Other Louisiana salt-dome fields also were headlined in the news reports. In 1911 and 1912, Pine Prairie had fair wells, and a Vinton well roared in as an 18,000-barrel gusher, thus introducing a fine field.[15]

By 1915, Louisiana had become an important oil-producing state. The Ferry Lake district, between two and three miles west of Mooringsport, was an important extension of the Caddo field. Here the Amateur Oil Company unexpectedly brought in a well that furnished incentive for extensive drilling. Other extensions were made in the De Soto and Red River districts, the old Naborton field being developed several miles both east and west, and the Crichton field several miles south of Gusher Bend production. The Grand Bayou district, lying on the boundary of the De Soto and Red River parishes, practically connected the Gusher Bend and Naborton districts when Kelso and Graham drilled a well that had an initial production of 1,500 barrels of oil.

Almost as important as these oil developments was the discovery of the enormous Elm Grove gas field, twenty miles south of Shreveport, in Bossier Parish. This was thought to be a part of the Monroe gas field of more than 350 square miles, discovered in 1916, which by January 1, 1930, had yielded 1,056,000,000,000 cubic feet of gas.[16] The Atlas Oil Company, representing the Potter-Palmer interests of Chicago, had taken the lead in the development of this field. By 1917 it took in four or five parishes in the northeastern corner of Louisiana.

The Dallas Oil Company, after protracted experimental drilling, also brought in a 1,200-barrel well in the north end of Bossier

---

[15] Frequently wild promotional plans were launched during the development of such a field. In 1918 the Edgerly-Vinton field was advertised as the place upon which three great underground streams of oil, running from the Arctic Circle, converged and formed "one great underground stream," flowing under Vermilion Parish and Edgerly-Vinton field.—"Oil Field Events," advertising sheet of an oil company "Oil, 624.25-T135," Records of the Geological Survey, Correspondence branch, National Archives.

[16] Powers, *loc. cit.*, 34.

Parish, thereby starting a new leasing movement. Another interesting oil field was at Homer, where exploration began in 1917, and the third well drilled in the area came in on January 12, 1919, as a 2,500-barrel producer. The field was developed rapidly and soon reached its peak. By this time, too, Caddo's producing area extended twelve miles in length and five miles in width,[17] consisting of separated pools at Mooringsport, Oil City, Jeems Bayou, Monterey, Harts Ferry, Vivian, Black Bayou, and Pine Island.[18]

Standard Oil (New Jersey) officials had watched with great interest the development of prolific Southwestern oil fields. Two of these men, James A. Moffett, Sr., and Colonel F. W. Weller, were instrumental in organizing the Standard Oil Company of Louisiana (a subsidiary of the New Jersey company) under the laws of Louisiana, on April 13, 1909, with a capital of $5,000,000, which eight years later was raised to $10,000,000.[19]

The Standard Oil Company's second major step was in starting the construction of its pipe-line system in May, 1909. It completed an eight-inch line from Ida, in Caddo Parish, to Baton Rouge, 270 miles distant. At Ida this line connected with the Prairie Pipe Line (old Arkansas Division), which in turn joined with the Oklahoma Pipe Line running across Oklahoma and up into Kansas, thus affording continuous pipe-line connection from the fields of these states to the Baton Rouge refinery or an ocean outlet.[20] In addition, steel barges were designed to carry oil by river to various points in Louisiana and Arkansas.

Then Weller took the third step in planning by selecting a 225-

[17] In 1920 Louisiana's maximum annual petroleum output was 35,712,000 barrels, or 8 per cent of the nation's total, and placed Louisiana fifth among the producing states. From 1901 to 1923, the state had produced 290,927,000 barrels of crude oil. In 1920, 1921, and 1922 it ranked fifth in producing natural gas, with a three-year cumulative total of 186,545,000,000 cubic feet.—Director of the United States Geological Survey to Senator Jos. A. Ransdall, February 16, 1924, in File No. 625, La., U.S.G.S., Department of the Interior Files, National Archives.

[18] G. C. Matson, *The Caddo Oil and Gas Field, Louisiana and Texas*, in U. S. G. S. *Bull. No. 619*, 13 ff.

[19] Weller became president of the company and supervised the building of the refinery. Amos K. Gordon, secretary-treasurer, was purchasing agent. C. H. Haupt was chief engineer; Will Gottschall, resident engineer; and Cal Clark looked after the building of stations on Standard's eight-inch trunk line from northwestern Louisiana to Baton Rouge.

[20] MS dated October 12, 1931, Files, Public Relations Office, Standard Oil Company (N. J.), Louisiana Division.

acre cotton farm on the high ground about two miles north of Baton Rouge as a refinery site, on three sides of which were railroads—the Illinois Central on the west, the Frisco on the north, and the Louisiana Railroad and Navigation Company on the east.

Presently a work crew started the erection of the plant. A September storm delayed construction, but the crew was doubled and the work was pushed. In October, it was reported that most of the crude stills and all the steam stills and condensers were in place; that the agitators, refined-oil tanks, and crude tanks were going up, with some tankage completed; and that the boilers were being set up and the 100-foot brick smokestack on the boiler house was nearing completion. The first crude stills were charged on November 15, 1909,[21] thus starting what was to become one of America's largest refineries.[22]

Texas salt-dome fields shared with Caddo to some extent the newspaper space devoted to oil. Hoskins Mound, Humble, and Markham furnished a few gushers in 1910, but the region's oil yield was below that of the previous year and its next year's record was much the same. Humble declined almost half a million barrels, although during seven years, 1905–11, it had produced 33,754,728 barrels of crude oil.

Spindletop was also in a tailspin. For the first time since its discovery, this field in 1911 produced fewer than 1,000,000 barrels, or 998,093 barrels of crude oil. Yet in a decade it had an output of 42,773,650 barrels of oil. From 1910 to 1911, according to one authority, Sour Lake had declined by 102,692 barrels of oil, its output being 1,408,977 barrels. In the same period Saratoga dropped under the million mark. Batson produced 1,018,102 barrels, thereby reaching a grand total of 24,069,362 barrels since 1903; and Markham increased in production, being credited with 527,323 barrels. In the four years since it had been in the producing column, down to

[21] *Oil Investors' Journal,* Vol. VIII, No. 10 (November 20, 1909), 20, announced that crude runs would begin by January, 1910, but construction was completed earlier than was expected.—Standard Oil news release, furnished the author by W. B. Cotten, Jr., Public Relations Department.

[22] The Hexagon Sales Company advertised that the Standard Oil Company had faith in Louisiana's "greater oil fields" when it established the refinery. See "Oil Co.—624.25-T135," in Records of the Geological Survey, Correspondence of the Geologic Branch, National Archives.

1911, it had to its credit 1,138,453 barrels of crude oil, with a promise of a better yield in the future.[23]

Thus Markham was the only bright spot in the Texas Gulf Coast fields; but during the next six years Damon Mound, New Iberia, West Columbia, and Goose Creek proved that there was plenty of oil yet in this region. Damon Mound was a new field in 1916, with the completion of several good gushers, the initial well being estimated at 10,000 barrels. In the next year more than thirty rigs were running there. Humble continued to be active, with 474 wells completed during 1916 and new production reaching 265,450 barrels.[24] At New Iberia, a rank wildcat field, two producing wells were completed during August and September, 1917. The field's first well was a bare producer, but its second, drilled by the Gulf Refining Company of Louisiana, made 1,500 barrels of oil.

Saratoga spurted to the front in 1916 with two gushers, but soon declined again; and Sour Lake went as high as 25,000 barrels a day, not counting the two days when the Humble-Gulf No. 15, Hardin County, was running wild. Production there had taken a meteoric rise during the autumn; but, as at Saratoga, its fall was almost as rapid. Several good wells were brought in on the Hardin County tract by the Humble-Gulf companies[25] and by the Traver Oil Com-

---

[23] *Fuel Oil Journal*, Vol. I, No. 5 (March, 1912), 3.

[24] *Derrick's Hand-Book*, 1916–19, IV, 22.

[25] Humble owned jointly with Gulf an eighty-acre lease out of the holdings of the Hardin County Oil Company at Sour Lake. The Humble Oil Company was first chartered under the laws of Texas, in February, 1911, with an authorized capital of $150,000, which was increased in October of the next year to $300,000 when the company entered Oklahoma, acquiring valuable properties there. Producing properties were added at Humble, Sour Lake, and Goose Creek. On June 21, 1917, Humble's capital stock was raised to $4,000,000, its name changed to Humble Oil and Refining Company, and its directors increased from seven to nine. Officers of the company were R. S. Sterling, president; W. W. Fondren, R. L. Blaffer, W. S. Farish, and H. C. Wiess, vice-presidents; and Miss F. P. Sterling, secretary-treasurer. A short time later Standard Oil (N. J.) bought a substantial interest in Humble, paying $17,000,-000 for 40,000 shares of stock.

Humble's oil production in Oklahoma climbed from 661,671 barrels in 1917 to a peak of 1,601,960 ten years later, and when it declined to 551,292 barrels in 1929, the company disposed of its properties. In 1918, Humble's oil output in Louisiana was only 7,437 barrels, but within three decades it had jumped to 8,141,410 barrels. In Arkansas, Humble began operations in 1921, producing 303,856 barrels of crude oil, and by 1925 reached a peak production of 2,383,278 barrels. The company did not enter New Mexico until 1929, when in six months its oil output was 105,962 barrels, but by 1947 its production had grown to 1,747,985 barrels. Texas remained Humble's chief strength with a net production of 113,369,883 barrels of crude oil

pany. Then the prize well, the Humble-Gulf's No. 14 came in on December 5 with an initial flow of 12,000 barrels of oil a day. By the following spring, the output from this well was worth more than $500,000. In January, 1917, the same companies completed their No. 15 well, with an initial production estimated at from 12,000 to 15,000 barrels, but after running wild for two or three days, it "sanded up" and could not be made to flow again. Later, production declined rapidly.

Goose Creek was a better field, although up to 1917 it was still classed as an "enigma." "Life at Goose Creek nowadays is just one darned sand after another," paraphrased the Galveston *Daily News,* on Monday, October 1, 1917. "And each sand means an addition to Goose Creek's wealth, and consequently the wealth of the coastal belt."

October, 1916, saw Goose Creek in the beginning of its boom, although a Houston syndicate well had been drilled there as early as June 2, 1908. Interest was kindled in August, 1916, with a new gusher, and a short time later available land at Goose Creek was plastered with leases, and the oil industry was watching closely developments in the field. At that time no fewer than thirty derricks had been erected. Following the first gusher, C. T. Rucker brought in another well, a 6,000-barrel producer from a 2,000–2,200-foot sand on the Gillette one-acre tract, a tract which sold a short time later for $50,000.

Had operators been content with this sand, Goose Creek would have declined in production. Soon, however, the Gulf Production Company drilled on through the 2,000-foot horizon and at 2,600 feet brought in an 8,000-barrel well. This brought a new boom to Goose Creek. It was reported that a Houston shoe-store clerk owned a fourth interest in this well, netting him an income of more than $1,500 daily, a story that was used by small-company promoters to bring out additional capital for Goose Creek development.

in 1947. Humble was serviced by its own extensive pipe-line system and refineries and speedily became one of the region's leading oil companies.—H. C. Wiess to Miss Larson and Miss Ellsworth, October 2, 1945, Standard Oil interviews, New York; Hines Baker to Miss Larson and Miss Ellsworth, October 9, 1945; W. N. Finnegan, Jr., to C. C. Rister, July 20, 1948; *Oil Trade Journal,* Vol. VIII, No. 4 (April, 1917), 54; Walter Skinner, "Humble Oil and Refining Company," in *Oil and Petroleum Manual* (1927), 94.

Oil! Titan of the Southwest

Other wells followed in rapid succession. Production grew, and then Goose Creek oil jumped to $1.00 a barrel, credit-balance price; and on contract price it went as high as $1.25 a barrel, keeping stride with prices paid in other fields.[26]

Scores of 3,000-barrel wells were drilled at Goose Creek, several of 5,000 barrels, and three of 12,000 barrels daily. Then on August 5, 1917, came the record-breaker Simms-Sinclair No. 11 Sweet well, flowing between 30,000 and 35,000 barrels of oil a day. This well was located near the center of the field. It flowed for two days and then "sanded up." Nevertheless, the field's output remained steady, ranging from 31,350 barrels in March, 1917, to 66,000 barrels in September.

In 1918, Goose Creek was the only oil field in the Texas Gulf Coast that showed an increase in production, reaching its peak with a yearly oil output of 8,943,635 barrels. This was because of offshore drilling by both the Gulf Production Company and the Humble Oil and Refining Company.[27] When the field's output reached 30,000 barrels daily, the drillers began to find salt water, and Goose Creek's production again dropped, going as low as 17,-000 barrels daily. And then, one Sunday, the Gulf company completed a well at 3,000 feet in the mid-eastern part of the field, with a 2,850-foot well completed near the creek a short time previously. Once more Goose Creek had temporary excitement.

Other Texas Gulf Coast discoveries came in later years. On January 15, 1918, a new and very prolific sand was found at West Columbia when the Tyndall-Hogg No. 2 Hogg made twenty-five barrels an hour, and the field ended the year with a production of 186,350 barrels of oil, which grew to 5,611,000 in 1919.

Hull, in Liberty County was another of these fields. Here, on July 22, 1918, the Republic Production Company and the Houston Oil Company of Texas brought in their No. 3 Fee well for an initial

[26] In 1918 crude sold for a higher figure than ever before in the history of the Gulf Coast. On February 15, the pipe-line companies posted quotations at $1.35 in all fields except Spindletop, where the price was $1.40. On August 1, the Oil Division of the Federal Fuel Administration, a war-created commission, through the War Service National Petroleum Committee, fixed $1.80 per barrel on Gulf Coast crude, and this price remained in force until January 14, 1919, when the pipe lines posted a reduction of $1.50, except for Spindletop, for which the Gulf Pipe Line Company quoted $1.55.

[27] *Derrick's Hand-Book*, 1916–19, IV, 36.

106

output of 1,000 barrels a day at 2,352 feet. The Barbers Hill field was discovered on September 14 of the same year. In the next year, on April 4, the Gulf Production Company completed its No. 2 well at Blue Ridge, on the Blakely "C" lease, as a 1,200-barrel producer.

In 1921 two other strikes were made, one at Pierce Junction and the other at Orange, the latter making 4,000 barrels a day, thus proving the fourth productive horizon there. In 1922 new fields were opened at Big Creek, Stratton Ridge, and High Island, but these were small and production was minor.

IX

Exploring the Red River Uplift

I N JANUARY, 1901, North Texas farmers living along the Red River Uplift, twelve or fifteen miles north of the Clay County–seat town of Henrietta, Texas, read avidly the newspaper accounts of the Spindletop oil discovery. They were excited by what they read, for they, too, had found oil, oil seeping into their water wells. But they did little more at the time towards commercial production than talk of the possibilities of a second Spindletop.

The actual date of the Red River Uplift discovery well was not until the next year, 1902. Farmer Lochridge was drilling a water well on his farm when, at a depth of approximately 150 feet, the drill struck a sand that showed only oil, thus ruining his proposed water well. Although he abandoned further drilling, the launching of what was first called the "Henrietta oil field" may properly be dated from his discovery.

Experienced oilmen were attracted to Lochridge's community, but few understood the rock formations. The discovery well was on a broad, flattish divide, here and there showing outcroppings of what were widely known as the "red beds," belonging to the Wichita formation of the Permian series.

The recent arrivals knew only that this was oil country and proceeded to negotiate leases. Within a year they had sunk other wells and found oil at depths varying from 150 to 300 feet. Each well produced from ten to forty barrels of good 32–33-gravity (Baumé), paraffin-base oil, similar to that of the Corsicana field, and described as yielding "54 per cent water white distillates," kerosene 35 per cent, and gasoline 10 per cent.

During 1905 more than 66,000 barrels of oil were shipped to refineries, nearly 10,000 more were used in field boilers, and about

108

26,000 barrels were put in tank storage. In this year, eighteen companies and individuals owning wells in the new field produced daily 500 barrels of oil, 400 of which were shipped by rail to market. The Clayco Oil Company, representing the Higgins Oil and Fuel Company, one of the most important firms in the field, built tank storage of 37,400-barrel capacity and a pipe line to the boom town of Petrolia, which grew up on the northern flank of the field. A smaller pipe line, owned by Brown and Wigham of Wichita Falls, connected the oil field with this new town. These companies levied a railroad gathering charge of ten cents a barrel.

With the rise of Petrolia, Henietta lost its North Texas oil town primacy. Petrolia boosters, like those at Beaumont, proclaimed the merits and future possibilities of their community. "What Petrolia has got," one said, "is a hotel, drugstore, barber shop, livery stable, bank, grocery store, hardware and furniture, meat market, two oil well supply houses, two telephones, one lumber yard and a big trade in all lines of business."[1] Of course, he did not mention the dives, shanties, and tents cluttering Petrolia's oil field.

By 1907 the Petrolia field had 169 shallow producing oil wells. The Navarro Refining Company, successor of the Clayco Oil and Pipe Line Company, piped the oil from the field to the railroad. In October, this company brought in the first gas well at a depth of 1,500 feet. The well had a four-minute pressure of 470 pounds to the square inch and a capacity of 8,000,000 to 10,000,000 cubic feet a day. Two other gassers of approximately the same production were drilled the next year.

There was no other oil development along the Texas side of the Red River during the next few years, although several test wells were drilled. But Petrolia's gas production was important, supplying twenty-three towns and cities in northern Texas by 1913, the average price of Petrolia gas being twenty-five cents per 1,000 cubic feet.[2] The Lone Star Gas Company built a pipe line to Fort Worth and Dallas, a distance of approximately 140 miles, and the field became the sole source of gas for these two cities.

The Petrolia oil and gas field had a longer life than oilmen had

[1] Henrietta *Independent*, Friday, December 8, 1905, p. 4, col. 2.
[2] William B. Phillips, "Petroleum in Texas," in *Engineering and Mining Journal*, Vol. XCIII (January–June, 1912), 97.

predicted. The operators had no great expense. The wells were shallow, and ten or twelve of them could be pumped by a central power unit. But Petrolia had passed its peak by 1910. The total amount of oil produced up to the close of 1914 was a little over 2,-000,000 barrels. And at that time the Petrolia field was by far the greatest producer of the 10,000,000,000 cubic feet of gas annually available in Texas.[3]

About thirty miles west of the Petrolia field, W. T. Waggoner also drilled some deep wells, but for water and not oil. During drought seasons the tanks and ponds on his south Wilbarger County ranch dried up and his cattle suffered. Planning deep wells and artesian water, he started to drill. He sank one well near a Fort Worth and Denver Railroad cattle-shipping station, called Beaver Switch (later Electra in honor of his daughter), in extreme western Wichita County. This well was about one and one-half blocks north of the present Electra railroad depot. He drilled a second well south of the railroad and a third a block south and west of the present Electra Municipal Light Plant; but in all of them he found only salt water and traces of oil.

Waggoner was disappointed that oil ruined his water wells. "I wanted water," he told a reporter later, "and they got me oil. I tell you, I was mad, mad clean through. We needed water to drink ourselves and for our cattle to drink. I said, 'damn the oil, I want water.' "[4]

Waggoner's last well, in 1904, was no better. It was drilled to a depth of 1,700 feet, but still he found no artesian water and pulled the casing. The hole caved in and formed a cavern resembling the size and depth of a shallow, dug well. Oil rose in it to within a few feet of the surface. Yet when this fact was known throughout the community, it caused no great excitement. Townsmen, ranchmen, and farmers, however, found the oil valuable for "doping" tick-afflicted cattle, for painting the insides of hen houses to drive away the "blue bugs," and for kindling fires. Near-by settlers drew the oil from the cavern by fastening lard or syrup buckets to the end of ropes or tomato cans to bailing wire.[5]

[3] U.S.G.S. *Bull. No. 629*, 30. Later, helium was another valuable by-product.

[4] "Tom Waggoner Talks of Olden Days," in *Oil and Gas Journal*, Vol. XVIII, No. 47 (April 23, 1920), 64.

Exploring the Red River Uplift

News of the Electra oil phenomenon quickly spread throughout northern Texas, and soon oil scouts arrived to explore the country. Waggoner leased most of his ranch to the Producers Oil Company, a subsidiary of The Texas Company, which presently spudded in a test well. A Houston news release, on April 6, 1909, commented on the progress of the well. A "well is being drilled on the W. T. Waggoner place, about 300 yards from the Fort Worth and Denver depot at Electra, Texas," the item explained. "At 500 or 600 feet a sand 12 or 15 feet thick was penetrated and from this formation several barrels of 36-gravity oil were bailed."[6] When the well was drilled deeper, it was dry and was abandoned. Producers Nos. 2 and 3, although drilled to more than 1,800 feet, were also dry holes.

Nevertheless, the Producers Oil Company hoped that it would eventually reach a pay sand and continued to drill. Its No. 4 Bywaters, on August 9, 1910, and its No. 6 Waggoner, on December 13, 1909, at a little more than 1,800 feet, found traces of oil before the company completed its No. 5 Waggoner as a fifty-barrel producer, on January 17, 1911. In this well, along the western flank of the several Electra pools, oil was found at a depth of 1,852 feet. The well was drilled by W. H. Ellinger and his son-in-law, Clyde Rogers. The Producers Oil Company, seeking for a time to maintain strict secrecy concerning its discovery, established an armed guard at the site, and built a wire-fence barricade about the well to keep curious spectators away. But it was impossible to withhold news of the finding of oil from the public.

Meanwhile, another crew—S. E. ("Dad") Massingill, Bill Chaffee, and Hal Hughes—drilled the Clayco No. 1 well, in block No. 2 of the H. and S. N. Railroad survey, two and one-half miles north of Electra, on the Putnam and Woodruff farm,[7] on April 1, 1911,[8]

[5] Data furnished the author by Mrs. N. D. Cooper, Electra, Texas. Mrs. Cooper lived in Electra at the time the well was drilled and more than once used the oil.

[6] *Oil Investors' Journal*, Vol. VII, No. 21 (April 6, 1909), 28.

[7] The Clayco No. 1 well was spudded in during October, 1910. Its location was near the center of the tract of land adjoining the Electra townsite on the northeast. The quarter-section, originally school land, of the discovery well had been settled in the eighteen-nineties by the Norwood brothers, and was later sold to Nick Coble, who, in turn, disposed of it to Nick Cooper, in August, 1906. Then Cooper sold the farm to Messrs. Putnam and Woodruff of Port Henry, New York, in 1908. Later the New Yorkers leased the tract to the Clayco Oil Company.—Cooper MS.

[8] At the end of the first nine months of production after the drilling of the Clayco No. 1 well, the pipe-line runs from the Electra field (up to December 31) amounted

approximately one and one-half miles northeast of the No. 5 Waggoner (Producers No. 5).

Local tradition has it that during the night of the discovery, A. F. Dennison, Clayco's field manager, was called by one of his crew, who brought the news that the well was "bubbling." Dennison, too sleepy to get up, instructed the messenger to return to the well, cut the fires, and wait until daylight. But the gas-powered oil would not wait; by daybreak, it was cascading one hundred feet into the air from the well, spraying the surrounding grass and trees.

Ben Donnell of the Wichita Falls *Daily Times* hurried to Electra to cover the discovery for his newspaper. He found the well "spouting a stream of oil at intervals of from five to fifteen minutes . . . steadily growing more frequent." The oil had been turned into a pipe and conveyed several hundred yards from the well into an earthen tank. Oilmen from Tulsa, South Texas, and Louisiana were arriving on every train, and Electra was a bedlam of excitement. Donnell said that fancy prices were being paid for leases within a radius of three miles of Electra, offers of $150 an acre bonus having been refused on April 3, and that it was believed that they would reach $500 an acre before the end of the week.[9] Tents and buildings sprang up overnight as if by magic, and Electra became a second "old woman who lived in a shoe."

Other wells at Electra were drilled in rapid succession. The Clayco No. 1 well brought a drilling campaign that saw 101 wells producing oil in the Electra field by the end of 1911, with a total output of 899,579 barrels of oil. The Clayco No. 3 well, drilled to 1,890 feet, was the best, averaging 1,600 barrels daily. The deepest well, a "duster," in 1911, was 3,985 feet. Most of the oil came from a

---

to 892,204 barrels of crude oil, all but 70,000 barrels of which went to the Magnolia Petroleum Company. Car shipments for the same period were 510,598 barrels.— *Fuel Oil Journal,* Vol. I (January–February, 1912), 3.

[9] MS, Donnell's original "Oil Well at Electra a Wonderful Gusher," written on April 3, 1911, in the files of the Wichita *Daily Times.* See also Wichita Falls *Daily Times* (twenty-fifth Anniversary "Electra's Discovery Well Clayco No. 1"), April 1, 1936, p. 2, col. 1. A. T. McDannald says that "there were numerous sales put on in the early Electra days wherein the producer would acquire a small tract of land in a cheap area, either wildcat or where it was already proven dry but near the Electra field, and sell off in twenty-foot or thirty-foot lots . . . , wherein the buyer owned his drilling site of 20 x 30 feet and an undivided interest, which would run into the thousandth part of a well the producer usually promised to drill."—McDannald to C. C. Rister, May 17, 1946.

'Robson's Views of Petrolea and Vicinity," about 1905

Oil and Gas Journal

Electra, Texas, Clayco No. 1 oil well and drilling crew.
Left to right: driller, R. T. Craig; fireman, S. C. ("Dad")
Massengill; derrickman, Clabe Moody; floorman, Limba
Weathersby

photograph by Dink M. Robb

Overflowing Burkburnett oil tanks

Wichita Falls News

Burkburnett at the height of the oil boom

Fred Sehmann

depth of 1,000 to 1,200 feet, although the deepest sands, 1,700 to 1,900, were good producers.[10]

Wichita Falls, approximately halfway between Petrolia and Electra, shared in the oil boom. "Coal Oil Johnny," the shuttle train between Electra and Wichita Falls, did a thriving business, carrying excited businessmen, promoters, and sight-seers to and from Wichita Falls. But Wichita Falls wanted its own field and offered $5,000 for the first well within a radius of six miles of the townsite.

From 1904 to 1913 northern and northeastern Texas enjoyed an oil boom that promised better days to come. A contemporary production table reveals the growing importance of the petroleum output in this part of Texas.

NORTHERN TEXAS OIL PRODUCTION (barrels), 1904–13[11]

	Corsicana	Henrietta	Powell	Marion Co.	Electra	Total
1904	374,318	65,455	129,329	_____	_____	569,252
1905	311,554	75,592	132,866	_____	_____	520,282
1906	322,622	111,072	673,221	_____	_____	1,117,905
1907	226,311	83,260	596,897	_____	_____	912.618
1908	211,117	85,963	421,659	_____	_____	723,264
1909	180,764	113,485	383,137	_____	_____	681,940
1910	137,331	126,531	450,188	251,717	_____	969,403
1911	128,526	168,965	373,055	677,689 .	899,579	2,251,193
1912	233,282	197,421	251,240	362,870	4,227,104	5,275,529
1913	158,830	344,868	282,476	262,392	8,131,624	9,184,252

By 1912, Electra had blossomed into a major oil field. Wells were completed producing from 50 to 1,200 barrels per day at varying depths—580, 965, 1,035, and 1,900 feet. The oil was of excellent quality, varying in gravity from 38 to 42 degrees Baumé, and containing "35 per cent kerosene, 19 per cent gasoline, 4 per cent unsaturated hydrocarbons, and 3.2 per cent paraffin wax."[12] It was fortunate, too, that the field had a commercial outlet. The Fort Worth and Denver Railroad furnished an excellent tank-car service,

[10] By October, 1911, the major producing companies were Producers Oil Company (3,300 barrels), the Corsicana Petroleum Company (2,500 barrels), and the Red River Oil Company (2,500 barrels).—*Engineering and Mining Journal*, Vol XC (July–December, 1911), 1031.

[11] *Mineral Resources of the United States, 1913, Part II, Nonmetals*, 435.

[12] C. A. Warner, *Texas Oil and Gas Since 1543*, 229.

and before the end of 1911, The Texas Pipe Line Company and the Pierce-Fordyce Association had both started building pipe lines from the field.

Electra's growth was spectacular, following the usual pattern of oil booms. The town was served by four major pipe lines, gathering oil from a district in which ultimately 8,500 wells have been drilled. In and about the town were five gasoline plants, a refinery, two cracking plants, twelve oil-field supply houses, a steel-tank manufacturing plant, five machine shops for all sorts of oil field equipment, and six welding shops. Oil's pay roll was more than $400,000 a month. This advantage, when coupled with the town's being the center of a rich cattle-raising and farming country, guaranteed its growth in the future.[13]

Still later, in February, 1917, oilmen's interest at Electra was revived by the completion of a 175-barrel well at a depth of 1,500 feet on Beaver Creek, eight miles southeast of the town.

This and other lucrative pay sands found at Electra led to an intensive exploration of northern Texas, and within a few years small oil and gas wells had been drilled in Wichita, Shackelford, Archer, Palo Pinto, and Stephens counties. In 1913, The Texas Company completed a gas well at Moran, Shackelford County, and another well fifteen miles north of Albany, which produced from twenty to thirty barrels of oil a day. By the end of 1913 the northern Texas fields were yielding 15,009,478 barrels of oil.

There is little doubt that Electra was the forerunner of the Burkburnett oil boom. Officials of the Corsicana Petroleum Company, which had absorbed the Clayco Oil Company, met in a Dallas hotel in 1911 to discuss the possibilities of Burkburnett oil, on the basis of oil play at Electra. Scouts advised that chances were good; consequently, within a short time a rig was on the ground and drilling started.

The rig on Corsicana's No. 1 Schmoker went up just south of Burkburnett, and on July 8, 1913, the well came in as an eighty-five-barrel producer from a sand at 1,837 feet. For a short time the field experienced great activity; then it settled down to minor production. June 10, 1916, brought another temporary revival of interest

---

[13] Abby Wheelis Cooper, "Electra a Texas Oil Town," *The Southwestern Historical Quarterly*, Vol. I, No. 1 (July, 1946), 47.

when C. C. Bradford completed a small five-barrel well at the shallow depth of 643 feet. Still, these operations were only an earnest of the boom days in store for Wichita Falls and near-by towns, fabulous days hardly surpassed elsewhere in Texas since Beaumont's oil discoveries.

Wichita Falls became the hub of the northern Texas oil region and quickly climbed from the rank of an obscure village to a fast-growing oil town. Refineries, equipment houses, hotels, major business concerns, and quickly spreading residential districts were evidences of municipal growth.

Iowa Park, about twenty miles west of Wichita Falls, followed Burkburnett as a new oil field, when on January 27, 1913, the Forest Oil Company completed its Ferguson farm well for an initial flow of twenty barrels of crude oil a day at a shallow depth of 486 feet. And later, several producing sands were tapped in this field at horizons above 1,000 feet. As in other shallow fields, however, each well's production was small, although for many years Iowa Park maintained a steady output.

These discoveries, when compared with the opening of the fabulous Burkburnett townsite field, paled in commercial significance. "Fowler's Folly," as the field's first well was called, on July 29, 1918, launched a craze for stock and lease jobbing.

S. L. Fowler was a farmer owning land adjoining Burkburnett on the north, on Outer Block No. 6, and according to local tradition had planned to move to a more inviting community when his wife persuaded him to linger long enough to try for oil.[14] Fowler studied the trends of development about town and concluded that from all surface indications his farm was favorably situated for oil. He finally persuaded J. A. Staley, W. D. Cline, and some other men to invest in his wildcat venture. Cline put in his cable-tool rig, his own services, and those of his "tool-pusher" for $1,000 in stock; Fowler contributed his farm for drilling sites and $500; Movel Fowler, his brother, put in $500; and J. A. Staley paid in the same amount. One article of their agreement provided that drilling was to continue until oil was found, provided the drilling did not exceed 1,700 feet. If oil and gas were found in paying quantities, then those signing the agreement would form a company under the laws of

[14] Wichita *Weekly Times,* August 2, 1918, p. 1.

Oil! Titan of the Southwest

Texas, to be known as the Fowler Oil Company, with a capital of $12,000.[15]

The promoters' faith was rewarded; on July 29 their well blew in as a 2,200-barrel gusher, from a sand at 1,734 feet. Previously, the only production about Burkburnett at approximately the same depth had been on the F. R. Knauth farm, Block 40, on the Red River Valley Lands subdivision, more than one and one-half miles southwest of town.

The fact that within three weeks fifty-six drilling rigs were set up on the townsite of Burkburnett proved the new field's significance. The Magnolia Petroleum Company had two two-inch pipe lines connected to the discovery well, and The Texas Company was building a four-inch line to run from 5,000 to 6,000 barrels of oil daily.

Soon the town had become a forest of derricks, some lots furnishing space for two or more rigs. By August 1, Burkburnett resembled "a hive of bees at swarming time." Crowds thronged its streets, public places, and near-by well locations; and automobiles dashed here and there, as fast as the two inches or more of dust which overlaid the road and blinded and choked the motorists would permit.[16]

Gusher after gusher increased frenzied deals, drilling, lease, and royalty operations, and general oil-field excitement. On the north side of town, nearest to the discovery well, lots were leased for as much as $1,000 each. One resident who a short time previously had offered his house and lot for $1,500 without attracting a buyer, now leased a part of his property for $3,600, with the usual royalty provision. C. H. Featherston says that on one occasion he and his associates bought a lease for a small sum and he promptly walked across the street and sold it for $14,000. "There were, of course, hundreds of similar deals," he explained.[17] The Wichita Falls *Daily Times* of July 29, 1918, reported that town lots 75 by 150 feet

[15] After the second well was drilled, the Fowler Farm Oil Company sold its interest to the Magnolia Petroleum Company. "We sold our lease, with its two wells," said Cline, "for $1,800,000 cash which President E. R. Brown paid in three checks—one for $800,000 and two for $500,000 each."— C. C. Rister's interview with Hon. W. D. Cline, at Wichita Falls, Texas, September 18, 1947.

[16] Wichita Falls *Daily Times,* August 1, 1918, p. 1.

[17] Featherston to Rister, November 3, 1947.

were leasing for $1,000 and that the town would soon be "liberally sprinkled with derricks in backyards and gardens."

Operators and investors worked for quick returns because Fortune might smile today and frown tomorrow. Quickly Burkburnett and Wichita Falls became infested with stock swindlers, honest and dishonest lease and royalty *entrepreneurs*, real-estate promoters, and speculators of all shades of character. A Wichita Falls reporter on August 2, 1918, wrote of "throngs of visitors walking the streets [of Burkburnett] all day and until late at night. . . . To say that Burkburnett presents a busy scene does not begin to express conditions in that little city, where all is activity and where the main street is thronged with visitors from both near-by and distant points. . . . Oil companies are being formed on the sidewalk or in the middle of the street."[18] Hotels, rooming houses, and private dwellings were not able to accommodate Burkburnett's milling crowds, and Wichita Falls was swamped by persons seeking homes, board, and rooms. Many a "to your health" was drunk at local "blind tiger" bars and in hotel rooms; and stock promoters were on every street corner, in hotel lobbies, drugstores, and railroad stations to catch the crowd.

From Burkburnett the field spread northwestward, then southeastward. The Burk-Waggoner Company completed a 2,750-barrel test northwest of town at a depth of 1,705 feet, on April 29, 1919, to launch afresh bogus stock operations and wild lease and royalty transactions. There, too, close drilling was the order of the day; as it was southeast of town when, in the fall of 1919, the Texhoma Oil and Refining Company completed its No. 1 Daniel well at 1,300 feet for a daily output of 225 barrels.

In 1919, Burkburnett and the new Waggoner pool produced 31,604,183 barrels of crude oil. At that time Burkburnett had a cumulative oil production of 40,000,000 barrels.[19]

This was not all. A local field guide of January, 1919, listed 289 incorporated and joint-stock companies in the field, capitalized at $159,034,000. These had only recently been organized. There were also 168 producing wells and 207 others being drilled.[20] "Never be-

[18] Wichita *Weekly Times*, August 2, 1918, p. 1.
[19] *Oil City Derrick's Statistical Abstract of Petroleum, 1916–1919*, 41.
[20] *Ibid.*, 4.

fore has land sold at the rate of $180,000 an acre," wrote an observer, "as happened at Burkburnett, and never before have investors put in $100 in August and sold their properties in February for $1,750, as happened in Burkburnett." Twelve pipe-line companies served the region, and three refineries at Burkburnett and nine at Wichita Falls processed daily 27,800 barrels of crude oil.[21]

Hardly had excitement over the Burkburnett oil field subsided when the Kemp-Munger-Allen Oil Company completed a test in May, 1919, on the Munger lands, twelve miles southwest of Iowa Park, for an initial production of five barrels of crude oil daily at a depth of 1,771 feet. This opened what later came to be known as the K-M-A field, not so prolific as Electra and Burkburnett but important enough to keep the county's production at a high level.

By the fall of 1919 the northern Texas fields were fairly well proven. And by the end of the year its oil production was more than twice as great as in the preceding year, reaching a total of 53,385,-915 barrels, with a selling value of over $120,000,000.

[21] The pipe-line companies were: Central Conduit Company, Crude Oil Marketing Company, Gulf Pipe Line Company, Hockaday Pipe Line Company, Humble Oil and Refining Company, the Liberty Pipe Line Company, Magnolia Petroleum Company, the Panhandle Refining Company, the Producers Pipe Line and Storage Company, the Texas Gulf Refining and Pipe Line Company, and The Texas Pipe Line Company. The refineries at Burkburnett were: the Burkburnett Refining Company, the Constantin Refining Company, and the Victor Refining Company. At Wichita Falls were the American Refining Company, the Commonwealth Refining Company, Fisher and Gilliland, the Lone Star Refining Company, the Panhandle Refining Company, the Power Oil Refining Company, the Red River Refining Company, the Sunshine State Oil and Refining Company, and the Texas Gulf Refining and Pipe Line Company.—*Hughes' Burkburnett and Wichita Falls, Texas, Oil Development Guide and Directory* (1919), 94–97.

In addition, Fort Worth had seven refineries and five more in process of building; Iowa Park had two; and Dallas had four with one building.—*Statistical Abstract,* 42.

X

Oklahoma Steals the Show

THAT NO GREAT AMOUNT OF MONEY had been made on Oklahoma and Kansas oil prior to 1914 is the interesting conclusion reached by Tom Galey.[1] A few operators reaped fair profits at Glenn Pool and at Cleveland, but oilmen of large means were little interested. "When the Galbreath-Chesley well uncovered the Glenn Pool there were a few who came, saw, and conquered," says Galey, "but there were many who came, saw, and went away."[2] Among the oil firms to "conquer" were the Gypsy Oil Company, the Prairie Oil and Gas Company, The Texas Company, the Associated Producers, and a few others.

Yet Oklahoma had stolen the show from the other Southwestern states. In 1905 it produced only 24.49 per cent of the crude-oil output of these states. Then came Glenn Pool. By 1906, Oklahoma had reached first place, with 50.08 per cent of the region's oil. This rank was maintained for more than two decades because of the discovery of such fine fields as Cushing, Healdton, and Garber. Then in 1928 Texas again claimed primacy, never again to be challenged.

After Glenn Pool, half a decade passed before the Cushing field startled the oil world. Its fine-quality oil at last drew most of the major operators to the Mid-Continent region.

The new field, twelve miles from Cushing, was discovered by C. B. Shaffer. His discovery well on the Wheeler farm, about a mile north of the present site of Drumright,[3] barely preceded another brought in by C. J. Wrightsman. Tom Slick[4] had previously ex-

[1] Galey MS, as cited.
[2] *Ibid.*
[3] In S31-T18N-R7E.
[4] The *Literary Digest*, Vol. XLVIII (March 14, 1917), 568, has an interesting account of Slick's part in developing this field. Also see a manuscript with the date

plored and acquired leases to much of the surrounding country. Shaffer's well was completed on March 10, 1912, for an initial daily production of 400 barrels of oil from a sand at 2,319 to 2,347 feet, known in later years as the Wheeler sand. And for more than a year and a half this and the Layton sand produced the entire output of the Cushing field.

A contemporary observer said that "the newly discovered Cushing oil field had carried battle-scarred oil men off their feet. . . . Production is found everywhere in an area six miles north and south and five miles east and west,"[5] a region of rolling hills cut by the Cimarron River. Of the forty-six wells that had been drilled early in November, 1912, only one was dry and four were gassers. Some wells blew in with an initial daily production of 1,500 barrels of high-grade oil, which then sold at seventy-six cents a barrel.

News of Cushing's prolific production and its great fortunes brought prospectors and speculators from every direction. They came from Pennsylvania, Ohio, Indiana, West Virginia, Illinois, Texas, California, and Wyoming. The sole topic of conversation on Oklahoma railroad trains and in stations was Cushing oil and the lucky strikes that men had made. The ragged, unkempt little town of Cushing was presently overwhelmed by a noisy excited army of men—millionaires, laborers, hoboes, gamblers, prostitutes, and men of small means—all hopeful that fortune would smile on them. Men with surface-pipe boots and swedge-nipple pants, red eyed and keen eyed, close mouthed—prospectors, prompters, pimps, scouts, scalpers, and scavingers—were everywhere, overflowing the hotels, boardinghouses, shanties, and tents.

Cushing pool halls closed at midnight, so that men could sleep on the tables, under the tables, and in chairs, at from fifty cents to one dollar a head. At dawn the "crum bosses" cleaned out the places. Indeed, Cushing was but repeating the behavior of many another oil-boom town, and doing it uproariously and wantonly.

line, "Bristow, Okl., June 7," in F. S. Barde Papers, envelope marked "2224," Oklahoma Historical Library, Oklahoma City. Slick made a tidy fortune at Cushing. He had formed a leaseholding syndicate with B. B. Jones, a Bristow banker, and Charles J. Wrightsman, a Tulsa lawyer. Presently, Wrightsman sold his leaseholdings, it was reported, for a million dollars.

5 Envelope No. 2224, "Cushing, Ok., Dec. 21," Barde Papers, Oklahoma State Historical Library, Oklahoma City.

Oklahoma Steals the Show

"A blind man could easily make his way at night from Cushing to the heart of the oil field, at the new town of Drumright," commented one man.[6] Materials of every kind were hauled by wagon from Cushing, and one who made the journey heard the rattle and clang of the heavily loaded freight wagons and the shouting of the drivers. Here he passed a six-horse wagon laden with a steam boiler with its smokestack and other equipment. Next came a wagon creaking and straining under a mass of wire cable. In fact, from Cushing to the oil field, endlessly it seemed, there were wagons loaded with steel pipe for the oil wells, derrick timbers, lumber for stores and dwellings, and merchandise for the storekeepers. So much used was this oil-field road during a dry season that it had been pounded as hard and as flat as a floor. The broad wagon tires had polished and smoothed it until it glistened.

On one trip from Drumright a traveler counted 276 outfits, all outward bound from Cushing. With all the tumult—the creaking and groaning wagons, the shouting, and the cracking of whips— still each day the Cushing freight yards, already stacked with oil-field supplies, seemed to accumulate more oil-field materials.

This oil-field road was so crowded with freighters and all kinds of horse-drawn vehicles that another route was laid off for automobiles; and they raced along it in a stream until they were compelled to travel part of the way on the freight road. Then came blockades and delays and impatience. A road from Cushing to Drumright fourteen miles long allegedly was passable on horseback or by Ford and was locally called "the road from Jericho to Jerusalem."

Drumright, as well as Cushing, had its social chaos and lawlessness. The oil workers' wages were from six dollars to fifteen dollars a day. They spent their money freely to relieve the monotony and toil. Drumright had no moving-picture show, nor was there a vaudeville house. But whiskey peddlers came to town, and Tiger Creek Avenue tore loose. "By merely turning one's head," said an eyewitness, "it was an easy matter to see a dozen fights in full blast at the same moment. Men fought to a finish, and others did not interfere for as it was a waste of time to mix in other men's quarrels —you might have one of your own if you became too 'auspinarious.' "

[6] *Ibid.*

121

Oil! Titan of the Southwest

Then the lid was clamped down; both Cushing and Drumright had to obey the law. The oil producers "from a business standpoint are all prohibitionists," the eyewitness added, "though individually they may be booze-fighters, as many of them are." They knew that if their men got drunk, they would not show up for work, which, in turn, closed down field operations; or, if they showed up for work with a hangover, a driller might make a crooked hole or a "derrick monkey" cause a fatal accident. Thus, the producers backed the efforts of United States marshals and local peace officers by contributing a fund of $5,000 for the rigid enforcement of law. And presently Tiger Creek Avenue and other centers of lawlessness became whiskeyless and the roar of the six-shooter was no longer a common sound.

Cushing's oil-field development came amazingly fast. Slick and Jones struck a 150-barrel producer at 2,181 feet ten miles east of Cushing; and two miles farther east, Wrightsman[7] and Jones brought in a gas well yielding 5,000,000 cubic feet of gas a day. By January, 1913, the Cushing field produced 11,000 barrels of oil a day, and increased production to 20,000 barrels in the next month.[8] In February, in spite of bad weather, sixty-seven wells were drilled —sixty-four oil wells, four gas wells, and one "duster." As a result there was a temporary spurt in production, then a rapid decline. In March, the daily yield was 23,000 barrels of oil; in April, 18,000 barrels; and by June, 16,000 barrels. Oilmen generally saw in this decline the end of the boom and prepared to move out; but before they could do so, a deeper prolific sand was reached.

On November 30, 1913, the Prairie Oil and Gas Company sent a test well down to the Bartlesville sand[9] to a depth of about 2,600 feet, and struck a large gusher. Excitement was intense. Within thirty days Cushing production moved up from 25,000 barrels to 60,000 barrels a day, and wells came in with an initial daily production of 4,000 and 5,000 barrels. By May of the next year, 155 steel tanks, each with a capacity of 55,000 barrels, were under construction, providing a general storage of 8,525,000 barrels. Each tank

[7] Wrightsman later became an important Oklahoma oil producer at Cushing, Healdton, and elsewhere, and was known for his interest in public affairs.

[8] *Mineral Resources of the United States, 1913, Part II, Nonmetals*, 1032.

[9] In S3-T17N-R7E.

Oklahoma Steals the Show

cost $12,000, making a total investment of nearly $2,000,000. This construction was designed to bring Cushing's storage to 200 tanks and to give employment to 2,000 mechanics, each of whom was paid $4.50 a day.

During the first half of 1914, Cushing's daily oil output from the prolific Bartlesville sand reached 140,000 barrels; and the estimated production from all sands in this field approached a high of 280,000 barrels of oil.[10] At one time 160 wells from the Bartlesville sand alone yielded 160,000 barrels of oil. This flood of oil broke the market—the posted price of crude oil in this field dropped from $1.05 in April, 1914, to 40 cents a barrel in February, 1915, and hundreds of thousands of barrels of oil were sold at almost any price.[11]

Cushing's great bonanza was the north end of the oil field. Here the Lete Kolvin, Barney Thlocco, Emma Coker, Sarah Rector, Katie Fixico, and Tommy Atkins leases were the envy of all oil producers.[12]

The McMan Oil Company also reached the Bartlesville sand at 2,599 feet near the site of the present town of Oilton.[13] The well had an initial production of only 150 barrels of oil a day, but it stimulated other exploratory drilling. As a result, production was found between Oilton and Drumright, near the village of Pemeta; and south of Drumright another pool was discovered near the Shamrock post office. Wells in this area were in the Bartlesville sand[14] at 2,700 feet, some making as high as 8,000 barrels a day. At first, oilmen thought that these new discoveries represented new fields, but subsequent drilling proved that they were parts of one great field, generally known as "Cushing."

Cushing had not yet seen its best day. In January, 1915, deeper production was found in the northern part of the field, where a well's daily output of oil reached as high as 10,000 barrels. Consequently, old wells were deepened to reach the new pay. In April, Cushing's daily oil output reached an ungauged peak variously

[10] *The Daily Oklahoman* (Oklahoma City), July 3, 1915, p. 9, col. 5.
[11] Charles E. Bowles, "Oil History in Brief," in *Oklahoma*, Vol. I, No. 9 (December, 1927), 13–14; U.S.G.S. *Bull. No. 658*, 9; manuscript on "Cushing Oil Field" in the files of the Mid-Continent Oil and Gas Association, Tulsa, Oklahoma.
[12] George F. and J. Paul Getty, *The History of the Oil Business*, 38.
[13] In S2-T19N-R7E.
[14] The quality of oil from the Layton, Bartlesville, and Wheeler sands ranged from 38 degrees to 42 degrees Baumé. The producing area of Cushing was about fourteen square miles.—U.S.G.S. *Bull. No. 658*, 9.

Oil! Titan of the Southwest

estimated at from 300,000 to 330,000 barrels. By the end of 1919 the Cushing oil field covered thirty-two square miles and had a cumulative production of 236,000,000 barrels of crude oil, or 17 per cent of all the oil marketed in the United States.

The rapid development of the Cushing oil field came opportunely. Although the United States was not drawn into the World War until 1917, its supply of oil was of great help to the Allies. In later years the English statesman, Viscount Curzon, was reported to have said that "the Allies floated to victory on a wave of oil." Oil made it possible to transport millions of soldiers to Europe's battlefields, and to supply England and France with gasoline for airplanes, tankers, and other motor vehicles. A major part of this "sea of oil" came from Cushing and Healdton.

Oklahoma Oil Production, 1891–1913 *

Year	Barrels	Year	Barrels
1891	30	1903	138,911
1892	80	1904	1,366,748
1893	10	1905	8,562,716
1894	130	1906	18,618,583
1895	37	1907	43,524,128
1896	170	1908	45,798,765
1897	625	1909	47,859,218
1898	1,020	1910	52,028,718
1899	2,230	1911	56,069,637
1900	6,472	1912	51,427,071
1901	10,000	1913	62,500,000
1902	37,100	Total	377,947,850

* *Mineral Resources of the United States, 1914, Part II, Nonmetals*, 898–99, includes Oklahoma production with Kansas for 1905 and 1906 and lists production for 1913 as 62,500,000.

Cushing producers found six oil sands (the Layton, Jones, Wheeler, Skinner, Bartlesville, and Tucker) ranging in depth from 1,000 to 3,000 feet. The Layton was the first oil sand reached, at 1,400 feet. Many good wells were found in it, and the quality of its oil was excellent. The Wheeler sand was reached about 2,300 feet and proved to be the main producer until February, 1914. Both the big Drumright and Dropright wells were mainly in the Wheeler sand. But the Bartlesville sand became the field's sensation, first located about two miles east of Drumright. Here this sand was reached at 2,600 feet and the wells were big producers.

The Cushing field was discovered in March, 1912, and Healdton in August, 1913. Cushing reached its peak in May, 1915, with 310,-000 barrels of crude oil a day. Healdton was to be almost as sensational; it reached its peak in 1916 with an estimated daily output of 95,000 barrels of crude oil.[15]

The Healdton oil field—north, west, and south of the town of that name—was in a rolling hill country, twenty-three miles west of Ardmore, on the western border of Carter County and twenty-three miles north of the Red River.[16] Its oil was found in anticlinal sandstone layers in the "red beds" of the Permian series.[17]

Healdton's first well was drilled by a wildcatter named Palmer, in the late eighteen eighties or early eighteen nineties, on what later became the Mrs. C. L. McClure farm, the land at that time being unallotted. Palmer used a primitive spring-pole drill rig, and found small production at about 425 feet. Greatly excited, he capped the well, hurried to Ardmore, and sought to acquire leases; but he was told that this was Indian land and not subject to leasing. After a few days he left Ardmore but returned several years later and renewed his efforts for drilling rights. He drove with two Ardmore residents, A. C. Cruce and Mike Gorman, out to the well, which they found full of oil. Then he pledged his new friends to secrecy until he could solve his lease problem; but this he failed to do. Not long afterward he was killed while on an exploratory trip to South America.

More than a decade passed before the Healdton oil field was exploited. In 1907, Roy M. Johnson moved to Ardmore and became owner and editor of the Ardmore *Statesman*. He soon learned of a Healdton oil-field possibility and, being a wide-awake editor, sought

[15] *The Daily Oklahoman* (Oklahoma City), Wednesday, April 22, 1914, Sec. B, p. 1, col. 4. The *Oklahoman* estimated the state's output for 1914 at 77,000,000 barrels, which showed the influence of the Healdton field. On October 1, 1916, the total yield from the Cushing field alone had reached 165,000,000 barrels of crude oil.— U.S.G.S. *Bull. No. 658*, 9.

[16] Gilbert L. Robinson, "History of the Healdton Oil Field" (unpublished Master's thesis, University of Oklahoma, 1937), 1.

[17] *Mineral Resources of the United States, 1915, Part II, Nonmetals*, 648.

to promote its development. Later, in company with Edward Galt, A. T. McGhee, and Captain Francis B. Cooke (as guide), he hired a livery rig and drove out to the field. The four men had little difficulty in finding the old Palmer well;[18] then they examined water wells in the vicinity and found traces of oil on them.[19] This encouraged Johnson and Galt to organize the Plains Development Company (a co-partnership; later, the Crystal Oil Company) to acquire leases, and to begin drilling.[20] A thrifty schoolteacher, Miss Odessa Otey, soon to become Mrs. Roy Johnson, made a loan of a few hundred dollars to the partners; and subsequently Johnson, to acquire additional funds, mortgaged his *Statesman* for $2,000, at 12 per cent interest, to W. E. Corbin of Berlin, Vermont, thus advancing the latter to the partnership.

Previously, Sam Apple and Wirt Franklin, Ardmore lawyers, had bought a farm in the vicinity of the well.[21] They, too, learned of the Palmer well from a tenant and planned to secure leases preparatory to starting a drilling campaign. But Johnson and Galt persuaded them to transfer their holdings to the Plains Development Company and to accept in exchange a one-fourth interest in the company.

Then the new firm checkerboarded its holdings, now totaling 7,000 acres, and gave alternating leases to J. M. Critchlow of Titusville, Pennsylvania, who represented Scottish capital, in return for a contract to drill three wells. When oil was struck, Critchlow's holdings were transferred to the Red River Oil Company (later the Dundee Petroleum Company). The Red River Oil Company completed its first well on a site in the north edge of Section 5, fortunately near a pond, since water for drilling was a necessity. Had the company chosen the south half, it would have drilled a dry hole.[22]

H. P. Nichols, driller for the Red River Oil Company, started his

[18] In S5-T4S-R3W.

[19] The *Daily Ardmoreite* (Ardmore, Oklahoma), August 12, 1923.

[20] Robinson, thesis, 3. The Atoka Agreement, permitting leasing of Indian land, was consummated on April 23, 1897. The officers of the Crystal Oil Company were Wirt Franklin, president; A. T. McGhee, vice-president; Edward Galt, secretary; and Roy M. Johnson, treasurer. The company was capitalized at $50,000.

[21] In S8-T4S-R3W.

[22] "The Healdton Oil Field, Carter County, Oklahoma," in U.S.G.S. *Bull. No. 621*, 13–14; Carl H. Beal, "The Decline and Ultimate Production of Oil Wells," in *Bull. No. 177*, Petroleum Technology 51, 148–49.

Oklahoma Steals the Show

well on the Apple-Franklin property about the middle of July, 1913, and completed it on August 4 as a twenty-five-barrel producer at about 920 feet.[23] The drilling time was only eighteen days and the cost less than $5,000. Then the No. 1 McClure well was started near the Palmer well and was brought in as a "sixty-foot gusher," or for an initial flow of 300 barrels daily.

Hundreds of oilmen, scouts, and local citizens from Ardmore and from Waurika, twenty-five miles west, as well as men from more distant points, came to watch the new well. The Sun Oil Company (through its subsidiary, the Twin State Oil Company) entered the field on October 6, 1913, by leasing 1,000 acres from the Crystal Oil Company. It also planned a pipe line to connect with its Electra–Port Arthur line. Crystal contracted with William G. Skelly, at present a prominent oilman of Tulsa, to drill ten wells.[24] A short time later the observant Skelly secured a lease of twenty acres on the Woodruff farm, in Section 31, that proved to be the richest part of the field.

By 1913 major lease and royalty bartering had started. In fact, all royalty trading reached its first prominence in Oklahoma at Healdton and was later developed into a big business at Seminole. Here Robert A. Hefner, now of Oklahoma City, is credited with having developed a royalty-purchase form calling for the "first barrels of oil" produced each day. This means that purchasers bought one or more (specified) barrels of royalty oil each day for the life of the lease.

[23] A reporter estimated the initial flow of the well at 200 barrels.—*Daily Ardmoreite,* August 10, 1913. On November 11, 1913, Nichols and Westheimer completed a good well on C. R. Smith's farm at 477 feet.

[24] W. G. (Bill) Skelly was one of the best-known Mid-Continent oil-field operators of the nineteen-twenties. He entered the Eldorado, Kansas, oil field shortly after the No. 1 Stapleton well had been drilled. He and his associates built a refinery on an eighty-acre tract and two years later, on October 2, organized the Skelly Oil Company. Then followed a period of rapid expansion: in 1920, into the Teeter pool, in Kansas, and Hewitt, Oklahoma; in 1923, by the absorption of the Midland Refining Company; in the next year, by large production at Smackover, Arkansas, and in the Texas Panhandle; and two years later, by entering the fields of western Kansas, Louisiana, New Mexico, and others in Oklahoma. Skelly's 160-acre Hendricks lease in West Texas, which ultimately yielded 8,000,000 barrels of crude oil, had come into production by 1928.

By 1948 the Skelly Oil Company was one of the Southwest's most successful oil companies in co-ordinating production, refining, and marketing. Its leases, production, refining, and marketing represent every part of the vast Southwest.

127

Oil! Titan of the Southwest

Although the 1913 oil output was not great, by the end of the following year it had so increased as to make Healdton a major field. Drilling expanded mainly northwest-southeast, and the field assumed an elliptical form, with a maximum width of two and one-half miles and a length of six and one-half miles, covering fourteen square miles.

No doubt the rapid development of Healdton was partly due to the low cost of drilling. An Ardmore drilling contractor, C. H. Lamb, stated that a Cushing well cost from $15,000 to $20,000, while a Healdton well rarely cost more than $4,000. Some of the best wells had an initial production of from 4,000 to 5,000 barrels of oil a day.

Healdton, with the nearest railroads at Ardmore on the east and Waurika on the west, was hardly prepared to store and market such a flood of oil. Temporary storage tanks and earthen reservoirs were entirely inadequate, and there was much waste. Presently a railway, built by John Ringling of circus fame, connected the field with Ardmore. The Oklahoma, New Mexico and Pacific Railway was projected westward from Ardmore, through Wilson, about five miles from the Healdton field, but its limited tank-car service gave little relief.

When the discovery well was brought in (August 4, 1913), pipe-line accommodations to the Gulf Coast refineries were near at hand. Among these was the Magnolia Petroleum Company's pipe line, from the Electra field in Texas, the nearest point on its route being about forty-four miles to the southwest. The Petrolia station, of The Texas Company's line, was about thirty-seven miles distant; and this same company's pipe line from the Cushing field to the Gulf was about sixty-nine miles to the southeast. There was a small six-inch pipe line running from the old Wheeler field (a small field, discovered in 1904, between Healdton and the Arbuckle Mountains) to Ardmore; but it belonged to the Santa Fe Railroad and was used to carry fuel oil to Ardmore from the wells owned by the Santa Fe (the Coline Oil Company).

The Magnolia Petroleum Company in 1912 had built a pipe line to connect the Cushing field with its Texas refineries.[25] The line ran

[25] The Magnolia Petroleum Company was formed on April 24, 1911, from the John Sealy Company. John Sealy became president and later chairman of the board.— *Magnolia Oil News* (Founder's Number), April, 1913, 21. By January 3, 1917,

west of Healdton and made it practicable to extend a branch line into the Healdton field.[26] Shortly after the discovery of the Red River Oil Company's No. 1 well, representatives of the Corsicana Petroleum Company[27] visited Healdton, took a sample of the oil, and sought to buy producing property. Later, D. C. Stewart, manager of the Magnolia pipe-line department, told Healdton operators that his company had high-grade oil, that it needed all this oil it could get and would pay the current price, $1.03. Pending the completion of his company's pipe line, he furnished the producers with steel tanks, expecting them to pay only the expense of installation. Then about the middle of December, 1914, the Magnolia Pipe Line Company, capitalized at $500,000, was organized as a common carrier under the Oklahoma state law. It owned an eight-inch line, about twenty-six miles long, connecting at the Oklahoma-Texas boundary with the Magnolia Petroleum Company's pipe line at Addington, Oklahoma, from which point a six-inch branch line was laid on to the Healdton oil field.

In addition, Magnolia invested heavily at Healdton. By September 30, 1914, it had built forty-five miles of gathering lines, three 55,000-barrel steel storage tanks, and a pumping station. It also owned pumping stations at Mud Creek and at Waurika. Then on September 21, it had leased from its parent firm, the Magnolia Petroleum Company, the latter's eight-inch main pipe line and equipment, extending from the Red River to Fort Worth, Texas. Two 55,000-barrel tanks at Fort Worth were a part of the equipment. The entire distance from Healdton to Fort Worth was about 125 miles. The pipe line was opened for Healdton oil on March 11, 1914.[28]

On January 26, the Magnolia Pipe Line Company had begun to

Magnolia had 1,245 producing wells in Oklahoma and North Texas and was drilling, or preparing to drill, 80 additional wells. Its pipe lines at that time included 1,033 miles of eight-inch trunk line; 120 miles of six-inch trunk line; 90 oil and gas engines, developing 8,500 h.p.; 28 main-line pumping stations; 226 steel storage tanks of 10,000,000-barrel capacity; and other properties. By its purchase of all the properties of the McMan Oil Company in Oklahoma and Kansas, except restricted Indian leases, on January 3, 1917, Magnolia became one of the largest crude-oil producers in the United States.—*Oil Trade Journal*, Vol. VIII, No. 2 (February, 1917), 3.

[26] The *Daily Ardmoreite*, October 7, 1913.

[27] An affiliate of the Magnolia Petroleum Company.

[28] Joseph E. Davies, Bureau of Corporations, *Conditions in the Healdton Oil Field*, March 15, 1915, 3.

buy and store oil preparatory to the opening of its pipe line; and it had notified the Healdton producers that its price on Oklahoma crude oil of 32 degrees gravity and above would be $1.03 per barrel at the wells, the prevailing price paid by the large pipe-line companies in other Oklahoma oil fields.

On February 2, 1914, Mid-Continent oil was priced at $1.05. But on March 2, 1914, the Magnolia Pipe Line Company announced that until further notice it would pay only 70 cents a barrel for Healdton crude oil under 32 degrees gravity Baumé test; but that it would pay $1.05 for oil above 32 degrees, claiming that much of the Healdton oil was of low gravity and usable only as fuel oil.

This caused a great deal of dissatisfaction among the producers, who appealed to the Oklahoma Corporation Commission for protection. They charged that Magnolia practiced discrimination and employed monopolistic practices among the producers. Two days prior to the hearing, set for March 13 by the Commission, the Healdton operators met in Ardmore and selected a committee of twenty-five members to represent them. Then the Commission postponed its hearing, giving Wirt Franklin[29] and his independents time to organize the Ardmore Independent Oil Producer's Association (March 14).[30]

Later the Commission held several hearings. At the first meeting both sides of the controversy were given opportunity to present their arguments. The Corporation Commission's inspector reported that much of the Healdton oil he had examined was found to be under 32 degrees Baumé, and that the odor of sulphur was noticeable over the field. In his opinion, Healdton oil could easily be rated

[29] Franklin played a conspicuous role as champion of the independent producers and as one of the organizers of the Independent Petroleum Association of America, at Colorado Springs, on June 11, 1929, where he made the keynote address. Franklin was named the Association's first president.

[30] Shortly a new move of wider scope was launched by Robert A. Galbreath and Wirt Franklin in a mass meeting of independents at Oklahoma City, on April 23, 1914. Two hundred and fifty men assembled. C. F. Colcord was elected president and M. C. French, secretary. E. E. Brown, Wirt Franklin, and Robert Galbreath composed the board of directors. They appealed to Congress to supervise interstate pipe-line companies, not to permit them to engage in production and refining of oil, and to prohibit discriminations in pipe-line runs. The United States Supreme Court's decision in June, 1914, defining all oil lines, except refiners' private lines, as common carriers and under the jurisdiction of the Interstate Commerce Commission, helped the independents' cause.

as fuel oil.[31] At the second hearing a short time later the Commission's special inspector reported an estimated total output for Healdton's thirty-seven wells at approximately 7,000 barrels a day. A producer asked if the Magnolia Pipe Line Company could handle this much oil, to which the Magnolia official replied that his company could accept as much as 10,000 barrels of oil daily.

Events now moved swiftly. On March 23 the pipe-line company gave notice that it would take only 4,000 barrels of Healdton crude oil a day, when the estimated field output was 10,000 barrels. Three days later, the company stated that after March 26 its price on all grades of Healdton crude would be seventy cents a barrel at the well. Then on April 13 and 20 there were other reductions of ten cents each, bringing the price down to fifty cents a barrel. Magnolia justified its policy on the ground of the heavy and inferior quality of Healdton oil, which could not compete with the finer-quality oil from Cushing.

The pipe-line company's policy was challenged, the producers again lodging a protest with the Corporation Commission. At the time of the first ten-cent cut, on April 13, Magnolia's counsel presented his case before the Corporation Commission and producers at Ardmore, explaining his company's action and outlining its plans to take care of Healdton oil, such as the building of a refinery at Fort Worth, especially equipped to refine Healdton crude oil, the erection of storage tanks at Fort Worth, and the increase of the company's pipe-line capacity by building additional pipe-line and pumping stations. But the producers asked why Magnolia could not take 10,000 barrels of oil daily as it had promised the Commission on March 13. The counsel replied that no one could foresee the difficulties of Healdton's oil transportation problem when this promise was made. Since then, he said, Magnolia's tests had showed that Healdton crude oil should be considered only as fuel-oil crude.[32]

Thus, no final settlement was reached at the Ardmore meeting. Magnolia's cut in price had thrown on the producers the burden of

[31] *Conditions in Healdton Oil Field*, H. L. Wood's report, Exhibit 2, p. 94.

[32] Healdton crude oil averaged a gravity of about 30 degrees Baumé.—James H. Gardner, "The Oil Pools of Southern Oklahoma and Northern Texas," in *Economic Geology*, Vol. X, No. 5 (July–August, 1915), 423.

storing their surplus oil, and they could do little else than build large ground reservoirs, and waste was great. Yet the staggering output of Cushing oil had modified the commitments of all pipe-line carriers.

The producers again took their grievance to the Oklahoma attorney general, and he, in turn, charged that the Magnolia Pipe Line Company was guilty of illegal acts in unreasonable restraint of trade, and had "engaged in forbidden practices in purchasing and piping oil from the Healdton field, including discrimination between different producers in its purchases of oil." Subsequently, however, this charge was not pressed.

Out of the heated controversy at last came a temporary settlement, embodied in the Corporation Commission's official order, No. 814, of May 7, 1914.[33] By it the Magnolia Pipe Line Company should within a week from May 5, 1914, begin taking Healdton crude oil at a daily average of 8,000 barrels; and on or before July 1, 1914, and until April 1, 1915, should not take less than a daily average of 12,000 barrels. Magnolia was to erect four 55,000-barrel steel tanks in the Healdton oil field, and, in addition to its daily agreed-upon runs, it was to clear the leases of all stocks of accumulated oil which were in a merchantable condition and pay the owners upon delivery at the rate of fifty cents a barrel for the quantities delivered. Magnolia was also ordered to provide pipe-line connection and loading facilities on the main line of the Chicago, Rock Island and Pacific Railroad at or near Addington;[34] and it was to charge only a reasonable rate when producers offered oil in carload lots.

The Commission named Wirt Franklin as field umpire and Vern Calvert as inspector for the Healdton field to investigate all oil runs and the output of all wells, and to apportion the quantity of oil which should be taken from each producer.[35] One-half of Calvert's salary ($150 a month) was to be paid by the producers and one-half by the Magnolia Pipe Line Company. The order was to remain effective until April 1, 1915.

[33] *Conditions in the Healdton Oil Field*, Exhibit 1, p. 91. The *Daily Ardmoreite* of May 7, 1914, gave Wirt Franklin credit for effecting this compromise.

[34] This part of the order was later changed to permit loading racks at Waurika instead of Addington.

[35] Art L. Walker was Oklahoma's first state conservation officer.

Oklahoma Steals the Show

Calvert began his duties almost immediately. He took gauges of the field, which showed an estimated average daily yield of 49,596 barrels of crude oil. This was the monthly record.

Healdton Oil Production for Six Months

Date	Wells Reported	Estimated Daily Yield
1914		Barrels
June 24	---	49,598
July 25	---	53,085
August 25	242	58,431
September 25	255	65,171
October 24	259	66,173
November 25	263	68,855
December 24	268	68,058

At a Commission hearing in August, Magnolia's counsel, George C. Greer, again sought an adjustment with the producers at Ardmore, pointing out that the ruined export trade and financial disturbance growing out of the European war had made the Corporation Commission's "proration" order of May 7 hard to meet. His allegations were proved to such an extent that the Commission finally allowed a new agreement, by which the pipe-line company was permitted to reduce the quantity of oil to be run, beginning September 1, 1914, from 12,000 barrels to 8,000 barrels of oil a day, until January 1, 1915. The producers agreed to accept part-payment for their oil in scrip issued by the pipe-line company, bearing interest at the rate of 6 per cent per annum.

In August, 1914, an electrical storm started what proved to be one of the most disastrous fires that ever visited an Oklahoma oil field. Practically every producer at Healdton suffered loss, the total quantity of oil destroyed being estimated at from 375,000 to 400,-000 barrels.

On top of this disaster, on September 30, the Magnolia Pipe Line Company advised the Corporation Commission and the Attorney General that, beginning on October 6, its price on Healdton crude would be reduced to forty cents a barrel. But the Commission would not approve this reduction and forbade the producers to sell their oil at less than fifty cents a barrel. Therefore, pending another hearing before the Commission, Magnolia did not put its new price into effect.

The hearing was held at Ardmore on October 22 and 23. There the pipe-line company's witnesses testified to the cost of raising crude oil to the surface and of gathering, overhead costs, and so on, and at the same time directed attention to the comparative quality and refining value of crude-oil products from Cushing and Healdton. At the close of the hearing, Magnolia announced that it would continue to take Healdton crude at fifty cents a barrel in such quantities as it could use, estimating its needs at from 6,000 to 8,000 barrels. The Commission issued no order, requiring only that the pipe-line company take as much oil as it needed to fill its current requirements.

Meanwhile, crude-oil production climbed steadily, but fortunately the demand also increased. American oil consumption practically doubled during the period 1912 to 1915. Not only had there been a rapidly mounting Allied need for oil during the first year of the war, but domestic consumption was equally large. H. G. James on December 9, 1915, wrote: "Five months ago there was a tremendous overproduction of crude in the Mid-Continent field. Cushing was the talk of the oil world."[36] At that time the posted price of crude was forty cents a barrel and private sales were reported as low as twenty-six cents. Premiums paid a few months previously ranging from three to ten cents a barrel had completely disappeared. Gasoline drugged the market and went begging at one cent a gallon, and kerosene was going to storage because of a lack of buyers.

Then came a remarkable change. Beginning in August, the Prairie Oil and Gas Company reduced its storage surplus of crude oil from 52,000,000 to 47,000,000 barrels in Oklahoma, and by October it began to draw upon its reserve at the rate of 37,500 barrels a day. Other major operators were doing the same thing, and the result was an upward swing of the market. By December, the posted price of crude oil was $1.00 a barrel and private sales were made as high as $1.40. In some instances crude oil cost Kansas re-

[36] H. G. James, "Refining Industries of the United States," in *Statistical Abstract*, 74.

fineries $1.70, and a scramble for "raw material" among the refineries amounted to a near riot. Gasoline jumped in price to twelve and one-half cents a gallon f.o.b. refinery, kerosene rose to three cents a gallon, and fuel oil from sixty to seventy-five cents a barrel.

This sudden change in the American domestic market, favorable to the petroleum industry, was caused, no doubt, by a "spectacular arithmetical progression" in the manufacture of motor cars. The number of automobiles built in 1901 exceeded the total number of cars sold in the preceding six-year period, and in the next year the number equaled the cumulative total up to that time. During each of the following thirty years the automobile increase over each preceding year ranged from 10 per cent to 50 per cent. In 1910 the first closed car was introduced, and the windshield and folding top became standard equipment. In 1914 there were 1,504,304 motor cars manufactured in the United States; and in the next year, 2,075,750. (In this year, too, an electrically heated carburetor was invented for burning kerosene in automobiles.) Manufacturers reported that they had enough orders to keep their factories in operation for six months even if they did not receive another order. This, of course, meant a tremendous consumption of motor fuel and helped to put the market in a healthy condition.[37]

At a time when the Cushing field was nearing a daily mark of 250,000 barrels of crude oil, carriers put forth desperate efforts to handle the field's output, even when the market was low. But the Prairie Oil and Gas Company and the Gulf and Texas companies took little more than half the field's output either by tank car or pipe line. Still, dozens of loading racks were built on the Santa Fe Railroad at Cushing, at Yale, and at other points. The Santa Fe constructed a branch line from Oilton to Drumright, and the Frisco tapped the Shamrock pool.[38]

When the Cushing oil field was discovered, there were only thirteen refineries in Kansas and Oklahoma, which processed not over 30,000 barrels of crude oil daily. The rest of the field's output,

[37] *Ibid.;* B. E. Hull, "Memorandum," MS, February, 1946, p. 4. In 1910 the airplane was first used in warfare, when Italian aviators caught a Turkish army in a ravine and showered it with bombs. In 1919, the United States began to furnish England with fast and comfortable motor busses.—*Oil and Gas Journal—The Oil City Derrick* (Diamond Jubilee edition), August 27, 1934, 162.

[38] Galey MS.

about 160,000 barrels, was purchased by pipe-line companies—the Prairie, the Gulf, and the Texas companies—for their own refineries. The Prairie Oil and Gas Company ran its oil northward; and the Gulf and Texas companies southward, to Gulf Coast refineries. But by 1915, at the peak of Cushing's production, Kansas and Oklahoma had fifty-five refineries processing 75,000 barrels of crude oil daily. Still all storage was overflowing, and some producers became refiners rather than face a considerable loss.[39]

Cushing's transportation problem also was partly solved by 1915. In fact, by 1914 Cushing's pipe-line capacity had practically been doubled by the building of new lines to refineries at Sapulpa, West Tulsa, Ponca City, Okmulgee, Bristow, and Vinita. The McMan Oil Company built an eight-inch line from Cushing to Ringgold, Texas, just south of the Red River; and the Sinclair and Ozark interests laid others. Among the largest shippers of crude oil were the Magnolia, Gunsburg and Foreman, White and Sinclair,[40] White Oil, and the Uncle Sam companies; while the major pipe-line operators remained the Prairie, Gulf, Texas, and Magnolia-McMan interests.

By 1915 property transactions of major companies were common. The largest occurred when the Roxana Petroleum Corporation (an American subsidiary of the Royal Dutch Shell Oil Com-

[39] A discriminating market and the high gasoline content of Cushing crude oil caused Kansas and Oklahoma refiners to change from local field crude oil to Cushing oil. The Milliken refinery switched from Nowata and Rodgers counties to Cushing; the National Refining Company and Cudahy Refining Company at Coffeyville, Kansas, changed from Montgomery and Chautauqua fields to Cushing; the Chelsea Refining Company abandoned the Chelsea-Alluwe area; The Indiahoma Refining Company prorated purchases from the Okmulgee district and bought Cushing oil; the American Refining Company built a new refinery at Cushing to take the place of an old one at Okmulgee; and the Uncle Sam Company left eastern Kansas for Cushing.—Galey MS.

[40] Sinclair Oil and Refining Corporation, now Sinclair Oil Corporation, was organized in May, 1916, and at that time took over the properties of the Sinclair Oil Company, the Chanute Refining Company, the Cudahy Refining Company, and the Milliken Oil Company, and others. From these accessions, Sinclair extended its holdings in the Cushing field, Garber, the Osage area, Healdton, in northeastern Oklahoma, and Kansas, with a pipe-line system connecting with refineries at Cushing and Vinita, Oklahoma, and Chanute and Coffeyville, Kansas. Soon after the company's organization, it became active in Texas, particularly in the Ranger field and around Wichita Falls. Presently, too, refineries at Kansas City, Chicago, and Houston were built and a pipe-line right-of-way secured. From these beginnings, Sinclair, by 1940, had extended its operations throughout the Southwest.

Drumright, Oklahoma, about 1916

Carter Oil Company

Oilton, Oklahoma, one month old

Standard Oil Company (N. J.)

Ponca City, Oklahoma, two weeks old

A. A. Forbes photograph
Ponca City Chamber of Commerce

Ponca City today

Ponca City Chamber of Commerce

Oklahoma Steals the Show

pany) took over the holdings of the Dundee, Allma, and Samoset companies at Healdton, including 18,500 barrels of production daily with considerable acreage, the price being $3,000,000.[41] Roxana also purchased the properties of the Devonian Oil Company in Cushing—8,500 barrels of production and ten 55,000-barrel steel storage tanks for $1,950,000.

In September, 1915, the Carter Oil Company[42] took over the John Markham, Jr., Yarhola, and Manuel leases in the northern part of the Cushing field for $2,000,000. At this time the Yarhola lease

[41] The Roxana Petroleum Corporation is the same company, with two name changes, as the Shell Oil Company, Incorporated. The Royal Dutch–Shell group, the parent organization, entered the United States oil business in 1912, acquiring Oklahoma properties under its trade name, Roxana Petroleum Company of Oklahoma. At this time it acquired control of the Signal Oil Company, the Kingbell Oil Company, the Parris Oil Company, and the Standard Oil and Gas Company of Oklahoma (with their properties) from John A. Bell, head of the Bell Steel Company of Pittsburgh. In September, 1912, the Paova Oil Company, the Helmic Oil Company, the Quintuple Oil Company, and the Clephane Oil Company, controlled by L. C. Sands, also a Pittsburgher, were purchased. Meanwhile Roxana had established headquarters in Tulsa; and in 1919, under the trade name of Roxana Petroleum Corporation, it moved to St. Louis, but left exploration and production divisions in the Mayo Building, Tulsa.

Its expansion was rapid. It moved into Cushing and Healdton (1915) by acquiring the Alma Oil Company, the Dundee Petroleum Company, and the Samoset Oil Company. During the nineteen-twenties it entered the Tonkawa oil field, Oklahoma; North Texas, about Wichita Falls; Smackover, Arkansas; several fields in Kansas; Louisiana, discovering the oil fields of White Castle and Iowa; and West Texas. It had also established a wide-ranging pipe-line system, several refineries (at Cushing, 1916–17; Wood River, Illinois, 1917; Arkansas City, Kansas, 1923; East Chicago, 1926; and Houston, 1928) and marketing facilities. On April 1, 1939, the present Shell Oil, Incorporated, emerged from the consolidation of three Shell firms, and the St. Louis and New York offices were merged in September, 1940. The headquarters of the exploration and production departments, formerly in St. Louis, were now moved to Houston.—Information from K. F. Beaton, Shell Oil Company, in letter of September 13, 1948.

[42] Both the Carter and Prairie were Standard Oil subsidiaries. The Carter Oil Company was organized by Colonel John J. Carter of Titusville, Pennsylvania. The company became a Standard Oil enterprise when on January 24, 1908, Standard acquired 19,950 shares of its 20,000 shares. In August, 1917, the company's capital stock was increased from $2,000,000 to $25,000,000.

Carter entered the Mid-Continent area on September 27, 1913, when it qualified to do business in Oklahoma. Two years later it acquired the Manuel and Yarhola leases near Oilton and, before the end of the year, other properties at Healdton. Also in 1915 the Carter Company entered the Eldorado and Augusta fields of Kansas and then quickly moved into other Southwestern oil-producing states.

In 1940, Carter produced 54,000,000 barrels of oil and its total cumulative production reached 366,000,000 barrels. At present, the Carter Oil Company is under the alert presidency of Oscar Schorp.—Manuscript copy, "Early History of the Carter Oil Company," furnished the author by C. D. Watson, Public Relations Department, Carter Oil Company, Tulsa, Oklahoma.

was making 7,500 barrels of crude oil daily and the Manuel lease was of unknown quantity, although later it produced 12,000 barrels of oil daily. This transaction brought the Carter Oil Company into Oklahoma, and at the close of the year it was one of the largest concerns in the state, being next to the Prairie Oil and Gas Company in its holdings of oil in storage. In December, 1915, the Carter company took over the Russell and Skelly holding on the Ward 120-acre lease[43] in the Healdton field, with approximately 4,000 barrels of crude oil daily from nine wells. The deal also included three 55,-000-barrel tanks. The largest big-company deal, however, came in 1916 when the Cosden Oil and Gas Company paid $12,000,000 for the holdings of the Hill Oil and Gas Company in the Shamrock pool.

Both the Carter Oil Company and the Standard Oil Company of Indiana[44] engaged in active buying of Cushing crude oil in 1915. The Carter Company purchased sixty 55,000-barrel steel tanks from the Quaker Oil and Gas Company, about forty tanks from the White and Sinclair interests, and thirty-eight from Gunsburg and Foreman, as well as building a large number of its own. Standard Oil started late to buy tankage but took over thirty-two tanks from W. C. McBride; 740,000 barrels storage from B. B. Jones; and forty tanks from the Oklahoma, Katy, and Slick oil companies. Prices for this storage ranged all the way from $1.00 to $1.40 a barrel.

At both Cushing and Healdton, frenzied leasing, the buying and selling of royalties, and the appearance of numerous fly-by-night oil companies gave more conservative operators many uneasy moments. Small acreages were quickly drilled by these speculator-operators, and major companies and producers felt that they must develop their holdings for protection, or to meet offset-well

[43] In S6-T4S-R3W.

[44] Standard of Indiana was originally organized by the parent Standard Oil Company to take over refining at Lima, Ohio, and Whiting, Indiana. As the crude-oil flow to these two refineries diminished, more crude was sought in the Middle West and Southwest. Standard entered Kansas soon after the discovery of the Neodesha field and a short time later erected a new refinery at Sugar Creek, Missouri, a suburb of Kansas City. Starting in 1919 by acquiring controlling interest in the Dixie Oil Company, Standard broadened its operations. In 1921, Standard bought controlling interest in Midwest Refining Company; in 1925, an interest in Pan-American Petroleum and Transport Company, later built to 78 per cent; in 1930, in McMan Oil and Gas Company, owning acreage in the rich Yates field of western Texas; and in 1935, important Yount-Lee producing properties of Texas and Louisiana. At present its holdings are found in every important oil-producing area of the Southwest.

requirements. By 1915 crude-oil production had clearly outrun demand, and Oklahoma's surplus reached 200,000,000 barrels. Experienced oilmen predicted that the state's oil industry faced disaster unless something were done to curtail this swelling output.

But man-made curbs on production were unnecessary. Cushing reached its peak output in 1915 and started a swift decline; and Healdton passed its zenith a short time later. But other pools were found. As early as 1914 developments in the Blackwell field, in Kay County, west of the proved Mid-Continent zone, led to exploratory drilling; and as a result, during the next year minor pools were found in older fields. In the fall of 1914, Dorsey Hager, a California geologist, came to Tulsa and later entered into a partnership with Mowry Bates. Then Hager mapped for the Chanute Refining Company acreages owned by Bert Garber and others which now compose the Garber oil field.

Near Garber, on the Hoy farm, in September, 1917, the Sinclair Oil and Gas Company brought in a 200-barrel oil well from a sand at 1,130–1,156 feet, later named the Hoy sand.[45] After this the Garber field spread rapidly. Sinclair also completed a well in Arbuckle limestone, in this Garber field (in S18-T22N-R3W),[46] which proved to be Oklahoma's greatest producer up to that time—27,000 barrels of oil a day, in siliceous limestone, at a horizon of 4,085–4,100 feet.

The Garber field is notable for its eleven different oil horizons, of which the major ones are the Hoy (900 feet), the Hotson (1,500 feet), the Belveal (1,750 feet), the Garber or Billings (2,100 feet), and the siliceous-Arbuckle (4,100 feet). The field showed Permian red rocks at the surface and was on a well-defined dome of the subsurface Nemaha Mountain. During the latter part of 1917 its daily oil output averaged 2,000 barrels, and quadrupled its yield two years later. By the end of 1918 the field had 760 producing wells. It reached its peak in November, 1925, with a daily 71,875 barrels of crude oil.

The Yale pool, found by deep drilling west of Cushing, became an important producer during 1914–17. By the end of 1917 it was yielding 500,000 barrels of crude oil a month from the Wilcox horizon at 3,580–3,600 feet. Later, five pay zones were found here.

[45] In NE NE NE of S25-T22N-R4W.
[46] T. O. Bosworth, *Geology of the Mid-Continent Oilfields*, 107–108.

Oil! Titan of the Southwest

The most notable new oil territory exploited during this period (1916–17) was that just south of the Kansas boundary, in Kay, Noble, and Garfield counties, some distance west of the older fields. Blackwell, Newkirk, Ponca, Billings, and Garber became well-known oil place names. At Blackwell a number of the deep wells had initial flows of 1,000 to 2,000 barrels of oil a day. At Newkirk early production was at 500 feet, but three years later a better sand was reached at 3,000 feet. Ponca was first drilled as a gas field at 500 feet, then as an oil field at 1,500–1,600 feet, and in 1918 the best pay sand was tapped at 2,100 to 3,900 feet. In 1917 the Billings field came into production, and in several months it reached a peak output of about 1,000,000 barrels of oil from sands ranging between 1,000 and 2,300 feet.

Then north of the Kansas line and about seventy miles west of other producing territory, the Augusta, El Dorado, and Towanda fields were discovered during 1916 and 1917. Earlier, in 1911, Henry L. Doherty, a New York public-utilities investor, bought three gas companies that were piping natural gas into Kansas from the Hogshooter field east of Bartlesville. One, the Wichita Natural Gas Company, had piped gas from this field to Wichita, Kansas, and such other near-by towns as Newton, Wellington, Winfield, Augusta, and El Dorado; a second company supplied Iola smelters; and a third sold gas to the Joplin and Miami zinc field and to adjacent towns.

Doherty's Kansas-Oklahoma manager, A. J. Deischer, employed the well-known Oklahoma geologist, Charles N. Gould, to prospect for a new gas-producing area, since the Hogshooter field was practically exhausted. Gould made several surveys in Osage County and other areas in northern Oklahoma and then went to Augusta, in southern Butler County, Kansas. Previously, in 1912, Erasmus Hayworth and his son had mapped anticlines at El Dorado and Augusta, two gas wells had been found, and a small company organized to supply Augusta with the fuel.

At Augusta, Gould and his assistant hired a team and buckboard and drove out to these gas wells; and after a cursory examination they discovered that the wells had been located, by chance, on a well-defined anticline. They spent several days tracing and mapping the anticline and found that it ran northeast and southwest for a distance of twelve miles, crossing the Walnut River almost as far as Udall.[47] Then they returned to Bartlesville and made their report to Deischer, who, at Gould's suggestion, sent lease men into the territory to secure oil and gas leases on several thousand acres on and about the anticline, along a strip twelve miles long and two miles wide. Next, Deischer sent two parties with alidade heave table and rod into the area to prepare a contour map. Again with Gould's advice, the site of Deischer's first well was chosen, about two miles south of Augusta, which was drilled as the first producer in what came to be a large and productive gas field.

The Doherty interests had a number of leases in the El Dorado field, which produced prolifically. These formed the basis of the Empire Gas and Fuel Company, organized by Doherty and his associates, and became the main stem upon which several small companies were grafted, all forming the Cities Service Company.[48]

The Augusta oil field was discovered by the Continental Oil Company, a former Benedum-Trees company, after the opening of the gas field.[49] The field's first gusher, and the one which really opened the pool, was drilled (in the NE S17-T28S-R5E) and was credited with an initial production of 1,700 barrels of oil. The El Dorado field, which shortly overshadowed Augusta, was discovered by the same company, in October, 1915 (in S29-T28S-R5E), although it was a minor producer. At first, oilmen believed that these

[47] Unpublished account of Dr. Charles N. Gould's geological surveys in Kansas and Texas, written for the author on December 2, 1946.

[48] Cities Service operates in substantially all branches of the petroleum industry, owning oil and gas leases, principally in the Mid-Continent and Gulf Coast area. The company produces, purchases, refines, and sells crude petroleum and its products (gasoline, lubricating oil, fuel oil, kerosene, and other products). It has absorbed several other companies operating in the Southwest. In 1941 it took over the Indian Territory Illuminating Oil Company with its extensive holdings in Greater Seminole and Oklahoma City.

[49] In 1885, Isaac E. Blake of Ogden, Utah, and other Utah and Wyoming businessmen organized the Continental Oil and Transportation Company to distribute petroleum products. Ten years later the company was reorganized as the Continental Oil Company to concentrate still on the distribution of the oil products of other companies. But in 1924 it merged with the Mutual Oil Company, yet carrying the name of Continental, but adding crude-oil production and refining to its activities. Five years later, it also absorbed the Marland Oil Company and moved its headquarters to Ponca City, to its newly acquired refinery. Continental expanded both its production and refining of oil in the Southwest. At present it has 6,000 wells in Oklahoma, Kansas, Texas, Illinois, Indiana, New Mexico, Louisiana, Colorado, Wyoming, Montana, California, and Canada; refineries that are well distributed over the Southwest; and nearly 1,500,000 acres of land under lease for future development.

two discoveries represented two pools, but eventually they saw that they were connected by production and were practically one field.[50]

The development of the Augusta–El Dorado district was slower than that of other Mid-Continent fields, largely because the Empire Gas and Fuel Company owned the greater part of the field and was not forced into competitive drilling. But these fields became so prolific that Kansas production rose from 11,500,000 barrels of oil in 1916 to 38,000,000 barrels in 1917. The principal oil sand was known as the Varnar sand, although other major production came from a 1,750-foot horizon. The best wells in the Augusta field flowed as much as 12,000 to 15,000 barrels a day, while at El Dorado and Towanda some wells had initial production of 18,000 and 25,000 barrels. By the end of 1919 these Butler County pools had yielded more than 100,000,000 barrels of oil from an area of about forty square miles.[51]

Refinery demands, fortunately, took an upward turn to take care of steadily mounting crude-oil output in Oklahoma and Kansas. And such large firms as the Prairie Oil and Gas Company, Gulf, Texas, Sinclair, Cosden, Chapman-McFarlin, and Magnolia so increased their purchases as to take care of the reserve and leave the market in a healthy condition.

[50] Galey MS, as cited, 83 ff. The Towanda pool was a short distance southwest of, adjacent to, and a part of the El Dorado field. See map, frontispiece insert, T. O. Bosworth, *op. cit.* See also Raymond C. More and Winthrop P. Baynes, "Oil and Gas Resources of Kansas," in *State Geological Survey of Kansas, Bull. 3,* 22–23.

[51] Bosworth, *op. cit.*

XI

The Ranger Oil Boom

B Y 1920 petroleum had entered a new era. Several factors pointed toward a change during the period, 1915–20, among which were the growing importance of the automobile industry, a demand for a better quality of gasoline, and the rapidly mounting output of crude petroleum.

Earlier, President Moffitt of the Standard Oil Company of Indiana had said that "the great concern for the future would be . . . high grade petroleum to meet requirements in the manufacture of fuel for gasoline engines." Edward L. Doheny, in *Hearst's Magazine* of April, 1919, added: "Ere long oil-driven machinery will enable man to conquer the air, till the soil, utilize the seas, accelerate communication on a scale not dreamed of today. We are about to enter the oil age—the age of motorization."

Concrete evidence of this change was that the oil industry had already proposed improved refining processes—the Burton, Rittman, Snelling, Wells, Kelsey, Washburn, and others. Yet only two of these, the Burton and Rittman, were beyond the experimental stage. The Standard Oil Company of Indiana had tried the Burton process by 1915 and was installing it in all its plants, and the Rittman process for the manufacture of benzol and toluol used in high explosives was also in successful operation at Pittsburgh. The Cosden company had a small cracking plant in Oklahoma.

It is also worthy of note that the first cracked gasoline was sold at a discount over first-run gasoline and was considered an inferior product. It was only after the antiknock feature became important that cracked gasoline came into its own.

Meanwhile, the nation's petroleum output was staggering; in 1914 it amounted to 290,302,000 barrels. Then new Oklahoma and

Oil! Titan of the Southwest

North Texas fields increased production far beyond the oilman's fondest dream. By 1918 the North Central Texas oil fields were the most spectacular ever recorded in history. Drilling operations covered an area larger than one-half that of the New England states, and the number of men employed by the industry and its many branches outnumbered General W. T. Sherman's legions in their sensational march to the sea. The money invested exceeded the total investment (including profits and losses) of the combined mining rushes in the history of the American continent.

Oil prospecting in North Central Texas had started almost as early as along the Gulf Coast. In 1890 an Abilene "Well Committee" had sought to kill two birds with one stone. Since the city needed water, the committee proposed to drill an artesian well, which might also tap a "gas oil reservoir."

Arriving at this decision, the committee entered into a contract with J. P. Miller and Company of Chicago, on May 31, 1890. The names of such well-known men as O. T. Anderson, Henry Sayles, and Ed S. Hughes appeared on the committee. Miller agreed to furnish all drilling equipment and "to complete your well in a workmanlike manner." His charge for drilling was to range from $4.50 a foot from 1,000 to 1,200 feet to $8.00 from 2,400 to 2,500 feet. If he struck "oil gas or a sufficient flow of water" at less than 1,000 feet, the committee could require that drilling cease. But it must then pay him for 1,000 feet of drilling. Miller proposed to start drilling with a "not less than ten-inch inside drive pipe" and promised to complete the well, if it went to 2,500 feet, with a four and one-fourth-inch pipe.[1] He also agreed that his company was to receive no pay until the well reached 2,500 feet, unless drilling was stopped before that depth by the committee.

This No. 1 J. P. Miller was started about July 25, 1890, at a site a short distance southwest of the Abilene High School building and, according to the well log, reached a depth of 2,223 feet on

[1] Henry Sayles, Jr., the son of an Abilene committee member, furnished the author with a photostatic copy of the Miller contract and the well log. In addition, he supplied other materials relative to oil development in western Texas.

Other members of the committee were: Thead. Heyck, Jas. H. Parramore, Otto W. Steffens, D. W. Wristen, H. A. Porter, D. G. Hill, G. A. Kirkland, W. L. Gatlin, and S. F. Steere.

144

The Ranger Oil Boom

March 5, 1892. Then, since neither oil nor water was found, the well was abandoned and the contract voided.

Almost four decades elapsed before central West Texas experienced its first great oil boom. As an earnest of what was to come, however, in 1912 the Texas Pacific Coal Company of Thurber sank some test holes for coal about 700 or 800 feet deep along the Leon River, seven miles south of Ranger, and found slight indications of oil. Three years later another test was made about ten miles east of Ranger and three miles west of Strawn, which reached 1,000 feet and struck an oil sand. The well flowed several hundred barrels of oil daily, according to Dr. A. K. Wier, who helped to secure the leases.[2]

Thus began the Strawn part of the Ranger field. Shortly a number of companies were formed in Ranger and Eastland. Wells were drilled northeast and northwest of Ranger, and others were sunk near Eastland; but they were dry, since they were too shallow to reach the prolific Ranger oil formations.

Following these tests, Ranger's oil fever was allayed until October 30, 1916, when the Texas Pacific Coal Company completed a 200-barrel well from the Smithwick lime, at 3,105 feet, on the Parks ranch, seven miles southeast of Breckenridge and twenty-five miles northwest of Ranger. The company then leased several hundred acres of land in Stephens County and drilled a number of test wells, most of them near Caddo, about twenty-five miles north of Ranger. No great amount of oil was found in any of these wells. Similar exploratory work was carried on in Comanche, McCulloch, and Young counties, one experiment resulting in the North American Oil and Refining Company's small oil well at South Bend.

Ranger citizens were not yet satisfied, but they could not raise the necessary capital among themselves to drill the deep test that seemed advisable. Moreover, a severe drought throughout the region had brought business stagnation and threatened insolvency for struggling firms. Therefore, in March, 1917, John M. Gholson and other Ranger businessmen went to Thurber and laid the matter before W. K. Gordon, then general manager of the Texas Pacific

---

[2] Mrs. Jimmie Wagner, "The Ranger Oil Boom" (unpublished Master's thesis, Southern Methodist University, August, 1935), 10.

Coal Company.[3] They convinced him of the accuracy of geologists' predictions—that oil might be found in a deeper formation than had yet been reached. Gordon agreed to drill four tests to a depth of 3,500 feet if the Ranger promoters would secure leases to 10,000 or 15,000 acres of land. This was good news, and the visitors returned home to proclaim it. An enthusiastic Ranger mass meeting followed, resulting in property owners' signing lease agreements involving 25,000 acres of land, for which they received twenty-five cents an acre in cash and, in addition, an annual rental of one dollar an acre for seven years.

Under this agreement, in the spring of 1917 Gordon's contractor, Andy Urban, spudded in his first well on Mrs. Nannie Walker's farm on the northern outskirts of town. The drillers of this well were George Dunkle and John Dunkle. In August a strong flow of gas was encountered, but drilling was continued. At 3,400 feet a drill bit broke off, and the well was abandoned, the gas being allowed to flow from the open well. Then a second test was started on the J. H. McCleskey farm, about two miles southwest of town. As the drilling neared the 3,000-foot level, Gordon kept in daily contact with his New York office; and when the well had reached 3,200 feet, he was ordered to abandon it. But he stubbornly held on, and on October 21, 1917, at 3,431 feet he drilled into a "black lime," and the well roared in at an estimated daily flow of 1,700 barrels of oil.[4]

It is difficult for one who has not seen a major oil-boom town to picture what followed. In a brief, one-paragraph sketch, Ray L. Dudley graphically portrays Ranger's transition. "I visited Ranger before the second well was completed," he related. "It was a typical little central West Texas town with a few false-front stores and the inevitable 'commercial hotel,' a large residence which had been given over to taking care of the drummers who were forced to stay

[3] W. K. Gordon, a Virginian, came to Texas in 1889 as a mining engineer in the employment of the Texas Pacific Coal Company of Thurber, previously established by Colonel R. D. Hunter and Edgar L. Marston. In pursuit of his work, riding horseback over the Thurber region, Gordon became convinced that the country contained oil. This belief he held to steadfastly, although geologists had reported adversely. Finally the Texas Pacific Coal Company permitted Gordon to send a local young man, Luther Davenport, over the territory in a buggy to procure leases, which ultimately amounted to 300,000 acres in Eastland, Stephens, Throckmorton and Palo Pinto counties.—MS supplied by Mr. Gordon of Fort Worth, Texas.

[4] Ranger *Daily Times,* 1919–34 (Fifteenth Anniversary edition), p. 18.

[5] Ray L. Dudley to C. C. Rister, March 29, 1946.

in the town. I should imagine that there must have been at least three or four bedrooms in this hotel. Then I saw the oil companies and supply companies move in. I saw warehouses built, stores built, and a pasteboard hotel. I saw the lawless element follow quickly in the wake of oil. I saw streets which, though muddy in pre-oil days, had become quagmires from the unexpected and unparalleled usage to which they were subjected. I saw thousands come in where hundreds had been before. And then I saw the boom slacken off. I saw the supply stores move their personnel to other and more promising areas; I saw the flush production drop off to a rather disappointing pumping production. I saw hotels abandoned. I saw an office building, which would have done credit to a fair-sized town, standing empty. I saw a ghost town."[5]

But this transition took place over months and years. It is necessary to enlarge on Mr. Dudley's pen picture, for the McCleskey discovery well, as has been said, "caused the whole oil fraternity of the United States, with their dubious hangers-on, to be 'tossed into the air' ... and then dumped into the lap of Ranger."[6] Within six months the population of quiet little Ranger grew from 1,000 to 6,000, and within the next year it was converted into a milling, seething mass of 25,000 or 30,000, most of whom were men. The No. 3 well of the Texas Pacific Coal Company (now reorganized as the Texas Pacific Coal and Oil Company) was drilled on the Davenport farm as an offset to the No. 1 McCleskey, and on March 1, 1918, it came in as a 2,000- to 3,000-barrel producer. The fourth test on the Hagaman farm, one and one-half miles north of Ranger, was also a fine producer. Then, as though it were not to be an exception, the No. 1 Walker well, that had produced only gas for several months, on the morning of January 1, 1918, awakened Ranger townspeople by its mighty roar, flowing millions of feet of natural gas. This was followed six weeks later by a second blast from the well bringing in a gushing oil well, worth upward of $500,000.

By this time scouts and lease men of the major companies were everywhere trying to acquire properties near the producing wells.[7]

[6] Wagner, *op. cit.*, 15. See also *Oil Trade Journal*, Vol. IX, No. 9 (September, 1918), 97–98.

[7] David Donoghue states that the Prairie Oil and Gas Company sent eight lease men to Ranger in December, 1917, and that lease prices jumped immediately.—Donoghue to Rister, May 29, 1947.

Oil! Titan of the Southwest

The Fort Worth *Record* of November 22, 1917, estimated that more than $1,000,000 had been spent for leases up to that time. But the Texas Pacific Coal and Oil Company had almost completely leased the field, and some of its properties skyrocketed to $8,000 an acre, which it then subleased to others. The Prairie Oil and Gas, the Magnolia, and the Humble companies drilled a part of these leases on a 50–30 basis. Thus, within a short time the Texas Pacific had become one of the most powerful corporations of the Southwest. This condition, together with the fact that deep drilling costs ranged between $35,000 and $100,000 a well, and the added high wartime labor and materials costs and a limited water supply, just about excluded independents and small companies from the main field, although they leased marginal properties. In fact, many a Texas oilman cut his eyeteeth on the hard edge of these wildcat deals; or, as J. S. Bridwell humorously puts it, "I learned for the first time that one could be an oilman without being a Pennsylvania Dutchman or an Irishman."[8]

Independents and small companies fanned out beyond the Ranger field proper, leased many thousands of acres, and started drilling. By July, 1918, four hundred tests were drilled in thirty-five North Central Texas counties. Drilling operations alone cost $15,-000,000, allowing an average of $30,000 for each test. A small per cent of these tests were drilled 4,000 feet or deeper. For a 4,000-foot hole the pipe costs $24,000, derrick (wooden) and preparation, $3,000; drilling contract at $3.50 a foot, $13,000; and fuel and water, $5,000; bringing the total to $45,000, with deeper holes reaching $75,000 or more.[9] And because of this periphery movement, other important pools were discovered—the Gray-Hightower of the Panhandle Oil and Refining Company, the Parsons, and the Sinclair-Earnest. Northwest of Ranger, the inimitable wildcatter, Barney Carter,[10] opened the "Lake sand" below the Ray, Scott, and Harrison sands, at depths varying from 1,200 to 2,800 feet.

Other operations were just as venturesome. A young school teacher, C. M. Caldwell, from the Breckenridge country, came to

---

[8] Bridwell to C. C. Rister, March 27, 1946. A. T. McDannald was in the field early. His first royalty check amounted to $11,000.—McDannald to Rister, May 17, 1946.

[9] *Oil Trade Journal*, Vol. IX, No. 7 (July, 1918), 83–85.

The Ranger Oil Boom

Ranger with his friend, B. S. Walker, seeking his fortune. One night they lay on two secondhand cots in a hotel room, seven by eight feet. There was a beaverboard wall between them and a room occupied by three Oklahomans, who that night discussed spending $100,000 for leases around Ranger. "I did not eavesdrop," says Caldwell, "but I got the 'dope' that they wanted leases in a certain direction. Before daylight the next morning I was patting those farmers on the back, by ten o'clock I had a bunch of leases assembled. I came into Ranger strut[t]ing like a turkey gobbler in March, and delivered the leases to these boys."[11]

As the drilling area spread rapidly, most of the region east and immediately south of town proved to be unproductive, but that north and west was rich. One of the best parts of the field was the John York Survey, the "Golden Block," a two-mile area in which were the Norwood, the Boyd, the E. Roper, the J. T. Roper, and the Harrison leases. But a smaller zone of forty acres, the Brewer pool, was more spectacular, producing more than $2,000,000 worth of oil and launching a frenzied drilling campaign. During the latter part of 1917, Ranger produced 93,053 barrels of oil, and in 1918 its output climbed to 3,107,000 barrels. During 1919, when the field had reached its peak, operators had found eight oil horizons, five of which were sands and three limes; but the most prolific formation still remained the Ranger or McCleskey sand.[12]

Among the largest Ranger producers were the Prairie Oil and Gas Company's No. 1 Emma Terrell, the Texas Pacific Coal and Oil Company's No. 1 S. E. Norwood, and the Ohio-Ranger Oil Com-

[10] Carter's rapid climb as an independent producer started with these Ranger operations. He began without funds. He landed in Ranger shortly after the McCleskey well came in and sought to buy a milk shake in a drugstore. But he was told that there was no milk in town. Then he decided to install a dairy. He went to M. H. Hagaman and leased two hundred acres of grazing land, returned to Abilene, Texas, and borrowed the money to pay for the lease and to buy a local dairy herd of thirty-eight cows, and launched his new enterprise. Meanwhile he watched his opportunities and picked up leases and royalties, and thus became an outstanding independent operator.

[11] Caldwell to Rister, March 27, 1946. Both Caldwell and Carter later became liberal contributors to Hardin-Simmons University, Abilene, Texas.

[12] U.S.G.S. *Bull. No. 736-E*, 134.

pany's No. 1 Eli Perkins. The initial daily production of these wells was 7,000, 11,000, and 8,000 barrels respectively.[13]

In quality, the Ranger crude oil was second only to that of Pennsylvania. It had a heavy, greenish-black color, with a gravity varying from 39 to 42 degrees Baumé. In 1917 it sold for $2.60 a barrel; but with the great need of the United States and Europe during World War I, the price advanced to $4.25.

As prospectors pushed out from Ranger seeking new oil pools, a rich strike was made in the Merriman community southwest of Ranger. The community Baptist church was over the center of this pool. The congregation was offered a large sum for drilling rights on its two-and-one-half-acre church lot; but this it refused, its own members underwriting the drilling of three wells, since some of them had already received large royalties on their own properties. The Reverend W. T. Hamor's congregation then voted to designate 85 per cent of the income from oil to the co-operative program of the Baptist General Convention of Texas and to retain the remaining 15 per cent for building a new church after the oil-boom days passed. The building was completed in the early nineteen twenties. From lease money on the lot a $5,000 government bond was given to the Southwestern Baptist Theological Seminary and a like contribution was made to the Buckner Orphans Home.

An agent of Eastern capitalists sought to lease the cemetery but was told that the church did not own this property.[14] Subsequently the trade journals and newspapers published the story that the indignant church members had turned down $1,000,000 rather than see their dead disturbed. Indeed, Will Ferrell wrote a lengthy poem, "There's a Churchyard down in Ranger," praising the brave little congregation and its pastor for their stand.[15] "Merriman is not for sale," Ferrell reports a deacon telling the agent. Heroically, he pictured the Baptist church "Standing guard above the gravestones in a lot that's not for sale."

But like many another oil-field story, the Merriman graveyard narrative had little basis of truth. The Reverend Hamor states that

13 *Ibid.*, 133–43.

14 *Ranger Texas and the Ranger Oil Field*, 30, 31, pamphlet in E. DeGolyer's library, Dallas, Texas; *Oil Trade Journal*, Vol. IX, No. 9 (September, 1918), 82.

15 Ranger *Daily Times*, 1919–34 (Fifteenth Anniversary edition), p. 4.

the Baptist church could not lease the cemetery, even had it desired, for its donor had deeded it to the dead.[16]

Boyce House described vividly the chaos and confusion of the oil field after the McCleskey discovery well in his book, *Were You in Ranger?* At least for a time poverty and want were banished, and the devastating drought was forgotten. Hundreds sought Ranger for employment and found it, and hundreds of others were needed. The surge of the town's spectacular growth, while many derricks all about could be seen spewing their black wealth into the air, gave employment to all. Ranger was in a real sense "the fountain-head of oil used in Aladdin's Lamp." Girls behind the cash counters drew $60 a week, mule-skinners $7 a day, roughnecks and day laborers $12 and $15, tool dressers $20, and rig builders and drillers $25 to $30 plus an occasional handsome bonus.[17] Every day saw a new crop of wealthy persons created from frenzied speculation in oil leases and real estate.

A visiting newspaper correspondent reported that Ranger had suddenly taken on the appearance of a city. "New business houses are going up as fast as carpenters can be secured," he said. "Several new business houses have been contracted for and work has already started on an elegant building for the First National Bank."[18] The McCleskey hotel was opened in the spring of the next year. When men left their hotel rooms in the morning to go to the oil field, their beds were rented and occupied by others without a change of linen. Even overstuffed chairs in hotel lobbies were rented.[19]

This relieved the congestion to some extent, although the throng of men who sought every restaurant and eating place found the meal problem difficult. The café operator could not have on hand enough food for the hungry hundreds who swamped his place, and sometimes small stands, occupying narrow holes in the wall, served odoriferous hamburgers at fabulous prices and in turn paid as high as $250 a month rent for their space. All food prices were high—steaks $1.50 to $2.50, ham and eggs 75 cents, and a glass of milk

---

[16] W. T. Hamor to C. C. Rister, September 19, 1947.

[17] Ruth Terry Denney, "A Short History of Ranger, Texas" (unpublished Master's thesis, Hardin-Simmons University, June, 1941), 184; Ranger *Times*, 1919–39 (Twentieth Anniversary edition), p. 14.

[18] Fort Worth *Record*, November 22, 1917.

[19] Denney, *op. cit.*, 203.

and a piece of pie 50 cents. Water sold at five cents a glass. Tips were expected and given and sometimes amounted to more than the price of the food. Small restaurants were quickly established in tents and shacks, over the door of one of which appeared this sign, "Our Cooks Eat Here!"[20] Out of a party of five who ate meat for dinner at one restaurant, according to a visitor, two became ill.[21]

In rainy weather, Ranger, like other oil-field nerve centers, was plagued with mud. Main Street became a loblolly, with slush oozing on to sidewalks. Men and women wore boots. And at the foot of Main Street, teams were employed to draw heavily laden wagons from hub-deep mire. As the long trains of wagons, each loaded with heavy oil-field equipment, moved up and down the street, groaning with their burdens, the constant and frantic churning of the hooves of the horses, mules, and oxen pulling them threw mud on the store fronts, so that persons inside could not see out the windows. To bog across this quagmire at street intersections was hazardous. Not uncommonly, men in hip boots did a thriving business, charging five to twenty-five cents each to carry passengers "piggy-back" across the street or to transport them on sleds or in boats.

The Texas and Pacific Railway's gross receipts at Ranger served as a barometer of the town's prosperity, climbing from $94,098 in 1917 to $8,146,309 in 1919. The avalanche of supplies—oil-field equipment, lumber, groceries, and dry goods for Ranger's firms, and other articles—cluttered up the railroad's freight yard. Tipping the switchman and local employees often speeded up freight deliveries, the tips ranging from $10 to $500, depending on the importance and bulk of the shipment. At first, on January 29, 1919, the division superintendent declared a temporary embargo so that he could clear the congestion, but without great success. Hundreds of loaded cars occupied every foot of the railway siding and sidings at near-by towns. Then other parallel switches were built, but they, too, were soon jammed with rolling stock. In the freight depot, boxes and crates were strewn about and piled high, while gangs of baggage-room and platform workers labored long hours to bring order out of confusion.

[20] Ranger Texas and the Ranger Oil Field, 12.

[21] "Ranger Is Country's Newest and Most Picturesque Boom Town," in The Oil Trade Journal, Vol. IX, No. 9 (September, 1918), 97–98.

No. 1 McClesky oil well, Ranger, Texas

W. K. Gordon

Breckenridge, Texas, 1921

Early Desdemona, Texas, oil field

The Ranger Oil Boom

The Texas and Pacific operated five east and west passenger trains between Ranger and Fort Worth, each pulling from seven to fifteen coaches—all crowded to the doors.

Jake Hamon, an oilman, sought to solve this freight and passenger problem. He addressed several hundred businessmen in the present Ranger *Times* Building, proposed a new road, the Wichita Falls, Ranger and Fort Worth, and asked for a subscription of $250,-000 to build it. Businessmen and oilmen supported his proposal. This displeased Texas and Pacific officials, who refused to grant Hamon a crossing of their right-of-way; but he made the crossing one night while angry officials and workmen of the rival road stood by threatingly. "Ranger . . . took on a movie studio aspect at seven p. m. Monday night," said an eyewitness, "when 200 operatives of the Wichita Falls, Ranger and Fort Worth Railroad stepped in, cut the T. and P. tracks, tied up the traffic all night, and completed the crossing."[22] Hamon built his line on northward and helped to relieve the congestion.

Dirt roads running from Ranger to the oil field could not accommodate the confused welter of traffic, although they had served the farmers and ranchers satisfactorily. In dry weather powdery dust marked them for mile on mile, hanging above the ground like "a cloud by day." It settled on the green trees, changing their color to an ashen gray; and the deep chugholes and ruts in the road made uncertain the movement of heavily laden wagons.

Major companies often used huge dapple-gray Percheron horses for teams, sometimes with six to twelve of them pulling one wagon, and occasionally in trains of fifteen to twenty wagons. It was an impressive sight to stand by the roadside and watch these "patrician horses" pulling the long trains of wagons. But oxen were shipped in to pull the heavy loads of machinery and boilers in wet weather. When pulling these through quagmires, they sometimes sank up to their bellies in mud.

No expense was spared to keep the horses in fine fettle and to maintain for them the best of equipment. The Percheron horses wore harness that cost more than a complete ensemble for a well-dressed woman. The hames were incased in sixteen-inch housing, made in West Virginia and weighing seventeen pounds. Each set of

[22] Ranger *Daily Times*, March 16, 1920.

153

harness contained 600 rings, ranging in size from one inch to three inches. The cost of the housing was $35, the rings $150, and the harness $150, making the gear for one team cost $670.[23] A horse's headdress was made of red flannel and green poolcloth, with strings of white rings and loops laced by a leather strap and with long red tassels hanging from their headbands.

The oil field had many miles of pipe line, with Ranger as the center of these arteries of steel. Most of the major companies either started lines from refining centers toward Ranger or built branch lines to the new field. Four pipe lines were built to each of the fully three thousand wells that dotted the field—a high pressure gas line to operate the engine or boiler, a water main to cool the engine and furnish water for steam, a pipe line to carry away the oil, and another to deliver "wet" gas to the casing-head plants. Feeding and gathering lines radiated like octopus arms from the mains, while the mains extended over hills and valleys. Seven major pipe-line systems—the Texas, the Prairie, the Humble, the Magnolia, the Sinclair, the United Producers, and the Gulf—radiated from the field—northward to the Great Lakes, southward to the Gulf of Mexico refineries, or eastward to other refineries.

Ranger had a few small refineries and a casing-head plant but no large refineries. However, major and small company tank farms provided storage for more than ten million barrels of crude oil.

A human deluge inundated the Ranger oil field, month by month, during the hectic years of flush production. Men came from every direction and from every walk of life—financiers, businessmen, promoters, and investors; contractors, lease men, land men, company lawyers, abstracters, and scouts; mule-skinners, tool dressers, roustabouts, drillers, carpenters, rig builders; merchants, and vendors; restaurant men and hotel keepers; professional men; and people of every persuasion, including criminals and thugs. They came from widely separated places, from Pennsylvania to California and from Canada to Mexico. Some were from Russia and Romania, and from Egypt, India, and the isles of the sea,[24] which, when added to the native classes, formed a varied social amalgam.

[23] *Ibid.*, 1919–39 (Twentieth Anniversary edition), 41; Wagner, *op. cit.*, 47.
[24] "Ranger Is Country's Newest and Most Picturesque Boom Town," *loc. cit.*

The Ranger Oil Boom

Ranger quickly overflowed its population bounds into suburban and neighboring community districts. Tent and shack towns sprang up. Shacks of rough boards, part wagon box, sheet iron, and tar paper—dirty, greasy, and unkempt—sprawled irregularly and closely spaced in the valleys and on the hills about town. Some housed the oil-field workers; and others were hell holes—gambling places and rowdy dance halls and all manner of vicious establishments. In and around these, like moths about a candle, gathered unsavory characters—men and women suited to squalor and filth.

This social backwash infested Ranger as well as the near-by oil field. Whiskey dives, "cabarets," and gambling halls defied the law. There were such places as the Blue Mouse Cabaret, on South Austin Street, and the Grizzly Bear in the same block. Then in the next block was the Oklahoma Cabaret, and across the street, the Jensen Cabaret. Later there were the Wilson Cabaret and others. Each of these places furnished "entertainment" for oil-field workers. Gambling, whiskey, and "working" women contributed an atmosphere that bred crime and violence.

Small wonder Ranger had five murders in one twenty-four-hour period and that during the next several months thugs shot at Peace Officer Ingram twenty-seven times (without a hit). Car thieves, hoodlums, and crooks of every sort stalked the streets at night. It was not unusual in the morning to find the body of a dead man in a street or alley. One night two "toughs" held up the Oklahoma Cabaret, took its cash, killed a policeman who chanced to be present, backed out the door, and fled. They barricaded themselves in a roominghouse; but angry citizens aided the officers, surrounded the house, and helped to arrest the two men, who were sent to the penitentiary for long terms.

The crime wave was broken by two spectacular events. Adjutant General Thomas D. Barton of Texas had kept an eye on Ranger's lawlessness. It was publicly known all through North Texas that Ranger's Commercial Hotel was being operated as a gambling house and saloon. He therefore sent Captain R. W. Aldrich to make arrests. Aldrich arrived at Cisco on Friday night, February 11, 1922, and was met by Rangers Sam Walker, M. N. Koonsman, and W. L. Lesueur from Breckenridge, and by County Attorney Dunnam. He drove with the combined party to Ranger, making a detour of

155

Eastland so that friends of Cleve Barnes and Alf Jordon, operators of the Commercial Hotel gambling hall, could not give warning of the Rangers' approach.

Aldrich's coup was completely successful. A few minutes before ten o'clock on Saturday night, while the gambling resort was crowded, the peace officers deployed about the building. Aldrich sent Koonsman and Walker up the fire escape at the rear, and he and Lesueur entered the front and climbed the stairs to the third floor, where the gaming tables were located. The gamblers were caught red handed, ninety of them, ten or a dozen others having escaped. The Rangers also took much gambling paraphernalia, and cards and money from the tables.

Aldrich took his prisoners before Justice of the Peace McFatter; but "Kid" Jordan, one of the proprietors, appeared and assured McFatter that he and his partner, Cleve Barnes, would stand good for the prisoners' appearance in justice court the next morning. True to his promise, Jordan appeared and paid the fines of eighty-seven of the men, three others having been proved innocent.[25]

The local Rotary Club delivered the final body blow to Ranger's crime wave. In 1922 members of this civic organization, aided by policemen, raided liquor joints and gambling dens, seized liquor valued at $16,000, and poured it into the streets. Aldrich said that the Commercial Hotel could not have been operated so openly "without the knowledge of the local peace officers."[26] Knowing that an aroused citizenship would tolerate racketeering and crime no longer, the gamblers, hoodlums, and even a peace officer or two left town.

This concluded Ranger's experiences as described by Mr. Dudley. Yet its swirling crowds, wild speculation, traffic congestion, mud, growing pains, and lawlessness were little different from those of Electra, Burkburnett, and other oil fields that had preceded it. The oil industry had not yet reached maturity, when orderly development, deep drilling, heavy costs, scientific exploration, and state control of production helped to eliminate chaos and waste.

[25] *Report of State Ranger and Martial Law Activities of the National Guard of Texas, 1921 and 1922*, 3–4; Ranger *Daily Times*, March 18, 1921. The musty old record book of the Justice of the Peace is yet in the possession of a Ranger hardware merchant, who during the oil-boom days served as justice of the peace.
[26] *Ibid.*, 4.

The Ranger Oil Boom

Early in 1919 North Central Texas was described as "slopping over" with oil. It was admitted, however, that Ranger seemed "to have fallen into the 60,000 bbl.-per-day class" and would probably do no better, although later in that year it reached a peak of 73,000 barrels a day from 636 wells spaced over 120 square miles. But the field soon "blew its top" (its reservoir energy) and then began a swift decline. Ranger crowds dispersed, going to Desdemona, Breckenridge, or other Texas fields; banks failed; businesses moved out; and deflated Ranger groaned under a heavy bonded indebtedness. Wallace Pratt says that Humble hired him as its chief geologist because of his knowledge of Ranger and that the Standard Oil Company of New Jersey bought a one-half interest in Humble on the strength of the company's Ranger holdings. And then Ranger "plopped"![27]

[27] Pratt to E. DeGolyer, March 2, 1945, in DeGolyer papers, Dallas, Texas.

XII

Desdemona and Breckenridge

B Y 1920, Ranger, Desdemona, and Breckenridge had seen little
of Edward L. Doheny's "oil age," referred to in the previous
chapter, if it meant new techniques. Cable-tool drilling rigs,
eighty-four-foot wooden derricks, ox-drawn freight wagons, indiscriminate prospecting and well-location, bogus company stock
operations, and profligate waste were yet common.

Still, oil promoters favored "surface geology." If a geologist
recommended a certain surface structure, the promoter was inclined to lease it. Then he drew prominent businessmen into his enterprise. Often astute bankers, merchants, and manufacturers, having had great success in their own business, were persuaded to
enter this gamble, ignorant of its hazards and not able to resist the
tantalizing lure of fabulous wealth. Their previous successes were
worth little in their new roles.[1]

Science was late in coming to the oil industry. At best the early-
day oil industry was financially hazardous, even for the most seasoned oilman, for geology, engineering, electric prospecting, and
logging were yet in their infancy. For example, in 1918, 25,687 wells
were drilled in the United States, of which 17,845 were oil wells,
2,229 gas, and 5,613 dry.[2] Since the average cost of drilling a well
was $11,144, the total expenditure for dry holes was enormous.

But occasionally wildcatters blundered into success. One has
but to call the roll of early-day oil fields to find this. It was true at
Ranger and at Hogtown, although scientific exploration was occasionally employed at both places. Hogtown was a small inland
village which stood near the boundaries of Comanche, Eastland,

[1] An interesting account of this period's prospecting and promoting is found in
J. C. Yancey, *Why and Where Oil Is Found,* 17 ff.

158

and Erath counties, south of Ranger, in a region of rolling hills and scrub mesquite, elm, and oak. It was on the sloping banks of seepy Hog Creek[3] and was like many another inland Texas town of the Cross Timbers—poor, static, and all but dead, although neighboring farmers fared well. Reaching back from the village of one or two tumble-down stores (that featured tobacco, snuff, sardines, and a little flour), a blacksmith shop, a gin, and a post office were sun-baked farms and ranches.[4] It was a fine country for watermelon, fruit, cattle, horses, and large families; but there was practically no one who had any inkling that it would ever become one of the richest spots in North Central Texas.

Yet Hogtown's settlers had resolute faith. If Strawn had oil, why could it not be found at Hogtown? Indications were just as promising. Some argued that "damp gas" in many community wells was the same gas that was in Strawn oil wells, that oil was on the water in Hog Creek and its tributaries. One man said that by studying a map he had proved that if a straight line were drawn from Petrolia on the north to Strawn on the south, it would also pass through Hogtown.

Hogtown settlers voted to back this belief with money. On the evening of February 2, 1914, approximately one hundred citizens met in the Hog Creek schoolhouse about two miles south of town and formally launched the Hog Creek Oil Company. The presiding officer appointed a committee to write a constitution and by-laws, to lease the surrounding farms, and to buy a cable-tool drilling rig. The Hog Creek Oil Company financed its own well by the sale of stock. A member of the company was permitted to purchase only a limited amount of the stock, at ten dollars a share.

When the company had raised between $1,200 and $1,500, it spudded in its test well on the west side of Hog Creek, on a small plot of ground owned by the village barber, J. W. Carruth. When the well reached about 900 feet, funds were exhausted and drilling was stopped. Another assessment was made on the members, and drilling was resumed until the well reached more than 1,500 feet, where it was finally abandoned.[5] Had this well been located one

[2] *Petroleum Facts and Figures* (First edition), 119.

[3] Tradition has it that Hog Creek was so called because early settlers allowed their hogs to feed on acorns from the post oaks growing along the creek's banks.

[4] Mrs. George Langston, *History of Eastland County.*

hundred yards farther north, it would have been the field's discovery well.

A short time later, Tom Dees, an Oklahoman, came to Hogtown and leased about 2,000 acres of land. He moved in a Star rig and began drilling just a short distance up the hill from the first well, but soon he, too, ran short of funds and abandoned the well.

Before Dees' well was drilled, R. O. Harvey and associates of Wichita Falls, Texas, sent two men to Hogtown to examine the country and procure leases. One of these was W. E. Wrather,[6] geologist, and the other was L. H. Cullum, lease operator. Shortly after their arrival, while exploring a creek on George Knowles' place, the geologist Wrather found an anticline which he thought to be oil-bearing.

Then on the night of October 1, 1917, Cullum met community farmers in a second schoolhouse mass meeting, out of which grew a new Hog Creek Oil Company, from which the Harvey group leased more than 6,000 acres of land at two dollars an acre.[7]

The Maples Oil and Gas Company contracted to drill a Hog Creek well for half-interest in a 5,000-acre lease. This company, composed of F. B. Barrett, Mike Benedum, Joe Trees, John Kirkland, and others, let the drilling contract to Pete Hoffman of Illinois, who shipped his rig to DeLeon, from which point it was hauled by wagon through the country to a site picked by Wrather on Joe Duke's farm.[8]

This was the well that blew in as a strong gasser on the night of September 2, 1918. The well caught fire from the tool dresser's forge and lighted up the countryside, causing a large crowd to assemble. After three days, Harvey succeeded in extinguishing the flames with high-pressure steam from four boilers. By September

[5] John Derwin Palmer, "History of the Desdemona Oil Boom" (unpublished Master's thesis, Hardin-Simmons University, August, 1938), 7 ff.

[6] At the present Mr. Wrather is director of the United States Geological Survey in Washington, D. C.

[7] The Minute Book of the Hog Creek Oil Company is now in possession of J. R. Palmer of Stephenville, Texas, who served as secretary of the meeting and who supplied the author with copies of the minutes of October 1, 6, 10, 13, 16, and December 18, 1917, and August 13, 1918. At the meeting of October 6, Cullum agreed to bring to Desdemona a standard rig, to drill a well to the depth of 3,500 feet, providing oil were not found at a shallower depth, if the Hog Creek Oil Company on its part would lease 5,000 acres of land.

[8] Palmer, op. cit., 10 ff.

the well was completed as a 2,000-barrel oil producer from a black lime formation at 2,960 feet.

As at Ranger, thousands of people rushed to Desdemona, as Hogtown was now called. The town came to life much as Ranger had. A land of peanuts, corn, and cotton suddenly blossomed into an oil field. Leases were sold at extraordinarily high prices. Unlike Ranger, where most of the first leases were in the hands of one large company, Desdemona was a small-company oil field. R. O. Harvey *et al.* had only 6,000 acres; his block did not include some of the most profitable leases. Numbers of operators and small companies, therefore, rushed in to secure valuable properties. Some leases were large, but many were small. In one instance, a lease was let for one-hundredth of an acre.

By the last of October the No. 1 Duke well was gauged at an estimated daily flow of 3,840 barrels of oil; and the Knowles well, about two hundred yards south and west of the No. 1 Duke, the next to be drilled, came in with an estimated daily production of 8,000 barrels. Then came No. 2 Duke, a larger well than No. 1 Duke. Harvey *et al.* (including Kell, Kemp, and others), Benedum Trees and Company, and the newly created Tex-Pen Company soon started ten more wells in the immediate vicinity, and by January of the next year had proved the new field as a heavy producer. Indeed, by January, 1919, literally hundreds of wells were being drilled. Four hundred yards southeast of the Duke was the famous Payne gasser, with an estimated daily flow of 30,000,000 to 40,000,-000 cubic feet of gas that could be heard twenty-five miles away. The Hogg well, one mile northwest of the No. 1 Duke, was the field's major producer—with an estimated 15,000 barrels of oil per day.[9]

As the oil field developed, the Desdemona townsite was one of its richest parts. But the field was soon found to be not so large as had been believed. A rectangle drawn one-half mile south of the Duke well, extending three miles north of the Duke, one mile east and two miles west, included Desdemona's heaviest producing area.

Transportation facilities could not adequately care for production. Steel tanks soon overflowed, and earthen reservoirs and dams

[9] John D. Palmer, "Glimpses of the Desdemona Oil Boom," in West Texas Historical Association *Year Book*, Vol. XV (October, 1939), 51.

across creeks and gulleys were made. On one occasion traffic between DeLeon and Desdemona was blocked by a stream of oil three feet deep flowing across the road.

Jake Hamon's Wichita Falls, Ranger and Fort Worth Railroad building northward from Dublin promised a quick outlet for Desdemona oil and a boost for the town, but when local citizens could not raise $200,000 to support the road, the promoter built, a short distance south of Desdemona, his own town, known as Jakehamon, and is believed to have reaped a fortune in town-lot sales. But after the boom Jakehamon became a ghost town.[10]

Much of the oil from the first wells had to be hauled to near-by towns in tank wagons; but pipe lines were soon laid to the railroad at Gorman and DeLeon. The Humble Oil and Refining Company was shortly in the field, although Magnolia took care of most of the oil transportation, storage, and refining. A number of independent refineries were built at Desdemona, and others were constructed at Stephensville, Gorman, and Dublin. Meanwhile, the Humble Oil and Refining Company began building its Comyn station and an eight-inch pipe line from Stephens County to Houston, through Comyn, six miles west of Dublin.[11]

Pipe-line crude-oil runs measured to a large degree Desdemona's importance as an oil field. Because of a lack of transportation facilities, this field reported no pipe-line runs until September, at which time, in one month, 19,871 barrels of crude oil were gathered; and DeLeon, Desdemona's chief loading center, reported 757,510 barrels. In addition, a part of Desdemona oil was being loaded at Kennison and Comyn stations. In September, 1920, however, Desdemona showed an astonishing decline when it loaded only 87,-506 and DeLeon 129,635 barrels, with a corresponding decrease in pipe-line runs at Comyn and Ranger. Both Desdemona and Ranger had reached their peak production in July and August, 1919.[12]

[10] The Ranger *Daily Times* of September 15, 1919, proclaimed, "This new town in the heart of the Duke-Knowles Field will be opened on Monday, September 22."

[11] Stephenville *Tribune*, March 28, August 15, and September 5, 1919; Dublin *Progress*, April 11, May 2, September 12, 1919; and Gorman *Progress*, March 17, June 2, and June 16, 1921.

[12] Texas Railroad Commission reports, 1919, 527–30; 1920, 151–59.

Desdemona and Breckenridge

Desdemona dropped from its peak of 7,375,825 barrels of crude oil a year to 2,767,115 barrels by 1920.[13]

Gas venting was a cause of Desdemona's oil-field decline. Producers gave little thought to conservation. Ofter a gas well was allowed to flow for weeks in the hope that it might blow into an oil well; and "gushers were allowed to gush" to promote oil-stock sale and to satisfy curious visitors who had never before seen a flowing oil well. An early-day Desdemona observer has recently stated that one-half this field's potential output was lost because of the producers' ignorance of conservation methods. Within less than a year many of the flowing wells became pumpers.

The pay zone was lime shale, and the oil contained so much paraffin that within a few days after a well was completed, the paraffin would completely clog the well, so that it would go dry or produce a very small amount of oil. Several methods were tried to reopen wells, the most common of which was to run the tools every three or four days. This was sufficient agitation, but at the same time it was expensive to keep a string of tools hanging in a completed well and a crew sufficiently large to handle the work of agitation, when each man drew from $14 to $18 a day.

During 1918 and 1919, North Central Texas was oil mad. Millions were invested and millions taken out in profits and other millions lost in wildcat operations. Yet North Central Texas oil production in 1919 was twice as great as in 1918. In 1918 the output amounted to 20,384,915 barrels of crude oil; in 1919, to 53,385,915 barrels, valued at over $120,000,000.

Naturally, widespread, intensive prospecting was inaugurated. The geographic extent of the oil-producing area was staggering to the mind. In a territory embracing Young County on the north and Brown County on the south, and from a line drawn north and south through Fort Worth, west to a line drawn similarly through Amarillo, a territory that prior to 1917 produced only a few hundred barrels of oil daily, by the end of the next year brought to the surface millions of barrels. A few months after the No. 1 Duke well was found, fields constantly widened, with wildcatters drilling in more than fifty counties. North Texas counties that showed production by the close of 1918 were Wichita, Wilbarger, and Archer; and

[13] *Texas Almanac,* 1927, 259.

in North Central Texas, Palo Pinto, Eastland, Comanche, Brown, and Stephens.

The industry's big fellows literally threw money into North Central Texas wildcat prospecting. By 1919 their discoveries called for a maze of pipe lines and a large refinery movement, with plants, in various stages of progress, at centrally located points. Places where refineries were in operation, under construction, or proposed, were Dallas, with four refineries operating and one building; Ranger, three operating, two under construction, and four proposed; Fort Worth, seven operating and five building; Brownwood, four operating; Cisco, two; Electra, two; and other towns in the area with one or more.[14]

The finding of the Breckenridge oil field, about thirty-five miles north of Ranger, was the third outstanding event in North Central Texas oil history; and it, too, led to the discovery of near-by pools, such as at South Bend. At Breckenridge, cowboys ceased to be cowboys and farmers left the farm; schoolteachers became prospectors and promoters; and clerks grew rich on leases and royalties, although hundreds of investors lost their savings.

In the early fall of 1911 three prospectors, Messrs. Miller, Puffenburg, and Perkins, calling themselves the California Oil Company, came to Stephens County and leased the W. H. Green and J. W. Crudington properties. Then they sank a test well on the Crudgington farm, eight miles northwest of Breckenridge; but after drilling 2,400 feet without finding oil, they abandoned the well and left the country.

Caddo was the first of the Stephens County towns to enjoy oil prosperity. In May, 1916, a small amount of oil was found on the W. L. Carey farm near town, at a depth of 2,740 feet. A short time later the L. W. Wright well at the edge of town came in for approximately 300 barrels of crude daily and continued as a small producer for about three years. The R. Q. Lee well beside the highway, one mile east of Caddo, was the next producer, and was pumped profitably for four years. The Manning well, one and one-half miles east of town, was a better producer, with an estimated daily flow of 2,500 barrels. But the Sandidge well, in 1918, was the field's best, flowing an estimated 15,000 barrels a day. The field was limited, however, and its average output was small.

Desdemona and Breckenridge

Breckenridge, the county seat of Stephens County, according to Judge Caldwell, "ran a population of about 600 in the summer to 800 or 1,000 in the winter while school was 'on.' "[15] By 1919 or 1920 its population had grown to 40,000 living within two miles of the courthouse.

In 1911, prior to the beginning of drilling about Breckenridge, the Producers Oil Company, The Texas Company's producing branch, had secured leases to 50,000 acres of land south and southeast of town, paying the nominal sum of ten cents an acre for a ten-year period. Later, in 1914, the Gulf Production Company also leased several thousand acres, paying twenty-five cents an acre. The Texas Company did the first drilling, on the Park Ranch, eight or nine miles south of Breckenridge, and brought in a small producer; but their No. 2 well, drilled a short distance from the first, was better. Yet neither well started a Breckenridge boom, as had the No. 1 McCleskey at Ranger. Nor did the No. 1 Lauderdale well, northwest of the No. 1 Parks; nor, at first, the No. 1 Smith gas well.

But when the Smith gasser turned into an oil well, spraying oil on the surrounding mesquite and post oaks, the boom was on. Royalty prices leaped, leases soared, and thousands of oil hunters, shyster lawyers, lease men, big company representatives, and the usual oil-field hangers-on rushed in from depleted Petrolia, from the yet important Electra, and from flush-producing Burkburnett on the north; and from the booming fields of Ranger, Desdemona, and Sipe Springs on the south. "The streets are crowded with traffic to the outlying fields day and night," said a visitor.[16] The newcomers were rough and ready and experienced in hazardous oil play. "Catch as catch can" and "no holds barred" were their only creeds.

The No. 1 Stoker launched Breckenridge's townsite drilling. But the No. 1 Chaney, on February 4, 1918, was more important; it blew in for a huge production.[17] Two hundred derricks rose in town, and within five years two thousand oil rigs could be seen from the top of the courthouse.

In some instances owners of 50x100-foot lots became wealthy.

[14] *Derrick's Hand-Book,* IV (1916–19), 29, 43.

[15] C. M. Caldwell to C. C. Rister, March 27, 1946.

[16] Alf Burr, "North Central Texas Has Many Big Wells," in *Oil Trade Journal,* Vol. XII, No. 5 (May, 1921), 26–28.

[17] Dallas *Morning News,* July 30, 1920.

Neighboring towns had refused permits to drill within the corporate limits; but not so Breckenridge. Here property owners effected agreements whereby within a block they would share their interests in such oil as might be found. A lease on their lot was then offered to someone who wished to drill.

Townsite drilling brought almost certain success. "It is claimed," said W. G. Steret, "that not one well in this two and a half miles (city limits after incorporation) has been drilled that was not proved to be a fine producer."[18]

On September 1, 1921, Humble's No. 1 Keithly blew in at 3,648 feet, and by afternoon of the second day it was making an estimated 60,000,000 feet of gas daily, spraying oil and salt water, blown by the wind, for a distance of two and one-half miles; but after two weeks it was brought under control. Finally, on January 1, 1921, Breckenridge reached its peak production of 115,000 barrels of crude oil a day, after which its decline was rapid.

The rise and fall of Breckenridge as a major oil field is seen in the following table of production. The crash started in 1921, and

Breckenridge Crude Oil Production, 1917–25

Year	Barrels	Year	Barrels
1917	36,219	1922	14,925,000
1918	790,243	1923	10,062,000
1919	10,514,216	1924	7,129,000
1920	23,852,050	1925	5,729,000
1921	31,037,710		

within a few months it brought ruin to many a Stephens County operator. The price of oil dropped to one dollar a barrel. Many operators, hopelessly in debt but who had earlier made great riches, now turned back to their cow pastures and cotton and grain fields. There were a few, like Cliff Caldwell and Breck Walker, who had made more conservative investments and had salvaged tidy fortunes for themselves.

Most of the Breckenridge banks closed their doors in the face

[18] *Ibid.*, October 9, 1920.

of this catastrophe. A few held off insolvency for months by reorganization; then they, too, crashed. The First National Bank was saved by its loyal directors—Walker, Caldwell, Jack Black, Will Black, C. E. Martin, and Glenn Russell—who assessed themselves $1,200 each for each one-hundred-dollar share of stock they owned, making a total of $990,000. Neighboring boom towns—Necessity, Wayland, Frankell, Parks, Crystal Falls, Leeray, and Gunsight—boasted from one to three banks during the flush times, none of which survived the crash.

The oil boom's impact on Breckenridge's rate of growth and its social structure was marked. On January 1, 1920, Breckenridge's population was 1,500; and one year later 30,000. In one month it had an estimated increase of 10,000. Most of the wells shut down on week ends to pay the men, who swarmed into town, unshaven, unkempt, and smeared with crude oil. The town took on a carnival appearance, with its packed streets, its crowds sweating and milling, and its motley array of characters, some upright and others careless of morals and companions, looking for diversion. And they found it—brothels, red whiskey, cheap hamburger stands, cafés, gambling dens, and picture shows.[19] Again social chaos appeared.

Both Desdemona and Breckenridge had to contend with lawlessness because both towns had grown quickly into restless, shifting oil towns. By June, 1919, Desdemona's main business section was four blocks long, with a population of 2,000. Many who came cared little for law and order; and, indeed, many came to take advantage of the town's turbulence. Highjackers, bootleggers, prostitutes, gamblers, former convicts, and bad men generally made up the human dregs. Robbery and murder were current problems, and saloons and other establishments catering to crime and vice were run wide open without restriction. Throughout the day women solicited their "clients" about the streets, even going to the derricks. Highjackers also visited the derricks to levy their tribute on the workers. When the workers did not have money, they were told to bring it the next day and leave it at a designated place. First the American Legion and then the Texas Rangers threw their weight

[19] Loy William Hartsfield, "A Brief History of Breckenridge and the Stephens County Oil Fields," in West Texas Historical Association *Year Book,* Vol. XII (July, 1936), 111.

on the side of law, and finally the criminal population went on to other, more open fields.

The Stephens County jail records show that from 1890 to 1904 there were never more than twenty-two persons imprisoned during any one year. In contrast, during the one month of November, 1920, two hundred offenders were jailed, and down to the close of 1921 the monthly average was about two hundred lawbreakers. But with the decline of the oil field, local peace officers and Rangers drove out the criminals and thugs.

Yet oil-field improvements, promising better things, had also appeared, not only at Breckenridge but at Desdemona and Ranger. Automobiles and trucks gradually supplanted wagons and teams, dispensing with teaming contractors; new boardinghouses and company camps brought better sanitation and convenience; the rise of casing-head gasoline plants pointed toward conservation; and business and public structures were material evidences of oil's impact. Presently newly built courthouses became the scenes of mighty and heated legal battles over royalty, lease, and other oil-field problems.

By 1925 there were people who freely predicted the end of the Breckenridge oil field, who said that all its wells would soon be plugged. But acidization saved the field. Chemists had found that hydrochloric acid dissolved calcareous material just as it did in limestone wells.

This was the basis of a successful oil-well test at Breckenridge. From this beginning, the Chemical Process Company was formed and pushed its recovery work throughout the Mid-Continent area. This firm was the first commercial treating company to acidize Texas, Oklahoma, and Louisiana wells. Experience proved that 2,000 to 3,000 gallons of acid was sufficient for a well, at a cost of about $360, and that many acidized wells increased their oil output almost 100 per cent. The life of the Breckenridge field was practically doubled; and in later years, Jake Sandefer and other stripper-well operators made the wells again commercially profitable. Jake was an outstanding independent producer of this area—alert, shrewd, and everlastingly active. The Breckenridge oil field is not so spectacular today as it once was, but it is yet an active, producing oil field.

XIII

Along the Mexia Fault Zone

SINCE SPINDLETOP DAYS oilmen had believed that the Gulf Coast's salt domes were the chief oil reservoirs of Texas. Then the discovery of Electra, of Burkburnett, and of other Texas fields far removed from the Gulf Coast caused many operators to have less faith in the salt-dome theory.

Yet those who accepted the salt-dome idea offered the Gulf Coast's sustained oil output as proof of their belief. West Columbia produced 5,000,000 barrels of petroleum in 1919; 9,000,000 barrels in 1920; and 12,000,000 barrels in 1921. The Hull oil field, opened in 1918, was extensively developed during the next two years, producing more than 8,000,000 barrels of crude oil; and deeper drilling in Orange County, in the Cow Run pool, added still more to salt-dome oil, bringing the county from 470,000 barrels of oil in 1921 to 5,345,000 barrels in the next year.[1]

This increasing Gulf Coast oil output kept alive the salt-dome theory. But central East Texas discoveries, especially at Mexia and Corsicana, when added to those of North Texas, proved that oil-bearing formations could be found elsewhere in Texas, far beyond the Gulf Coast.

Corsicana had been the first of the "Mexia Fault Zone" fields, as they were called later.[2] A drill crew had found oil while drilling for water. Gas was also discovered around the turn of the century, enough to supply the town with a much-needed fuel until the field

---

[1] *Mineral Resources of the United States, 1921, Part II, Nonmetals,* 256.

[2] A term used by Frederic H. Lahee, "Mexia and Tehuacana Fault Zones," in *Structure of Typical American Oil Fields,* I, 307. See also map on page 306. E. H. Sellards and Leo Hendricks refer to the same structure as the "Luling-Mexia-Talco Fault System." See "Occurrence of Oil and Gas in Texas," in *Texas Mineral Resources,* 185–86.

declined after a few years. The gas field yielded almost the entire production of Texas until 1909, when Clay County's gas fields were developed, of which Petrolia was the most important. Petrolia sold gas to Fort Worth and Dallas until it had exhausted its supply, and its operators by 1912 had passed the initiative of finding a new source of gas back to others along the "Mexia Fault Zone."

Thus, 1912 became a year of crisis for the natural-gas industry of Texas, a year in which a new venture was launched—the Mexia Oil and Gas Company,[3] to explore the possibilities of gas near Mexia. This company, headed by Blake Smith,[4] drilled nine wells without finding more than a showing of gas, but Smith persuaded the contractor to sink two other wells for the price of one. Luckily, the eleventh and last test was completed as a dry gasser, thus securing Mexia its fuel needs with enough left over to supply Corsicana, Waco, Teague, Groesbeck, and Mart.

For a short time the Mexia gas field had large production, yielding in 1915 an estimated 2,331,057,000 cubic feet of gas. Five years later, however, like Corsicana and Petrolia, it also showed signs of exhaustion; and, in fact, from a commercial standpoint, it failed Mexia at a time (during the early nineteen twenties) when thousands of newcomers rode into town on the crest of a wild oil boom.

But stockholders of the Mexia Oil and Gas Company were not defeated. They believed that their depleted gas field was over or near an important oil pool, and they were willing to back their belief by offering a half-interest in their 2,000-acre lease block to any promoter who would drill a deep test for oil. In 1919, Colonel Albert E. Humphreys' Homaokla Oil Company rejected such an offer; but J. Julius Fohs, its consulting engineer, believed in Mexia's oil claims and joined with W. A. Reiter to drill a well. The two men secured a 3,000-acre block of leases and the support of John A. Shephard of Muskogee, Oklahoma, to put down a test well. Fohs and Reiter then

---

[3] Nanine Simmons of the J. K. Hughes Oil Company, Mexia, Texas, supplied the author with her manuscript titled, "The Mexia, Texas, Oil Field."

[4] Blake Smith formed an association of one hundred Mexia businessmen who agreed to pay $1,000 each toward the drilling of ten wells. After several dry holes had been drilled, a number of the original sponsors dropped out and refused to pay their dues, but Smith carried them in his organization until the gas well came in.— Mexia *Evening News*, November 24, 1920, p. 1, col. 3.

took over the lease holdings of Smith's Mexia Oil and Gas Company, raising their own lease block to 5,000 acres.

Shephard started his test well on the L. W. Rogers farm, three miles west of Mexia, in September, 1919. He spudded it in with a light portable rig to hold the leases, and later moved in a larger standard rig and began drilling. But the well posed many problems. At 109 feet, Kheitlinger, the driller, lost the hole and finally skidded the derrick to a new site. Here, too, he met with delays, running the expense of the test beyond Shephard's original estimate. Therefore, near the end of 1919, without funds, Shephard offered a one-half interest in the Rogers well to the highest bidder.

Humphreys, who had been watching the development of the Mexia enterprise, now re-entered the scene. He bought out Shephard's interest, except three leases, and resumed drilling.

Humphreys, formerly a Colorado silver miner, was not an oil-field tenderfoot. He and Fohs had been among the first operators at Boynton and Blackwell, Oklahoma. They had blocked acreage at Billings, had found the eastern extension of the Pine Island pool, Louisiana, and had discovered and owned most of the available acreage in the Big Muddy pool of Wyoming. They had also operated near Nocona, Texas, and in Montague County and elsewhere, and understood the hazards of the oil game.[5]

Some of Humphreys' friends thought that the Mexia venture was his greatest gamble in that it seemed less likely to be successful than anything he had hitherto undertaken; but they were wrong. On November 19, 1920,[6] the Rogers well came in, justifying the local diehards' faith in Mexia's oil possibilities. The well had a daily average of only fifty barrels of oil, but it stimulated Humphreys and his associates to undertake more extensive operations.

A trace of oil had showed in the No. 1 Rogers well earlier in November, and Humphreys instructed his driller to cease drilling. Then he began the erection of a 1,600-barrel tank and completed

[5] For a readable account of the Balcones Fault development, see P. J. R. MacIntosh, "The Wonder Story of Texas Oil," in *Texas Monthly*, Vol. II (July–December, 1928), 597–611.

[6] Prentiss T. Moore, "Mexia Well Making Slow But Steady Flows," in *Oil Trade Journal*, Vol. XII, No. 1 (January, 1921), 20. See also Mexia *Evening News*, Saturday, November 20, 1920, p. 1, col. 3; November 22, p. 1, col. 3. These and other copies were supplied by Editor Womack.

arrangements with The Texas Company for a small pipe line to the field and a loading rack at Mexia. In addition, he and Fohs perfected two new organizations, the Humphreys-Mexia and the Humphreys-Texas companies.[7] After completing these organizations, Humphreys leased 12,000 acres of land about the well, including acreage along the fault line and about Mexia and Groesbeck. Then the well was completed.

Fohs announced that it would be the policy of the Humphreys-Fohs companies "to prove up the field" and to "conserve as much of the oil as possible"; and in keeping with this proving policy, a short time later, he and Humphreys started eight new wells at Mexia and Groesbeck. Next, they purchased a 352-acre refinery site from Joseph Nussbaum and Company, two miles south of Mexia, and made arrangements with the H. and T. C. Railroad for the building of a dam to impound a 135-acre lake for the use of the refinery and the railroad shops.[8]

It was not until 1921, when the Mexia yearly oil output stepped up to 5,500,000 barrels, that the full significance of the No. 1 Rogers discovery was realized. By May, 1921, the boom had gained headway, when Humphreys completed his second well, the No. 1 Blake Smith, as a 300-barrel well, and several derricks were marking Mexia's western sky line, over an area approximately seven miles long north and south. One mile northwest of Mexia the Occidental Oil Corporation also completed its No. 1 Liles well for 500 barrels of crude oil daily.

But "Mexia . . . pushed itself into the limelight," said an oil field correspondent, when the No. 1 Henry well came in, a short distance southwest of Mexia and south of the discovery well.[9] Its initial flow was estimated at 1,200 to 1,500 barrels of crude oil daily and by the latter part of the week it had almost doubled its flow.

Sensational well completions continued. The No. 1 Desenberg, drilled by the Western Oil Corporation, at a depth of 3,059 feet spouted a black stream of oil over its 110-foot derrick on Sunday morning, August 21, 1921, flowing at the rate of 18,000 barrels every

[7] Mexia *Evening News*, September 23, 1920, p. 1, col. 3–4; *ibid.*, November 26, 1920, p. 1, col. 3.

[8] Moore, *loc. cit.*, 19–20; Mexia *Evening News*, December 3, 1920, p. 1, col. 3.

[9] Fort Worth *Star-Telegram*, May 9, 1921, p. 13, col. 5; Mexia *Evening News*, May 9, 1921, p. 1, cols. 2–5.

twenty-four hours.[10] Later in the day, the No. 1 Adamson turned out to be the largest well in the field, producing hourly 1,000 barrels of oil.

Overnight the news of these two gushers spread, and literally streams of people poured into Mexia, formerly a sleepy little Cotton Belt Railroad town. Mexia bulged at the seams, jumping from a population of 4,000 to 40,000 within a few days. Hotels, rooming houses, and private homes were wholly unable to supply the necessary accommodations. Many visitors spread newspaper pallets on a green sward in front of the *News* office, or slept in their automobiles, in tents, or on the freight-depot platform.

Transportation facilities were equally inadequate, and the Dallas-Houston highway that ran through Mexia was swamped with people and supplies headed for the new oil bonanza. Hacks, buggies, and wagons predominated, although automobiles were also present in a limited number.

Daily, new derricks helped to define the field. Mexia's so-called "Golden Lane," its heaviest oil-producing area, was about one-half mile wide, the derricks extending in a continuous line along the fault. During 1921 this field's oil output increased steadily, the total being nearly 5,000,000 barrels. Next year it rose to 35,120,000 barrels, and continued to increase until February 12, 1922, when a single day's production reached 176,000 barrels of crude oil. This was the peak, after which the field began the usual decline, well after well going on the pump.[11]

Fohs and Humphreys did not wait for the field's depletion; they continued their exploratory work, and on December 14, 1921, brought in the Currie pool in Navarro County, midway between Corsicana and Mexia. Currie was never a large pool, its peak output being about 13,000 barrels daily from twenty-two wells. A Kosse well in the next year produced at the rate of several thousand barrels of oil a day, for about two days; then it stopped producing and was afterwards ringed by dry holes, mute evidence of the cost of wildcatting.

[10] Simmons MS, 6.

[11] In January, 1923, the Humphreys interests still owned a large part of the field's daily production—about one-third of the field's 60,000 barrels a day.—*Oil Weekly*, Vol. XVIII, No. 1 (January 6, 1923), 33.

Oil! Titan of the Southwest

Notwithstanding Mexia's decline in oil production, in 1922 Texas attained a new record in petroleum production, with a yield of 118,684,000 barrels, a 12 per cent increase over the previous year. But Oklahoma continued to lead the oil parade with 149,571,000 barrels, or 30 per cent of the nation's total output.

Luling, in the cedar and post-oak country, fifty-four miles east of San Antonio, where the Mexia Fault crossed the San Marcos River, was the scene of the next major oil play. Here an Easterner, Edgar B. Davis of Brockton, Massachusetts, was to hoist his flag among the great wildcatters of Texas.

While still a young man, Davis got a job in a shoe factory and ultimately became treasurer and sales manager of the Charles A. Eaton Company. Later, his health failed and his physician recommended an ocean voyage. Edgar accepted the doctor's advice and joined his friend, Walter Mahony of New York, on a trip round the world. The two men had not passed through the Suez Canal before British fellow travelers told them about plantation rubber that could be produced at one shilling (twenty-four cents) a pound.

Davis was interested, for he knew that rubber sold on the American market at $1.25 a pound. Later he was influential in getting the United States Rubber Company to plant rubber in Sumatra and himself directed the planting of the first 5,000,000 plants in this profitable enterprise. After an association of eleven years with this company, he retired and opened an office in New York City to promote the manufacture of automobiles for the masses.[12]

Edgar Davis's brother Oscar had recently bought $75,000 of the stock of the Texas Oil and Lease Syndicate, having properties in Caldwell County. He asked Edgar to go down to Texas to manage these holdings, promising him one-third of the profits. Edgar accepted and was soon on his way to assume his new responsibilities.

There was little in the small town of Luling, with its wooden sidewalks and unpaved streets, to arouse interest. But Edgar was content; he believed that God had sent him to Luling. He took over his brother's and associates' interests, helping to form the United North and South Oil Company by absorbing the holdings of the

[12] Davis to Rister, April 21, 1948. Mr. Davis also supplied a copy of his Thanksgiving address at the Twenty-fifth Anniversary Jubilee Celebration of the discovery of the No. 1 Rios.

Texas Southern Oil and Lease Syndicate and by giving the stockholders share for share in the new company.

Presently the Mozelle well was completed as a dry hole and two other wells were started—one on the Cartwright tract and another on the Thompson lease. They were also dry holes. Then Oscar lost interest in his Texas holding and sold it to Edgar, who, in order to buy, was forced to sell British war bonds at a loss of two dollars on the pound. The company drilled three other wells simultaneously, one of them the No. 1 Rios, which on August 9, 1922, came in as a flowing well of about 300 barrels of oil daily.

With the bringing in of the No. 1 Rios, Davis's toughest fight had just begun. "I was broke," he writes. "I had to sell my fine New York office furniture, and my Packard car to get money to come to Texas. We could not meet the payroll and I hope never to forget the loyal support of our office force and the men in the field. . . . Then providentially, I always have thought, Miss Mabel A. Johnson, my Brockton secretary (now Mrs. Lundgren) discovered at my summer home at Buzzards Bay, Massachusetts, a block of securities which I had forgotten . . . and which kept us going for a while."[13] Then the completion of the No. 2 Rios and other good wells brought better times.

Among the men who came to Luling after the completion of the No. 1 Rios were Magnolia officials, who later agreed to buy 1,000,000 barrels of oil at fifty cents a barrel. This contract furnished Davis with desperately needed funds to develop his property. Magnolia not only laid a pipe line to the field but also loaned the United North and South $300,000. Later, on June 11, 1926, Davis sold his interests to Magnolia for $12,100,000, half in cash and half in oil.[14] At that time the field had 215 wells producing about 17,000 barrels of oil daily, proof enough that Davis's faith was amply rewarded.

Meanwhile, Corsicana, twenty-nine miles north of Mexia, basked in the glory of her early-day oil-discovery tradition, although the town still profited from its shallow wells. But now it was shocked into action by the prolific Powell oil field, eight miles east of town.

[13] Davis MS, 3.
[14] Kenneth Foree, Jr., *Citizen of Luling*, 8.

Oil! Titan of the Southwest

January 7, 1923, was the date of Corsicana's awakening, with the oil discovery at near-by Powell. The occasion was the Corsicana Deep Well Company's[15] No. 1 J. H. Burke well strike, eight miles southeast of town, Sunday at midnight, flowing by heads at the rate of 350 barrels daily from the top of the Woodbine sand at about 2,970 feet.

Next day, the editor of the *Sun* wrote: "People are registered at the various hotels in the city from every section of the United States —New York; Chicago; Cincinnati; Lancaster, Philadelphia, and Scranton, Pennsylvania; Dallas, Fort Worth, Waco, Houston, Mexia, and Kosse, Texas; and many other cities too numerous to mention."

The townsmen held their breath. Hardly had they ceased their shouts of enthusiasm when the well choked with cavings. To solve this problem, the Humphreys' interests agreed to put up $50,000 to complete the well and to drill an offset, if the Corsicana company would furnish Humphreys with 5,000,000 barrels of crude at seventy cents a barrel when its properties were developed.

After this deal the Corsicana Deep Well Company erected derricks for two additional tests, and the Humphreys Company also started two wells on its J. O. Burke fifty-acre lease, about one-half mile south of the discovery well. Also Cosden's No. 1 J. V. Bounds well soon blew in while the tools were being run, and flowed at the rate of 1,000 barrels of oil a day. And on the west side of the field, at 3,215 feet, The Texas Company's No. 2 Slaughter well picked up the pay sand and made several heads of about forty barrels of oil.[16]

Then there followed a short period of decline when wells drilled on three sides of the No. 1 Burke test filled with salt water; and it was not until May 5 that interest was revived by the J. K. Hughes Development Company's No. 1 McKie, an 8,000-barrel gusher, about one and one-half miles southeast of the discovery well. But as a crew of fourteen men arrived to begin their "tower" (shift) and came up on the derrick floor to install a control-head, the well burst

---

[15] The Corsicana Deep Well Company's officers were W. H. Warren, president; R. K. Blackshear, secretary; and R. A. Caldwell, treasurer. Its capital was $100,000, and its shares had a face value of $10 each.—*National Petroleum News*, Vol. XV (January 10, 1923), 51; Corsicana *Daily Sun*, January 8, 1923, p. 1; *ibid.*, January 9, 1923, p. 1.

[16] "New Producing Area Opened by Wildcat Near Corsicana," in *Oil Weekly*, Vol. XXVIII, No. 1 (January 13, 1923), 33.

into flames and burned them to death. The fire raged for eleven days before it was brought under control.[17] Then the well was gauged as a 5,200-barrel producer of 36-degree gravity oil from a depth of 2,841 to 2,844 feet.

On May 26 the Thompson well reached the Woodbine sand at 2,911 feet and roared in as a 12,000-barrel producer, starting a major boom. The country was alive with big-company land men and independent scouts. A steady stream of trucks and wagons, moving in derrick timbers, rotary outfits, camp houses, and miscellaneous equipment, from Mexia and elsewhere, choked the roads at all hours of the day and night; and field men from Arkansas, Oklahoma, and Texas flocked into Corsicana seeking employment.

Major companies hastened to develop offset properties; and pipe-liners, who heretofore had waited for developments, worked feverishly to connect with the new production. The Prairie Oil and Gas Company built a four-inch line from Currie, as did Humble, and the Humphreys Company completed another. The Texas Company extended its six-inch line from the Corsicana pump station; and Sinclair started surveying a right-of-way from Mexia.[18] Oilfield installations spread as if by magic, with derricks crowding the sky line.

On October 22, 1923, Powell had a total of 322 wells, the output of each averaging daily 567 barrels of petroleum. The producing area extended from a point about one-half mile north of the village of Navarro in a north-northeast direction to a point approximately one mile west of south of the small town of Powell, from which the field got its name. The south end of the field was the richest part, with the two-thirds of a mile–square John Harris survey producing more than one-half the flush production. The remaining or older area's output was approximately 140,000 barrels.[19] As in other Texas oil fields where little thought was given to gas conservation, the reservoir pressure soon declined, the water table moved up the slope of the formation, and daily production declined to 150,000

[17] Corsicana *Daily Sun*, Wednesday, May 9, 1923, p. 1; *ibid.*, May 10, 1923, p. 1; and May 21, 1923, p. 1.

[18] *Oil Weekly*, Vol. XXIX, No. 6 (June 16, 1923), 40.

[19] Paul Wagner, "Powell Tops Santa Fe Springs in Flush Output of Production," in *National Petroleum News*, Vol. XV, No. 44 (October 31, 1923), 25.

Oil! Titan of the Southwest

barrels of oil. Powell reached its peak on November 13, 1923, with 354,893 barrels of oil daily; but during 1924 it still was a major field, yielding 40,000,000 barrels.[20]

Mexia Fault Zone Fields, 1921–27[21]

Week Ended	Daily Avg. Production Barrels	Week Ended	Daily Avg. Production Barrels
MEXIA			
Oct. 15, 1921	1,000	April 8, 1922	108,000
Nov. 19, 1921	55,000	July 20, 1922	66,000
Jan. 14, 1922	147,000	Sept. 17, 1927	10,000
POWELL			
June 2, 1923	5,000	Dec. 1, 1923	172,000
July 14, 1923	50,000	Dec. 15, 1923	93,000
Aug. 18, 1923	98,000	Jan. 5, 1924	77,000
Aug. 25, 1923	140,000	Mar. 8, 1924	140,000
Oct. 13, 1923	180,000	Mar. 31, 1924	98,000
Oct. 20, 1923	250,000	Jan. 3, 1925	62,000
Nov. 10, 1923	315,000	Sept. 17, 1926	15,000
Nov. 24, 1923	275,000		
WORTHAM			
Nov. 29, 1924	7,000	May 16, 1925	52,000
Dec. 27, 1924	56,000	July 25, 1925	30,000
Jan. 17, 1925	154,000	Sept. 17, 1927	3,000
Jan. 31, 1925	83,000		

Later, in July, 1926, Nigger Creek made headlines when the Transcontinental Oil Company's test on the Rosen farm, about five miles from the Mexia oil field, had an initial flow of 2,900 barrels of crude oil. There was a frenzy of leasing, with acreage selling as high as $7,000, but soon salt water appeared in the wells, and September saw the end of the boom. Other oil strikes of lesser importance at Cedar Creek, in Limestone County, and Van in Van Zandt County, were enough to keep oilmen interested in East Texas.

By 1925 the "Mexia Fault Zone" had produced 204,760,967 barrels, as the following table reveals.

[20] *Petroleum Facts and Figures* (First edition), 105.
[21] *Ibid.*, 108.

Along the Mexia Fault Zone

Mexia Fault Zone Oil Production, 1921–25[22]

	1921	1922	1923	1924	1925
Mexia-Currie	4,716,805	35,120,405	20,085,395	15,614,955	7,569,690
Corsicana-Powell	305,335	245,705	32,361,150	33,500,525	17,528,055
Luling	———————	————————	958,055	10,210,396	9,706,346
Wortham	———————	————————	————————	————————	16,838,150
Total	5,022,140	35,366,110	53,404,600	59,325,876	51,642,241

Oil, black and greasy, was literally transformed into gold, all along the "Mexia Fault Zone," from Corsicana on the north to Luling on the south, changing society, booming towns, building roads, schools, and churches, and bringing agricultural and industrial improvement. Farmers, who heretofore had eked out a precarious subsistence in the midst of poverty and squalor, now grew prosperous on lease and royalty income, or profited from oil-well production; small-town and hamlet investors received huge dividends from shares in local oil companies; and enterprising businessmen, formerly merchants, lawyers, barbers, and café proprietors, headed or were directors of newly created oil concerns. The community's oil wealth permeated every level of society.[23] For all, the several fault-zone fields, stretching brokenly across Texas, from north to south, became indeed a "golden" fault zone.[24]

[22] *The Texas Almanac and State Industrial Guide, 1927*, 258–59.

[23] Mexia, a village of 2,500 people, became a town of 25,000 to 30,000, or 50,000 if the oil field were included. This rapid rise in population brought social chaos and similar conditions at Powell, Luling, and Wortham. The bootlegger was a new kind of a leach, but he was of the same feather as the gambler, the dope peddler, and the highjacker. Befuddled peace officers could not cope with such widespread outlawry, and the Texas Rangers were called in. At Mexia, they closed the "Winter Garden," at Wortham, within 250 yards of a deputy sheriff's home, the "Chicken Farm," and other places of ill-repute, confiscating gambling devices (roulette wheels, crap, blackjack, and poker tables, and chuck-a-luck) and large amounts of whiskey, arresting 602 undesirables, and driving out the underworld leaders.

Luling's "Gander Slue," on the banks of the San Marcos River, the dividing line between Caldwell and Guadaloupe counties, where shady characters could dodge back and forth to evade the law, met the same fate. The Rangers cleaned it out. There was no local jail, so the criminals were carted away to other prisons or chained temporarily to trees. Ranger action was drastic but it brought beneficial results; the "rings," the "operators," and the "entertainers" were jailed and fined or scattered.— *Report of State Ranger and Martial Law Activities of the National Guard of Texas,* 1921 and 1922, 7; McIntosh, *loc. cit.*, 603.

[24] A contemporary authority estimated that the United States oil industry supported approximately 1,100,000 officials and employees. To this could be added operators of filling stations, placed conservatively at 225,000; stock and bond holders and owners of royalty and lease interests, 1,500,000. One-eighth of the crude oil

179

Oil! Titan of the Southwest

A short distance south of the Luling field, The Texas Company found a new and important field at Darst Creek. Its initial well, the No. 1 Dallas Wilson, was completed on July 10, 1929. The new field was developed so rapidly that by the following February it had forty-four wells and an estimated daily potential of 44,768 barrels of crude oil.

From Luling and Darst Creek, tireless wildcatters pushed southward into a new area, the Laredo district, along the Reynosa Escarpment, through Webb, Zapata, and Jim Hogg counties. And minor production was found at Mirando City, Schott, Mid-Oujelos, and Aviators. Gas fields were developed at Cole, in southwestern Duval County, east of the Escarpment, and the Carolina-Tex in Webb, north of Mirando City; but there were no major discoveries. Then in the Minerva pool, north of Rockdale, in Milam County, another Mexia Fault field was discovered, which by 1923 produced 230,000 barrels of oil; but it, too, soon started a swift decline.

Between the Powell and Mexia oil fields, Richland in Navarro County and Wortham in Limestone and Freestone counties, in 1924, were two other discoveries that added to the fault-line fields. Richland never reached major production, but Wortham for a short time promised to become a second Powell. The Boyd Oil Company, a Humphreys subsidiary, found a 2,000-barrel well in its No. 1 Boyd, on November 22, 1924, and a few days later caused considerable excitement by bringing in its No. 1 Simmons, a 10,000-barrel gusher. The field was then drilled recklessly, without regard to well-spacing and gas maintenance. Within two weeks, more than one hundred derricks dotted the field, which grew to three hundred derricks seven days later. In January, 1925, the field's output was 3,509,768 barrels of oil, but the rapid depletion of the gas pressure caused a corresponding decline in oil production.

---

produced went to landowners as royalty. In 1926 royalty oil was about 90,000,000 barrels, worth $1.60 a barrel. "All oil produced, 775,000,000 barrels, was worth at the wells $1,302,000,000." See *Petroleum Facts and Figures* (First edition), 102.

XIV

Competition in Oil

ENORMOUS though the oil output of the Mexia Fault Zone fields was by 1925 (reaching annually 51,642,241 barrels), it was only a minor portion of the vast oil flood produced by the many other Southwestern fields. By this time Southwestern oil loomed large on the national horizon—so large that it becomes necessary to investigate just how this regional yield fitted into the bigger national scheme.

For forty years after the Drake well of Pennsylvania was discovered in 1859, the market demand for oil was fairly steady. Crude-oil production had been relatively small in the beginning and increased only slightly in succeeding years. Oil was still bought for medicinal, lubricating, and illuminating purposes. Then the unprecedented Spindletop gusher of 1901 rocked the oil world, stepped up the tempo of production, forced the industry into the fuel-oil market, and within a few years stimulated wide use of fuel oil by steamers, locomotives, and factories. Refinery improvements also introduced a better quality of kerosene.

Despite this progress, the rapid increase of crude-oil yields during the next two decades swamped the market and made necessary the broadening of its base. Again necessity became the mother of invention. The steadily improved internal-combustion engine not only caused expansion in the automobile industry, but also increased the demand for gasoline and lubricants. This was fortunate, for within this period oil yield had increased 800 per cent. The rapidly growing number of automobiles was a great boon to the oil industry, "for," it has been asserted, "everything in the oil industry that lies behind the advent of the automobile is relatively as unimportant as is the present . . . harness business in comparison with its

181

status prior to the automobile."[1] By 1910 there were 458,500 passenger cars and 10,000 trucks in the country; but the total of all motor cars jumped to 10,463,295 in 1920, and in the next half-decade to 22,001,393. Surface highway mileage grew correspondingly, reaching 521,915 by 1926, with 35,000 miles surfaced in this year.

The growth of these two giant industries was vital to the economic welfare of the nation. The automobile revolutionized rural transportation, appreciably altered urban transportation, afforded a quick and inexpensive means of travel, and reduced the significance of distance as a factor in social and business relations. And the increase in automobile and oil production was parallel. Between 1919 and 1926, automobile manufacturing jumped 121 per cent, and petroleum products, which furnished fuel and lubricants for motor cars, 114 per cent.[2]

By 1920 the petroleum industry had become a chain of four links: production, transportation, refining, and marketing—each with its distinctive, intricate problems and organization. An increasing crude-oil yield soon overflowed prepared storage and made necessary the extension of pipe lines and the wide use of tank cars and tankers to transport it to waiting refineries and a market. A healthy market depended upon increasing consumption, which, in turn, required a diversified output from the refineries. That they met this challenge successfully in 1920 is demonstrated by the wide variety of products distilled from crude oil, such as benzine, gasoline, kerosene, gas oil, lubricating oil, fuel oil, paraffin, petroleum coke, and many others—totalling, in fact, about three hundred separate products. By January 1, 1921, there were 415 refineries in the United States with a capacity of 1,888,800 barrels—and 44 additional refineries were being built.

The building and maintenance of pipe lines was another facet of the diversified, complex industry. The pipe line had come to be the chief transportation agency for the oil companies. By 1920 there were 34,000 miles of main trunk lines and 11,500 miles of gathering lines. This vast network of underground transportation had come a long way from the simple line built by Henry Harley in 1865, from Benninghoff Run to Shaffer's farm on the Oil Creek, Pennsylvania, railroad.

[1] *Petroleum Facts and Figures* (First edition), 86. [2] *Ibid.*, 92.

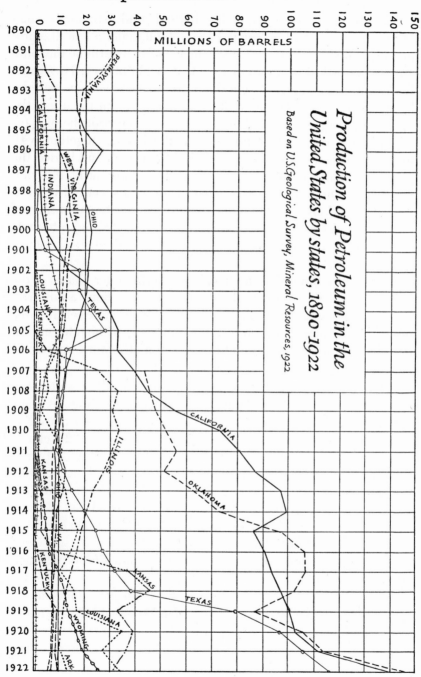

MILLIONS OF BARRELS

Production of Petroleum in the United States by states, 1890-1922

Based on U.S. Geological Survey, Mineral Resources, 1922

Oil! Titan of the Southwest

After decades of trial, pipe-line building and maintenance had become an important industry. For the building of a line, the promoting company sent out a "surveying gang" to determine the route and to acquire by purchase or agreement a right-of-way. Then came the "right-of-way gang" to cut down trees, clear the way, and deliver pipe at convenient intervals along the route for the use of the "stringing gang" soon to follow. These men strung out the pipe for the "pipe-laying gang," who screwed the lengths together with tongs. Finally, the "ditching gang" dug the trench and buried the pipe from eighteen inches to three feet deep. Ordinarily, the composite pipe-line personnel consisted of forty to seventy-five men, who averaged laying from one-half to three-quarters of a mile of pipe a day. When completed, the pipe line was divided into units for administrative purposes, with a superintendent in charge of each segment.[3]

The same complexity had developed in the other phases of the oil business. This expanding industry, indeed, became a powerful leaven for all Southwestern economic life, for the states of this area produced the major portion of the nation's oil, with states east of the Mississippi River dropping to a position of minor importance.

In 1922 Oklahoma still led the oil parade of all the states, but with the development of the bonanza fields of the Los Angeles basin, it was crowded by California. Oklahoma's 149,571,000 barrels of crude oil represented an increase of 30 per cent over 1921, chiefly because of the flush production at Burbank, Bristow, Hewitt, Lyons-Quinn, and Tonkawa. More than 24,000,000 barrels came from Burbank alone; and Oklahoma was generally productive. In January, 1923, the Oklahoma Geological Survey listed 243 oil- and gas-producing areas in the state. California's 138,468,000 barrels of crude oil, an increase of 23 per cent over its yield in 1921, was made possible by developments at Long Beach, Santa Fé Springs, and Huntington Beach.

Texas, third in rank, yielded 118,684,000 barrels, an increase of 12 per cent over its 1921 production. The Mexia and Currie fields,

---

[3] Interview with B. E. Hull, the Texas Pipe Line Company, Houston, Texas, February 27, 1946.

No. 1 Desenberg well, Mexia, Texas, 1921

Fred Sehmann

Osage lease sale, Pawhuska, Oklahoma, June 14, 1921

Osage Indian Agency, Pawhuska

Competition in Oil

with a combined yield of 35,000,000 barrels, made substantial contributions to the total; and Luling, Powell, and Wortham gave the Mexia Fault Zone still greater prominence in the next two years.

Kansas retained its fourth rank, but with a decreasing lead over Louisiana, which remained fifth. Kansas' rank was kept because of new developments in Butler, Marion, and Greenwood counties. Prolific Butler County had increased the state's production to over 35,000,000 barrels of crude oil. This increase was principally in the Towanda pool, an extension of the Augusta-Eldorado fields, in Towanda township. Louisiana crowded Kansas with its new Haynesville yield of 19,939,000 barrels of crude oil. Wyoming held sixth place, Arkansas seventh, Illinois eighth, and Kentucky ninth, passing West Virginia, Pennsylvania, and Ohio.

Working within the frame of this rapidly expanding and complex industry were three types of operators. First was the colorful wildcatter, an independent operator, who generally worked in unproven territory and sometimes far beyond known production. Essentially he was a plunger and a gambler, an up-and-down, in-and-out operator, playing the game recklessly. Some early wildcatters made and lost several fortunes and are yet active, still following an oil will-o'-the-wisp. They prowl the little-known regions, swamps, hills, and valleys, in their endless search for underground wealth. The urge of discovery draws them on; they seek hidden oil pools and formations whether the market is low or high. And it is through their wildcatting that great fields have been discovered— Glenn Pool, Cushing, Burkburnett, Mexia, Luling, Haynesville, Rodessa, and East Texas. Bob Galbreath, Tom Slick, Roy Johnson, Wirt Franklin, Frank Buttram, Scott W. Heywood, W. B. Hamilton, Barney Carter, Edgar B. Davis, Colonel Albert E. Humphreys, and "Dad" Joiner are a few of the notable wildcatters of the nineteen twenties. Sometimes the wildcatter organized his own company, with himself as the central figure, and at other times he was a lone wolf, an individualist in a highly competitive industry.

Then there were the thousands of small companies, hastily conceived and often poorly organized and staffed. In Texas, out of 1,050 new stock companies formed in 1918 and 1919, only seven paid dividends. Six of the largest companies produced more than half the oil brought to the surface, upon which dividends to the amount of $76,000,000 were paid.[4] In Oklahoma, the Corporation Commission estimated that only one dollar was returned out of every $550 invested in stock companies; and in Kansas, in 1916 and 1917, only twelve out of 1,500 new companies showed profits.[5]

It may accurately be concluded that the Southwestern oil industry was hazardous for the operator of limited means. Once-great shallow oil fields presently declined and finally settled down to a few barrels a day by stripper operations, a business not lucrative for the wildcatter and in which even the minor company was promised small returns. During the early days of development, oil sands were found at shallow depths and only primitive drilling rigs and a little capital were required. Hence, the drilling of a dry hole need not be financially ruinous. But the shallow fields were soon exploited and deeper horizons were sought, making necessary, of course, stronger drilling rigs and scientific data compiled by competent geologists. Competition became keen, at a time when ruthless methods were common. Business ethics had not yet invaded the oil fields. A small company with a minor lease acreage, poor equipment, and scanty capital could not compete on favorable terms with a giant corporation with many hundreds of thousands of acres in leases, vast storage, pipe-line, and drilling facilities, sometimes large refineries—and adequate capital.

Indeed, the hazardous "oil game" gave way to co-ordinated "oil business." For example, of the 23,133 wells drilled in the United States in 1917, according to Charles E. Bowles, "16,365 (or about 71 per cent) came in oil, 1,966 (or about 8 per cent) came in gas while 4,802 (or about 21 per cent) were 'dry holes.' "[6] It is significant that most of these dry holes were drilled by wildcatters and small-company operators. The large producing companies had the advantage of the services of geologists and technicians to direct exploration and drilling, and as a result their percentage of dry holes was much smaller.

Many similar examples could be cited to show that the "gasoline era" favored the large-scale operations of highly capitalized major companies. In 1920, there were about 16,000 crude-oil producers in

4 *Oil Weekly,* Vol. XVI (February 21, 1920), 64.
5 Dorsey Hager, *Oil Field Practice,* 250.
6 *The Petroleum Industry,* 54.

the United States, with oil yields varying from one barrel a day to seventy thousand barrels. But 58 per cent of the nation's 378,367,-000 barrels of oil were produced by 32 companies, and the other 42 per cent by the remainder of the 16,000 companies.[7] Thus, it became obvious that, to make money, the small companies and independent operators needed the technical advice, the engineering and geological services, and the varied facilities that had given the major companies this production advantage.

Yet many independent operators and small companies, led by fearless and experienced businessmen, weathered this uncompromising competition. State laws governing pipe-line operations and monopolies helped them. In at least two instances state governors invoked martial law to stabilize the market. In addition, independents presently had access to consulting engineers and geologists, and the major companies bought their crude oil.

The advent of the major-company era, its "catch-as-catch-can" business ethics, its trend toward monopoly, and its interlocking interests brought fierce legal battles. The Standard Oil Company was yet enmeshed with its late nineteenth-century odium, gained because of its trust operations, discriminations, and monopolistic controls. In the Southwest, however, its operations were more circumspect. True, in Kansas, its subsidiary had been charged with price-fixing and pipe-line favoritism, and in Oklahoma another subsidiary was accused of monopolistic operations in more than one field; but these charges were never substantiated. In both areas a limited pipe-line and railroad outlet and a poor market were more important factors restricting local operations.

In Texas, the Standard Oil Company was jolted by two adverse

[7] Companies producing over 1,000,000 barrels of crude oil in 1919 were Associated Oil Company, Barnsdall Corporation, the Carter Oil Company, Cosden Oil and Gas Company, Doheny companies of California, Galena Signal Oil Company of Texas, General Petroleum Corporation, Gulf Oil Corporation, Humble Oil and Refining Company, Magnolia Petroleum Company, McMan Oil and Gas Company, Mid West Refining Company, Ohio Cities Gas Company, Ohio Oil Company, Oklahoma Production and Refining Corporation, Prairie Oil and Gas Company, Producers and Refiners Corporation, Roxana Petroleum Company, Santa Fe Railway, Shaffer Oil and Refining Company, Shell Oil Company of California, Standard Oil Company of Indiana, Standard Oil Company of California, Standard Oil Company of Louisiana, Sun Oil Company, The Texas Company, Texas Pacific Coal and Oil Company, Tidewater Oil Company, and Union Oil Company of California. See Bowles, *op. cit.*, 72.

court decisions. Its subsidiary, the Waters-Pierce Oil Company, was ousted from the state in 1907 on a charge of violating a Texas anti-trust law and was assessed penalties amounting to $1,623,900, a judgment that was affirmed by the United States Supreme Court in June, 1909. Four years later the parent company was also driven from Texas on a similar charge by the Hunt County District Court.[8] This was a staggering blow, for Texas was soon to become the nation's major oil-producing state.

No less important was the Supreme Court's affirmation of a Texas court's dissolution decree in 1911, after five years of litigation, whereby the "Jersey Company" (Standard Oil Company of New Jersey) was enjoined from voting stock of or exerting control over its thirty-three subsidiaries. The subsidiaries, in turn, were enjoined from paying dividends to the parent company or permitting it to have any control over their management. John D. Rockefeller, who had built Standard's vast interests, lived to see the day, however, when several of these subsidiaries became larger than the parent company in 1911, and when each actively competed with the others in a vastly greater field of operation. One authority regards this dissolution as being this era's most important functional step in corporate realignment.

A writer for *Fortune* magazine, in June, 1945, stated that the Supreme Court's action in affirming the Texas court ouster "ripped thirty-three important subsidiaries out of Standard (N. J.), including Standard Oil Co. of New York and Vacuum Oil Co. (now Socony-Vacuum Oil Co.), Standard Oil Co., Indiana, and Standard Oil Co. (California)." Quickly, Standard rehabilitated itself through investments at home and abroad and soon had a higher rate of earnings than any other American company.[9]

In later years the terms "Standard Oil Group" and "Standard Oil Securities" were still bandied about by Southwesterners as if by artifice or subterfuge the Standard Oil Company of New Jersey

[8] No. 10, 232, The State of Texas *vs.* the Magnolia Petroleum Company *et al.*, in the District Court of Hunt County, Texas, Eighth Judicial District court records, Greenville.

[9] During the depression, Standard gave hint of its new public-relations policy by drawing from its surplus to the extent of $100,000,000 to maintain its unbroken dividend payment record. "In this sense," continued the *Fortune* writer, "the Jersey company is a model to U. S. business, showing that private enterprise as well as government can counter the business cycle."

still managed to control its former subsidiaries. This was not the case. Each subsidiary was a separate organization, controlled its own activities, and engaged in active competition with all other members of the former Standard group. So far as the controlling ownership in these companies was concerned, a federal authority admitted in 1927: "There is no longer unity of control of these companies through community of interest."[10]

Powerful new companies, the so-called independents,[11] had also sprung up—Phillips, Skelly, Sinclair, and McMan. Like other major companies, each of these had its far-reaching lease holdings, hundreds of producing wells, myriad installations and administrative divisions, legal staffs, and scientific personnel. And each successfully competed with such older companies as Gulf, Shell, and Sun. It became necessary, however, to effect agreements for the interests of all and to observe certain oil-field customs. These practices began a movement that later grew into the reasonably circumspect corporate ethics commonly observed by the major companies and producers of today, in the interest not only of genuine conservation but of business self-preservation. No doubt, too, this trend has been strengthened and partly shaped by state law, oil-commission control, and court decisions.

[10] Federal Trade Commission, *Prices, Profits and Competition in the Petroleum Industry,* December 12, 1927.

[11] Each company was an independent only in that it was not controlled by another company.

XV

An Osage Monte Carlo

IMPORTANT as was the petroleum yield in Texas, from Mexia, Powell, Currie, Luling, and Wortham, Oklahoma kept stride with its Burbank, Garber, and Tonkawa, and helped to lift the nation's total production to a new peak in 1922 of 447,000,000 barrels, an increase of 18 per cent over the previous year. The United States oil output was 65 per cent of the world's total. This tremendous amount of oil taxed all storage facilities and broke the market. At the end of 1922 the producers', pipe-line, and tank-farm stocks reached 273,000,000 barrels, a quantity sufficient for 165 days, as contrasted with a 130-day supply at the end of 1921.

During the nineteen twenties geologists thought that Oklahoma had reached its peak of oil production, that it would "continue to produce for a number of years at a high rate," and then decline. And as late as 1928 a government scientist predicted that only a "slight production" would be found "75 or 100 years from now." But six years previously the United States Geological Survey and the American Association of Petroleum Geologists had been more encouraging in their jointly prepared estimate of "1,340,000,000 barrels of oil probably remaining in the ground in Oklahoma" that could be recovered by improved methods.[1] This estimate was drawn up after the discovery of the Burbank oil field but before that of Tonkawa.

Oklahoma's part of this increased production was largely the result of an extensive and intensive exploration movement. In fact, operators in all the nation's fields were engaged in drilling old and

[1] Philip T. Smith to John Nuveen and Company, September 28, 1928, MS, in U.S.G.S., Geologic Division, Department of the Interior, file "No. 624–27,–Okla.," National Archives.

new areas. They drilled 24,000 wells for oil and gas, bringing the total of producing wells to 285,000. Of these, Oklahoma completed 6,148 wells, of which 4,149 were oil wells, 571 gas, and 1,428 dry.[2]

Oklahoma operators still were inclined to favor cable-tool over rotary drilling, using two kinds of derricks: a 74-foot derrick with four-and-one-half–inch rig irons; and an 82-foot derrick with four-inch rig and calf irons, costing $950 and $1,250 respectively.

This was only a small part of an operator's expense. Ordinarily he paid his drillers and tool dressers fourteen to sixteen dollars a day, and other workers in proportion. Drilling costs depended on several factors, the most important being the depth of the well, the kind of strata encountered, the number of water-bearing formations, and the skill of the driller. A well 1,200 feet deep might conceivably cost $10,000 or go as high as $30,000; and a well 3,000 feet deep might cost $60,000, although in Oklahoma, when conditions were understood and drillers were competent, deep wells were completed for as little as $20,000.[3]

The average expense of drilling Oklahoma wells in 1921 had increased to $35,509, largely because of the greater depth of drilling. In fact, in the preceding year an important wildcat well had entailed a total expenditure of $250,000. One expert of that period gave these drilling-cost percentages for a 4,150-foot well under normal conditions: drilling, 45.8; casing, 19.4; rigs, 11.8; fuel, 8.2; day work, 5.0; miscellaneous labor, teaming, and freight, 4.0; water,

[2] *Mineral Resources of the United States, 1922, Part II, Nonmetals,* 359.

[3] Director George Otis Smith, U.S.G.S., to Mrs. H. H. Willes, Geological Division, Classified Files, Department of the Interior, file "No. 624.2," National Archives. Another authority states: "In 1912 the average cost of drilling the wells of one of the largest companies in Oklahoma had increased to $3,169. In 1913 it had gone to $4,667; 1914, $6,744; 1915, $8,321; 1916, $6,917; 1917, $7,880; 1918, $11,144; 1919, $21,353; 1920, $26,437; 1921, $35,509; 1922, $23,999; 1924, $23,745; 1925, $27,333. The big jump to $35,509 per well occurred in the days when rig builders were getting $20 a day; drillers and tool dressers $14 to $16; and everything connected with the drilling of a well or the operation of an oil property had gone to top price.—*Petroleum Facts and Figures* (First edition), 125.

Drillers who served their apprenticeship during these hectic days often started with ramshackle rigs and poor equipment and later reached the height of major success. Among Oklahoma's operators of this class were Bob Kerr and Jim Anderson, Lloyd Noble, Harry Franklin, W. T. Payne, W. G. (Bill) Skelly, and John E. Mabee. These men presently headed firms whose rigs were employed in many Southwestern fields.

3.1; torpedoes, 0.5; other equipment, 0.3; and miscellaneous, 1.9; making a total of 100 per cent.[4]

By 1920 significant innovations had appeared, pointing toward a new oil era. First, by 1913, oil companies were gingerly accepting the work of geologists. In the northern part of the Mid-Continent region, in 1914 a professor of geology at the University of Kansas, Erasmus Hayworth, and his son had mapped Eldorado; and Charles N. Gould and Everett Z. Carpenter had similarly charted the Augusta anticline. Gould and Carpenter were employed by the Empire Gas and Fuel Company, the geological department of which Carpenter had organized on August 1, 1913.[5]

Geological work in these Kansas fields was not the first in the Mid-Continent region, but it created interest in this science and caused operators to turn increasingly to geologists for advice. H. B. Goodrich engaged in commercial work in Oklahoma as early as 1903, when he went from Houston, Texas, to Ardmore, to do field work for the Coline Oil Company, a subsidiary of the Santa Fe Railroad. He located the first Santa Fe well at the Wheeler oil seepages in May, 1904.

Goodrich remained with the Coline Oil Company until 1910, also doing consulting work for others. From 1910 to 1911 he explored for oil in Bolivia, and two years later reported on the Cushing field for the United States Bureau of Mines. Later, he was engaged by the Dundee Petroleum Company at Healdton, after which, in 1915, he moved to Tulsa to become a consulting geologist.

The United States Geological Survey encouraged Indian Territory oil prospecting by calling the attention of commercial geologists to anticlines in southeastern Oklahoma similar to the Appalachian folds of the Pennsylvania and West Virginia oil fields. These oil-sand outcrops in the Ouachita Mountains near Redden in Atoka County and Jumbo in Pushmataha County, and gas seepages in the folded Pennsylvanian strata at Soda Springs, east of Checotah, and on Ash Creek, fifteen miles northeast of McAlester, were indeed well defined.

The Oklahoma Geological Survey, founded by Charles N. Gould, also made a marked contribution to the advancement of

---

[4] Charles B. Eliot, *Petroleum Industry of the Gulf Southwest*, Part II, 63, 64.
[5] E. DeGolyer to C. C. Rister, November 1, 1947.

petroleum geology in this state. Its reports, prepared by instructors and students of the University of Oklahoma and published by the survey, had a direct bearing on the development of Cushing, New-kirk, Ponca City, and other fields, just as federal surveys had aided at Glenn Pool, Healdton, Billings, and Bristow, in the Osage country, and in other oil-producing areas.

The Oklahoma Geological Survey furnished two men, D. W. Ohern and Frank Buttram, for independent work. In the fall of 1913 they resigned from the Survey to become geologists for the Fortuna Oil Company, which later met with increasing success.[6] It opened the Yale, Cement, Morrison, Ripley, and Ingalls oil fields and the Cushing gas field. Buttram made a plane-table survey of Cushing for the state in 1913,[7] and in 1916 he and Ohern did extensive field work at Cement, in Caddo County. A gas well had been drilled on the Funk farm, three miles east of Cement a short time previously. But the Oklahoma Star Oil Company brought in the Kunsemuller well, Cement's first oil well, in 1917. This well encountered sufficient oil at a depth of about 1,700 feet to encourage further drilling, and as a result, the Fortuna Oil Company started active operations. By 1921, Cement had developed into a minor oil field, thirty-six wells having been drilled, of which twenty were oil wells and four gas wells.[8]

Among other scientific workers in Oklahoma before and shortly after 1920[9] were M. J. Munn, Carl D. Smith, Robert H. Wood, and Everett Carpenter, of the federal Survey; and Charles N. Gould, Pierce Larkin, L. L. Hutchison, Irving Perrine, Charles H. Taylor, L. C. Snyder, and others of the state Survey.[10]

Petroleum geology scored a decided advance in 1913, when, on August 1, the Gypsy Oil Company organized a geological department under M. J. Munn, and the Empire Gas and Fuel Company followed with another, under Everett Carpenter. Munn had the

[6] *Oil and Gas in Oklahoma,* Oklahoma Geological Survey *Bull. No. 40,* I, 6.

[7] U.S.G.S. *Bull. 726-B,* 71; Frank Buttram to C. C. Rister, June 10, 1948.

[8] *Bull. No. 40,* I, 6. as cited. For Buttram's report of the "Cushing Oil and Gas Field, Oklahoma," see Oklahoma Geological Survey *Bull. No. 18.*

[9] On January 1, 1913, E. W. McCrory at Tulsa organized the geological staff for Guffey and Gillespie.—*Oil and Gas Journal—The Oil City Derrick* (Diamond Jubilee edition), August 27, 1934. The subsurface at Healdton was mapped by the United States Geological Survey in 1915.

[10] *Bull. No. 40,* I, 6, as cited.

good fortune to delineate the dome on the Boston lease in the Osage country and to outline the Cushing field, where the Gypsy Company secured extensive leases in the south end of the Drumright area. Later, his department mapped many of the folds which in later years became oil fields, including the Fox field. By 1914 his department included thirty men, and their work caused other oil companies to employ geologists in 1915.

"It was not until the last few years," wrote a member of United States Geological Survey in 1921, that "the application of geology to oil field operations has been of increasing importance in bringing in new pools."[11]

Petroleum engineers appeared about the same time. The Bureau of Mines, established in 1910 with J. A. Holmes as director, encouraged the operators' use of scientifically trained engineers and aided the oil industry in solving many of its most vexing problems. Subsequently Bureau engineers served as company executives, and its publications became the media for the education of operators in drilling methods for oil and gas and economical production. As many companies branched out into refining, transportation, and marketing, their organizations grew so much that each department had to have competent men to direct operations. Into this changing condition engineers appeared, bringing equipment, drilling, and refining improvements. For example, by 1916 the published accounts of J. A. Pollard and A. G. Heggem and J. O. Lewis and W. F. McMurray on the use of mud-laden fluid in oil and gas wells had appeared.[12] In the next year the six-inch California-pattern rig irons were used in the Mid-Continent fields, and soon manufacturers could not supply the demand of the rig builders, causing other manufacturers to enter the rig-iron business. George E. Burton suggested the use of a diamond drill, and in 1919 such a drill was used at Sawyer, Oklahoma. It deepened a hole from 2,200 feet, where it had been drilled by a cable-tool rig, to a depth of 4,920

11 *Mineral Resources of the United States, 1921, Part II, Nonmetals,* 309.

12 E. DeGolyer states that the mud-laden-fluid technique introduced by the Bureau of Mines was supposed to seal off and conserve gas but that it did not work; that petroleum engineering developed as an offshoot from petroleum geology; and that most early petroleum geologists, such as J. O. Lewis, John Suman, and Charles Millikan, were trained as geologists and gradually built up the petroleum engineering profession.—E. DeGolyer to C. C. Rister, April 2, 1948.

feet and gave the operator very definite information about the formation penetrated.

For a time technicians and processes were forgotten by Oklahoma operators in their mad scramble for Osage oil. Burbank, in a sense a second Cushing, was the greatest of all Osage fields.

From 1916 to 1920, Oklahoma had produced more than 100,-000,000 barrels of petroleum a year, except for a drop to 87,000,000 in 1919. But in the next two years it made large gains because of the finding of new pools and the extension of old ones, among which were Hewitt, Beggs, Bristow, Deaner, Burbank, and others in Okmulgee, Creek, Carter, Okfuskee, and Osage counties.[13]

Nestling under the eastern brow of a hill in the high Osage tableland country of northern Oklahoma, twenty miles east of Ponca City, was the small town of Burbank, a cluster of a few wind-beaten homes, near the center of which were a post office, a blacksmith shop, and two or three stores. It was a typical village in this rolling prairie country, and near-by ranchmen and farmers came there once or twice a week to buy supplies.

Osage Indians also occasionally came to purchase tobacco, flour, meat, calico, denim, and blankets. Since 1872, when the federal government had moved them to this former Cherokee country, between the ninety-sixth meridian and the Arkansas River, literally an unoccupied left-over land, they had been desperately poor, depending on the government's annuity and the cattlemen's lease money. This dual income, plus what they earned by their own efforts, met their simple wants; but, as in the case of other Oklahoma reservation Indians, their future prospects were not bright.

Just as it seemed that the lot of the Osages was hopeless poverty, the horizon brightened—the Foster lease, small oil and gas fields—then Burbank! After the first oil and gas discoveries, previously mentioned, an active prospecting, leasing, and drilling campaign was carried on. This brought the Osages the comforts of life. Then Burbank oil gave them fabulous wealth and placed them, per capita, among the richest people in the world.

Prior to 1912, when the first Osage oil- and gas-lease auctions were held under a wide-spreading elm tree near the Agency building at Pawhuska, enough Osage oil and gas finds had been made to

[13] *Mineral Resources of the United States, 1921, Part II, Nonmetals, 254, 256.*

promise a better future. Such discoveries as Avant, Okesa, Osage City, and Wiser in 1904–1905 and Bird Creek (1906) kept prospectors interested. In 1911 another small field was found near Skiatook, the last discovery before the first of the auction sales. Then followed Wildhorse (1912), Hickory Creek, Landon, and Quapaw (1914), South Elgin (1915), Barnsdall and Hominy (1916), Domes, Nelagoney, and Pershing (1917), Almeda (1918), and Pawhuska, Pearsonia, Pettitt, and X-686 (1919)—all before the finding of Burbank.[14]

The region west of Range 8, the western half of the Osage country, was first opened for public leasing at Pawhuska on December 9, 1918, after nine auctions had already been held disposing of 178,611 acres of land for $13,195,574.36. This was an unexplored territory and had long been a topic of conversation among operators. At this auction representatives of several companies—Gypsy, Guffey-Gillespie, Marland, and Carter—bought leases in a few scattered tracts in Ranges 5, 6, and 7. And soon important tests south of Foraker were drilled by Gypsy and Guffey-Gillespie but were disappointing. North of Foraker, the Gypsy test on the White Horn allotment was better, a little oil being found in the Mississippi lime at 2,880 feet. And even other tests that were unsuccessful had condemned only local spots of a vast area.[15]

In 1919, Frank Fisher of the Carter Oil Company brought the first string of tools into what is now the Burbank oil field, putting down a test on S9-T26N-R6E, on two small anticlines. Although he had mechanical difficulties, he finally brought in a gasser. Then, in September, 1920, he drilled an offset which came in with a small oil flow. But before he had completed this second test, on May 8, 1920, Marland electrified northern Oklahoma by completing a 150-barrel flowing well[16] on the Bertha Hickman farm in a sand (2,949–3,001 feet) at first believed to be the Burgess but later found to be the Bartlesville.[17]

Later, in 1920, the National Exploration Company (now Roxana Petroleum Company) brought in the biggest gusher in the

[14] *Bull. No. 40,* I, oil and gas fields listed chronologically. For a short time the town of Pershing flourished, then became a ghost town.

[15] Galey MS, as cited.

[16] In the SE¼ S36-T27N-R5E.

[17] J. P. D. Hull *et al., Structure of Typical American Oil Fields,* I, 220.

southeast corner of the southwest of Section 4-26-6. It made 3,450 barrels of oil the first twenty-four hours.

Burbank was drilled methodically, primarily by large companies. At first, the area between Carter's production[18] and Marland's was thought to separate two fields, although sand depths and the oil were similar. But soon it was established by other discoveries that they were the same. The field spread in all directions from the discovery wells. Yet the major trend of development was to the north; consequently, such operators as the Gypsy Company, Waite Phillips, Phillips Petroleum Company,[19] Skelly, and Comar, in ad-

[18] In S9-T26N-R6E and S36-T27N-R5E.

[19] Phillips Petroleum Company represents the success story of two brothers, Frank and L. E. Phillips, who had earlier climbed the ladder of success the hard way. Frank as a poor lad had served as a Creston, Iowa, barber, became a proprietor of all the town's shops, came to Bartlesville, Indian Territory, as a bond salesman and holder of oil and gas leases. L. E. attended rural schools, and worked his way through the Western Normal College of Shenandoah, Iowa, by serving as a janitor and waiting on tables. Both men had marked business ability. In Bartlesville, Frank helped to organize and became president of the Citizens Bank and Trust Company, which opened for business in December, 1905. There L. E. joined him shortly to look after their joint oil and gas properties, which by 1917 they had incorporated as the Phillips Petroleum Company.

From its beginning, Phillips enjoyed unusual success, advancing from a $3,000,-000 enterprise with 27 employees in June, 1917, to a closely integrated major oil company with assets of approximately $500,000,000 and more than 16,000 employees in 1947. Soon after incorporation, in 1918, the company held 7,000 acres of Osage leases, with ninety oil and gas wells and five strings of tools running, and other Oklahoma properties in the Bartlesville and Morris-Okmulgee districts and in the Healdton-Fox area. In Kansas, it held 2,200 acres at Eldorado and other leases in the Potwin and Augusta districts and Greenwood and Cowley counties. In Texas, it entered the oil-producing area embraced by Eastland, Stephens, Parker, Young, and Palo Pinto counties.

In addition, it began processing crude oil, and established its pioneer Hamilton gasoline plant, two miles from Bartlesville, its Osage plant, between present Wooloroc and Bartlesville, in October, 1917, and August, 1919, respectively. In July, 1918, Frank Phillips announced to his stockholders net earnings at the rate of $740,808 per annum, more than seven times the company's requirements on preferred stock.

At the end of 1947, Phillips had developed into a major oil company, holding 4,435,303 acres of leases, having drilled during the year, or participated in drilling, 546 wells; finding twelve new oil fields; transporting 65,163,974 barrels of crude oil and products through its 2,632 miles of trunk pipe line and 810 miles of gathering lines; and owning refineries at Borger, Texas, Kansas City, Kansas, Okmulgee, Oklahoma, and Sweeny, Texas. These refineries processed more than 35,498,483 barrels of crude oil. Mr. Charles E. Cummings, public relations department, Phillips Petroleum Company, furnished the author with photostatic copies of announcements to stockholders, 1918–20, sketches of Frank and L. E. Phillips and the Phillips Petroleum Company, and other data.

197

vance of production, commenced to buy acreage at surprisingly low prices in Kay County.

By September, 1921, the Carter Oil Company was Burbank's biggest producer, having twenty-three of the sixty-three wells and 5,445 barrels of oil a day of a total of 22,570 barrels.[20] Other operators of importance were Producers and Refiners Corporation with six wells, Gypsy with four, Roxana-Marland Refining Company with eight, National Exploration Company with five and Tidal Osage Company with three. By 1922 the field was producing 75,000 barrels of crude oil daily.

The Sapulpa Refining Company's wildcat test in SW¼S15-T26N-R5E became a 500-barrel well on January 16, 1923, extending the field several miles northwest in Kay County, thereby justifying these leases. These wells were characterized by large gas volume and extremely heavy sand saturation. Here, in fact, was the richest part of the field, which quickly brought Burbank to its peak on July 21, 1923, with a daily oil output of 121,700 barrels.[21] The *Wall Street Journal* of March 24, 1923, announced that such major companies as the Phillips Petroleum–Skelly Oil Company, the Gypsy Oil Company, the Prairie Oil and Gas Company, the Sinclair Oil and Gas Company, Carter Oil Company, and Cosden Oil and Gas Company had led in Burbank's development, spending a total of $29,625,200, until the oil field finally covered 132 quarter-sections or 33 square miles.[22] These investments paid handsome dividends. Indeed, there is little doubt that the Osage country was largely responsible for the development of the Skelly, Phillips, Gypsy, and Sinclair companies into major Oklahoma producers.

Under Section 3 of the Osage Allotment Act of June 26, 1906, and as amended on March 3, 1921, all oil, gas, and other minerals

[20] The Mid-Continent Oil and Gas Association sought through a voluntary producers' agreement a temporary stoppage of drilling in the Mid-Continent area but met with no success. See *The Plan, Rules and Regulations of the Committee on Conservation and Conciliation of the Kansas-Oklahoma Division of the Mid-Continent Oil and Gas Association.*

[21] *Petroleum Facts and Figures* (First edition), 112.

[22] Cushing covered thirty-six square miles and up to 1925 had produced 250,000,000 barrels of oil, or an average of about 11,000 barrels to the acre; and Healdton covered thirteen square miles and had produced approximately 131,000,000 barrels of oil, or an average of close to 15,000 barrels to the acre.—Mid-Continent *Bull.*, May 15, 1925, p. 5.

were to be reserved for the Osage tribe as a unit; and leases for operating such properties were to be made by the Osage tribal council with the approval of the Secretary of the Interior. Under this authority, Osage auction sales were held periodically after 1912.

After May, 1920, when Burbank's discovery well blew in, thirteen Osage land auctions were held at Pawhuska, up to and including that of March 28, 1927, disposing of 532,876.75 acres. Enormous lease prices were paid. In one instance the Midland Oil Company gave $1,990,000 for 160 acres.[23]

At the end of each quarter, per capita payments were made to the 2,229 enrolled Osages, or their heirs. These payments on a yearly basis and the value of one share are given in the following table:[24]

Year Ending June 30	Number of Payments	Amount of Each Share	Total Amount
1916	4	$ 384.93	$ 858,008.97
1917	6	2,719.98	6,062,835.42
1918	6	3,672.33	8,185,623.57
1919	7	3,930.00	8,759,970.00
1920	9	8,090.00	18,032,610.00
1921	7	8,600.00	19,169,400.00
1922	4	7,700.00	17,163,300.00
1923	4	12,400.00	27,639,600.00
1924	4	11,600.00	25,856,400.00
1925	3	9,300.00	20,729,700.00

These Pawhuska auction sales became an Osage Monte Carlo in spirit—in truth, accompanied by a far greater exchange of money than at all of celebrated Monaco's Monte Carlo transactions. Millions were not made or lost by the turn of the wheel, but by competitive, and sometimes capricious, bidding. Frequently the bidder lost all sense of value and proportion, whether he was a representative of a large company or an independent producer.[25]

Naturally, the Osages took full advantage of what they had to sell. The royalty demanded, and fixed by the government, was one-sixth, and one-fifth on leases averaging over one hundred barrels

[23] *Petroleum Facts and Figures* (First edition), 140.
[24] *Ibid.*, 140.
[25] Galey MS, as cited.

199

to the well. In addition, the lessee had to pay the Indian surface owner thirty-five dollars for the drilling of every well, one hundred dollars up for each drilling location near a house, and a fee for the erection of each tank. Small wonder the individual Osage garnered lavishly!

The total cumulative bonus paid for Burbank 160-acre tracts by 1929 was $63,784,300, not including the nominal cost per acre on the Kay County side of the field. The bonus acreage average was approximately $2,745. The eight-year Burbank production, including both the Osage and Kay County parts of the field, to the end of 1928, was about 160,541,000 barrels of crude oil, which sold during the period, 1920–28, at an average of $1.78 a barrel. The gross amount from the sale of this oil was $285,762,980, upon which producers paid in royalty $45,899,711. Then the operator paid all development costs—drilling 2,100 wells, figured conservatively at $78,750,000; lease improvement; field gathering lines; vacuum stations; and other miscellaneous expenses.

This was not all. In four auction sales, from March 5, 1919, to February 3, 1920, inclusive, each Osage—there being enrolled 2,260 —received $7,707.34 as a cash bonus in addition to a pro rata payment of one-sixth royalty on all oil produced and three cents per 1,000 cubic feet of all gas at the well. With a daily Osage area output of 45,000 barrels of oil and approximately 500,000,000 cubic feet of gas, the total oil and gas royalty paid each member of the Osage tribe was $3,635. In 1919 it was about $7,000. One Osage family of eleven—a father, a mother, and nine children—during ten months of 1919 and January, 1920, received about $55,000 in cash bonuses and oil and gas royalties.

H. L. Wood, an oil-field reporter, attended the auction sale of February 3, 1920.[26] He found the "usual large and speculative crowd" present, more than five hundred men and women having journeyed to Pawhuska either to bid on the two hundred tracts or to enjoy the bidding of big and little speculators against each other. There were 178 tracts offered for lease east of Range 7 and 22 west

[26] "Our Government's Biggest Gambling Center at Pawhuska," in *National Petroleum News*, Vol. XII, No. 6 (February 11, 1920), 34; "More than $3,000,000 Was Paid for Leases at Recent Osage Sale," in *Oil Weekly*, Vol. XVI, No. 6 (February 7, 1920), 20.

of Range 8. The Tulsa train was late, and the versatile auctioneer, Colonel E. E. Walters of Skeedee, Oklahoma, did not offer the first tract until 10:30 A.M., then recessed for lunch and started again at 1:30 P.M. Since the day was cloudy and cold, with rain in the morning, there was little milling about outside; and a theater was used to accommodate the crowd.

A full-blood Osage lawyer, John Palmer, began proceedings by presenting Walters with a fine diamond ring, a gift for securing so much oil money for the Osages. This was a ceremony that oilmen present could hardly be expected to enjoy, for in the one auction of October 6, preceding, bonuses offered on 34,670 acres of land amounted to $6,056,950. After Palmer's presentation remarks, the clever auctioneer, with a booming voice, expressive gestures, and entertaining humor, opened the bidding. No doubt in the past his direct appeals to the crowd had added millions of dollars to the Osage tribal fund, and made the auctions 100 per cent effective.

The Phillips Petroleum Company and associates were the largest buyers,[27] purchasing seven 160-acre tracts for $495,000 and paying the top price of $222,000 for tract No. 75, NE¼S20-T22N-R10E in the Wildhorse Creek district east of Hominy. For Wildhorse properties, the Marland Refining Company and the Phillips Petroleum Company were rival bidders on 160 acres, carrying the bidding from $1,000 to $201,000, which were finally "knocked down" to Marland. The three 160-acre tracts offsetting this purchase on the east, north, and west, were in Sections 17, 18, and 19. The Carter Oil Company paid $154,000 for one quarter-section; the Guffey-Gillespie acquired three, paying $70,000 for a 160-acre lease west of Hominy; the Amerada[28] paid $55,000 for Tract 31; the

---

[27] The Phillips Company announced in January, 1920, that it had 415 producing oil wells on sixty different properties and 12 gas wells. It owned 23,000 acres in Louisiana on which were producing oil wells and had recently purchased 248 acres at Caddo, Texas, with nine oil wells. In addition it had new properties in the Ebling Field, Butler County, Kansas.—*National Petroleum News*, Vol. XII, No. 1 (January 7, 1920), 56.

[28] The Amerada Petroleum Corporation was formed in Delaware on June 4, 1919. The name "Amerada" was taken from the first part of "America" ("Amer") and the last part of "Canada" ("ada"), since in its beginning it was in part financed by British funds. By February, 1926, Amerada was controlled entirely by American interests.

No. 1 Signs, in the Osage country (in S33-R18N-T5E), February 12, 1920, was Amerada's first southwestern well and was completed as a dry hole. Its first oil was

Riverland Oil Company, $91,000 for Tract 32, both in S16-T22N-T9E, just east of Hominy.[29] At the end of the day the auctioneer had sold 29,533 acres, for which he had received $3,102,700.

Even Pawhuska church members caught the Monte Carlo spirit. The Methodists and Presbyterians served a chicken dinner at noon, the Methodists charging $1.50 and the Presbyterians $1.00; and at night during a recess from 6:00 o'clock to 7:20, the Christian church did honors. After dinner Walters auctioned a quilt for thirty dollars, probably figuring that some shorn lamb needed more cover for his bed. The last lot was sold at 9:45 P.M., the tired Tulsa oilmen not reaching home until 1:00 A.M.

Within a few years, and sometimes a few months, the Osages changed from blankets to bank rolls. Some took their riches soberly, made their investments wisely, and lived conservatively. But a majority spent lavishly. Formerly, they had lived in the country and had worn blankets and moccasins, and their living expenses had been slight. Now they bought luxuries—automobiles, pianos, surreys, fancy blankets, and trinkets. The Osage country became an Indian paradise. Max Ball says that some Osages bought Cadillacs and Pierce-Arrows and then abandoned them beside the road if a tire blew out.[30] One Indian, seeking unquestioned social supremacy, bought a new shiny black hearse. That the federal government permitted such wanton expenditures and did not plan long-range investments for the benefit of the tribe represents another failure in the aimless Indian Bureau program.

Pawhuska's Monte Carlo spirit overran the bounds of the Osage country. Burbank, Shidler, Cooper, Apperson, and Webb City became boisterous oil towns. Burbank boasted a population of 2,500 to 3,000, with a thriving business center, equipment houses, and 250 teams pulling the familiar heavily laden freight wagons. But with the decline of the oil field, decadence set in. Today Burbank

sold from the No. 1 Hun-Kah-Me (No. 1 Hominy) in S16-R22N-T9E, on July 13, 1920. It then operated in Seminole County, in the Cromwell field, at Tonkawa, Beggs, Duncan and Cushing during the nineteen-twenties; and elsewhere in the Southwest in later years.

[29] On December 30, 1919, the Osage lessees had set up the "Osage Oil and Gas Lessees' Association" to protect their interests and rights in the Osage Country and to promote a better understanding with the Indians and the Department of the Interior.—*Ibid.*, 74.

[30] *This Fascinating Oil Business*, 349.

lives only in its past, its bank and businesses having moved elsewhere. The Richardson Hotel, an imposing two-story structure, reminds the curious visitor of the hosts of tired oil-field men who once sought its friendly accommodations. Cooper, Apperson, and Webb City, too, are content to see other thriving towns all about, their laurels having turned to willows.

Tonkawa, thirty-four miles west of Burbank, was the next oil field to assume major proportions in northern Oklahoma. This region was explored geologically by a Professor Bowers of the Department of the Interior as early as 1883. During the Osage boom, "Spot" Geyer, the head of Marland's geological staff, decided that the Tonkawa anticline was a good place to drill. But dry holes had already been drilled in this area and other geologists said that they "couldn't see" Geyer's proposal; consequently, Marland had difficulty in selling leases.[31]

The Humphreys Petroleum Company had given Marland a 160-acre lease for a test well.[32] Prairie put in $2,500 "dry-hole" money,[33] and another Marland subsidiary, the Kay County Gas Company, put in $5,000. Then Cosden joined Marland in the enterprise and the test was made; and on June 29, 1921[34] the well came in, flowing initially 1,000 barrels a day from a sand at 2,658–2,660 feet, the oil testing 41–43.9 degrees Baumé.[35] Marland had drilled nine dry holes before he found this producer.[36]

The field was a money-maker from the start. By April 1 of the next year enough oil had been produced to pay for all operating costs, the total output having reached 675,000 barrels. Although the first well was in the southernmost part of the field, it remained for the northern area, along a township line between 24 and 25-1 west to be the major producer (the upper Hoover at 1,900 to 2,000 feet, the lower Hoover at 2,100 feet, the Tonkawa at 2,625 feet). There were three big producing oil sands, giving the field its popular name of "Three Sands." Later several other oil sands were found.

[31] *Daily Oklahoman*, September 23, 1923, Sec. F, p. 2, cols. 1–4.

[32] In the northeast corner of S16-T24N-R1W.

[33] A wildcat well was often a joint company enterprise shared in by two or more companies. The money that was contributed was called "dry-hole money," for percentages proved that a majority of such tests were dry holes.

[34] Ira Rinehart, *Report on the Oil Situation in North Central Oklahoma*, 43.

[35] Oklahoma Geological Survey, *Bull. No. 40*, I, 256.

[36] Rinehart, *op. cit.*

Oil! Titan of the Southwest

Within two years Tonkawa had surpassed Burbank as a producer, reporting 112,112 barrels of oil daily to 110,400 for Burbank.[37]

Tonkawa had several unique features. First, it had huge gas wells that resulted in that area's becoming one of the greatest casing-head gasoline-manufacturing centers of America. By September, 1923, there were eight such plants in the field and others were building. In April, 1921, twenty gas wells showed an initial daily open flow of 408,250,000 cubic feet of gas, or over 20,000,000 cubic feet for each well. From July, 1921, until September, 1923, 525,000,-000 cubic feet of gas had been mudded off and 112,000,000 shut in. Then, second, the ever present need of mudding off the gas in drilling oil wells and conserving gas in others, introduced rotary rigs. The Southwestern Petroleum Company used the first rotary rigs at Tonkawa to solve the problem of gas interference, after which other companies followed suit until they were generally used.

Third, Tonkawa leases commanded high prices. Here again was the spirit of Monte Carlo, the sky being the limit in competitive bidding for leases, and without an auctioneer. Sixteen months after the Marland-Cosden discovery well was drilled, one company paid $1,300,000 for a lease on 400 acres in the northern part of the field; and on February 1, 1923, the Blackwell Oil and Gas Company sold its interests, including the John Ruzek lease, a 160-acre tract, in the northern part of the field, for $2,000,000, or at the rate of $7.00 per share for approximately 300,000 shares. Enormous prices were paid for 40-acre, 80-acre, and 160-acre leases, and in some instances $2,000,000 in royalty were rejected on 160 acres. Sam McKee, a Tonkawa farmer, had refused that amount on his 160-acre tract that was producing 8,000 barrels of oil daily. By June, 1923, Tonkawa royalty interests were estimated at $100,000,000.[38]

The fourth unusual feature in the development of the Tonkawa

[37] *Daily Oklahoman,* June 10, 1923, Sec. B, p. 5, col. 1.

[38] All available Tonkawa acreage was sought for. And like Jennings, Louisiana, and Merriman, Texas, Tonkawa or Three Sands had its graveyard-drilling controversy. A contractor obtained a lease on a churchyard within the Tonkawa field and selected a drilling site near a grave in the adjacent cemetery. But neighborhood farmers, armed, refused to allow him to drill. The matter came before Judge Claude Devall's district court of Kay County and the final judgment was against the operator, the decision being that the location was within thirty-two feet of a grave and must therefore be abandoned.—*Daily Oklahoman,* Sept. 23, 1923, Sec. F, p. 2, cols. 1–4; A. R. Parker to Albert R. Parker, October 24, 1947.

oil field was its adequate pipe lines and storage. By May 1, 1923, fifteen pipe lines were running Tonkawa crude and eleven more were under construction, making a total of twenty-six. This movement to run Tonkawa crude was prompted by its high gravity and the desire of major companies to secure it. These twenty-six pipe lines could handle 185,000 barrels of crude oil daily. The field was also dotted with large-capacity storage tanks, capable of storing a million barrels of oil. The Marland company stored a vast amount of Tonkawa crude at Ponca City, and various other companies stored oil elsewhere.

Billings had become a minor producing oil field before the Burbank pools were developed. In February, 1917, the Midco Petroleum Company of Tulsa drilled the discovery well on the Hoover farm. The well made 250 barrels of oil daily from a sand at 2,115–2,136 feet. The well was drilled deeper and showed for 150 barrels of oil in a deeper sand (2,344–2,351 feet), in September, 1919. When later the limits of the field were defined (practically a square section), the Midco Petroleum Company and the Humphreys Petroleum Company controlled the producing acreage. In 1922 the field's daily output was 1,158 barrels from seventy-three wells.[39]

Garber,[40] about twenty-five miles southwest of Tonkawa, also developed as an important but minor field on September 10, 1917, when the Exchange Oil Company (a subsidiary of the Sinclair Oil and Gas Company) Hoy farm well had an initial daily production of one hundred barrels of oil in a sand at 1,130–1,156 feet, called the "Hoy sand." Following the completion of the first well, the Garber field was developed rapidly, as Roxana, Healdton Oil and Gas, Cosden, Marland, Atlantic,[41] and other companies had leased close-

[39] Rinehart, op. cit., 19.

[40] Dorsey Hager came from California to Tulsa in the fall of 1914 and later entered into partnership with Mowry Bates, formerly a tool dresser of the Gypsy Oil Company. The two men mapped the block of acreage owned by Bert Garber and others, where later the Garber oil field was discovered. Oklahoma Geological Survey Bull. No. 40, I, 6.

[41] The Atlantic Refining Company entered the Southwest in 1918 by acquiring property in the Newkirk pool and by drilling in the Osage country. Next, it extended its operations into Texas, in 1919, at Sipe Springs; and into Kansas in 1920, Louisiana and Arkansas in 1922, and New Mexico in 1930. By 1928 its production had increased to 24,000 net barrels daily, this quantity representing 35 per cent of refinery runs, which had increased from 44,000 barrels in 1918, to 70,000 barrels in 1928. To insure prompt delivery of Atlantic's West Texas crude oil and to avoid paying the

in tracts and started drilling. Later, on April 6, 1925, Sinclair drilled into the Ordovician limestone pay with a 2,600 barrel well.[42] This opened a deep, rich pay horizon which temporarily challenged Tonkawa's oil output. Tonkawa, too, had its deep pay horizons, with two to five derricks sometimes standing in a cluster, each representing a different production level. On March 15, 1927, Garber's total gross production was but 17,876 barrels of oil.

In fact, the early and mid nineteen twenties saw new and conspicuous black splotches on the Southwest's geological maps, each locating a recently discovered oil field. Among these, Haynesville, Louisiana, and El Dorado and Smackover, Arkansas, next claim attention.

It should be remembered that Osage riches were not typical of the profits made in other Oklahoma and Southwestern oil fields. The per capita Osage income was amazingly high, but that of other oil-producing areas was small. For the most part the quest for Southwestern oil was highly speculative. Fortune was as fickle with the oil hunter as she was with the gold prospector. Thousands of eager investors lost heavily in both bogus and honest oil companies, and other thousands lost just as heavily in lease and royalty trading.

That the quest for oil was financially hazardous is seen in the drilling records of the Southwestern states. About 30 per cent of all the wells drilled in Oklahoma and approximately 40 per cent in Louisiana and Texas from 1920 to 1922, in both proven and wildcat areas, were dry.[43] And in wildcat territory this percentage was substantially higher.

---

then high tariff rates, the company's subsidiary constructed a ten-inch pipe line running 580 miles from Winkler, through Midland, to Atreco, Texas; and in 1930 this line was joined with another ten-inch line running 78 miles between Hobbs and Midland. In addition to its Pennsylvania refineries, Atlantic also has a 38,000-barrel-capacity plant at Atreco. At present its oil production is from about 2,800 company interest wells in Kansas, Oklahoma, New Mexico, Texas, Arkansas, and Louisiana. It also has casing-head gasoline plants at Neale, Louisiana, and Magnolia and Mc-Kamie, Arkansas.

[42] Rinehart, *op. cit.*, 22.

[43] *Mineral Resources of the United States, 1921, Part II, Nonmetals,* 309 ff.; *ibid., 1922,* 417 ff.

XVI

Arkansas' El Dorado

IN THE NINETEEN TWENTIES, wherever there was oil in the Southwest, life was raw and crude, tempestuous and hazardous. In every major oil field—at Burkburnett, Ranger, and Mexia in Texas, at Burbank and Tonkawa in Oklahoma, or at El Dorado and Smackover in Arkansas—life was multifarious. Shrewd men, wealth-crazed, adventurous, and rash; trained oilmen, speculative and careful; men of science, engineers and geologists; bankers, merchants, preachers, schoolteachers, physicians, lawyers, ranchmen, farmers, and gamblers, shysters, and ne'er-do-wells—all were there.

Millions of dollars were spent recklessly and lavishly in the search for oil during this era, the tempo of which was heedless, maddening, and fast. The oil field's drive and excitement transformed the lives of men and communities. Social zephyrs became raging tornadoes that ripped up established custom and tradition and brought drastic change.

This was but one evidence of the nation's industrial transition during the nineteen twenties, which also affected manufacturing, railroading, mining, and city building. But the oil field's growing pains were the fiercest and most convulsive.

America had become oil conscious. Oil became the magic fluid that drew railroad trains, drove streetcars, pumped water, lifted heavy loads, greased factory wheels, flew airplanes, and propelled giant tractors, construction machines, and tanks. Through long arteries of steel, or by tank car, tanker, and barge, petroleum's blood banks, it kept pulsating cities of steel, the refineries—mazes of big and little pipes, cavernous roaring furnaces, towering stills, and large-dimension tanks. These cities of steel, with thousands of lights—electric, gas-torch, and the glow of furnaces and chimneys

Oil! Titan of the Southwest

—shining at night, worked day and night to process this black, magic fluid to power a dawning mechanized age, to answer the nation's industrial challenge.

In 1923, Max Bentley, in his brilliantly written "Smackover, and Seekers of Oil," well asked: "What was it that made a quarter of a million men in dozens of oil fields forsake the comforts of home life last year and drill 17,338 producing wells, and nobody knows how many dusters, to increase our production by only 78,000,000 barrels? . . . At $20,000 per well the cash-over-the-counter cost of those 17,338 actual completions was $36,000,000 or $4.50 for every barrel of two-dollar oil, two dollars being a fair average price the country over."[1] Then he estimated that if the average daily production per well in the United States was 4.9 barrels, a figure computed by the United States Geological Survey, the grand total for 1922 was obtained from 310,000 wells. "What mad logic justified this chase after rainbow gold," he asked, when the money spent in producing 78,-000,000-barrels increase would have paid for all the oil produced in the United States in any year prior to 1917? In fact, there was no mad logic; these oil-field expenditures were risky investments. Yet the compelling spirit back of them was magnificent; it was an excellent example of the driving buoyant force of American private enterprise.

The *Petroleum Age* of September 1, 1921, listed the oil-rich country of southwestern Arkansas, northwestern Louisiana, and eastern Texas as the "Triangle Field," just why, it did not say. But the name *"el dorado,"* popularly interpreted the "land of gold," said to have been applied by early settlers to southwestern Arkansas, would have been more appropriate. In 1843, when a Union County commission decided to move its records from Champagnolle, it picked a new townsite, far removed from the nearest settlement, laid off the streets, built a small log courthouse, and called the place "El Dorado."

This "land of gold," of course, is a traditional story of that region. Whether it is true or not, the fact remains that underneath the rolling, tree-clad hills were oil-bearing formations that one day would be worth far more gold than the combined holdings of Croesus and Midas. El Dorado and Smackover during the nineteen

[1] *Harpers Magazine*, Vol. XLV, No. 12 (December, 1923), 73–74.

208

twenties, and later Magnolia and Rodessa, became synonyms for petroleum and gas, the twin products of wealth far beyond the most ambitious dreams of the early settlers in the region.

Of these major oil fields, El Dorado was the first to have its boom. El Dorado had been a quiet rural town with dirt roads reaching back into prosperous farm communities, content with its surrounding beach and pine-forested hills; with its peaceful valleys; with its farms, from which it drew its trade; and with its fruit orchards, and its fields of corn, cotton, Irish and sweet potatoes, rye, broom corn, and millet. There was seldom any excitement or unusual event to break the town's even-tenored way of life. Day after day people went about their routine tasks, rested on the seventh day, then entered a new week expecting little change.

El Dorado's red brick courthouse gave the town proprietary right over Union County affairs. And on Saturday, roads were thronged with men on horseback and families in wagons and buggies, but not on other days. Saturday afternoon was a part of the week-end rest period for the farmers, who came to town to exchange eggs, butter, fresh vegetables, and melons for staple groceries, dry goods, and occasional luxuries.

Then strangers, keen-eyed and silent, wearing corduroys, heavy shoes, and leggings, showed up in El Dorado. At night they stayed at the local hotels but during the day they trudged through the dense underbrush of ravines and creeks, over the tree-clad hills, or across the pasture lands and farms, looking for "structure." These were oil prospectors, scientific and unscientific, who believed that Union County was oil country.

El Doradoans could hardly give credit to oil rumors. They had heard of oil, some of their friends had visited Texas and Oklahoma oil fields and had been a part of their excitement, bustle, and confusion, but they could not believe that Union County would ever witness such scenes. Then prospectors went away, and for a time peace and routine life returned. But soon other strangers came with long wagons loaded with derrick timbers, boilers, piping, and miscellaneous oil-field equipment. Derricks rose above the pines, and the nights and days were filled with foreign noises—the hiss of steam, the sound of hammer and saw, the clamor of the tool dresser's anvil, and the heavy rumble of wagons. It was only then that El

209

Oil! Titan of the Southwest

Doradoans became greatly interested, talked of lease and royalty offers, and speculated on oil prospects.

Next came the roar of escaping gas and geysers of oil, accompanied by hurry and scramble, crowds, frenzied transactions, and confusion; and soon El Dorado found itself the center of a new life, whether it wished it or not.

Arkansas had little oil prior to 1921.[2] True, a number of wells had been drilled, many of which became gassers and a few of which produced small quantities of oil. Forty-seven wells were drilled in 1910, thirty-seven of which made gas wells, raising the state's total to 103. Three years later five wells were drilled in four counties, but all were dry; and in 1914 a sixth duster was completed near Ozark.[3] Such failures as these made the El Doradoans doubtful of local success.

To a Tulsan, Bruce Hunt, goes the chief credit for El Dorado's oil discovery. In 1919 he borrowed $250 from his friend, Sam Arrendale, came to El Dorado, and leased 12,522 acres of land. He and a geologist, J. J. Victor, then "chose the Constantin Refining Company to drill the well and a division was made for drilling a test."[4]

A short time later Constantin's drilling crew was busy, day and night, on their No. 1 Hill, a short distance west of El Dorado.[5] On April 22, 1920, the drill bit into the Nacatoch sand at more than 2,200 feet, and a huge volume of gas, estimated at 40,000,000 cubic feet daily, roared from the casing head, with about eight barrels of oil.[6] Even then local people were not excited, for Fort Smith wells for many years had produced only gas.

It was not until January 10 of the next year that the El Dorado

[2] The Hunter Oil Company's well, about a 100-barrel producer, near Stephens, in Ouachita County, on April 14, 1920, was Arkansas' first oil well. By 1925 about 500 wells were drilled in this field, but all those producing oil were small. Two other minor oil fields were later discovered in this area; the Smart field, four miles northwest of Stephens, in December, 1940; and the Wesson field, three miles east of town, in September, 1945.—Fred H. Ward to C. C. Rister, March 13, 1948.

[3] *Mineral Resources of the United States, 1910, Part II, Nonmetals*, 320; *ibid.*, 1913, 1078.

[4] Juanita Whitaker Green, "History of Union County, Arkansas" (unpublished Master of Arts thesis, University of Texas, August, 1936), 80. Mrs. Mamie Smith McCurry, a well-known El Dorado operator, became associated with Hunt in the East Side Oil and Gas Company.

[5] Located in S1-T18S-R16W.

[6] *Oil and Gas Journal*, Vol. XVIII, No. 49 (May 7, 1920), 1; W. C. Spooner, *Oil and Gas Geology of the Gulf Coastal Plain in Arkansas*, 154.

payoff came, when the Busey-Mitchell interests completed their No. 1 Armstrong well,[7] which yielded from 15,000,000 to 35,000,000 cubic feet of gas and an initial 3,000 to 10,000 barrels of oil daily. By February, this well, choked back, still made 1,000 to 1,500 barrels of clean oil daily. The Shreveport Producing and Refining Company extended the field a mile farther south on March 19, by a well with a flow of 15,000 to 20,000 barrels a day. This "startled the oil fraternity" and made El Dorado "the youngest gold field of the Mid-Continent Mineral Section."[8] The field was almost two miles long, from north to south, and a mile wide. Then on May 7 and September 4, two other wells reached deeper horizons, the Meakin and the Tokio-Woodbine sands, guaranteeing that there would be major production in the field.[9]

El Dorado excitement knew no bounds. "Fully 5,000 strangers are making their headquarters in town," said an observer in February, 1921.[10] To handle this new situation, the Chamber of Commerce and city and county authorities joined hands to keep down profiteering and to keep out undesirables.

In May, acreage prices were high, one tract of sixty-five acres, half a mile from the Constantin Refining Company's new well, bringing $10,000; and Tulsa and Shreveport buyers paid $21,000 for another one-hundred-acre tract. Within four months after the Constantin's No. 1 Hill well became a producer, Captain Eugene Constantin was reported to have bought a chateau at Widville, justy forty-five minutes by taxicab from the heart of Paris, France. This estate of 780 acres was graced by a Louis XIII castle with a beautiful winding drive, banked with cedars and interspersed with flower gardens.[11]

Wildcatting and prospecting spread with the customary speed. "Derricks are blooming throughout the state regardless of geologists and mapped formations," wrote an enthusiast. "Hope is rampant."

El Dorado's boom continued to gain momentum. "Not less than

[7] Located in S31-T17S-R15W.

[8] *Times-Picayune* (New Orleans), Thursday, March 24, 1921, p. 1, col. 2.

[9] George H. Fancher and Donald K. MacKay, *Secondary Recovery of Petroleum in Arkansas*, 129.

[10] "El Dorado Well May Be Lost Thru Gas," in *Oil Trade Journal*, Vol. XII, No. 2 (February, 1921), 13, 102.

[11] *National Petroleum News*, Vol. XII, No. 18 (May 5, 1920), 38.

50 new rigs are already in route to El Dorado," asserted a field reporter.[12] Most of them were being shipped from Shreveport, Beaumont, Houston, and other rotary districts, since heaving shale in the wells called for rotary rigs. *The Oil and Gas Journal* predicted "a prolific oil pool there."[13] By August, 1921, derricks literally forested the oil field, which had reached its peak with an annual 1,746,294 barrels of oil. By June, 1921, more than 100 oil wells were drilled and 340 derricks were being built to start others. Three months later production had climbed to 74,364 barrels a week. In September, 1921, leaseholders cashed in at around $2,000 an acre, where a month previously the top price had been $1,000. The Southern Land and Oil Company, backed by Michigan capital, bought the Busey-Mitchell Oil Company interests at a handsome figure, and other large transactions were reported.

Some visitors pronounced El Dorado oil "dead," since for the most part it tested from 18 to 23 degrees Baumé. This caused the Standard Oil Company of Louisiana to post a price of fifty to seventy cents a barrel, much to the disappointment of producers who had expected eighty cents to one dollar a barrel. But low prices did not halt pipe-line operations. Arrangements were pushed to connect the field with refining centers. The Standard's ten-inch line from Wellers' Station, Louisiana, was approaching El Dorado, and the Louisiana Oil and Refining Company was expected to reach the field by July 4.

The Standard had about eight miles of eight-inch gathering pipe laid from its pumping station in the McKinney tract.[14] This new pumping station was beside the Rock Island Railroad tracks, and warehouses were being erected by the same company. The railroad was moving more than 400 cars of crude oil from the field every day, and an entire trainload of oil was billed for Canada from the Jean Anne well on the Rogers lease.[15]

The midsummer of 1921 also saw other rapid developments. The Gilliland Oil Company was working on a new pipe line from El Dorado to Haynesville; and prominent Shreveport oil operators

[12] *Ibid.*
[13] Vol. XVIII, No. 48 (April 30, 1920), 3.
[14] S5-T18S-R16W.
[15] *Oil Trade Journal,* Vol. XII, No. 6 (June, 1921), 17.

had organized a $2,500,000 company, the Shreveport–El Dorado Pipe Line Company, to connect with the new field, with branch lines to Homer and Haynesville. The Southern Oil Corporation laid a four-inch line to the Bradstreet and Widerman wells to transport oil to its new thirty-five-car loading rack on the Rock Island just south of the Shreveport Producing and Pumping Company's loading rack.[16] Tanks were also being built, although a large quantity of the oil was yet impounded in creeks, ravines, and open ground tanks. The Gladys Belle Oil and Gas Company had started construction for one tank on the Orell tract in Section 5, and the Boggs Oil Corporation had started work on another on the Belle lease in Section 31.

Meanwhile, active prospecting spread from El Dorado to all parts of southwestern Arkansas, and brought the discovery of other oil fields—Irma, October, 1921, and East El Dorado, Woodley, Smackover, and Stephens, in 1922. But Smackover was the king-bee of them all.

Smackover, a short distance north of El Dorado, also proved to be a part of Arkansas' *el dorado*. Prior to 1922 it had been a mere flag station of sixty souls on the Missouri Pacific Railroad. It had no urban ambitions and was satisfied with its tranquil life and rural wealth. But it, too, went through a revolutionary change after the discovery of the Oil Operators' Trust No. 1 J. T. Murphy well[17] on April 14, 1922, and emerged as a bustling town of 2,500 people. The Smackover oil field also had an enormous gas production. The discovery well flowed 30,000,000 cubic feet of gas a day, and other wells were even larger. The Murphy well tapped the Nacatoch sand at 2,024 feet, from which a strong head of gas blew out a crater 450 feet wide and 50 feet deep.

The V. K. F. Oil Company's No. 1 Richardson well[18] was Smackover's first oil well, and within the next year 1,000 wells were completed which produced 25,000,000 barrels of oil, thus making Smackover Arkansas' greatest field.

Several oil-bearing formations—the Nacatoch, the Meakin, and the Graves sand, and the Smackover limestone—made the field

---

[16] *Ibid.*
[17] Located in S8-T16S-R15W.
[18] Located in S29-T15S-R15W.

much richer than the one at El Dorado. From the Nacatoch sand came the largest oil well, a 25,000-barrel producer, which Bentley eloquently described as the largest oil well in America, that had filled a 1,000-barrel sand-tank in twenty minutes. Other wells yielded 5,000 to 10,000 barrels daily.

Smackover had both light and heavy oil. Light oil, 23 to 28 degrees A. P. I., was found in the Meakin sand and in the Louan district; and the heavy oil, 18 to 23 degrees A. P. I., in the Nacatoch, Graves, and Blossom sands. The field reached its peak in 1925 with an annual 69,000,000 barrels of oil, 9,500,000 barrels of which were light and 59,500,000 heavy. But after it had passed its peak, Smackover started a swift decline, just as El Dorado had; and on January 1, 1930, of the 2,998 producing wells, 962 yielded daily 5,290 barrels of light oil and 2,036 produced 41,837 barrels of heavy oil, making a total of only 47,127 barrels.

Both El Dorado and Smackover had experienced prodigal waste, as had all other major oil fields of the Mid-Continent up to this time. Both fields had large volumes of gas so that their wells had adequate lifting force for the oil. But gas was burned in giant torches or vented to the air, sometimes being allowed to flow with the hope that the gas would change to oil. Oil, too, was wasted recklessly. An *Oil Trade Journal* reporter noticed that the Smackover field was "dotted with lakes of oil, lying at the mercy of the elements."[19] A dry period or a heavy rain might cause the earthen banks to crumble, thus releasing the precious fluid into creeks and bayous; or a bolt of lightning wreak more widespread havoc. In both fields, tens of thousands of barrels of crude were in earthen reservoirs, awaiting pipe lines and steel tanks, from six months to a year before they were generally available, although heedless drilling went on.

But on the credit side of the ledger, both fields had made an enormous contribution to the state's wealth by the turn of the next decade, more than one-third of a billion barrels of petroleum. The Smackover field alone had 330,000,000 barrels; and, in 1925, produced for the state's severance tax more than 70,000,000 barrels of oil.[20] Then the immediate impact on the economic and social life

[19] *Oil Trade Journal*, Vol. XIV, No. 1 (January, 1923), 13–14.
[20] Arkansas Oil and Gas Commission, *Midyear 1940 Survey of the Oil and Gas Industry in Arkansas*, 5.

of the region was noticeable. El Dorado's dirt streets disappeared under concrete; the red brick courthouse was supplanted by one of stone; and modern office buildings, stores, churches, schools, and beautiful homes were built. Although Smackover was a smaller town, it, too, was similarly changed.

Within little more than a decade, active prospecting finally brought an oil-producing zone from the Urbana field of Union County on the east to Fouke in Miller County on the west, including such minor fields as Champagnolle, Lisbon, Schuler, Stephens, and Magnolia.

Northwestern Louisiana, commercially and geographically, was also a part of what early settlers had called "the land of gold." Within this region, Caddo, as has been pointed out previously, was Louisiana's oil mainstay from 1904 to 1933, producing 140,000,000 barrels of the state's one-half billion barrels. But it was a neighbor to other great fields. In 1920, the Homer oil field (in T21N-R7 and 8W),[21] in Claiborne Parish, produced 21,508,000 barrels of petroleum of the state's 35,714,000 barrels; and by 1933 its total output was 64,500,000 barrels, the field ranking second in the state. Homer's initial production was from the Nacatoch sand, on the upthrow and north side of a fault. After the discovery of the field in May, 1919, it was drilled quickly and reached its peak in 1920 with 22,182,836 barrels of oil.[22]

The Haynesville oil field, also in Claiborne Parish, and north of Homer, was northwestern Louisiana's third *el dorado* field, lying off the eastern edge of the Sabine Uplift.[23] Its first well, drilled by the Smitherman-Anderson Company,[24] on March 30, 1921, was completed as an 8,000-barrel oil well in the Blossom sand at 2,850 feet and was followed by a wild leasing and drilling campaign, although through the efforts of the Conservation Department, operators agreed to drill no closer than 330 feet of property lines. In this

[21] *Report of the Division of Minerals, Department of Conservation, 1926–1928* (New Orleans), 18.

[22] *Oil Weekly*, Vol. XVI, No. 1 (January 10, 1920), 20; *Hearings . . . on H. Res. 441, September 17, 18, 19, 21 and 22, 1934*, Part 2, pp. 985 ff.

[23] Mainly in T23N-R9W.

[24] James E. Smitherman organized the company and helped to secure the company's 30,000-acre lease block. C. B. Smitherman was a member of the discovery well's drill crew.—Interview with C. B. Smitherman, January 6, 1948.

first year the field produced 3,000,000 barrels of crude oil; and in the next year it climbed to its peak, 20,299,911 barrels. But its decline was as swift as Homer's. In 1929 its yearly crude oil output was but 2,631,817 barrels.

Other northwestern Louisiana fields during the nineteen twenties—Bellevue, Cotton Valley, De Soto—Red River, Elm Grove, Urania, and Zwolle—had threatened to divert operators' attention from these major oil fields, but no one of them became a major field.

Northern Louisiana Oil Production, 1920–29[25]
(Thousands of barrels)

District	1920	1921	1922	1923	1924	1925	1926	1927	1928
Bellevue	-----	-----	1,050	2,351	1,749	1,129	789	472	323
Caddo	6,336	5,342	4,498	4,178	4,319	4,067	4,749	5,789	4,798
Cotton Valley	-----	-----	-----	-----	1,211	3,348	2,914	1,968	1,731
De Soto	-----	719	531	429	353	305	321	541	463
Elm Grove	-----	-----	-----	220	217	212	222	222	185
Haynesville	-----	3,161	19,939	10,496	6,720	4,604	3,328	2,600	2,150
Homer	21,508	13,030	5,673	3,581	2,837	2,296	2,033	1,785	1,548
Red River	5,923	2,844	1,778	1,207	1,231	1,074	1,037	1,070	1,109
Urania	-----	-----	-----	-----	-----	10	3,669	3,321	2,487
Other fields	-----	77	100	7	-----	-----	-----	-----	-----
Totals	33,767	25,173	33,629	22,469	18,637	17,045	19,062	17,768	14,794

A late arrival was Rodessa, about thirty miles northwest of Shreveport, the fourth of northwestern Louisiana's great fields. Here was found a far-flung reservoir of oil along a fault line that straddled the Louisiana-Texas boundary north of Shreveport and that furnished its own gas lift for 50,000 barrels of crude oil daily as late as 1937.

As far back as 1910 wildcatters had prospected the Rodessa area, hoping to find oil; and from that date until 1925, a total of ten tests were drilled along the Rodessa trend. The Latex Community Oil Company drilled the deepest of these tests in 1922, located on the same twenty-acre tract on which the discovery gas well was drilled years later; it was abandoned at a depth of 3,266 feet.

After the drilling of these tests, Dan L. Perkins, a consulting geologist of Shreveport, studied carefully the area's well logs and

[25] Charles B. Eliot, *Petroleum Industry of the Gulf Southwest*, 23.

Lunch counter, Smackover, Arkansas

Album of Mrs. Mamie Smith McCurry

Aerial view of Lion Oil Company refinery, El Dorado,
Arkansas

Lion Oil Company

In Smackover mud

Album of Mrs. Mamie Smith McCurry

Loading rack of Union Pipe Line and Refining Company,
El Dorado

Album of Mrs. Mamie Smith McCurry

concluded that a fault existed northeast-southwest across the area and leased 6,000 acres centering about two and one-half miles southwest of the town of Rodessa.

Here Perkins and W. J. Stauffer of New Orleans drilled a test to 3,003 feet, which they abandoned as being structurally low. The next year Perkins interested the Ohio Oil Company in his lease, and seven wells were drilled on the block during 1926 and 1927, all of them dry.

The Ohio Oil Company then turned the leases back to Perkins, who a short time later, entered an agreement with the Humble Oil and Refining Company. But Humble failed to drill, and the leases again reverted to Perkins.

Still presevering, he persuaded R. W. Norton, an independent producer of San Antonio, Texas, to enter a partnership with him. On August 21, 1929, Norton spudded his No. 1 O. J. Hill well,[26] which was finished on August 3, 1930. This was Rodessa's discovery well, completed at a total depth of 5,509 feet in the lower Glen Rose section of the Trinity Group, about 300 feet from a well drilled in 1921.[27] The No. 1 Hill had a daily potential of 11,242,000 cubic feet of wet gas. The gas rights in this field were then sold to the United Gas Public Service Company.

But for five years the field produced only gas[28]—in 1934 making 13,934,264,000 cubic feet, the third largest gas-producing field in Louisiana that year. The first oil well was not found until July 7, 1935. On this date the United Gas Public Service Company completed its No. 1 Young well as a fair producer (about one and one-half miles north of the Hill well), at 6,048 feet. The oil found had a pure paraffin base. Then the rush began, with wells going down like magic. Rodessa's production reached a peak in 1936 with 19,-224,232 barrels of oil.

Here again was a striking example of waste. Some companies

[26] Located in the S/2 of S33-T23N-R16W.

[27] "Report On The Rodessa Oil Field," mimeographed copy, Railroad Commission of Texas, Austin, December 15, 1937, 1–2; Sunday *Item-Tribune*, March 14, 1937.

[28] The gas field consisted of a strip of land about one and one-half miles wide in a northwest-northeast direction and about five miles long in a northeast-southwest direction lying in the south half of T23N-R16W and the northwest corner of T22N-R16W and extending into the eastern portion of Cass County, Texas.—*Twelfth Biennial Report of the Department of Conservation, state of Louisiana*, 1934–35, 404.

which "ten-spotted" (one well to every ten acres) their properties were charged with overpulling. By the fall of 1936 the amount of gas flared daily reached 700,000,000 cubic feet, causing a startling drop in reservoir pressure. Commissioner William Rankin warned Governor Richard W. Leche that the field's gas pressure would soon be depleted unless the waste problem was solved. As a temporary measure the commission issued Order No. 7, limiting Rodessa gas wells to 12,000,000 cubic feet of gas a day and its oil wells to 6,000,-000 cubic feet a day.

The Conservation Commission used this as a basis for its new policy, not recognizing "distillate" wells, allowing gas wells the previously fixed allowables and limiting oil wells to not more than 2,000 cubic feet of natural gas per barrel of all oil brought to the surface. This laid the basis of a long-term oil output, making Rodessa one of the state's greatest producers. By the end of 1945, Rodessa had produced 86,272,000 barrels of crude oil.[29]

Petroleum has in a real sense made an *el dorado* of the region embraced in southwestern Arkansas and northwestern Louisiana, thus fulfilling the forecasts of its first settlers. More than a half-billion dollars have come from oil, bringing prosperity to the region and hope to its people.

[29] "Louisiana Oil," in *The Link*, Vol. X, No. 3 (March, 1946), 4.

XVII

Texas Forges Ahead

INTERWOVEN with Texas petroleum history during the half-decade, 1925–30, like the scarlet strand in the English navy rope,
appears the influence of men of science, of the geologists, and of
the geophysicists (as Alexander Duessen and E. DeGolyer[1] in their
employment of the seismograph and torsion balance in the salt-
dome fields). During 1925 alone, seven new salt domes were discovered by geophysical methods, in each case when there was no
surface evidence of a dome such as elevations, gas, oil seeps, and
paraffin dirt.[2]

The friendly state rivalry of oil production in the Southwest in
some respects was like an ancient chariot race, although run in
relays, with Oklahoma's oil chariot, pulled by such tired thorough-
breds as Glenn Pool, Cushing, Healdton, and Burbank, well out in
front until the last lap of the race. The Texas chariot was running
second, with Louisiana, Arkansas, and Kansas strung along the race
course, and in that order.

The Texas oil chariot was pulled by a mixed team—the up-and-
coming giant thoroughbreds, Yates, Hendricks, and Borger; the
jaded nags, Electra, Burkburnett, Ranger, Breckenridge, Desde-

---

[1] DeGolyer has been the recipient of some of the highest honorary awards in
the industry, including the Distinguished Service Award of the Texas Division, Mid-
Continent Oil and Gas Association; the A.I.M.E.'s Anthony F. Lucas Medal, and
the John Fritz Medal of the Four Founders Society.

[2] L. H. Friedman, "Geophysical Methods Replacing Wildcat Drilling," in *Oil
Weekly*, Vol. XL, No. 11 (March 5, 1918), 84.

The seismograph is a portable instrument that measures earth sound waves (set
off by dynamite charges) on a sensitive paper by a ray of light photographing the
sounds' impressions. A torsion balance is an instrument that measures minute differences in the gravitational attraction of the earth at different places.—Max Ball,
This Fascinating Oil Business, 73–76, 71–72.

Duessen to Rister, February 27, 1947; *Fortune*, January, 1946, 130.

mona, Mexia, Powell, Luling, Spindletop, and Humble; and many small broomtail nags. But the strength and drive of the thorough-breds more than offset the feeble efforts of the other members of the Texas team to pull this state out in front by 1928.[3]

Oil-production figures show how Texas' primacy was won. In 1925 Texas increased its oil production by 10,000,000 barrels; in 1926, by 22,000,000 barrels; in 1927, by 50,000,000 barrels; in 1928, by 40,000,000 barrels; and in 1929, by 39,000,000 barrels.[4] During the next year oil fields had been opened in practically every geographical division of Texas, although they were widely separated and the grades of oil, size and depth of wells, and types of producing formations differed greatly.

Texas oil fields multiplied in proportion to the rapid spread of prospecting; yet most of the discoveries were minor. But two new producing areas—the Panhandle and West Texas—were so extensive as to stagger the belief of experienced oilmen, so extensive, indeed, as each to command later chapters in this narrative.

Texas-wide prospecting and wildcatting were responsible for a number of minor oil-field discoveries during 1925–30 and for the extension or deepening of old fields.[5] In North Central Texas were the Cook Ranch field, in Shackelford County; the Fry Pool, in Brown County; and the Hooser field, in Cooke County. In 1928 major flush production was found in the Greyback field, in Wilbarger County, where light-oil wells were completed with daily initial flows of several thousand barrels, only to fizzle when once the reservoir pressure of the field declined. But these discoveries led to widespread exploration in Brown, Cooke, Coleman, Shackelford, and Wilbarger counties and to other minor discoveries, as in Foard County. Nevertheless, Archer, Cooke, and Wilbarger continued to be the leading counties of the region. North Central Texas fields, whether major or minor, were profitable because their oil sands were shallow and conditions favored independent wildcatters with limited means.[6] In 1929 the region produced 52,046,000 barrels of petroleum as compared with 49,459,000 barrels the preceding year.

[3] Charles B. Eliot, *Petroleum Industry of the Gulf Southwest*, 31.

[4] For Texas's oil output for each of these years, 1925, 1926, 1927, 1928, and 1929, see *Mineral Resources of the United States, Part II, Nonmetals*, 329–30, 358–59, 536–37, 645–47, and 457–61 respectively.

[5] *Ibid.*

Texas Forges Ahead

Prospecting was also active along the Balcones and Mexia fault zones during this period, and minor pools were found and old ones extended. Yet the Mexia-Powell-Wortham area continued its production decline.[7] In 1926 the shallow Thrall-Minerva area was the center of attention and showed a substantial oil output. The Nigger Creek field, which will be treated more fully later, was an exciting trial of a geologist's theory, to prove only in part correct. And in August, 1927, Cedar Creek, in Limestone County, and Dale, a serpentine field, in Caldwell County, were opened but later were classed as minor. Geologists gave the most attention to the finding of oil at Boggy Creek, on the boundary of Cherokee and Anderson counties, since this field was the first one found on an inland salt dome, which, of course, led to a search for others. Then the Bruner field, near Luling, was discovered in 1928, beginning inauspiciously with small Austin Chalk formation wells but growing in importance when sizable production was found a year later in the Edwards lime.

The Van oil field discovery, in Van Zandt County, on October 14, 1929, served to rivet the eyes of oilmen on East Texas, and in that sense acted as a curtain raiser for the huge East Texas field of the next year. The Van field was on a large, well-defined structure and caused much speculation. Its output in 1929 reached 144,000 barrels of oil, although its first well was not brought in until the middle of October. The Pure,[8] Sun, Shell, Texas, and Humble com-

6 "Wildcat Completions Feature Week in North Texas," in *Oil Weekly*, Vol. XL, No. 8 (February 12, 1926), 30. Among the North Central Texas oil pools discovered during this period were Overall (March 8, 1927), the Sealey-Smith (February 10, 1928), the Weaver (February 3, 1929), and the Moody (May, 1929), in Coleman County; the Dyer (July 3, 1927), and the Storm (November 25, 1929), in Eastland County; the Thompson (July 29, 1929), in Comanche County; the Thalia (October, 1927), in Foard County; the Otto (March 24, 1927), in Cooke County; the Costello-Root-Thodes (July 29, 1929), in Palo Pinto County; and the Dunigan (October 6, 1929), in Taylor County. See "Summary Report of New Pools," Records of Petroleum Administration Board, Natural Resources Records Office, National Archives, Washington, D. C.

7 L. E. Bredbert, "Revival of Drilling in Old Fields," in *Oil and Gas Journal*, Vol. XXVIII (June 20, 1929), 42. Bredbert described the Graham field as having "an important present."

8 The Pure Oil Company, the Ohio Cities Gas Company, the Oklahoma Producing and Refining Company, and the Humphrey Oil Company are pillars upon which grew the present Pure Oil Company, among the youngest of the major independent oil companies of the United States. Since the Pure Oil Company opened the Cabin Creek, West Virginia, oil field on December 18, 1914, it opened the Van

panies consolidated their leaseholdings and inaugurated a unit plan of operation, with each company sharing profits and expenses in proportion to their holdings. The result was that there were few dry holes out of 600 wells drilled, and the field, which had produced 110,266,334 barrels of oil up to January 1, 1938, still had a considerable reservoir pressure.[9]

Van's output, and that of the Bruner or Salt Flat field of Caldwell and Guadalupe counties, helped to lift the East and South Central Texas areas from a production of 27,368,000 barrels of petroleum in 1929 to 40,445,000 in 1930. Bruner alone produced 13,286,000 barrels of oil in 1929, only to decline to 7,305,000 barrels in the next year.

Excluding Van, oil production in other East and South Central Texas fields along the Balcones fault and scattered pools like Boggy Creek, Thrall, Pettus, and Calliham, showed a satisfactory gain in 1930. Darst Creek, including the smaller Manford field, was registered on the region's oil column for the first time in 1929, with 243,000 barrels; but in the next year it rose to a respectable 11,424,000 barrels.[10] However, production in other fault-line fields fell off, as at Salt Flat. Yet new discoveries at Chapman, a Williamson County serpentine field, and at Pettus in Bee County, compensated for this loss. In addition, extensive wildcatting in Bee and Goliad counties brought other minor discoveries, with Kerr County reporting a small producer.

Southwest Texas,[11] including oil fields in Jim Hogg, Webb, and Zapata counties, and in Duval County, except the salt-dome field at

---

field of East Texas, the Sweet Lake, Gueydan, Ganado, and Louise fields of the Gulf Coast region, new fields in Michigan and southern Illinois, the Cumberland and Pauls Valley fields of Oklahoma, the Worland pool in Wyoming, and the Dollarhide field, Andrews County, in West Texas. Pure has also secured substantial interests in such fields as Seminole and Edmond in Oklahoma; East Texas; Winkler, Goldsmith, Keystone, and McCamey in West Texas; Cooper in New Mexico; and the Bosco field of Coastal Louisiana. At present it owns pipe lines, tankers, terminals, and refineries in five states.

[9] C. A. Warner, *Texas Oil and Gas Since 1543*, 191; *Mineral Resources of the United States, 1929, Part II, Nonmetals*, 458.

[10] *Ibid.*, 1930, 816.

[11] Known as the "Laredo district," embracing the producing fields of Aviator-Schott, Carolina-Texas (gas), Cole (gas), Charco-Redondo, Jennings (only gas), Henne-Winch-Fariss, Mirando Valley, and Randado.—P. W. McFarland, "Laredo District Texas," in *Structure of Typical American Oil Fields*, I, 389.

Texas Forges Ahead

Piedras Pintas, had added its name to the oil-producing regions of Texas by 1922. And seven years later it produced 3,850,000 barrels annually. Still no new fields were opened, and it is difficult to assign specific causes for this region's success, although the completion of a great number of shallow wells could have been a factor. By 1929 new fields at Driscoll in Duval County, at Escobar in Zapata County, at Palo Blanco in Brooks County, and near Roma in Starr County, had increased the importance of this area. The Roma field marked the most southerly point at which oil had been discovered in the United States.

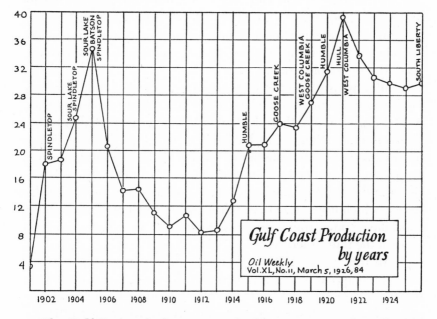

Gulf Coast Production by years
Oil Weekly
Vol. XL, No. 11, March 5, 1926, 84

The Gulf Coast salt-dome region had been a major oil-producing district of Texas since the days of the Lucas gusher.[12] In 1925 it reported an increase of 3,803,000 barrels over the previous year, chiefly because of oil play at South Liberty and mounting effectiveness in finding new fields and deepening old ones. The South Liberty salt dome, in Liberty County, discovered in 1904, produced but slightly and only from shallow wells until January 1, 1925, when the Winifree Oil Company brought in its No. 1 Pickett well for

[12] See a production table in *Oil Weekly*, Vol. XL, No. 4 (January 15, 1926), 103.

about 750 barrels initial production from a sand 3,419 to 3,480 feet deep. Since the land on all sides of the discovery well was leased in small tracts, a frenzied drilling campaign followed, with a consequent dissipation of the field's reservoir energy. In this mad scramble, approximately 196 wells were drilled, of which 148 were productive. All told, South Liberty yielded 4,500,000 barrels of oil for the year.

Moreover, the comeback of Spindletop added zest to the region's operations. Other fields, too, hit the comeback trail, as at Pierce Junction (the dome's west side), Big Creek, and Blue Ridge. Exploratory drilling added Gay Hill in Washington County, Sugarland in Fort Bend County, and Boling in Wharton County. The Gay Hill discovery was particularly interesting from the point of view of geology, as it was the first time that production was found in the Cook Mountain formation.

Contemporary records reveal many interesting narratives of what otherwise might be classed as unimportant, commonplace events. For example, there is the Paul Wagner explanation of the discovery of the Nigger Creek oil field, near Mexia, in 1926.[13] Wagner relates that in the summer of 1924 a Dallas geologist, Leon J. Pepperberg, advanced a new fault-line theory. He believed that Mexia and Powell oil might not have migrated up the dip of the beds in which it was found, as other geologists thought, but that it could have come from a deeper formation,[14] the oil migrating up through the fault fracture.

With this in mind, Pepperberg sought a place where closure might be mapped in association with a Mexia-type faulting. One day while lunching with Heath M. Robinson, formerly of the United States Geological Survey and afterwards with the Humphreys Corporation, Pepperberg broached his novel idea. Robinson became greatly interested and told Pepperberg that he knew of a place where surface conditions met his requirements. A short

[13] Paul Wagner, "Geology Responsible for Finding New Oil Field West of Mexia," *National Petroleum News*, Vol. XVIII, No. 30 (July 28, 1926), 87–89; Leon J. Pepperberg, "Nigger Creek Field," in *Structure of Typical American Oil Fields*, I, 410.

[14] This area rapidly declined in production during 1925, going from a high of 3,600,000 barrels in January to a low of a little more than 400,000 in December.— H. H. King, "Mexia-Corsicana Decline Rapid During the Last Half of 1925," *Oil Weekly*, Vol. XL, No. 5 (January 22, 1926), 37.

Humble's Baytown, Texas, refinery under construction

Humble Oil and Refining Company

Humble oil refinery at Baytown today

photograph by Corsini
Standard Oil Company (N. J.)

Oriole gusher in the Batson field, July 4, 1903

Port Arthur, Texas, refinery today

time later the two men visited this place, the Nigger Creek area, and mapped its structure, taking the logs of previously drilled shallow wells on the Cochrum and Ross farms for data. The site was about five and one-half miles west of Mexia, in Limestone County, and three and one-half miles west of the south end of the Mexia oil field.

Their next step was to secure company backing to test their theory, but Mexia operators showed little interest. Finally, a third geologist, William E. Wrather of Dallas, who had discovered the Desdemona structure, was attracted by the possibilities of oil on an up-dip fault and provided the means of testing the theory.

He sold the idea to the Transcontinental Oil Company, whose headquarters were at Pittsburgh, Pennsylvania, a company which had earlier acquired the properties of Wrather and others during the Desdemona boom.

Transcontinental put George H. Gay, of its land department, into the Mexia area; and by February, 1925, he had blocked out about 1,400 acres of leases on the Nigger Creek structure, carrying the three geologists mentioned for a one-eighth working interest in the property if oil were discovered.

Then operations started, and on July 8, 1926, Transcontinental's No. 1 Rosson well came in at 2,846 feet in the Woodbine sand with an initial flow of 2,797 barrels during the first twenty-four hours.[15] The gravity of the oil was 39.9 degrees Baumé.[16] A week later the well still held a daily output of 2,600 barrels. Then twelve days later Transcontinental's No. 1 Cochrum was completed with an initial output of 4,000 barrels a day.

Meanwhile, lease and royalty operations zoomed, the trend broadening along a northeast-southwest direction, along the "inside" fault on which the Transcontinental well was located. But outsiders found that Transcontinental, the Pure Oil Company, and the Foster-Reiter Oil Corporation held most of the desirable leases.[17]

[15] D. C. "Blackie" Lee, driller; Oliver Mapes, floorman; D. E. Lancaster, fireman; J. O. Lancaster, floorman; and Joe Harris, derrickman, composed the drilling crew.

[16] J. P. D. Hull, "Discovery of Nigger Creek Oil Pool, Limestone County, Texas," in American Association of Petroleum Geologists, Bull. No. 10, 997.

[17] One writer mentioned that "leases were bought up to $50 per acre from below the town of Tehuacana to the Comanche Creek crossing of the Navasota River."— King, loc. cit., 37.

Oil! Titan of the Southwest

From the first, lease and royalty prices skyrocketed. Royalty owners asked from $4,000 to $6,000 an acre base for full one-eighth interest; and lease owners within a mile and one-half or two miles of the discovery well asked $2,000 an acre and more for their holdings. Major company land men would not buy at these prices and took up holdings elsewhere, up and down the West Mexia (Techuacana) fault line, in wildcat territory.

Nigger Creek's development thoroughly alarmed Oklahoma operators, who were already suffering from overproduction. This close-to-Mexia field could be served by near-at-hand pipe companies and its oil would soon be dumped on the market. In addition, it was believed that Nigger Creek was capable of making 100,000 barrels of oil daily within a period of sixty days or less.[18]

But Nigger Creek was disappointing. Between July 8 and September 10, the field's thirty-seven wells produced 539,995 barrels of oil, and up to January 1, 1937, a total of 1,585,470 barrels. The field reached its peak of 22,085 barrels daily on September 7, 1926, then settled down to a declining output. In the year of its discovery, the entire Mexia area—Mexia, Nigger Creek, Powell, Richland, Wortham, and smaller fields—produced but 20,494,000 barrels of oil; and in the succeeding years decline was rapid, production sinking to 4,621,000 barrels in 1930.[19]

A new oil find at Spindletop was more important. This field had produced a grand total of 48,782,604 barrels of petroleum by 1925, but in that year had declined to 428,873 as compared with 17,420,949 barrels in 1902. As early as 1917 the Spindletop Deep Well Company had sought a deep pay sand without finding it. And the Gulf Production Company completed its McFaddin No. 1 for 250 barrels of oil daily, but the well flowed only for a few days and was abandoned. Gulf then drilled four other tests, all of which were dry. In 1922 the Rycade Oil Corporation also drilled three deep tests at Spindletop but failed to find oil. South Texas State Fair visitors were electrified on the evening of November 14, 1925,

[18] A. F. Hinton, "Oklahoma Operators See Price Menace in Nigger Creek Pool of Texas," in *National Petroleum News*, Vol. XVIII, No. 30 (July 28, 1926), 35.

[19] There were 12,417,000 barrels in 1927; 8,353,000 barrels in 1928; 5,969,000 barrels in 1929; and 4,621,000 barrels in 1930.—*Mineral Resources of the United States, 1931, Part II, Nonmetals*, 816; Pepperberg, *loc. cit.*, 414.

when the news was brought that "Old Spindletop has brought in a new gusher!"

The Yount-Lee No. 2 McFaddin test, about 1,200 feet south of the field's southernmost production, had blown in as an 800-barrel producer from a sand at 2,588 feet, approximately 1,500 feet below the already known producing horizons. Frank Yount, a former foreman of a rice-threshing outfit and proprietor of a local garage, supervised the completion of the new well two days later. This well inaugurated extensive operations.[20] On January 13 of the next year the Yount-Lee No. 3 McFaddin, three hundred feet to the south of the No. 2, came in, making 5,000 barrels of oil a day from a sand at 2,780 feet. A week later the well increased its flow to 6,000 barrels through a one-inch choke, showing that it was not a flash in the pan. The depths of these two wells revealed that the slant of the dome was approximately thirty-five degrees.

Only three other oil companies moved at once to lease Spindletop properties. The Gulf and Sun companies acquired such additional acreage on the south and west side of the salt dome as the Yount-Lee Oil Company did not hold; and the Rio Bravo Company sought production on the Southern Pacific right-of-way, being a subsidiary of the railroad.

Yount-Lee sank six wells on the McFaddin tract and the Gladys City townsite, which it mainly controlled, and brought in producers that yielded small returns. Then Gulf, Rio Bravo, and Sun began drilling.[21] Gulf was the second company to find flank production with its No. 1 Weed, on an acre tract on the west side of the dome. This discovery, in July, 1926, at 2,824 feet, was good for 125

[20] *Oil Weekly*, Vol. XL, No. 5 (January 22, 1926), 30.

[21] In August, 1935, the Young-Lee interests were bought by the Stanolind Oil Company for $41,600,000, the third largest cash transaction (up to that time) in American business history.—*Beaumont* (American Guide Series), 118.

Stanolind Oil and Gas Company is a fully-owned subsidiary of Standard Oil Company (Indiana). In order to increase its exploration and oil production, Standard also obtained controlling interests in other organizations: in 1919, in the Dixie Oil Company; in 1921, in Midwest Refining Company; in 1925, an interest in the Pan-American Petroleum and Transport Company, later converted to about 78 per cent ownership; in 1930, the McMan Oil Company, with its rich Yates field acreage; and the Yount-Lee properties in Texas and Louisiana (obtained by Stanolind). In recent years, Stanolind has become a well-known Southwestern oil producer. Its parent company, Standard Oil Company of Indiana, engages in production, refining, and marketing.

barrels an hour, producing through two one-half-inch chokes, and was rated as an initial 3,000-barrel well daily.

The Gulf well had followed closely the Yount-Lee No. 5 Gladys City, having an open flow of 4,300 barrels daily at 2,760 feet. And this well was followed quickly by other Yount-Lee wells—No. 6 McFaddin, for 3,000 barrels daily, and No. 1 Davis, for 4,000 barrels daily.

Excitement mounted with each well completion. "Spindletop's yield of deep oil conceivably will reach as high as the total recoveries from caprock levels," Paul Wagner wrote.[22] And, indeed, for a short time this seemed possible. In 1926, Spindletop produced 13,441,000 barrels of oil, and in the next year it climbed to 20,751,-000 barrels. But this was its peak. In 1928 its output sank to 14,150,-000 barrels, in 1929 to 10,037,000 barrels, and in 1930 to 6,176,000 barrels, Spindletop yet ranking third among the Texas salt-dome oil fields.

Next to Spindletop was Humble, where important deep production had been found in 1917. By 1925 this field had to its credit slightly more than 50,000,000 barrels from the deep sand. The more active field, so far as drilling went, was Refugio, with Barbers Hill and Humble in second and third places, respectively.

In 1930, Refugio was the leading producing Texas Gulf Coast field. Its output had risen rapidly as one deep sand after another was discovered. But by April it, too, had reached its peak, with 40,000 barrels of oil daily and a yearly output of 11,485,000 barrels as compared with 1,990,000 barrels in 1929. Barbers Hill was second in production, with 7,441,000 barrels of oil in 1930 as compared with 4,552,000 barrels in 1929. This field had grown in importance with the discovery of deep sands late in 1928.[23] Here the oil sand was found under a ledge of salt, and it was necessary for the drill stem to bore through the salt plug, a drilling procedure that was tried elsewhere in salt-dome fields with material success.

The growing percentage of petroleum output by major oil companies during 1925–30 was as significant as the rise of scientific prospecting and operations. For example, after the Yount-Lee dis-

[22] "Spindletop, Famous in Oil History of Texas, Stages 'Comeback,' " in *National Petroleum News,* Vol. XVIII, No. 27 (July 7, 1926), 40.

[23] *Mineral Resources of the United States, 1930, Part II, Nonmetals,* 813–14.

Texas Forges Ahead

covery well found flank production at Spindletop, sixteen major companies held leases to the entire producing area. Mounting operating costs, as in deeper drilling, in scientific prospecting, pipelining, and refining, made it increasingly difficult for the independent producer and wildcatter to finance operations, and made possible the majority production of heavily capitalized companies. From a total Texas oil output of 31,443,244 barrels during the last quarter of 1925, ten leading companies produced 17,832,364 barrels.

Ten Leading Texas Companies[24]

Company	Fourth Quarter 1925	Third Quarter 1925	Second Quarter 1925	First Quarter 1925	Fourth Quarter 1924
Humble Oil and Refining Company	3,513,294	3,830,444	4,533,395	4,968,388	3,428,657
Gulf Production Co.	3,307,880	3,656,318	3,378,142	2,722,252	2,538,216
The Texas Company	2,430,441	2,760,166	3,184,793	2,590,554	2,237,132
Big Lake Oil Co.	1,723,221	1,166,302	1,202,442	--------	--------
Pure Oil Company	1,593,636	1,967,839	2,567,842	1,894,604	1,856,850
Magnolia Petroleum Co.	1,476,523	1,617,239	1,527,253	1,584,990	1,418,382
United North and South Oil Company	1,451,897	1,473,465	1,603,716	1,798,609	2,188,246
Group No. 1 Oil Co.	1,295,841	1,190,857	905,807	--------	--------
Republic Production Company	601,221	673,343	--------	--------	--------
Sun Oil Company	438,410	597,821	725,113	618,643	794,944
Totals	31,443,244	34,164,140	34,328,549	38,129,092	31,194,183

Equally interesting was the steady advance of the Texas Gulf Coast in industrial power. Such ports as Galveston, Houston, Texas City, Port Arthur, Beaumont, and Orange gave the coastal area excellent commercial advantages.

Houston was the largest port. From 1900 to 1930, Harris County, of which Houston was county seat, had grown in population from 63,786 to 359,329. By 1930, Houston had a population of 292,352, or 5 per cent of the state's total, and was one of its leading industrial cities. Its deep-water canal to the Gulf via San Jacinto River and Buffalo Bayou, a distance of approximately fifty miles, with a turn-

[24] *Oil Weekly*, Vol. XL, No. 12 (March 12, 1926), 79.

ing basin 1,000 feet wide, provided excellent advantages for refineries, shippers of crude oil, and for other industries.[25]

As early as June 30, 1923, 173 oil cargoes left the port of Houston
carrying 5,393,371 barrels of crude oil and oil products, bound for
the Orient, the Antipodes, England, the continent of Europe, the
West Indies, South America, and the Atlantic seaboard. These shipments were mostly products from seven refineries along the Houston Ship Canal and the crude handled by eight other canal firms.
Some of these had loading facilities that accommodated deep-sea
vessels, while others could discharge or load cargoes only into
barges. There were also many cargoes of crude oil delivered to the
refining plants by barges from the Goose Creek field. In 1929, Houston's exports, including crude oil, oil products and by-products, and
other commodities, reached 4,194,841 tons valued at $302,604,269.

The refining plants, with storage and docks, represented an investment of $35,000,000. Most of the crude oil going to these re-
fineries came from the Gulf Coast fields, except that going to the
Humble Oil and Refining Company and the Sinclair Refining Company, which had pipe-line connections with the Mid-Continent
fields.[26] Among other companies using the canal were the Houston
Oil Terminal, Deepwater, Magnolia, Rio Bravo, and Gulf.

Beaumont and Port Arthur also had petroleum and its products
as their chief exports, with a total shipping tonnage in 1925 of 2,-
359,082 and 7,736,708 respectively. Within a year after the Yount-
Lee Spindletop discovery, $5,000,000 was spent for new construc-
tion at Beaumont, and the young city had begun its climb to industrial power. In the decade to follow, construction started on six
banks, store and office buildings, a new city hall and auditorium, a
$500,000 hospital, two hotels costing more than $2,000,000, and
other structures to the value of $3,000,000 to $4,000,000.

The Neches-Sabine Canal had given Beaumont the same deep-
sea advantages as Houston, and six of the world's largest refineries,
with a total combined daily capacity of 365,000 barrels, made the
Beaumont–Port Arthur area the nation's greatest refining center.

[25] *The Texas Almanac and State Industrial Guide* (1925), 182; *ibid.* (1931),
136, 152, 200.

[26] Grady Triplett, "Houston as Outlet for Mid-Continent," in *Oil and Gas Journal*,
Vol. XXII, No. 15 (September 6, 1923), 56.

XVIII

Greater Seminole

WITHIN SEVEN YEARS, 1920 to 1926 inclusive, Oklahoma had produced a little less than one billion barrels of petroleum worth two billion dollars, and had drilled 42,000 wells, of which 26,600 were producers. In 1924, California ranked first in the output of crude oil, natural gas, and natural gasoline, worth $333,-292,000; but Oklahoma was second with an output worth $326,-833,000, and within two years regained first place.[1]

Texas forged ahead in 1928 only because of the steadily mounting oil output from the Panhandle and West Texas fields. Yet Oklahoma was also productive. As old fields hit their peak, then declined, new fields were discovered to maintain the high level of the state's output. For example, in the early nineteen twenties, as Burbank started to decline, operators seeking new oil bonanzas moved into a heretofore neglected area, central Oklahoma, and opened Greater Seminole and Oklahoma City, two of the most prolific oil-producing regions yet found in this state.

Before these fields were discovered, however, farther south, in the Healdton country, fifteen miles west and two miles north of Ardmore, the Hewitt field had supported the oil yield of other parts of the state to keep Oklahoma's place high. As early as October, 1916, while Healdton was yet in its heyday, William J. Millard had found and mapped the Hewitt structure, an anticline lying over a buried hill. And later, on June 5, 1919, The Texas Company's No. 1 A. E. Denny well tapped an oil sand from a depth of 2,084 feet for a daily yield of 450 barrels of oil.[2] By the following March

[1] Charles E. Bowles, "Oklahoma's Oil Production," in *Oklahoma*, Vol. I, No. 1 (April, 1927), 18–19; *Petroleum Facts and Figures* (Fifth edition), 91.

[2] George E. Burton, "Hewitt Oil Field, Carter County, Oklahoma," in *Structure of Typical American Oil Fields*, II, 290–91.

231

20, wells topping the Hewitt structure produced 11,805 barrels of oil. Also, gas was found when the Baker A. Strong well penetrated a gas sand at 240–258 feet, the well making 2,000,000 cubic feet daily.[3]

By the end of the next month Hewitt produced 10,423 barrels of oil daily from ten wells and had ten wells uncompleted—that is, they were producers but were being drilled deeper. But the field had not yet been outlined toward the west, east, and north.[4] In November, 1920, after deeper pay zones had been tapped, an intensive drilling campaign was started, and ten months later the field reached its peak of daily production when 570 wells yielded 43,902 barrels of oil. The total annual output was 13,095,000 barrels.[5]

Hewitt's Yearly Oil Output, 1920–29[6]
(In Barrels)

Year	Wells	Yearly Production	Cumulative Production
1920	396	7,426,000	7,603,876
1921	605	13,095,000	20,698,876
1922	692	10,690,000	31,388,876
1923	733	8,695,000	40,083,876
1924	796	6,905,000	46,988,876
1925	809	5,315,000	52,303,876
1926	793	4,202,000	56,505,876
1927	806	3,844,000	60,349,876
1928	808	3,380,000	63,729,876
1929	808	2,880,000	66,609,876

Hewitt could not keep stride with the output records of Burbank and Tonkawa, but it helped to maintain Oklahoma's high production record. Still, major fields must yet be found if Oklahoma were

[3] *Oil and Gas Journal*, Vol. XVIII, No. 36 (February 6, 1920), 70; "New Hewitt Pool May Have Shallow Pay As Well As Deep," in *National Petroleum News*, Vol. XVI, No. 12 (March 24, 1920), 60.

[4] *Ibid.*, April 28, 1920, 70.

[5] Other southern Oklahoma oil fields, although of minor production, which came into the limelight were Brock, January, 1921; Graham, in March, 1922; Sholem Alechem, 1923; and Ed Cox, 1926. Recent developments at Sholem Alechem indicate that it might surpass its early oil production.

[6] Burton, *loc. cit.*, 299.

to keep up its momentum of production. Fortunately, just when it seemed that all of Oklahoma's major fields had been discovered, the rich Greater Seminole country was found.

As the region was ultimately expanded, Greater Seminole embraced many oil fields, among them Carr City, Bethel, Earlsboro, Earlsboro East, Earlsboro South, Hotulke–West Earlsboro, Seminole City, Seminole East, Seminole North, Seminole West, Searight, Searight North, Bowlegs, Little River, Little River East, Maud, Maud South, Mission, St. Louis, and St. Louis East,[7] although strictly speaking a fewer number were included when the term "Greater Seminole" was first accepted.

By the summer of 1926, Seminole and Pottawatomie County operators were having almost daily meetings to discuss voluntary proration and well spacing and to consider production control. As Seminole City, Searight, Earlsboro, Little River, and Bowlegs were all coming in under identical operating conditions, those who attended these meetings suggested that a common name for the producing areas be accepted. Then Paul Hedrick, oil editor of the Tulsa *World,* offered the name "Greater Seminole," and another man suggested "Seminole Uplift"; but the first title seemed more appropriate to the producers and it was accepted.[8]

Wewoka, near the eastern border of Seminole County, was the first of these fields to have an oil boom. It was the county seat and had been the capital of the Seminole Indians until their tribal government ceased in March, 1906. Shortly after this, their lands, except those alloted in severalty, were opened to purchase and settlement by white people. By 1924 the Indians had not more than one-fifth of the county lands. The Indians held land in small allotments, a situation that made large leaseholding difficult in Seminole County during the oil development to come.

Wewoka nestled in a beautiful, rolling, tree-clad country of

---

[7] This group of fields from the date of discovery down to June 1, 1947, had produced a cumulative total of 896,555,000 barrels of crude oil. In April, 1947, they averaged 22,286 barrels of oil daily from 1,603 wells.

[8] Tulsa *World,* August 30, 1931. Hedrick wrote the author that Ray M. Collins, then umpire of this oil-producing area, had suggested the appropriateness of a common name. "One of the local newspapers call the play the 'Greater Seminole' field," he is reported to have said, "and it seems to fit." Others present agreed, and "Greater Seminole" became official.

rounded hills, low east-facing escarpments, gentle west slopes, and rich alluvial valleys along meandering streams. The sandy uplands were forested with blackjack, post oak, and, here and there, hickory; and the bottoms with pecan, sycamore, elm, and cottonwood. Checkerboarded redland fields, hedged by green forests, offered pleasing variety in the region. In this setting, life was tranquil, rural, and retired.

As early as 1902 the Wewoka Trading Company had drilled for oil on the B. F. Davis farm near town. Early in 1907 a gasser was brought in, but when the well was deepened, the hole was lost.[9] Another well was drilled about sixty feet northwest of the gas well and came in as a large producer at 1,600 feet, from what was later known as the "Wewoka sand," flooding a near-by stream before arrangements could be made to care for the oil. The well settled down to about 150 barrels of oil a day for more than two years. But in those days the price of oil was so low and transportation so inadequate that the well was never a paying proposition, and it later was drilled deeper and lost.[10]

Greater Seminole's development really began with the Smith well, one mile south of Wewoka. Here, as at El Dorado, Arkansas, and many another place, Wewoka's slow-moving tempo was shocked into frenzy when the R. H. Smith *et al.* No. 1 Betsy Foster well came in as a 2,800-barrel producer, on March 17, 1923.[11] Within a few months Wewoka more than doubled its population. Din and excitement, speculation, oil-field construction, the going and coming of wagons, buggies, and hacks, and the arrival of many visitors—all made up Wewoka's daily activity.[12]

An Oklahoma City reporter who visited the new field three months after the first well came in wrote an interesting account of what he saw and learned. By that time drilling had rapidly expanded to various parts of Seminole County, to the number of forty wells, ranging all the way from the North to the South Canadian rivers and from the east to the west boundaries of the county. Pro-

[9] The well was abandoned because of drilling miscalculations.

[10] *Daily Oklahoman* (Oklahoma City), June 24, 1923, Sec. B, p. 14, cols. 1–2.

[11] The Foster well was two miles southeast of town, in the NW¼ SW¼ NW¼, S33-T8N-R8E.

[12] Personal interview with J. C. Fore, who helped to block the first lease south of Wewoka.

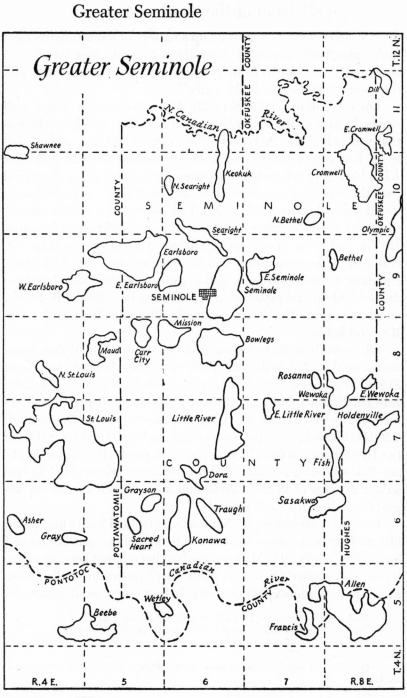

Greater Seminole

Dill

Shawnee

N. Canadian River

OKFUSKEE COUNTY

E. Cromwell

Keokuk

N. Searight

Cromwell

COUNTY

S E M I N O L E

N. Bethel

Olympic

OKFUSKEE COUNTY

Searight

Earlsboro

Bethel

W. Earlsboro

E. Earlsboro

E. Seminole

SEMINOLE

Seminole

COUNTY

Mission

Maud

Carr City

Bowlegs

N. St. Louis

Rosanna

Wewoka

E. Wewoka

St. Louis

Little River

E. Little River

Holdenville

C O U N T Y

Fish

Dora

Grayson

Sasakwa

Asher

Traugh

POTTAWATOMIE

Gray

Sacred Heart

Konawa

HUGHES

PONTOTOC

Canadian

River

Allen

COUNTY

Wetley

Beebe

Francis

T. 12 N.

11

10

9

8

7

6

5

T. 4 N.

R. 4 E.   5   6   7   R. 8 E.

ducers and refiners were putting up a battery of ten 250-barrel steel tanks, practically the entire townsite of Wewoka was leased, and community farmers were helping the county commissioners and the commercial club to build roads.[13]

On the following October 20, Magnolia's No. 1 Jones well reached a lower sand for 290 barrels of oil a day. This lower formation was called the "Sykes sand" at 3,183–3,200 feet, after Louis Sykes had completed his No. 1 Boggs well on June 24, 1924, for 1,100 barrels of oil each twenty-four hours. And when it seemed that the structure was closed in all directions, again Magnolia found a new horizon with its No. 1 Skinner well,[14] on the flank of the Smith sand (Wilcox) at 4,096 feet, on the following December 18. The well came in with an initial flow of 4,000 barrels daily. Operators were now in a dither, and Wewoka was crowded with major company scouts, land men, and engineers. From here they conducted widespread exploration, which soon brought the discovery of the Searight, Earlsboro, Seminole City, Bowlegs, and Little River oil fields.

Other wells at Wewoka reached the Hunton and Wilcox limestones, and by November 22, 1927, the field's daily average from 215 wells climbed to 10,326 barrels of oil. In the spring of 1927, Edward F. Shea and L. G. Mossberg[15] estimated that the field's recovery up to that time was 3,500,000 barrels from the Smith sand; 4,500,000 barrels from the Sykes sand; and 7,000,000 barrels from the Hunton and Wilcox limestones. Peak production in the Smith and Sykes sands was reached on June 12, 1925, when 134 wells had a daily average of 19,860 barrels; and in the Seminole sand on August 20, 1926, with 29,023 barrels.[16]

Cromwell, straddling the Seminole-Okfuskee County line, about fifteen miles northeast of the town of Seminole, became the second Seminole County oil field. Some gas had been found here previously, but it remained for the Wewoka development to kindle an enthusiasm for Cromwell wildcatting. In fact, a few months later, on

---

[13] *Daily Oklahoman,* June 24, 1923, Sec. B, p. 14, cols. 1–2.

[14] The No. 1 Skinner was in the northwest corner of S5-T7N-R8E.

[15] Paper read before a Tulsa meeting of the American Association of Petroleum Geologists, March, 1927.

[16] *Oil and Gas in Oklahoma,* Oklahoma Geological Survey *Bull. No. 40-BB,* 40–41.

Greater Seminole

October 2, 1923, the Cromwell Oil and Gas Company's No. 1 Bruner well was completed as a 312-barrel producer. Rapid development followed, peak production coming on August 20, 1924, with seventy-five wells making 62,391 barrels daily. Cromwell's decline is best seen in the fact that a year later (November 22) its total of 393 wells had a daily output of only 10,823 barrels of oil.[17]

Following Wewoka's and Cromwell's oil discoveries and operations, the small Bethel pool, midway between Wewoka and Cromwell, was found, when on December 9, 1924, the Independent Oil and Gas Company's No. 1 Cobb and Hill well was completed in the Booch sand as a 200-barrel well at about 3,200 feet.[18] Production here was confined to this sand, generally a water-bearing sand. Moreover, the Cromwell and Simpson formations that had been oil sands elsewhere were found here to be dry. Bethel's highest daily production was only 2,786 barrels.

Although the next few months comprised a period of widespread exploration, there was no great oil discovery. Then other new fields came fast—Earlsboro on March 1, 1926, Seminole City six days later, and Searight on April 21—three large fields in less than two months.

The town of Earlsboro in Pottawatomie County, about eight miles northwest of Seminole, gave the Earlsboro oil field its name, although the major part of the field lies in Seminole County. Morgan and Flynn's No. 1 Ingram was the discovery well, which made 200 barrels daily from the Earlsboro sand at 3,560 feet. But before excitement over this producer calmed down, on December 3, just over in Pottawatomie County and about a mile southwest of the Ingram well, the Gypsy Oil Company completed its No. 1 State well in the Seminole sand at 4,275 feet.[19] When the oil sand was hardly penetrated, the State well's initial daily output was 500 barrels. The well was deepened slightly, and its flow increased to 3,000 barrels; and, indeed, on December 3, when it was completed, it reached 8,050 barrels. Eagerly operators, lease and royalty jobbers,

[17] Oklahoma Geological Survey *Bull. No. 40,* III, 325.

[18] The Cobb-Hill well was located in NE¼ SE¼ NE¼, S7-T9N-R8E. Extensive wildcatting had been done in this area since 1921, and fair-sized gas wells had been completed in a shallow sand.

[19] The Ingram well was located in the NW¼ NW¼ SE¼ S10-T9N-R5E; and the No. 1 State was on the northeast corner, Sec. 16.

and fortune hunters rushed in. So rapid was the field's development that during the week ending August 9, 1927, its 135 wells reached a daily oil output of 205,286 barrels. But indiscriminate drilling and the general use of the air lift in production brought the Earlsboro field to swift decline. On the following November 1, its total daily oil yield from 248 wells sank to 148,361 barrels.

Earlsboro's high well production featured Greater Seminole's boom. Generally, Earlsboro wells ranged between 1,000 and 4,000 barrels daily, although a few produced as high as 14,000 barrels. Dr. Charles N. Gould believed that the field's high rate of production was due to "shooting and the application of air lift."[20] One expert declares that without the aid of the air-gas lift, Greater Seminole's peak would have been only about 240,000 barrels of crude oil instead of the 513,000 barrels it actually produced during the first week of August, 1927. If this is true, without the use of the air-gas lift there would have been no overproduction of light oil and no maladjustment of price levels.[21]

The Seminole field, or the Seminole City field, should not be confused with Greater Seminole, of which it was only a part. The Seminole City field had its center approximately one mile east of the town of that name and ultimately extended, north and south, for more than four miles and east and west for nearly two miles.

Early drilling at Seminole City dates from 1923, from W. B. Pine's 3,685-foot No. 1 Henry well in Section 22, which Pine abandoned after losing the hole. Then on March 7, three years later, on a cold, drizzly day, while a few spectators and a part of the Indian Territory Illuminating Oil Company's (I.T.I.O.'s) crew sat in a drill rig's "dog-house" to keep dry, a downpour suddenly drummed on the roof. But it was not rain; it was oil from the No. 1 Jones well, blowing in as a 1,100-barrel producer, from the Hunton limestone at 3,975 to 4,012 feet.

This was the start of another field in Greater Seminole.[22] Ten days later, the well had increased its twenty-four-hour flow from 960 to 995 barrels after the well had been deepened one foot. It

[20] Oklahoma Geological Survey *Bull. No. 40-BB*, 54. To shoot a well was to set off a charge of nitroglycerin in a "tight" sand to loosen it and give it more porosity. The air lift was when air was pumped under high pressure into the oil-bearing formation to augment the reservoir gas lift.
[21] Galey MS, as cited.

topped the Hunton lime at 4,006 feet. The I.T.I.O. had thoroughly geologized this region and held several hundred acres of leases in townships 9–6 and 8–6.[23]

The Amerada Petroleum Corporation kept interest alive, although little more, when it drilled a sixty-barrel well into the Seminole sand at 4,258 to 4,277 feet. But drilling activity went wild when the Independent Oil and Gas Company No. 1 Fixico Robert F. Garland well blew in on July 26, 1926. The Fixico gusher was a quarter of a mile east of the Jones well.[24] R. F. ("Bob") Garland and his wife, who had staked most of their possessions on this test, were the most anxious watchers when the bit penetrated the oil sand. And their waiting brought reward. Their well was a 6,120-barrel producer.

On August 11 the discoveries of the I.T.I.O. "bid fair to result in the development of a real field." This was soon apparent. Sixty-two operations were presently under way. The Fixico well improved with age, producing 5,524 barrels at the end of the week.[25]

Both major companies and independents now joined in an excited drilling campaign. The field was quickly expanded as the drillers and rig builders wallowed in the mud and snow that hampered their work all through the fall of 1926 and the following winter.

By November, Seminole City's oil output exceeded transportation and storage facilities, a condition that was aggravated by the growing output of Earlsboro and the two new fields of Searight

[22] The No. 1 Jones well was located in the NW¼ NW¼ SE¼ of Section 24, T7N-R6E. The I.T.I.O. had a major share of Greater Seminole's discoveries. When its Osage properties began to decline, H. V. Foster and his associates decided to look elsewhere for holdings. In 1921 and 1922, R. J. Metcalf made a survey of the entire Seminole area and discovered the line of faulting through Range 6 East. This influenced the company's action subsequently in leasing thirteen tracts of land in Range 6. From this beginning I.T.I.O. developed thirty-four leases in Greater Seminole.

[23] Oklahoma Geological Survey *Bull. No. 40-BB*, 46; A. F. Hinton, "Several Wildcat Showings of Interest as Oklahoma Production Declines," in *National Petroleum News*, Vol. XVIII, No. 10 (March 10, 1926), 53; J. F. Dwyer, "Oklahoma Field Operations," in *Oil and Gas Journal*, Vol. XXIV, No. 42 (March 11, 1926), 36.

[24] The Fixico location was in NW¼ NW¼ SE¼ Section 26. Its Seminole sand (the first "Wilcox") was reached at 4,065 to 4,073 feet.

[25] "Oklahoma Production Declines Slightly; Seminole Center of Interest," in *National Petroleum News*, Vol. XVIII, No. 32 (August 11, 1926), 35, and No. 33 (August 18, 1926), 35.

and Bowlegs. On February 22, 1927, the Seminole City field reached its peak production of 265,000 barrels daily. In the following May representatives of oil companies operating in Greater Seminole met in New York and agreed upon Ray M. Collins of Tulsa as field umpire, to work with an operators' committee, with authority to draw up a plan for production curtailment. From this move ultimately came a thirty-day program which prorated pipe-line runs and allowed only direct offsets to be drilled into the sand.[26]

On July 21, 1927, the Oklahoma Corporation Commission, in response to an appeal from Collins, issued an order returnable on August 5, 1927, forbidding the drilling of any wells in Greater Seminole outside of those pools then under development until the date of return. Then Seminole operators worked out a new agreement, continuing Collins as field umpire and providing that the combined crude-oil production at Searight, Seminole City, Bowlegs, and Earlsboro should be confined and limited to a total production of 450,000 barrels a day. Such a controlled program allowed the construction of pipe lines and storage to gain momentum, so that these handicaps were presently overcome.

Generally, Seminole City wells had an initial daily output of between 1,000 and 3,500 barrels, although some of them produced as high as 9,000 barrels when they were "shot" or operated by air lift.[27] Ultimately, the producing field expanded into 3,600 acres. Its oil varied in gravity from 40 to 42 degrees Baumé.

After nearly two years of work with cable tools,[28] F. J. Searight

[26] C. D. Watson, a seasoned Mid-Continent oilman, says that Seminole oil operators saw that some form of control was necessary, for the Seminole field came in at a time when oil was $2.50 a barrel. But prices continued to decline and finally reached a low of ten cents a barrel.—Interview with C. D. Watson, Public Relations Department, Carter Oil Company, Tulsa, April 10 and 14, 1945. A copy of this manuscript is in the files of the Standard Oil Company (N.J.), New York.

[27] Engineer S. F. Shaw is credited with devising the Seminole air-lift method.—Watson interview. Contemporary operators believed that the use of air lift brought water trouble more quickly than would have come with the normal development of the field, that it increased the corrosion problem. The Seminole field showed a rapid water encroachment. Of 319 producing wells on December 31, 1927, 122 of them were making water.—Blackwell *Tribune*, Sunday, November 18, 1928, Sec. 1, p. 11, cols. 6–7.

[28] Greater Seminole was the first important oil region in Oklahoma where the rotary drill was widely used. Wells were drilled by rotary to the Viola formation, casing was then set and cemented, the plug drilled, and the well finished with cable tools.

240

opened the next field in Greater Seminole, which was named for him, when his No. 1 312-barrel Youngblood well, four miles directly north of the town of Seminole, came in.[29] Six months later the company's No. 3 Youngblood, on the same quarter-section found the Seminole sand at 4,317 feet and flowed daily 4,572 barrels of oil. The field reached its maximum daily production during the week ending June 21, 1927 when forty-two wells had an average of 39,857 barrels.

Before the Bowlegs[30] oil discovery, the village of Bowlegs consisted of a big country store and a house or two. There was no main highway through the town and no railroad. The village's one bid for a visitor's attention was its name. Indian Territory Illuminating Oil Company's No. 1 Livingston well[31] is credited with opening Wilcox production at Bowlegs, in January, 1927.

While oil development was spreading north and west of Seminole, on June 18, 1926, the I.T.I.O. Company drilled a gas well in the basal sand of the Calvin series at a depth of 2,426 to 2,443 feet, about two miles northeast of Bowlegs and a short distance south of the Seminole City field; and, later, on January 4 of the next year, brought in the No. 1 Davis well,[32] a 5,500-barrel producer in the prolific Wilcox sand at a depth of 4,194 to 4,200 feet.

Then there were still other fields to follow before Greater Seminole was fully developed. The Little River field was opened by I.T.I.O.'s No. 1 House well,[33] on July 1, 1927, that reached the Seminole sand at 4,017 to 4,028 feet for an astonishing 13,541 barrels of oil a day, and within four months it had fifty-nine wells producing daily 45,361 barrels of oil, with a cumulative total of 2,644,-830 barrels of oil. Seminole City, Searight, Earlsboro, Bowlegs, and Little River were the prominent Greater Seminole fields during its peak production.

As previously mentioned, the first Wilcox-sand well in the Seminole City field was completed in the summer of 1926. Indeed, as

[29] This well was located in the SE¼ NE¼ SE¼, S33-T10N-R6E. Production was from the Hunton lime at a depth of 4,090 to 4,157 feet.

[30] The field was named for Lizzie Bowlegs, wife of Billy Bowlegs, on whose allotment the I.T.I.O. well was drilled.

[31] The location of the No. 1 Livingston well was S15-T8N-R6E.

[32] In the southwestern corner of S13-T8N-R6E.

[33] In S1-T7N-R6E.

Oil! Titan of the Southwest

the year 1926 closed, Greater Seminole's four centers of Wilcox production reached 160,000 barrels of crude oil daily. One of the most remarkable features of Greater Seminole's development was its speedy rise in production from a few thousand barrels daily in the Earlsboro and Hunton horizons to 160,000 barrels from the Wilcox sand. Within six months after the discovery of the Wilcox sand, the Seminole district was producing more crude oil than Glenn Pool, Healdton, Eldorado-Augusta, Burbank, and Tonkawa at their peaks.

Greater Seminole's Five Major Oil Fields, January, 1928[34]

Field	No. Wells Producing	No. Acres Producing	Total Production up to Jan. 1, 1928 (Barrels)	Yield Per Producing Acre up to Jan. 1, 1928 (Barrels)	Yield Per Producing Well up to Jan. 1, 1928 (Barrels)	Age Months
Seminole	319	3,600	54,795,543	15,221	171,459	17½
Searight	68	700	12,754,929	18,221	187,572	14½
Earlsboro	286	2,830	37,775,722	13,348	132,083	13
Bowlegs	292	2,980	37,617,193	12,623	128,825	12
Little River	93	940	5,188,523	5,519	55,791	6
Totals	1,060	11,050	148,137,080	13,406	139,741	____

In each of Greater Seminole's major fields, when adventurous firms competed with legitimate independents and major companies, operators worked with feverish speed, each determined that his neighbor should not drain the oil from under his lease. This reckless operation, of course, soon brought each field to its peak, exhausted its reservoir energy, and swamped the oil market. And the drilling of each unnecessary well not only shortened the life of the field but added greatly to the operators' costs. Seminole City drillers sank 3,500 test wells, at an average cost of $60,000 per well, with some going as high as $65,000, and with the total drilling cost reaching $210,000,000.

Seminole City reached its peak within a year, a record for an American major field. Here crude-oil floods repeated on a larger

[34] *Oil and Gas in Oklahoma,* Oklahoma Geological Survey *Bull. No. 40-BB,* 70.

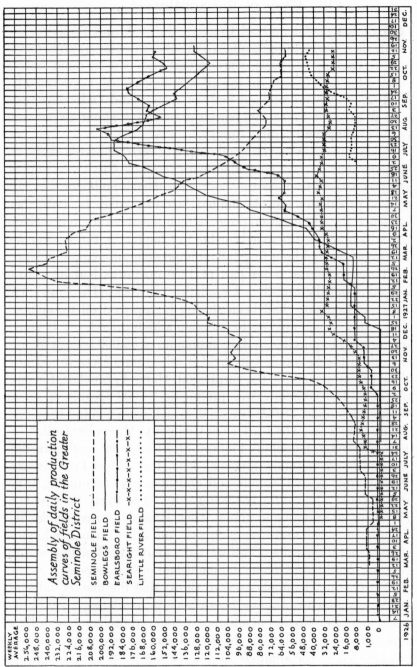

Assembly of daily production curves of fields in the Greater Seminole District

SEMINOLE FIELD ---------
BOWLEGS FIELD ———————
EARLSBORO FIELD —+—+—+—+—+—
SEARIGHT FIELD —x—x—x—x—x—
LITTLE RIVER FIELD ··············

35 Courtesy Oklahoma Geological Survey *Bull. No. 40-BB,* 69.

243

scale those from Glenn Pool, Cushing, Burbank, and Tonkawa.

Earlier, purchasing-company officials, watching apprehensively this swelling oil flood, warned that they would build only a limited tankage to care for the oil of independents. Consequently, by 1927, independents had built in Kansas and Oklahoma their own storage for 45,000,000 barrels of crude, or about 40 per cent of the total amount of oil in storage.

Oklahoma's skyrocketing oil output of 600,000 barrels daily, on January 29, 1927, was coincident with Seminole City's new high of 200,000 barrels. By February both state officials and operators saw that oil production must be limited. So on February 14, 1927, they launched the conservation program mentioned earlier in this chapter, which will be discussed further in Chapter 25. But emergency conservation could not forestall an impending oil-market collapse.

Throughout the latter part of 1926 operators had been concerned about the rapidly accumulating oil stocks. The Prairie Oil and Gas Company had been storing high-priced oil throughout that year and was anxious to maintain a high price level. It therefore offered to purchase a daily minimum of 35,000 barrels of outside oil in the Seminole City field if other purchasers would buy their pro rata share of the surplus oil. Harry F. Sinclair, for one, objected. His company was producing 34,000 barrels of oil in Greater Seminole, 28,000 barrels of which were coming from one eighty-acre lease. The Carter Oil Company, Magnolia, Gulf, I. T. I. O., Amerada, Stanolind, Phillips, Mid-Continent, and Barnsdall were inclined to follow Sinclair's lead. Indeed, on February 22, 1927, Carter posted Kansas and Oklahoma prices ranging from fifteen cents a barrel for 28–28.9-gravity oil to thirty-nine cents a barrel for 40-gravity and above. Then Humble posted similar reductions in North and Central Texas. And other major crude purchasers met these prices. This started a market decline that was to continue until after Greater Seminole had passed its peak.[36]

Yet Greater Seminole's record shows that the market value of crude was a factor of minor importance in regulating a field's development. For Greater Seminole experienced the greatest drilling campaign in the history of the oil industry, a movement that was not affected in the slightest by the market break. The large and

[36] Galey MS, 95 ff.

244

diverse number of operating leaseholders and the small area of the average leasehold was the main reason for the rapid development of the several fields.

Oil Storage in Oklahoma and Kansas[37]
(Barrels)

	1927 Approximate Average Shipments	1927 Approximate Additions to Storage
Prairie	175,000	6,100,000
Carter	125,000	4,100,000
Sinclair	90,000	3,700,000
Roxana	75,000	1,800,000
Magnolia	65,000	3,000,000
Gypsy	50,000	2,740,000
Empire	40,000	2,205,000
Texas	37,000	1,400,000

Greater Seminole's ten major fields steadily increased their oil flow until on July 30, 1927, their peak production, 527,400 barrels daily, was reached. Earlsboro, producing a cumulative 87,510,000 barrels of crude oil led the field; but Seminole City, with 81,546,000 was a close second. With the discovery of the Maud oil field (December, 1927), of Mission (June, 1928), and of East Seminole (May, 1929), Greater Seminole embraced 24,520 acres. But this was not all. Still other discoveries expanded Greater Seminole's boundaries into neighboring counties.

Greater Seminole so increased its crude-oil output that by September 1, 1929, it was the nation's premier high-gravity oil field. Since July 16, 1926, it had produced a quarter of a billion barrels of crude; and this oil output at the average price of $1.50 per barrel had brought the producers and royalty owners more than $300,-000,000. In fact, within a decade, Greater Seminole's red hills poured out their black treasure worth an estimated $1,009,996,749. But it was a sad fact that the Seminole Indians, owning the entire region before the white men came in, reaped very little of this vast wealth.

[37] *Ibid.*, 187.

Oil! Titan of the Southwest

Of more than one billion dollars paid the oil producers during this decade, one-eighth, or about $120,000,000, went to royalty owners, to say nothing of lease bonuses and delay rentals. A part of this billion dollars went in salaries and wages to business and professional men for goods and services, and much of it for oil-field (pipe lines, derricks, and refineries) and near-by town construction. Tax returns prove this. During the period 1926–34, when the assessed value of Oklahoma property as a whole was decreasing from $1,697,364,213 to $1,258,686,473, the value of Seminole County property increased from $14,868,034 to $32,751,989.[38]

Seminole City became the industrial capital of this oil *el dorado*. Eighty years earlier, the Chicago, Rock Island and Pacific builders had not dared to dream of a town on their long north-south railroad that would handle one-million dollars' worth of business in a month. But by 1936 this mark was passed, not by one town, but by two—Chicago, the world's major rail center, and Seminole City, Oklahoma's wonder oil town. For the most of 1927 Seminole City's Rock Island receipts even outstripped Chicago's, reaching a high of $1,606,900.

It is hard to describe Seminole City, Earlsboro, Wewoka, Bowlegs, and other Greater Seminole oil-boom towns. Seminole City, the largest town of the region, was perhaps most typical. Its every expression was disorder. Chaos and confusion; oilmen renting rooms in shifts; crowded noisy streets; 3,600 sweating and hard-working teams pulling oil-field equipment and supplies, filling the streets and highways; the raucous shouts of hucksters and drunken street ramblers; hastily built and odoriferous restaurants and hamburger stands; thousands of barrels of oil from newly-brought-in gushers spraying trees and grass; the stifling effects of escaping gas and the acrid scent of burning oil from wells and pits—all were part of Greater Seminole.

Quietly and swiftly, improvements came. Within the decade 1926–36 Seminole felt growing pains. Assessed property values more than trebled, deposits at the First National and First State banks increased five fold, and post-office money receipts jumped from $972 in August, 1926, to $5,958 in March of the next year. In-

[38] Seminole *Producer,* Seminole, Oklahoma (Tenth Anniversary edition), July 16, 1936, p. 1, col. 7.

deed, during the adjacent oil field's peak, 4,500 daily calls were made at Seminole City's post-office window, more than at New Orleans, Toledo, and San Francisco.

Almost by magic Seminole City was transformed, with electric lights, paved streets and sidewalks, sewage disposal, and other municipal improvements. Substantial brick business houses took the places of shanties and frame structures; and oil money built new, commodious church and school buildings.

Back of all these changes, of course, were alert men and women. Seminole City had men like O. D. Strother, who had early dreamed of an oil empire; Dr. W. E. Grisso, who pioneered Highway 48 through Seminole County, from north to south, and who backed other constructive enterprises; J. N. Harber, the cultured mayor of the town during the oil-boom peak years; and S. D. Powell, an alert "try-to-help" banker. And the women, too, working through local clubs and enterprises, sought to stabilize and dignify society —women such as Mrs. Claude Allen Bell, Mrs. W. E. Grisso, and Mrs. J. P. Sanford. For, indeed, it is the women whose influence and example in the community set the standards and determine the *mores,* even in an oil-boom town.

XIX

Oklahoma City's Bonanza Field

THE OPENING of Oklahoma lands to settlement on April 22, 1889, was eventful. Within a day hundreds of people came to the North Canadian River and established Oklahoma City; and for many weeks their ill-assorted tents, dugouts, and shacks, sprawling over the townsite, gave little evidence of a city's beginnings. These town builders were greatly handicapped by lack of an adequate water supply and the ordinary facilities of life.

The water problem was most acute, for these first settlers had to drink the brackish and sometimes muddy water from the river. Then an enterprising newcomer dug a well. By so doing he not only supplied his own household needs but established a thriving business; he charged his reluctant neighbors five cents for each cup of water. Angrily, they refused to tolerate such a monopoly and employed "a man versed in boring for oil" to dig a new well.

The well driller was successful in supplying their need. He then announced that he intended to drill an oil well. This was startling to the townsmen, but as was becoming of the settlers in this uninhibited land, they gave the new enterprise an enthusiastic send-off. The site selected for the well was near the intersection of what is now Northwest Fourth Street and the Santa Fe Railroad, then identified as "northeast of the hotel and on the edge of our thriving city."[1]

The site was impressively dedicated. Many people assembled to hear a Roman Catholic priest make a speech and to wish the promoters great success. Thus Oklahoma City's first oil well was

[1] Claude V. Barrow (oil editor, *Daily Oklahoman* and *Times*), unpublished manuscript on the Oklahoma City Oil Field. Mr. Barrow supplied the author with this manuscript and other materials.

started. And at approximately 600 feet it reached real pay—clear, cool water, as welcome to the townsmen as oil.

During the next two decades about twenty other oil tests were drilled in the Oklahoma City vicinity, "most of them honest ventures," says Barrow, "others purely promotions."[2] C. B. Ames, Marvin Armstrong, John Shartel, and others drilled one test a mile east of Putnam City[3] but abandoned it at 1,000 feet; and in 1900 L. C. Hivick drilled another unsuccessful well near Spencer. An Oklahoma City hardware merchant, E. J. Streeter, promoted a test in 1903 and reached a reported depth of 2,002 feet without finding oil. News of these efforts was printed far and near. Even the distant *Cherokee Messenger* (Cherokee, Woods County) on March 31, two years later, erroneously reported an oil well a short distance east of Oklahoma City. This and similar news items undoubtedly attracted oilmen, for during the next year three unsuccessful tests were drilled near Arcadia, east of Oklahoma City.

Geology should be given credit for the discovery of the Oklahoma City field. Two of the first geologists to observe Oklahoma City's favorable structure were George D. Morgan and Jerry B. Newby, "either in 1917 or 1919," Morgan stated later, and added: "I worked out the structure at Oklahoma City."[4] Newby's work was "north and northeast of Oklahoma City . . . in the early part of 1919."

In the fall of 1919, L. E. Trout studied the same area and late in the next year, or early in 1921, mapped what is now the southern part of the Oklahoma City field. His is reported to be the first structural map of that region. Four years later Trout, Claude Dalley, and L. R. Trout drilled a well near the Cleveland County line to a depth of 4,480 feet but found only traces of oil.[5]

In the same year John R. Bunn worked out a surface high north of the capitol for a deep test (7,180 feet) that was drilled by the Cromwell Oil and Gas Company. This well found several oil showings in the shallow sands but little more. Next year E. A. Paschal, in the employ of the Coline Oil Company, found the Hennessey-

[2] Barrow, "Early History—1," MS.

[3] In S14-T12N-R4W.

[4] Both Morgan's and Newby's statements are found in Oklahoma Geological Survey *Bull. No. 40-SS*, 6.

[5] *Ibid.*

Garber formation south of Oklahoma City, and Coline's chief geologist, C. T. Moore, negotiated three leases, all of which were later producing.

More credit for Oklahoma City's oil field, however, should go to the late G. E. Anderson, at that time on the faculty of the University of Oklahoma, but temporarily employed by the Indian Territory Illuminating Oil Company, fresh from its discovery of five Greater Seminole fields.[6] Anderson found a southward projecting nose, outlined on the Garber-Hennessey contact and running through Oklahoma City. Immediately I. T. I. O.'s geological department mapped this area, under the supervision of chief field geologist J. H. Derden, and his helpers, R. J. Riggs and C. W. Roop.

The Foster Petroleum Corporation joined with the I. T. I. O. in drilling the No. 1 Oklahoma City well on land purchased from Mrs. Celia Hall.[7] The site chosen for this test was about six miles south of the city. Drilling began on June 12, 1928, and as the well was deepened, it had several oil and gas showings, the most important being at 3,997 to 4,012 feet, where a strong daily flow of 47,000,000 cubic feet of gas was encountered.

On December 4, the No. 1 Oklahoma City well was completed. Previously the hole had partly filled with oil. And as the driller began to pierce a cement plug at 6,355 feet, the well blew in, tossing the tools up in the hole, within 2,500 feet of the surface, where they lodged, and some oil came through with the gas.[8] This was a few minutes past three o'clock in the afternoon. The well ran wild for an hour and a half before it was brought under control, producing 4,909 barrels of 40-degree gravity oil in the first twenty-four hours.

Oklahoma Cityans had become greatly excited by the reports about the new well. They had even imported a cannon which was kept loaded to fire when and if the I. T. I. O. well was completed as

[6] Homer H. Charles, "Oklahoma City Oil Field, Oklahoma," in *Bulletin of the American Association of Petroleum Geologists,* Vol. XIV, No. 12 (December, 1930), 1517.

[7] In "C SE SE Section 24-11-3W," Oklahoma County "Oklahoma City Wildcat Showing Oil," in *Oil and Gas Journal,* Vol. XXVII, No. 29 (December 6, 1928), 66.

[8] Actually the Cromwell Oil and Gas Company's No. 1 Edwards well of November 30, 1926, in SE SE SE of S15-T12N-R3W, about one mile north of the new field's production limits, was the first producer near Oklahoma City. This well produced off and on for nearly three years and in 1929 furnished fuel for drilling wells south of Oklahoma City.—Barrow, "Early History—1," MS.

a good producer. They were not kept waiting. Now they could celebrate.

At first geologists were uncertain what formation the oil came from, although they called it "siliceous lime," but they agreed that, regardless of its subsurface structure, the field was of mammoth proportions. Later the field's structure was found to be a faulted anticline, in which the formations ranged from the Mayes limestone of Mississippian Age to Arbuckle limestone of Cambro-Ordovician Age, that had been folded, truncated, faulted by one major fault, and then buried under Cherokee shale and other formations. The new field, together with the fields of Greater Seminole, brought the most important Sooner state oil-activity shift within many years.

The well's accelerating flow proved the worth of the field. On Monday, two weeks after the well came in, a gauge test showed that it was flowing at the rate of 5,971 barrels daily, and later it passed the 6,000-barrel mark when deepened to 6,455 feet.[9] In its first twenty-seven days the No. 1 Oklahoma City produced 110,496 barrels of oil, at a price of $1.56 a barrel.

The I. T. I. O.–Foster interests controlled the new field within a radius of two miles, or approximately 6,500 acres of leases except a few large tracts owned by T. B. Slick, Sinclair Oil and Gas Company, Coline Oil Company, Roxana Petroleum Company, and W. R. Ramsey. Only the Wirt Franklin lease of the Robert Lord section cornered on the southwest the half-section of the discovery well.[10]

This protection of the discovery well enabled I. T. I. O. to plan an orderly development. Owners of all near-by acreage agreed on twenty-one locations and to limit their drilling to one well in the center of each forty-acre tract (and the first eight wells were so spaced); and the I. T. I. O. persuaded the royalty owners of small tracts to accept this plan. But Tom Slick, holder of a twenty-acre lease, and the Sinclair Oil and Gas Company, owning leases south of the discovery well, rejected the voluntary forty-acre spacing. Yet, in subsequent drilling, operators shouted down voluntary restrictions. They spaced in the Arbuckle formation one well to 14.60 acres, and in the Simpson zone one well to 12.85 acres. Development in the rich Wilcox zone on the north end of the field became

[9] *Oil and Gas Journal*, Vol. XXVII, No. 30 (December 6, 1928), 33.
[10] *Ibid.*, map. Ramsey sold to Mid-Kansas, now the Ohio Oil Company.

a near stampede; wells were spaced as closely as possible, averaging one well to 2.1 acres on the west eighty acres of the northwest quarter of S2-T11N-R3W and one well to 6.18 acres over the whole north area.[11]

The operators also agreed that I. T. I. O. should have all the time it needed to complete its No. 1 Oklahoma City discovery well

Indian Territory Illuminating Oil Company's 6,000-acre lease block in Trosper Park area near Oklahoma City, showing other locations by December 13, 1928

COURTESY OIL AND GAS JOURNAL

in the Wilcox sand, since it was a field experiment. If the Wilcox sand produced, an additional four-day test period would be granted, after which the well should be shut in until the nearest offset well

[11] "Geology and Economic Significance of the Oklahoma City Field," in *World Petroleum*, January, 1935, 12.

could be started. But I. T. I. O. leases were so situated that this company could be forced to drill only twenty-nine wells to protect its boundary lines.

The recent general improvement of rigs and drilling equipment had made possible the drilling of the deep Oklahoma City field. I. T. I. O. and other companies used rotary tools with 122-foot steel derricks (24 by 24 feet at the base) until the pay sand was reached. Then standard tools were used to finish the well. In addition, at each well, batteries of four 125-horsepower and 30-pounds-working-pressure boilers helped to furnish power.

Generally, a well's depth had required only three strings of casing. The surface pipe was fifteen and one-half inches in diameter and was set at 250–300 feet and cemented with 250–500 sacks of cement. Next, a nine-inch casing was cemented at 4,798 feet with 1,500 sacks and the third string of seven-inch casing at 6,355 feet.[12] Then, after seven days, the plug was "drilled out and the well brought in by bailing the rotary mud down a sufficient depth so that the natural pressure of the well will clean the hole."[13] Later, a terrific gas pressure required the use of three extra-heavy gates and fittings at each well head.

The I. T. I. O. and Foster companies had 8,000 barrels of steel tankage near the discovery well by December 13 and an additional 6,000 barrels under construction. Temporary transportation was also promised, for the Empire Pipe Line Company was preparing to connect the well's storage tanks to the Turley Petroleum Company's loading rack at Oklahoma City, from which the oil could be shipped to refineries in Tulsa.[14]

The total drilling cost of the No. 1 Oklahoma City had been $57,000, exclusive of the pipe and rig. And the drilling time, from spudding in until the well was completed, was five months and twelve days. By 1930 the average drilling time for an Oklahoma City well was reduced to 113 days, and in 1933 and 1934, to 65 days.

For a short time Mid-Continent interest was divided between

[12] John Power, "5,000-Barrel Wildcat Near Oklahoma City to Open New Field," in *National Petroleum News*, Vol. XX, No. 50 (December 12, 1928), 24.

[13] Homer H. Charles, "Oklahoma City Oil Field, Oklahoma," in *Bulletin of the American Association of Petroleum Geologists*, Vol. XIV (January–December, 1930), Part II, 1530–37.

[14] *National Petroleum News*, Vol. XX, No. 50 (December 12, 1928), 24.

the Oklahoma City well and another in Sedgwick County, Kansas,[15] completed by the Marland Oil Company, about six miles northeast of the Wright pool, that had been discovered the previous summer near Wichita.[16] The Marland company controlled 3,700 acres of leases about this No. 1 Goodrich. Back at St. Louis, in the Greater Seminole area, a third producer, in the Simpson formation, the Prairie Oil and Gas Company's No. 8 Gammon, almost as large as the I.T.I.O.-Foster No. 1 Oklahoma City, was also completed.

But interest was divided only for a short time. The announcement of the new Oklahoma City field brought thousands of people, and as in smaller communities, shanty towns sprang up near the producing area. Bodine City was built south of the No. 1 Oklahoma City well and Emerson City flanked it on the east. Farther down the road, south of the well, the Sutton townsite was laid out, and soon half a dozen townsite offices were extolling the merits of another oil capital. All of these, within a year, had folded their tents and stolen away, like the fabled Arabs.

In fact, Oklahoma City became the new oil center. From the hour that the radio broadcast to the world that the No. 1 Oklahoma City had opened a major field, there started the growth of another Southwestern metropolis. Daily its Huckins, Wells-Roberts, Skirvin, and other hotels buzzed with excited, loquacious promoters, lease vendors, and speculators. Exuberance and optimism sparked a Chamber of Commerce dinner soon after the I. T. I. O.–Foster well came in, in the course of which a five-year building program designed to save Oklahoma City from boom-town chaos was formulated.

There was much speculation at this dinner about the new oil field's economic and social impacts. Todd M. Pettigrew, the principal speaker, senior member of the firm of Pettigrew and Myers, a New York investment house which launched Oil Shares, Incorporated, a $100,000,000 holding company, advised his listeners to prepare for a population of 400,000 by 1940. And in line with this expectation the Skirvin Hotel management announced a 150-room-addition building plan and the owners of the WKY radio station signed for a full NBC hook-up.[17]

15 The No. 1 Goodrich in 26S-1W.
16 Power, *loc. cit.*, 40.

Oklahoma City's Bonanza Field

The Ramsey brothers and T. B. Slick were heavily interested in near-by leases, the former having announced the location of their No. 1 Fortson well,[18] half a mile north and a little west of the discovery well. I. T. I. O. was drilling its second well,[19] and the Coline Oil Company, which owned the 160-acre lease adjoining the Ramsey acreage, had arranged for an offset to the Ramsey location. Indeed, so fast was development that Sinclair completed its No. 1 Stamper by June 20, 1929, the second producer in the field; and Coline brought in its 5,400-barrel No. 1 Old's well[20] seven days later in the lower Simpson sand, thereby convincing everyone that Oklahoma City was indeed a major field.

The new oil field's rapid northward expansion and the steadily mounting output of oil soon made two planned programs necessary.

Never before had so vast a metropolitan area been threatened by so vast a field. Oilmen realized this and co-operated with Oklahoma City officials to solve the many problems growing out of the singular situation. The I. T. I. O. Company employed a former Cleveland, Ohio, planning expert, Herbert Stanley, to work with the city officials and the Chamber of Commerce.

Lease by lease, oil development spread northward. As it approached the city limits, the city commission invoked an early-day business zoning ordinance to create limited drilling areas and thus prevent promiscuous encroachment. The first zone, "U-7," north of Southwest Twenty-second Street, on the east side of town, was established on May 10, 1929; and a second zone, north of Grand Boulevard, with North High Avenue on the west, was designated on December 3.[21]

There were few restrictions within a permitted zone. Derricks, slush pits, and steel and ground tanks invaded industrial and residential areas. Rigs reared their crown blocks in school yards, slush pits were dug on playgrounds, and storage tanks were built in alleys.

---

[17] Barrow, "Boom—1," MS.

[18] In the center of the SW NE of S24-T11N-R3W.

[19] In the center of the NE SW of S13-T11N-R3W.

[20] In S24-T11N-R3W, half a mile due west of the I.T.I.O.–Foster discovery well.

[21] "22–13a. U-7 Use. Regulations," Ordinance, No. 3615. "Published in Daily Record, May 16–17–18, 1929," Ordinance Record, XII, 452–3; Ordinance No. 3788, *ibid.*, "Published in Daily Record, January 2–3–4, 1930," 603; Ordinance No. 3678, *ibid.*, "Published in Daily Record, August 1–2–3, 1929"—all in the City Commission's files, Municipal Building, Oklahoma City.

Oil! Titan of the Southwest

On March 4 of the next year the U-7 zone, along with a strip across the south edge of the city, was opened under regulations; and five months later another zone was opened between Southeast Fifteenth and Southeast Twenty-ninth streets, and between North Byers Avenue and the Santa Fe Railroad on the west. A third zone was opened on November 25 between the Santa Fe Railroad and Santa Fe Avenue and north of Grand Boulevard, and still others came later.

At the same time state officials and operators approached the problems of proration and well-spacing. Slick and Sinclair championed a free-for-all field-production and spacing policy. This alarmed conservative operators, both in the Oklahoma City field and at Tulsa; and on May 2, Ray M. Collins, umpire of the Greater Seminole field, recommended that the Corporation Commission restrict the output of all Oklahoma fields, where wells made one hundred barrels or more a day. But his proposal was fought so bitterly by the free-for-all policy advocates that Commissioners Fred Capshaw and Roy Hughes denied Collins' application.[22]

During 1929 the oil-production problem grew weekly. The Oklahoma City oil field had gone into high gear, with news of gusher after gusher breaking into the state newspaper headlines. By the summer of 1929 several new wells were flowing 15,000 barrels daily. By September 12 there were fifteen producing wells in the field, making 60,000 barrels of oil daily, and nineteen others were drilling. An oilmen's committee, on the strength of this, asked the Corporation Commission for a thirty-day shutdown, saying that the field could well reach a daily output of 137,000 barrels by October 1. So fast had the field expanded during this year's development that the Oklahoma Secretary of State issued 102 charters to oil, royalty, and kindred companies. In addition, adding to the producers' embarrassment, over 1,000,000 barrels of potential oil were held back from production in West Texas fields, principally at Yates and Hendricks.

Several operator conferences had scheduled the subject of a shutdown of the Oklahoma City field. Then, late in August, 1929,

[22] For a discussion of the semivoluntary proration during this period, see Ray M. Collins, "Oklahoma to Need 90,000,000 Barrels," in *Oil and Gas Journal*, Vol. XXVII, No. 29 (December 6, 1928), 133 ff.

alarmed producers, purchasers, and state officials again met in Tulsa to consider this problem. Proration became an economic necessity. This was apparent when Commissioner Capshaw asked J. S. Sidwell, assistant superintendent of the Prairie Oil and Gas Company land department, what the production would be on January 1. Sidwell replied, "A minimum of 300,000 and a maximum of 500,000 barrels per day."

The Sinclair Oil and Gas Company, joined by a few other operators, opposed a shutdown, recommending instead a curb for each well of not less than one hundred barrels of oil a day. This time, however, the Commissioners supported the Greater Seminole umpire, and on September 11, 1929, issued their first order, No. 4804, applicable to the Oklahoma City oil field, calling for a thirty-day shutdown.[23]

Wirt Franklin, head of the Wirt Franklin Petroleum Corporation and vice-president and manager of the Cromwell-Franklin Oil Company, was a big acreage holder at Oklahoma City. He supported the Commissioners' order upon the express condition that the shutdown was to last only for thirty days and that at the end of that time the oil purchasers were to allocate pipe-line and tank-car outlets among all producers. He called upon representatives of the Carter Oil Company, the Prairie Oil and Gas Company, and the Empire Oil and Refining Company, the principal buyers, to support him in this, and they agreed to do so.

Two days later the Oklahoma City field, which had reached 67,507 barrels of oil daily on September 11–12, declined to 12,935 barrels, a gauge for a twenty-four-hour period, ending at 7 A.M., September 14. Of this amount, 4,985 barrels came from a new well that was allowed to flow twenty-four hours to "clean itself."[24]

The Oklahoma City Producers Association, under the presidency of Franklin, played a vital part in meeting overproduction and field-control problems. Franklin had championed the rights of

[23] In addition, this order required a period of seven days after the final string of casing was set and cemented. But the operator was permitted to drill the cemented plug and "bail the well for the purpose of allowing the water and mud to be expelled therefrom." See W. P. Z. German, "Legal History of Conservation of Oil and Gas in Oklahoma," in *Legal History of Conservation of Oil and Gas,* 157.

[24] Lawrence E. Smith, "Production in Oklahoma City Pool Shut in by State Order," in *National Petroleum News,* Vol. XXI, No. 38 (September 18, 1929), 29.

independents and controlled-field development since Healdton days. Supporting his and the Association's efforts were representatives of the major producers—J. S. Sidwell of the Prairie Oil and Gas Company, R. M. Williams and M. J. Kirwin of the I. T. I. O., H. V. Smith and Glenn Harroun of the Sinclair Oil and Gas Company, H. M. Stalcup of the Skelly Oil Company, M. M. Fleming of the Mid-Kansas Oil and Gas Company, and Ralph V. Boyd of the Shell Oil Company—all serving on important committees.

On September 25 the Association employed Otto B. Bradford as field umpire and set up a system similar to that at Greater Seminole, with Bradford serving as a liaison officer between the producers and the Corporation Commission.

When the Oklahoma City field was reopened on October 12, it was yet a good producer. In some instances the wells were better than they had been at the time of the shutdown. A twenty-four-hour gauge showed an output of 63,838 barrels of oil from fourteen wells eligible to start on that date, or 9,236 barrels higher than their total yield the day before the shutdown.

The Oklahoma City Producers Association and the oil company representatives working with it had ready a simple proration plan when the Commission's shutdown was lifted. Oklahoma City producers were divided into "A" and "B" classes, with each class permitted to flow its wells four days in succession during November and up to 40 per cent of each well's potential, with the allowable increased to 50 per cent in December. On January 27, 1930, the production of the Oklahoma City field was reduced to 25 per cent of its potential.

This plan was temporarily effective. By the end of 1929 there were 53 producing wells in the field, 161 drilling, "26 shutdown operations, and 27 wells shut down for proration";[25] and by March 10 of the next year there were 135 completed wells and 173 drilling wells or locations. At this latter date the estimated oil production of the field had been stepped up to an annual 14,500,000 barrels, and eight major companies had opened district offices in Oklahoma City.

Developments in the Oklahoma City oil field were of spectacular proportions for the remainder of this year. As in other fields with

[25] Barrow, "Proration raises its head," MS.

strong gas pressure, the terrific force of the sand blown from wells cut control fittings, caused wild wells, and brought the loss of hundreds of millions of cubic feet of gas and much oil, a part of it by fire. Such a fire came early in March when the Sinclair Oil and Gas and the Amerada Petroleum's No. 5 Kintner, on the east side of the field, blew out and burned 1,200,000,000 cubic feet of gas in twelve days before it was brought under control. Subsequent tests gave this well a potential of 300,000,000 cubic feet of gas daily.

Altogether the most awe-inspiring spectacle was staged by "Wild Mary Sudik." About daybreak on March 26, 1930, a tired drilling crew was leaving the hole at the No. 1 Sudik, an I. T. I. O.–Foster Petroleum well, in the south part of the field. The bit had just penetrated the top of the Wilcox horizon, where the crew had neglected to mud the hole. Then came a deafening roar, and a giant, uncontrolled gusher, estimated at 200,000,000 cubic feet of gas and 20,000 barrels of oil daily, blew in, cleaning the hole of mud and tools and buffeting the traveling block about as if it were a toy.

Frantically additional crews sought to aid in shutting down the well, but there was neither control head nor master gate. There was only enough surface pipe to make a connection. And it was only after a prolonged struggle of five days that a master gate was swung into place and anchored over the surface pipe. But it could not hold against the strong pressure which whipped out sand with the oil and gas and cut the steel fittings like an emery wheel.[26]

Men in slickers and steel helmets, wearing goggles, with cotton stuffed in their ears to keep out the deafening roar, worked courageously, urged on by company officials and spectators. Twice a day Floyd Gibbons, war correspondent and news commentator, broadcast "Wild Mary's" antics to a radio-listening world. "Wild Mary" was truly on a rampage. When it hurled millions of cubic feet of gas and a spray of oil high into the air, on March 26, a strong north wind caught the oil and blew it far southward, showering it on farms for five or six miles about, until they were covered by a black,

---

[26] *Oil and Gas Journal,* Vol. XXVIII, No. 28 (April 3, 1930), 48. The I.T.I.O. saved 25,945 barrels of crude oil, according to the *Journal,* by pumping that amount into storage tanks. Robert H. Dott (director, Oklahoma Geological Survey), "When Gushers Are Liabilities," in the files of the Oklahoma Geological Survey. Mr. Dott made available to the author this manuscript and other materials.

oily coat. And oily globules, like soap-bubbles, floated through the air to splatter homes in the university town of Norman, twelve miles away. Then, later, the wind changed, and a part of Oklahoma City also received an oil shower.

At last, on Sunday, April 6, the well was brought under control.[27] H. M. Myracle, with a crew of engineers and mechanics from the American Iron and Machine Company, built a special connection that was put on a rig and swung from lines inside the derrick. The workers, chancing death for perhaps the hundredth time, tore loose the remnants of the connections formerly used unsuccessfully, swung the die nipple into place, and with wrenches and tongs cut enough new threads on the surface pipe to cause the new control head to hold.

"Wild Mary's" rampage had been expensive. Thousands of acres of land were soaked with oil and farmers had to be compensated; 211,589 barrels of oil were drawn from pits, tanks, and streams, and much of it escaped. One can only surmise how much gas was wasted. Experts estimated the well owners' losses from $100,000 to $1,000,000, but the actual direct cost was less than $25,000.

In May, "Wild Mary's" antics were repeated by the Prairie Oil and Gas–Slick Oil's No. 1 Sigmon. It roared in with a huge gas discharge and ran uncontrolled for five days; and in the middle of the night on October 30, Morgan Petroleum's No. 1 Stout, called "Stout Fella," a mile from the principal business corner of the city, broke loose for three days and sprayed the city with oil. "Stout Fella" was an even greater menace to life and property than "Wild Mary," for a southeast wind blew a gray pall of gas toward Oklahoma City's skyscrapers and thickly settled areas. Workmen, wearing rubber coats and using copper-headed hammers, fought the wild gusher that was pouring out 100,000,000 cubic feet of gas and upward of 60,000 barrels of oil daily. Then the North Canadian, the waters of which were coated with oil, caught on fire outside the city and firemen fought the blaze that was creeping five miles down the river until they had it under control. Finally, after sixty-six hours, "Stout Fella" was also shut in. Its spray of oil had covered more than 1,000

[27] W. A. Spinney, "Oklahoma City's Output Increased," *ibid.*, April 10, 1930, 58; Earl Sparling, "Oil Hells in Oklahoma," in *Outlook and Independent*, Vol. CLVII, No. 6 (February 11, 1931), 214–17, 236–37, 238–39.

city residences and had sprayed the state capitol building with amber flecks.[28]

The new field expanded rapidly. On May 27, 1930, it reached the southeast edge of Oklahoma City when the Hall-Briscoe No. 1 Holmes well was completed for 17,000 barrels a day. In the following October the British-American Oil Producing Company entered the city proper with its No. 1 Eckroat well, thus presenting the city commission with a knotty problem. This city encroachment created a thriving business for "lease hounds." Where formerly lots had sold for $5.00, now they leased at from $500 to $1,000. And in the opposite direction, on June 21, the Continental Oil Company extended the field into Cleveland County with its No. 1 V. Sudik.[29]

But the city council had foreseen the oil field's envelopment of the city and moved to meet it on March 4 by issuing an ordinance, on the Oxford, Kansas, plan, prohibiting drilling within the corporate limits except in a U-zone (one north of East Reno Avenue and another across the south edge of the city.)[30] Drilling within a U-zone was limited to one well to a city block. The enlargement of zones from time to time took in much of the city. Injunctions and litigation followed, however, snarling the council's efforts and making uncertain a planned city program. Nowhere else had such puzzling oil-development problems confronted a city council.[31]

The state also had its legal problems. By January, 1931, the Corporation Commission could watch from the capitol's windows and see the shambles of its proration regulations. Both major and minor operators vied with each other in reckless drilling, in utter disregard of production regulations, and vented huge volumes of gas into the air. At one time it was conservatively estimated that seventy-five wells had a gas-oil ratio of 10,000 cubic feet of gas to one barrel of oil. It was estimated that 14,000,000 barrels of oil were produced illegally.

[28] Barrow, "Wild Mary—1," MS; Sparling, loc. cit., 214–15.
[29] In NW NW NE of S6-T10N-R2W.
[30] Barrow, "Oil—Alfalfa—1," MS.
[31] Governor W. H. Murray sought to aid the city commission in its efforts to promote an orderly oil-drilling program. In May, 1932, he declared the whole city to be a military zone and prohibited the drilling of wells in areas other than those created by the city ordinances. Two years later he set up another military zone within one mile of the executive mansion, but later reduced it to one-half mile. This was to prevent encroaching on state properties.

Oil! Titan of the Southwest

Foreseeing legal involvement, in the spring of 1930, the Mid-Continent Oil and Gas Association appointed a committee of nine lawyers to make a careful study of the state law of 1915 governing oil production.[32] After a careful study the committee concluded that the law was valid, except Section 2. In line with the committee's finding, the Corporation Commission drew up its order No. 5189, on June 30, 1930, imposing severe restrictions on the Oklahoma City field, citing the fact that the daily oil supply of the United States was 5,030,000 barrels as against a domestic demand of only 2,840,000 barrels a day. For this reason, the order read, production was being curtailed.

Meanwhile, the C. C. Julian Oil and Royalty Company, owner of an oil and gas lease covering three lots in an addition outside the corporate limits of Oklahoma City, sought to restrain the Corporation Commission from enforcing its orders as they applied to the

[32] Oil and gas associations have been effective agencies in promoting scientific oil-field development, production, and conservation. Topping the list of these organizations is the American Petroleum Institute, formed in 1919 as an outgrowth of the National Petroleum War Service Committee. Its objects are (1) "to afford a means of co-operation with the government in all matters of national concern"; (2) "to foster foreign and domestic trade in American petroleum"; (3) "to promote in general the interests of the petroleum industry in all its branches"; and (4) "to promote the mutual improvements of its members and the study of the arts and sciences connected with the petroleum industry."—*Petroleum Facts and Figures* (Second edition), 273. By 1930 the Institute, with its divisions of Production, Refining, and Marketing, had thousands of field men, technical men, and businessmen engaged in co-operative study, the findings of which were frequently published for the benefit of the entire industry. At present, the Institute, under the presidency of William R. Boyd, Jr., is regarded as the greatest single agency sponsoring rights and interests of oilmen and an orderly program of oil-field conservation and development.

The Southwest also has had local associations serving in much the same capacity but regionally. Among these are the Rocky Mountain Oil and Gas Association, the Kansas Independent Oil and Gas Association, the New Mexico Oil and Gas Association, and the Mid-Continent Oil and Gas Association. The Mid-Continent Oil and Gas Association was most truly a regional organization. It was formed on Saturday, October 13, 1917, in Tulsa, Oklahoma, primarily to co-operate with the federal government in supplying the armed forces with adequate petroleum products. Later, it sponsored the interests of all oilmen, local, state, and national, seeking "the advancement and protection of the petroleum industry in Kansas, Oklahoma, Texas, Arkansas, Louisiana, Mississippi, Alabama, and the other mid-continent oil states," a declaration of purpose from which it has not deviated. At present, the Association's administrative offices are Kansas-Oklahoma division, at Tulsa; the Texas division, at Dallas; the Louisiana-Arkansas division, at Shreveport; and the Mississippi-Alabama division, at Jackson, Mississippi. Texas also has its North Texas Oil and Gas Association, with its office at Wichita Falls; and its East Texas Oil Association, at Tyler, Texas.

Oklahoma City's Bonanza Field

Oklahoma City field, charging that the operators' committee and the field umpire had illegally ordered a Julian well to be shut in for sixty-five days before it was placed on production. The plaintiff contended that it was deprived of its constitutional right to develop and operate property as it thought fit and that the 1915 oil-conservation act was in violation of the Fourteenth Amendment to the federal Constitution. The case finally came before the Oklahoma Supreme Court, and on October 14, 1930, by a vote of seven to two, this body sustained the state law and the authority and orders of the Corporation Commission and denied the plaintiff's contention.

Another attack on the authority of the Corporation Commission of great significance was a suit brought by the Champlin Refining Company[33] in the federal court at Oklahoma City, in September, 1930, prior to a decision in the Julian case. Champlin sought a temporary, interlocutory, and, on final hearing, a permanent injunction restraining the Commission from enforcing its orders relating to the Oklahoma City field. The plaintiff had several wells on town lots in Oklahoma City additions and also owned an eighty-mile pipe line connecting them with its Enid refinery. It contended that the output of these wells was necessary to maintain the operations of the refinery. The federal judge refused to grant a temporary order restraining the Commission and his three-judge court on October 1, 1930, by a two to one decision, denied the plaintiff's application. In later years, the Julian and Champlin decisions strengthened the authority of the Corporation Commission and helped the conservation movement in other states.

[33] As is the case with other Southwestern refineries, the history of the Champlin Refining Company is that of its founder, H. H. Champlin, an Enid banker, hardware merchant, and real-estate investor. The refining company he founded was largely the product of a Garber lease, formerly owned by a Sinclair subsidiary that had been allowed to lapse. The lease proved to be a successful producer. Then Champlin purchased a small refinery near Enid, and began his new career. Pipe lines were extended into the Garber field, and later into Tonkawa, Seminole, and Oklahoma City. Tank cars were also acquired and bulk plants and filling stations were erected in Oklahoma, Texas, Kansas, Nebraska, Missouri, Iowa, Minnesota, Colorado, and Illinois. In 1935 the Champlin Refining Company built a gasoline pipe line from its Enid refinery to terminals in Hutchison, Kansas and Superior, Nebraska, a distance of approximately 300 miles—among the first product lines of this nature to be built. At present Champlin has approximately 4,000 barrels a day of crude oil production, 400 miles of crude oil pipe lines and a refinery capacity at Enid of 17,000 barrels. MS, "Champlin Refining Company," supplied the author by the Champlin Refining Company.

Oil! Titan of the Southwest

Market demand was a large factor in shaping the Oklahoma Corporation Commission's orders. But the price of oil was necessarily in part controlled by the oil output of other states. The huge oil production of East Texas by July, 1931, was decisive, causing posted prices to drop from eighty-nine cents a barrel at the beginning of 1931 to sixteen cents for 34- to 34.9-gravity oil.[34] Some panicky Oklahoma operators closed their wells and joined landowners to ask Governor W. H. Murray for drastic control measures.

Murray had been watching developments and now acted promptly. On August 4, 1931, he proclaimed a state of emergency, declared martial law within a fifty-foot zone about each well, and ordered the militia to take control of twenty-nine Oklahoma oil fields having 3,106 wells and to close all prorated wells until "the price [of oil] hits one dollar."

In his executive order, Murray cited Section 7955, Statute 1921, stating that it was unlawful to take crude oil from its stratum when there was not a market. He also charged that a certain oil company had "filched" the legacy of school children by operating in such manner that the state did not receive its just revenues, and that leaders of this company had met in Tulsa the preceding March and had conspired to bribe forty members of the legislature to impeach the Governor. This and "other monopolistic companies" had joined to depress the oil price and increase their earnings.[35] Whether his charges were true or false, Murray had his way.

The market was strengthened so that on August 24 one major purchaser announced his willingness to pay one dollar a barrel for crude; but others kept their quotations at seventy cents. In October, field control was lifted, with wells operating on a 5 per cent allowable. A short time later troops were withdrawn. In February of the next year the Corporation Commission changed its production ruling from a time to a percentage basis.[36]

[34] *Mineral Resources of the United States, Part II, Nonmetals*, 581; "Turning the Oil Tide With Rifles," in *Literary Digest*, Vol. CX, No. 8 (August 15, 1931), 6; "Militia Bill's Latest," in *Outlook and Independent*, Vol. CLVIII, No. 14 (August 5, 1931), 486.

[35] Executive Order 1460, "Calling Out National Guard and Declaring Martial Law and Ordering Military Control to Close Down All Prorated Wells," Secretary of State's Office, Oklahoma City, Oklahoma.

[36] *The Daily Oklahoman* (Oklahoma City), March 1, 1932, p. 17, col. 6.

Seminole, Oklahoma, during early development

Standard Oil Company (N. J.)

Seminole freight yard, 1928

Carter Oil Company

View from steps of capitol, Oklahoma City

Jacoby's Photo Service

Oil wells in residential area, Oklahoma City

Photograph by Corsini
Standard Oil Company (N. J.)

Oklahoma City's Bonanza Field

Soon violations occurred again, and on June 6, 1932, military law was once more invoked, with Colonel Cicero I. Murray in charge. The operators' proration committee and advisory committee were abolished and their records seized by the militia. A martial-law zone was extended about tanks and pipe lines, in addition to wells, and meters were installed to prevent "hot oil" from running. More than once the militiamen and workers engaged in free-for-all fights and "knuckle-dusting," and tear gas was not spared. But in the end the militia won.

Once more the Oklahoma City field was closed down entirely, except for wells making oil and salt water, from March 4 to 14, 1933. Gas wells and oil wells making 10 per cent water were not affected, except that the latter were given an allowable of one hundred barrels daily.[37]

The state legislature then buttressed Murray's efforts by enacting its famous proration law, House Bill 481, which was approved by the Governor on April 10, 1933. This law became the pattern for other states and was subsequently used by the federal authorities. The law required a proration staff (named by Murray on April 11) and reduced illegal production,[38] but carried over an old defect by basing proration upon well potentials without regard to acreage.

By 1935 drilling had reached Oklahoma City's northern limits. Phillips Petroleum Company's No. 1 Kendall, on Block 9 of the Durland Addition, was completed as a gasser on June 3, and then deepened to get oil. Early in October, the British-American Oil Producing Company drilled into the Wilcox zone with its No. 1 Mary Green well, northeast of the executive mansion, and proved a current theory that the field's major structure extended northward into this area.

This discovery was disquieting to many north Oklahoma City property-owners, for fashionable Lincoln Terrace, the University

[37] W. A. Spinney, "Governor Shuts in Oklahoma City Field, Charging Some Companies Greatly Overproducing," in *Oil and Gas Journal*, Vol. XXXI, No. 42 (March 9, 1933), 42.

[38] In a hearing before a House subcommittee in Washington, Hugh Irey, an agent of the Department of the Interior at Oklahoma City, charged that in July, 1934, 400,000 barrels of "hot oil" had been run in Oklahoma; and C. C. Brown, assistant proration umpire, stated that overproduction in the Oklahoma City field amounted to 188,753 barrels for July.—*Petroleum Investigations*, Part III, November 12, 13, 14, 16, and 17, 1934, pp. 1535 and 1543.

of Oklahoma Medical School and hospital grounds, and the executive mansion and state capitol properties were now well astride the newly found oil structure.

Then on March 24, 1936, an election was held, under a city ordinance, to create a new one-mile-square drilling zone, a niblick pitch from the capitol, immediately north of the state property on Twenty-third Street and west of an older zone. In a spirited campaign, the voters approved it.[39] Promptly the operators staked fifty-three locations in the new zone.

A storm of protest followed. Social clubs and politicians vied with each other in picturing unsightly derricks and slush pits and the smell of crude oil and gas about the executive mansion and capitol grounds. Governor E. W. Marland, too, was annoyed, for only recently he had donated three hundred truck loads of shrubbery from his Ponca City estate to beautify the capitol grounds.[40]

Marland, however, was also an oilman. He understood the danger of oil leases blocking in the capitol property and now began a valiant fight to protect state interests.

Meanwhile, Attorney General Mac Q. Williamson advised against Marland's opposing the city commission.[41] He told him that the seventy-acre capitol tract was within the city limits and that the city commission had exclusive leasing jurisdiction. Marland did not agree and called out the National Guard, charging that officials of Oklahoma City had "enacted arbitrary, discriminatory and unreasonable ordinances" and that "Foreign Corporations and private interests" on lands adjacent to the capitol grounds were endangering state oil lands.[42]

To find a way out, state Senator Knox Garvin from Duncan sought to lease the endangered land but met with a sustained protest from the city. Then Marland, thoroughly aroused, made Garvin a National Guard sergeant to save him from court action and named him as a state drilling superintendent. After ten days of

[39] Lawrence E. Smith, "200 Wells to Be Drilled in New Oklahoma City Field Extension," in *National Petroleum News*, Vol. XXVIII, No. 12 (March 18, 1936), 103.

[40] L. G. E. Bignell, "Big Wells Spur Activity in New Oklahoma City Drilling Zone," in *Oil and Gas Journal*, Vol. XXXIV, No. 46 (April, 1936), 9.

[41] Smith, *loc. cit.*, 25.

[42] MS, Executive Order 1981, April 1, 1936, in Secretary of State's Office, Oklahoma City, Oklahoma. Martial law was to become operative the next day. Tracts put under the ban were 1–100 and 37, 39, 41, 43, 44, and 45.

martial law, the State Board of Affairs awarded leases on sixteen separate tracts to the Sunray Oil Company[43] of Tulsa and on one tract to Anderson-Prichard Oil Corporation.[44] Sunray's bid was $372,000 and Anderson-Prichard's $3,055.[45] Immediately the city commission challenged the Governor in a legal action.

Marland, not to be outdone, put his troops to patrolling state properties with instructions to keep away court process servers. He also asked the Corporation Commission to find ways and means to prevent the operators from wasting gas and to save the state lands from being drained of oil by the adjacent leaseholders.

One process server did get by the watchful state troopers and laid a summons to court on Marland's desk, but the Governor refused to recognize it and told Garvin to proceed with drilling. With the state program thus adequately protected, on April 4, 1936, Marland drove down the first well-site stake near the executive mansion and launched with a flourish a state drilling campaign.

[43] Sunray Oil Corporation was organized in 1920. Its name was coined from the names of two business associates, A. W. Son, an incorporator, and a Mr. Ray, Son's business associate. The new company started with a debt of $145,000 and production only in Kansas. The Kansas leases were sold to pay off the debt, and Sunray purchased production property at Sipe Springs, Texas. Then came the purchase of other company properties and oil-field development. By 1925, Sunray had a production of 54,803 barrels of crude oil annually and was operating in Pawnee, Creek, Payne, and Lincoln counties, Oklahoma. Meanwhile other consolidations were effected and production expanded to other states. By 1930, Sunray's total net annual oil production had increased to more than 2,000,000 barrels. Today the company has more than 775 employees, has whole or part interest in 2,337 oil and gas wells in seven states, and in 1946 its refineries at Santa Maria, California, and Allen, Oklahoma, marketed more than $7,300,000 of petroleum products. C. H. Wright is Sunray's president and F. B. Parriott, chairman of its board. Data was furnished the author by Mr. Luther Williams, Public Relations Department, Sunray Oil Corporation, Tulsa, Oklahoma.

[44] J. Steve Anderson and L. H. Prichard had been partners in oil- and gas-lease trading and selling since 1918. In 1921 they acquired a small skimming plant at Cyril, Oklahoma, and operated it for the processing of specialties, particularly industrial naphthas. Two years later they purchased a second refinery in Kansas, dismantled it, and shipped it to Colorado City, Texas, where they rebuilt and operated it under the name of West Texas Refining and Development Company, and after Standard Oil Company of California had purchased stock, as the Col-Tex Refining Company. Anderson-Prichard began production with nine wells in the Sasakwa area in 1928 and by the end of 1931 operated twenty-nine wells at Oklahoma City. From these operations, properties were acquired and production came from Oklahoma, Kansas, Texas, and New Mexico by the nineteen forties.

[45] "Over a Hundred Oklahoma City Tests Amid 'Gushers' and Guardsmen," in *Oil and Gas Journal*, Vol. XXVIII, No. 38 (April 11, 1940), 15.

Oil! Titan of the Southwest

The oil press ridiculed Marland's martial law,[46] saying that his state soldiers were wearing "35 or 40 pound pistols," and that the outlook, plainly, was for fast action.[47] "But see how weakly it ended," continued the writer. "One judge [Ben Arnold] handled the affair." He handed down a decision spanking the Governor for resorting to martial law but at the same time supporting him by declaring that the city had no jurisdiction over state lands.

This ended the controversy. Subsequently offset wells were drilled directionally under Lincoln Terrace and derricks lifted their crown blocks about the impressive but domeless capitol and executive mansion as monuments to the Governor's practical turn of mind. As a result, the state's oil revenue was large, and at Marland's suggestion $1,000,000 of it was appropriated to construct a state office building.[48]

By 1935, Oklahoma City had the second largest single American oil field, embracing 11,000 acres. In it, 1,713 wells had been drilled, and from it had come 290,730,062 barrels of oil, according to a November 1 report of the Corporation Commission. The Wilcox zone had been most prolific, with 549 wells producing 192,-267,937 barrels, and next was the Simpson formation with 335 wells making 80,356,301 barrels. By January 1, 1940, Corporation Commissioner W. J. Armstrong said that the field's total yield was 475,-640,053 barrels, of which 357,932,000 barrels came from the Wilcox zone. The field then embraced 13,325 acres.[49]

In the operators' reckless development of the Oklahoma City field, waste had been flagrant. On top of the expense of drilling hundreds of unnecessary wells, many other costs must be added. One was the wanton venting of gas. In 1938, E. F. Schmidt of the Lone Star Gas Company of Dallas told the American Gas Association at Atlantic City that by 1935 there had been wasted in the

[46] " 'Popping' Gas, Waking Governor, Brings Conservation Hearings," in *National Petroleum News*, Vol. XXVIII, No. 17 (April 22, 1936), 25.

[47] *Ibid.*, April 29, 1936, 20-c.

[48] Budget Analyst Orval W. Hurst announced on January 29, 1948, that revenue from state land wells and leases that went into the public building fund amounted to $4,228,860.34. The peak year was 1937, when the state received $836,680.52. During the fiscal year of 1946–47 the state's oil revenue was $225,872.–*Daily Oklahoman*, January 30, 1948.

[49] Dal Dalrymple, "Oklahoma City Field Enjoying Another Periodic Flurry," in *Oil and Gas Journal*, Vol. XXVIII, No. 38 (April 11, 1940), 15.

Oklahoma City's Bonanza Field

Oklahoma City field, 1,200,000,000,000 cubic feet of natural gas, almost as much as the natural gas industry had piped to all its customers in the preceding year, worth approximately $441,000,000.[50] In the end this dissipated the producing formation's self-lifting energy and sealed in underground vaults hundreds of millions of barrels of oil.

Elsewhere over Oklahoma intensive exploration was carried on. As a result, there were oil discoveries in twenty-one Oklahoma counties during 1930–34. Among these Fitts, near Ada in Pontotoc County,[51] was the largest. Here Ed H. Moore *et al* had blocked leases on 1,160 acres upon which their No. 1 Wirick discovery well[52] was drilled on September 2, 1933, and within the next five years the field spread over 5,000 acres. Other discoveries were at Edmond, in Oklahoma County, in 1930; at Lucien, in Noble County, in 1932; at Crescent, in Logan County, in 1933; and at South Burbank, in Osage County, in 1934.

Oklahoma was yet a great oil-producing state. By 1939 it had yielded an all-years cumulative total of 4,500,000,000 barrels of petroleum.[53]

[50] Barrow, "1935–1," MS.

[51] The well was in S29-R2N-T6 and 7E.

[52] "Fitts, Pontotoc County," in "Summary Reports of New Pools," Records of the Petroleum Administration Board, Natural Resources Records Office, National Archives.

[53] U. S. Department of the Interior, Petroleum Administrative Board, *Operation of the New Pool Plans of Orderly Development Under the Code of Fair Competition for the Petroleum Industry* (pamphlet), 20–22; Bureau of Mines, *Crude Petroleum and Petroleum Products* (pamphlet), 953.

XX

Panhandle Oil and Gas

MANY SOUTHWESTERN OIL FIELDS had their leading actors—
Spindletop, its Anthony F. Lucas; Glenn Pool, its Bob Gal-
breath; Jennings, its W. Scott Heywood; Ranger, its W. K.
Gordon; and Luling, its Edgar B. Davis. The modest, retiring Uni-
versity of Oklahoma geologist, Charles N. Gould, was the Texas
Panhandle's discoverer.

On a late June afternoon in 1905 a heavily laden hack pulled by
tired horses splashed over the old Lee Crossing of the South Canadian River below the mouth of Pitcher Creek, about twenty-five
miles north of Amarillo. In the hack were Gould and his two youth-
ful assistants, E. F. Schramm and Tom B. Matthews. While crossing the Canadian, Gould noticed under the clear water a ledge of
white rock, dipping towards the east.

That night the travelers camped near the crossing. And after
supper Gould returned to the river and walked up it for a mile or
more to examine this dipping ledge, which he found to be a white
dolomite. In later years this formation, called the Alibates dolomite,
was the key used by geologists to run the region's surveying levels
for oil and gas.[1]

This summer of 1905 proved to be a busy one for Gould and his
helpers. They first worked the surface of the red beds in northeastern Potter and southeastern Moore counties, since known as the
John Ray dome. They next studied Sherman and Dallam counties,
mapping the cretaceous rock outcrops along Coldwater Creek; and
then they found the Bravo dome near the mouth of Trujillo Creek,

[1] Charles N. Gould, "The Beginnings of the Panhandle Oil and Gas Field," in the
Panhandle-Plains Historical Review, Vol. VIII (1935), 22–23; N. D. Bartlett, "Okla-
homa Professor Discovers Panhandle Oil and Gas Field," in Amarillo Sunday *Globe-
News* (Golden Anniversary edition, 1938), Sec. G-1, pp. 1–2.

in western Oldham County. Finally, they studied the triassic rocks along the Canadian River, in Oldham and Potter counties, and completed their season's work in the Palo Duro Canyon.

This concluded Gould's third field season in this general area, working under the United States Reclamation Service. At its close he published two United States Geological Survey Water-supply and Irrigation papers. In his second paper, *No. 191,* he mentioned three anticlines he had observed along the Canadian: the Bravo dome near the New Mexico line; the Tuck Trigg dome near the mouth of West Amarillo Creek; and the John Ray dome on which the discovery gas well was afterwards drilled, near the junction of Packsaddle and Big Canyon creeks.[2]

A decade passed before Gould had occasion to make practical use of his Canadian River dolomite discovery. At that time he was a consulting geologist in Oklahoma City. In May, 1916,[3] he went to Ardmore to do some work for two Amarillo men, M. C. Nobles, a wholesale grocer, and T. J. Moore, a traveling salesman. They wanted him to examine some leased properties near Tishomingo. Gould visited the tracts and then turned in an unfavorable report, much to his clients' disappointment.

Just before starting home, Nobles asked Gould if he knew of a favorable oil structure in the Amarillo country. At first Gould thought not. Then he remembered his Canadian River survey of 1905, when he had noticed three domes, and he told his visitors about them. Nobles and Moore were greatly impressed with what Gould had to say and persuaded him to return with them to Amarillo to revisit the site of his discovery.

From Amarillo a short time later, Gould, Nobles, J. M. Neely, and Dr. M. W. Cunningham, headed north by automobile, crossing the flat upland, buffalo-wallow plains, and finally came out on a high bluff south of the river. The panorama stretching out before them was like a map. Gould recognized in the rock strata of mesas and canyon walls and buttes, the outline of the John Ray dome and pointed it out to his companions. But they stared incredulously;

[2] U.S.G.S., *Geology and Water Resources of the Western Portion of the Panhandle of Texas, Water Supply and Irrigation Paper 154* (1906); *ibid.* 191, (1907).

[3] Nobles to Gould, April 22, 1929, in Gould papers. Dr. Gould furnished the author with this and other letters from his own personal file.

all that they could see were gulleys, rocks, red shales, and the vast sweep of prairie grass.

Nevertheless, they were shrewd businessmen. They knew that Gould was a competent geologist, successful in his previous work; and they were willing to accept his opinion now. Therefore, they commissioned him to make a contour structural map of the John Ray anticline and to locate a favorable drilling site on it.

Gould's assistant, Robert S. Dewey, came to Amarillo in March, 1917, and spent some weeks with a plane table and alidade, running levels on this Alibates dolomite structure. Gould thought that the dome's crest was near the Canadian, but Dewey found it to be just east of the John Ray dome, a prominent landmark, ten miles west of the river and about thirty miles from Amarillo.

At the same time Nobles and his associates secured oil and gas leases on approximately 70,000 acres of land lying on both sides of the river, allowing the property-owners the standard one-eighth royalty on all oil and gas found.[4]

Next, Nobles and his associates organized the Amarillo Oil Company, the articles of incorporation also carrying the names of H. A. Nobles, A. G. Stanley, T. J. Moore, J. S. Storm, S. F. Sullenberger, C. T. Herring, Lee Bivins, Frank Storms, and R. B. Masterson. The company was capitalized at a modest $10,000, one half of which was in cash and the other half in the value of the leases.

Then this new Amarillo Oil Company employed C. M. Hapgood of Oklahoma City to drill the well on the site selected. But before spudding in, two carloads of men drove out to the well site to listen to Gould's "dedication" speech. Gould told them that this was the most favorable location for oil and gas, but they would likely find gas. He warned, however, that he could not guarantee it. "The only way to find out," he said, "is to drill."[5]

This first well, then known as the Hapgood well but now called the No. 1 Masterson, was completed as a gas well on December 13, 1918, at a cost of $70,000. This was an expensive well for a $10,000 corporation to promote. But it produced 10,000,000 cubic feet of gas a day, which its sponsors subsequently piped to Amarillo.

Other wells were soon drilled to hold the company's leases, the

[4] *Ibid.*
[5] Gould's account of the affair to the author.

No. 4 Masterson, about two miles southeast of the discovery well, coming in from 1,670 feet as a 107,000,000-cubic-feet-a-day gas well.[6]

Amarillo was electrified. Lease speculation started, which in little more than half a decade caused 114 local companies to be organized, who for the most part peddled their stock to local buyers. And of $12,000,000 invested, $8,000,000 was paid out for worthless stock.

Gould's work was not yet done. He received so many requests for other surveys that he opened an office in Amarillo and employed a corps of assistants. Ranchmen and landowners daily asked him to search for anticlines and favorable oil structures on their properties.

Gould accepted many of these offers. In all, he and his helpers surveyed nine domes along the Canadian breaks, including such well-known sites as the Glenrio dome, on the Landergin and Odom ranches; the Boise dome, on the Landergin ranch north of Boise station; and the Alamosa and Indian Mound domes on the same ranch. They also made the first surveys of the Cliffside and Gentry structures, northwest of Amarillo, and the Bravo dome, near the mouth of Trujillo Creek. All of these ultimately became parts of the vast Panhandle oil and gas field.

None of the first Panhandle operators could conceive of the producing area's immensity. It was not until oil and gas wells began to dot the prairies and finally to prove an unbroken field that geologists began to speak of the huge proportions of the region. Geologically, they found under the ground a granite mountain, called the Amarillo Mountains, with its southeastern outcrop in the Wichita Mountains of western Oklahoma and far to the northwest its broad nose reaching towards Channing, in Hartley County. Farther south, in west central Potter County, was a circular oil and gas formation showing as a semicircle on the map.[7] With an average width of

[6] The wells were known as the Nos. 1, 2, 3, 4, and 5 Masterson; and the Nos. 1, 2, 3, and 4 Bivins, with only the No. 2 Bivins as a dry hole. The other wells averaged from 6,000,000 to 10,000,000 cubic feet of gas a day. Perry A. Little of Buffalo, New York, finally built a pipe line to the new field and supplied Amarillo with gas.—From manuscript furnished the author by H. A. Nobles of Amarillo.

[7] Map, in C. Max Bauer's "Oil and Gas Fields of the Texas Panhandle," *Bulletin of the American Association of Petroleum Geologists*, Vol. X, No. 8 (August, 1926), 734.

twenty miles, broadening to more than forty miles on its northern extension, the oil, and gas-producing zone stretched for 115 miles across Wheeler, Gray, Carson, Hutchinson, Potter, and Moore counties. Along the northern flank of this buried mountain, in sandy dolomite, in granite sand and gravel beds were oil accumulations.[8] This region was so vast that oil operators now had to adjust their appraisals in terms of counties instead of districts.[9]

Here was the world's largest single producing gas field. By 1934 the Amarillo Mountains' oil and gas zone embraced approximately 1,700,080 acres, of which 1,058,467 acres produced sweet gas and 391,613 acres sulphur or sour gas. The remaining 250,000 acres, along the north flank of Amarillo Mountains, was underlaid with a rich oil formation.[10]

Eugene S. Blasdel, who with P. H. Landergin promoted the first Panhandle oil well, wrote an interesting account of early developments. He related that on March 25, 1919, he and Landergin entered into a contract with Captain S. B. Burnett at Fort Worth, Texas, whereby they acquired a lease option on twenty sections of Burnett's 6666 Ranch in Carson and Hutchinson counties. Then they employed Gould and his field staff, Joseph M. Perkins, Leslie G. Hanson, and Robert S. Dewey, to survey their acreage. Meanwhile, the operators, having added W. H. Fuqua, on July 5, 1919, assigned eight sections of their leases to the Gulf Production Company for assuming their bond and for a promise to drill a test well. George E. Montgomery gave leases to Blasdel and Landergin on two Johnson ranch sections, immediately north of the Burnett ranch, to compensate them for their transfer of the eight sections to the Gulf Production Company.[11]

On August 5, 1919, the Gulf Production Company spudded in

[8] This buried mountain consists of a series of peaks: the westernmost, the Bravo dome, chiefly in Oldham County, the John Ray dome in Potter County, the Bush dome in Potter County; the 6666 dome in Carson County, the Le Fors dome in Gray County, and the Lela dome in Wheeler County. Helium is obtained from the Bush dome. The Bravo dome does not produce oil and gas.

[9] For geological analyses of the region, see Sidney Powers, "Reflected Buried Hills and Their Importance in Petroleum Geology," in *Bulletin of the American Association of Petroleum Geologists,*" Vol. VIII, No. 3 (May–June, 1923), 237–49.

[10] Railroad Commission of Texas, *Annual Report on the Panhandle Oil and Gas Field, July, 1937*, 1.

[11] Blasdel to Gould, October 4, 1926.—Gould papers.

a test well at a site selected on the west half of Section 118, Block 5 of the International and Great Northern Railroad survey, in Carson County. Actual drilling was begun on September 24, 1919; and the well was completed on August 4, 1920, at a depth of 2,411 feet, producing 50,000,000 cubic feet of gas a day. This was the first gas well within a radius of twenty-five miles.

Then, said Blasdel, Gulf began its No. 2 Burnett,[12] on November 20, 1920, and completed it on April 5 of the next year at a depth of 3,052 feet for an initial 175 barrels of oil a day, "the first oil well in the entire Panhandle."[13] He added that after five years it "was still making around 100 barrels a day."

The area about the Gulf's discovery well developed slowly. Its No. 2 Burnett produced 34-degree gravity oil that congealed at 50 degrees Fahrenheit, with a wax content; so there was little demand for it. Nor was there a pipe-line outlet. In 1923, Gulf had also drilled an 135-barrel oil producer on the Dial ranch in Hutchinson County; the W. W. Silk *et al.* had completed a 215-barrel No. 1 S. B. Burnett well in Section 93, Carson County, and announced plans for the erection of a 55,000-barrel steel storage tank; and The Texas Company had drilled its No. 1 Burnett, in Section 144, also in Carson County. These were all the Panhandle oil wells by the spring of 1923.

But others soon started. In June, the J. C. Whittington No. 1 Sanford test, in Section 82, H. and T. C. Block 46, southwestern Hutchinson County, came in as a flowing well, producing 38-gravity oil at a depth of 3,077 feet. This was the first Panhandle natural-flow well and created more interest in the Panhandle's oil possibilities. By January 1, 1925, Carson County had eight oil wells with an initial production of 1,110 barrels of oil a day. The *Texas Almanac* of this year stated that Carson County's oil industry was one of the chief industries and that its gas potential was about one-half-billion cubic feet.[14]

[12] In Section 106, I.G.N. Block 5, in Carson County.

[13] The generally accepted date of this discovery well is May 2, 1921. See Railroad Commission of Texas, *Annual Report of the Panhandle Oil and Gas Fields,* August, 1937, 1; Bauer, *loc. cit.,* 733; N. B. Bartlett, "Discovery of the Panhandle Oil and Gas Fields," in *Panhandle-Plains Historical Review,* Vol. XII (1939), 50; Pampa *News,* June 1, 1937.

[14] *Texas Almanac and State Industrial Guide* (1925), 258.

Oil! Titan of the Southwest

But during 1925 both oil-operator interest and activity increased. Early in January, Whittington's well on the Williams and Laycock property in Wheeler County came in at better than 1,000 barrels a day; and by April the Panhandle had twenty-six wells producing 2,900 barrels daily. Gray and Potter counties also reported oil discoveries, and the year closed with a production of more than 1,200,000 barrels of oil, with Carson and Hutchinson counties in the lead.

The year 1926 definitely put the Panhandle on the map with a yearly output of 25,551,000 barrels of oil, Hutchinson County producing 23,573,966 barrels of the total, with a daily output of 165,000 barrels from 813 wells.[15] C. A. Warner explains the field's rapid growth by comparing its 96 wells and 10,731 barrels of oil a day for the week ending April 15, 1926, with 174 wells averaging 48,985 barrels a day for the week ending June 19, 1926.[16] The Phillips Petroleum Company was the leading producer with an average of 8,330 barrels a day from twenty Hutchinson County wells; the Dixon Creek Oil Company was next with 5,410 barrels a day from nine wells in the same county; the Westex Oil Company third with a daily average of 3,325 barrels from three Hutchinson County wells; and the Wilcox-Pampa Oil Company fourth with a daily average of 2,892 barrels from four Gray County oilers.

The entire Panhandle—Carson, Dallam, Gray, Hartley, Hemphill, Hutchinson, Lipscomb, Moore, Ochiltree, Potter, Roberts, Sherman, and Wheeler counties—experienced new activity, with 204 locations and rigs, 280 wells drilling, and prospecting crews and land men as daily visitors.

On January 11, 1926, the Dixon Creek Oil and Refining Company gave great impetus to this oil play with its No. 1 Smith, a 10,-000-barrel-a-day well, opening the prolific Borger field, a short distance east of the present town of that name, in a broken, gulley-corrugated area. Excitement was intense. So rapidly was the field developed that nine months later it had 813 wells producing 165,000 barrels of oil daily.

In the weeks that followed geologists with their surveying instruments became almost as much an integral part of the scenery

15 Pampa *News*, June 1, 1937.
16 *Texas Oil and Gas Since 1543*, 261.

Panhandle Oil and Gas

as the horizon. From every direction both the large and small company advance guards poured in, with Oklahoma operators in the van. Chief among the Oklahomans were men of the Phillips Petroleum and Marland Oil companies. Phillips closed a trade with the Pulaski Oil Company of Tulsa to develop its Hutchinson County lease of 8,500 acres. The Marland Oil Company took over the Canadian River bed in Hutchinson County, and purchased protective leases on the river's opposite banks, and, in addition, launched a big drilling campaign.[17] But Texans, mindful of having their fingers burned at Ranger, another lime field, played a cautious waiting game. With wells making 1,000, 5,000, and 10,000 barrels daily, however, they soon forgot their timidity.

The year 1926 also brought the South Pampa field, in Gray County, by the drilling in July of the Shamrock Oil and Gas Company's Worley-Reynolds No. 1 as a 1,200 barrel well. And near-by Pampa mushroomed to boom proportions.

Amarillo, about fifty miles southwest of Borger, was crowded with strangers. Its hotels and rooming houses overflowed with oilmen. In 1926, N. E. Hubbard described the town as a fledgling city with half a dozen skyscrapers in various stages of construction. The Newspaper Feature Service of January, 1927, estimated its population at 52,680—the census of 1920 had listed it at 15,494. Its assessed property values jumped from $29,729,870 in 1925 to $39,808,810 in the next year, with building operations equal to a city of 200,000 population;[18] and its bank deposits climbed from $10,197,364 to $24,721,782 during the same period. Every town in the Panhandle —Pampa, Spearman, Shamrock, Panhandle, and others near the oil field—doubled or trebled in population.

At first the new oil field had no railroad outlet and no pipe lines, and hastily-built tanks and reservoirs could not hoard the oil wealth coming from the earth. Panhandle, thirty miles away, a small plains town but on the Santa Fe Railroad, became the field's freight center, handling tonnage second only to Chicago.

Rock Island Railroad officials observed this situation and started

---

[17] "Active Drilling in the Texas Panhandle," in *Oil Weekly*, Vol. XL, No. 7 (February 5, 1926), 46.

[18] W. E. Hubbard, "Oil in the Texas Panhandle," in *The Lamp*, Vol. IX, No. 5 (February, 1926), 13–19; *Texas Almanac and State Industrial Guide* (1927), 55.

building from Amarillo to capture a part of the oil-field traffic. The Santa Fe extended from Panhandle to connect with the new field. Immediately, it entered a race with the Rock Island, starting at Amarillo. And since the Santa Fe was nearest, it reached its objective first, building its station, Isom, and ran trains from there to Panhandle. Its spur track had cost $4,500,000. The Rock Island arrived later.

A. P. Borger, a townsite promoter of Tulsa, Oklahoma, secured a tract of 240 acres and founded Borger (sometimes called "Little Oklahoma") in February, 1926.[19] One visitor described it as "a wild, 'rootin-tootin,' 'snortin,' 'hell-raisin,' place,"[20] one of the most notorious Texas oil-boom towns. Its two-mile-long street was lined on either side with helter-skelter buildings—a "Betty Jane" Hotel, "Murphy's Dance Hall," a "Dewdrop Inn," a "Stagg Billiards and Pool" hall, one- and two-story rooming houses, ugly hot-dog stands and chili "parlors," barber shops, "entertainment dumps," drugstores, a bank, hardware stores, and groceries—all like the setting of Dawson's Klondike gold-rush days. But by the close of the year Borger had a population of between 10,000 and 20,000. The near-by oil field's development brought thousands of workmen with their families, and in addition, there were other thousands who came, ready to engage in any enterprise, legal or illegal. The result was that Texas Rangers finally took charge and brought order out of chaos much as they had done at Ranger and Mexia.[21]

Panhandle's oil production in 1927 reached 40,253,000 barrels, the year opening with a daily output of 150,000 barrels of oil from 805 wells. Gray County led the other counties with a total of 3,966,-412 barrels, but there was oil play all along Amarillo Mountains' north flank. Gray County's Gulf-Saunders and Bowers areas and Moore County's Morton No. 1 Reeder discovery well were headlined; and sustained production in Carson, Hutchinson and Wheeler counties kept the Panhandle in the Texas forefront.

By 1927 transportation had become fairly adequate. The first

[19] P. J. R. McIntosh, "The Wonder Story of Texas Oil," in *Texas Monthly*, Vol. III (January–June, 1929), 208.

[20] Edward B. Garnett, "Oil is Kind in the Texas Panhandle," in *World's Work*, Vol. LV (December, 1927), 168–74.

[21] *Report of the Adjutant General of the State of Texas for the Fiscal Year, September 1, 1929 to August 31, 1930*, 51–52.

gas pipe line completed from the Panhandle field to far-away markets was started in 1925, and all pipe lines aggregated 5,000 miles by 1932; and by June, 1937, the field served twenty-four lines of varying lengths.[22] Among these were the Northern Texas Utilities Company's sixteen-inch line to Wichita Falls, the Lone Star Gas Company's eighteen-inch line to Fort Worth and Dallas, the South Plains Pipe Line Company's sixteen-inch line to Lubbock and other West Texas towns, the Cities Service Gas Company's twenty-inch line to Kansas City, the Canadian River Gas Company's twenty-two-inch line to Denver, and the Consolidated Gas Utilities Company's fourteen-inch line to Enid, Oklahoma. Panhandle gas also went to Chicago, Minneapolis, and other northern cities.[23]

Oil pipe lines were also built to the field. By 1926 the Bar-Tex, Gulf, Humble, Magnolia, Marland, Pan-Tex, Plains, and Sinclair companies were running oil from the field to Amarillo, Kings Mill, Pampa, and Panhandle, while the major producers had built 2,845,-000 barrels of oil storage in Carson, Gray, and Hutchinson counties. And in the next year, the major companies were connecting with their trunk lines—the Prairie Pipe Line Company, an eight-inch line to Ringling, Oklahoma; the Humble Pipe Line Company, a ten-inch line to Comyn, in Comanche County; and the Gulf-Magnolia Pipe Line companies, a ten-inch line to Olden, in Eastland County.

Panhandle's enormous gas flow soon drew natural-gasoline plants. The first one was built in 1926, and others followed so quickly that on January 1, 1937, forty-three plants were in operation, having a combined capacity of 2,474,000,000 cubic feet of gas daily; and during November, 1936, they processed a daily average of 1,-139,723,000 cubic feet of gas and recovered an average of 921,540 gallons of gasoline a day, or approximately 50 per cent of the total natural gasoline produced in Texas.

Because of the great quantities of unmarketable residue gas from early-day gasoline plants, the carbon-black industry also came to the Panhandle, their smoke-smudges drifting over the plains like rain clouds. The first of these plants started operations early in 1927,

[22] Pampa *News*, June 1, 1937.

[23] *Texas Panhandle Field, A Study of Gas Wastage* . . . (Report of Engineering Committee, 1934), 12–13.

and after a decade thirty Panhandle plants burned a daily average of 646,697,000 cubic feet of gas in extracting an average of 934,505 pounds of carbon black, 96 per cent of the world's production.[24]

Since the formations which produce oil down structure are the same that contain sour and sweet gas over the structure's higher parts, activities in one part of the field directly affect those in another part. Naturally, this brought a clash between major and minor producers. Having access to great capital and their own pipe lines to market, nine major pipe-line companies supplying domestic and industrial gas to Chicago, Minneapolis, Denver, Dallas, Des Moines, and other distant points monopolized the field's pipe-line runs to their own advantage often leaving offset owners and near-by gas wells without a market.[25]

The Texas legislature sought to correct this abuse with its "Common Purchaser Act" of 1931.[26] This law was designed to afford equal marketing opportunities to all gas producers, under the Railroad Commission rules. Although the Commission issued no rules under this act, owners of sweet-gas wells with no light and fuel market, and with the sanction of the Commission, sought to force pipe-line companies to purchase their gas. Several suits were filed in federal courts by pipe-line companies to prevent the Commission from enforcing the new law. In one case (Texoma Natural Gas Co. vs. Railroad Commission), a three-judge federal court declared the state law invalid and granted the injunction.

In the next year, by its "Market Demand Law," the legislature sought to prorate gas in line with the market demand. The Railroad Commission was to ascertain the demand for gas in the field and to distribute it among the producers on a reasonable basis. This law, however, fared no better before the federal court than the other had. Pipe-line companies successfully enjoined it. The court refused to pass on whether an act, authorizing the proration of gas

---

[24] Pampa *News,* June 1, 1937.

[25] Maurice Cheek, "Legal History of Conservation of Gas in Texas," in *Legal History of Conservation of Oil and Gas,* 270.

[26] For a discussion of the state's battle to conserve its gas resource, see Col. Ernest O. Thompson, "Summary of the Development of the Panhandle Oil and Gas Field," in *Panhandle-Plains Historical Review,* Vol. XXI (1939), 13–23; Acts 1931, 42nd Legislature, 1st called session, c. 26, Sec. 2.

Charles N. Gould

Main Street, Borger, Texas, during oil boom

The Red Barn on the Yates ranch

Oil and Gas Journal

Pumping derrick near McCamey, Texas

Photograph by Bubley
Standard Oil Company (N. J.)

production for any reason other than to prevent waste, would be valid.[27]

Again defeated by a court decision, in 1933 the non-integrated owners of sweet-gas-producing acreage appealed to the legislature and had passed the "Sour Gas Law," later called the "Stripper Law," permitting owners of gas in all common reservoirs of more than 300,000 acres to use up to 25 per cent of a well's open-flow capacity for other purposes, including the manufacture of natural gasoline, "when there is no reasonable market for light and fuel." This law helped the natural-gasoline manufacturers, and soon several new stripper plants were built in the Panhandle and began operations on a large scale.

Unfortunately, this took the bridle off and threw conservation to the wind. Within a year 1,000,000,000 cubic feet of residue gas were daily blown to the air.[28] During 1934, for instance, forty-nine Panhandle natural-gasoline plants withdrew 1,577,257,939 cubic feet of gas a day from the reservoir, extracting per year at this rate 293,055,462 gallons of gasoline; but the twenty-six dependent carbon-black plants used only 449,270,435 cubic feet of the gasoline plants' residue gas.

The "popping" of more than one billion cubic feet of gas a day caused oilmen, gas producers, and even "stripper" operators much concern about Panhandle's reservoir energy. So once more, in 1935, the legislature sought to bring relief, with its comprehensive House Bill No. 266. This law made stripping illegal, restricted the use of sweet gas, allowed carbon-black plants to process sour gas, permitted the ratable taking of gas from all fields, gave the Commission the right to fix a gas-oil ratio for an oil field, set up a zoning program of a common field into separate proration units, and authorized lessor-operator unitizing agreements.[29]

The new law became effective for sweet gas on August 1, 1935,

[27] Cheek, *loc. cit.*, 274.

[28] R. D. Parker, "The Colossal Waste of Natural Gas in the Panhandle of Texas," in *Oil Weekly*, Vol. LXXVI, No. 4 (January 7, 1935), 35; Report of Engineering Committee, *Texas Panhandle Field, A Study of Gas Wastage* ... (pamphlet, August, 1934), 9 ff.

[29] The separation of the Panhandle field under this law into the East Field, West Field, and Sour Field is explained in the Railroad Commission's *Annual Report of the Panhandle Oil and Gas Field, July, 1939*, 2–3.

and for sour gas two months later. "As soon as the Commission's orders took effect in August, 1935," says Commissioner Thompson, the volume of gas wastage "dropped sharply." But again the law's validity was challenged in court by the pipe-line companies, and, after extended litigation, was stricken out. Yet the Commission made appreciable progress in preventing gas wastage and conserving the Panhandle's oil production under the authority granted it by the law. In June, 1937, an average of only 54,367,000 cubic feet of gas daily was vented into the air.

In its wording of the Consolidated case, the Supreme Court made it clear that the legislature might authorize the Railroad Commission so to allocate a common reservoir's production of gas that undue drainage from unconnected wells would be prevented. The legislature took its cue, and in 1937 enacted Senate Bill 407 authorizing the Commission to find the market demand for gas in the sour-gas area and to distribute its reasonable market demand among all producers. The Commission made such a survey in May, 1938, and placed the Panhandle's sour-gas area under proration to prevent undue and preventable drainage. Later, the Commission's order was sustained by the courts.

During this same period the Commission's oil-proration and conservation policy was being shaped. On August 14, 1930, its first oil-proration order relating to the Panhandle field was issued. The order was attacked by one operator shortly, but for the most part operators accepted proration, as improved from time to time by the Commission.[30]

After the first discoveries, the Panhandle oil and gas field developed slowly but steadily. By 1928 its gas-producing area embraced 1,500 square miles, with an estimated open daily flow capacity of 5,250,000,000 cubic feet. Much of the gas first produced came from upper producing formations, away from oil zones; consequently, it had little gasoline or lighter hydrocarbon liquids. But as drilling was extended to lower levels, near the oil formations, wells produced a large content of natural gasoline.

In Potter County, helium was found; and the federal government acquired a 20,000-acre lease in the Cliffside field, and later added another 30,000 acres. Previously the old Petrolia, Texas,

[30] Thompson, *loc. cit.*, 18; Warner, *op. cit.*, 272–73.

Panhandle Oil and Gas

field and another at Dexter, Kansas, had furnished the government with its sole supply. In April, 1929, the government built a plant near Amarillo, which by 1937 supplied 78,160,205 cubic feet of helium.

As the enormous Panhandle area was developed, oil and gas were found in four separate zones: the brown dolomite, the gray lime, the gray dolomite, and the underlying granite wash or disintegrated granite from the Amarillo Mountains.

By 1938 a total of 6,296 wells had been drilled, 90 per cent of which produced oil or gas or both. There were 3,120 oil wells and 1,498 gas wells. The gas wells for the most part produced sweet gas for pipe-line use. The field's cumulative oil production was 304,-208,920 barrels, with an average daily potential of 1,221,539 barrels and an allowable of 80,796 barrels; and the 1,798 gas wells had produced approximately seven trillion, six hundred billion cubic feet of gas, with a daily potential of 26,282,787,000 cubic feet.[31]

Panhandle maintained a fairly even oil output during the period, 1936–40. In 1936 its production was 22,357,000 barrels; in 1937, 27,617,000 barrels; in 1938, 23,556,000 barrels; in 1939, 24,-165,000 barrels; and in 1940, 26,700,000 barrels.[32]

[31] Railroad Commission of Texas, *Annual Report on the Panhandle Oil and Gas Fields, July, 1938*, 2 ff; Amarillo Sunday *Globe-News* (Golden Anniversary edition, 1938), Sec. G-1, p. 1.

[32] U. S. Department of the Interior, Bureau of Mines, *Crude Petroleum and Petroleum Products* (pamphlet, 1941), 955.

XXI

Permian Basin Discoveries

T HE VAST OIL-PRODUCING Permian Basin comprises 76,610 square miles of Texas and 12,000 square miles of southeastern New Mexico—88,610 square miles in all, an area greater than that of the two states of New York and Rhode Island. The Texas part is known also as West Texas.

Regional geology unfolds an interesting story. Many hundred thousand years ago the Permian Basin was a vast inland sea, larger than but comparable to the Great Salt Lake of Utah. In ages of time a limestone floor, then chemical layers of magnesium limestone or dolomite, anhydrite, and salt were successively deposited. And in succeeding ages mud-laden streams emptied their billions of tons of red clay and sand into this sea (on hydrocarbon-making plant and animal life), completely filling it. Finally, the bottom of the sea buckled and warped and created north-to-south mountain ridges of upward of three thousand feet in height, which in turn were covered during subsequent thousands of centuries by strata of other deposits, so that today the surface formations of the desert-like wastes of western Texas and eastern New Mexico blanket vast stores of hidden wealth hundreds of feet below.[1]

For many decades West Texas served indeed as a "No Man's Land" between Mexico, south of the Río Grande, and Anglo-Saxon civilization. It had been invaded by the cattlemen and sheepmen who eked out a precarious livelihood, but the land was arid and

[1] For a popular account of this geologic process, see *The Lamp*, Vol. X, No. 6 (April, 1928), 12–16. A more scientific view is found in T. P. McDonald's "Reconnoissance Report on the Permian Basin," in File No. 624.2—New Mexico, Feb. 11, 1930, U.S.G.S., Geological Records, Department of the Interior Records, National Archives; John T. Lonsdale *et al*, *Texas Mineral Resources* (The University of Texas Publication, No. 4301), 179–80.

much of it was in sand dunes, too barren for even the stockmen. Indeed, here was a semidesert, a land of little rain and less promise.

Many of the ranches were enormous in size but insignificant in value, the land often selling for as low as twenty-five cents an acre. The University of Texas had princely West Texas holdings, but its board of regents had little hope of profitable returns. Then the miracle occurred: West Texas became an oil empire. By 1938 it embraced ten major fields, two of which, if allowed to flow unrestrained, would equal one-third of the total oil production of the United States.

Permian Basin oil development began at Westbrook, a small Mitchell County town about ten miles west of Colorado City, the county seat. On a rainy, wintry day early in 1920, Steve Owens, general field manager of the Underwriters Producing Company, and Watt Collier, his wagoner, who with eight wagons had hauled the derrick timbers and equipment out to a site about two miles northwest of Westbrook, stood on a rock-rimmed butte overlooking the valley farther north.

"Unload your derrick timbers near that tank and stake a site for the first well," Owens is reported to have directed his companion. Collier promptly went down into the valley and staked the site of the No. 1 T. and P.–Abrams well, about 150 yards north of the tank.[2] This was the inauspicious beginning of the Permian Basin's oil development.

"Oil, Oil, Rumors of Oil!" was the headline that reached across the front page of the Colorado City *Record* on June 18, 1920, announcing the completion of the No. 1 Abrams well. Within twenty-seven years from this momentous discovery, thirty-five West Texas counties had 18,000 oil wells with a daily allowable of 650,000 barrels of oil and proven reserves of more than 3,200,000,000 barrels.[3] By 1945 the region's cumulative oil output had reached 1,563,164,-

[2] Interview with Watt Collier, Colorado City, Texas, December 28, 1948. Collier also helped to dig the slush pit and cellar, and to lay a field pipe line to a loading rack at Westbrook. At present the Standard Oil Company of Texas owns the block containing the No. 1 Abrams well, which is still a small producer. Near it is a marker bearing these words: "W. H. Abrams No. 1, Section 33, block 28, township 1, north T. & P. survey, 640 acres."

[3] Olin Culberson, member, Railroad Commission of Texas, "West Texas Oil," in *West Texas Today*, Vol. XXVIII, No. 6 (August, 1947), 5, 20.

012 barrels.[4] But West Texas has been a more prolific producer in more recent years, as will be related later.

When Owens came to Colorado City bringing several bottles of oil to prove that his well had struck pay, he did not know that he had unloosed a deluge of wealth. Nor did the Colorado City editor when he wrote: "Oil in Mitchell County. . . . The Golden Flood is Struck." No doubt he was expressing customary journalistic optimism. Nevertheless, he had talked with the field manager and had learned that the well was bailing from twenty-five to thirty barrels of oil a day for fuel and was estimated to have a daily potential of one thousand barrels.

"Excitement is running very high," the editor continued. "In less than 30 days Colorado expects to have a population of ten to twenty thousand. . . . 'Lease Hounds' are arriving on every train. . . . Prices are steadily climbing."

But if for a time excitement ran high, it eventually subsided, for the Westbrook field never became a major producer. Yet Colorado City, formerly a cow town, grew into an industrious beehive of oil speculation, leasing, and royalty trading. Enough oil had been found at Westbrook to cause experienced oil scouts to believe that West Texas at last could yield big dividends to its poverty-ridden landholders.

Farther north, three years later, in November, the Loutex Corporation brought in its No. 1 Moore well in Scurry County as a fifty-barrel producer of 28–29-gravity oil; and on August 1 of the next year, 1924, the new field's four wells yielded a total output of 25,000 barrels of crude. On June 8, 1925, the World Oil Company opened another minor field on the L. P. Powell ranch in Crockett County, about twenty-five miles south of the Big Lake field.[5]

In August, 1925, Mitchell County obtained its second field when the Magnolia Petroleum Company opened the Iatan field, with its No. 1 Mary Foster well that produced 150 barrels of 29–30 gravity oil daily from 2,858–2,872 feet. However, after four years, in 1929, the cumulative production of both the Westbrook and Iatan fields amounted to only 6,427,124 barrels of crude oil.

Big Lake was to be West Texas' first bonanza field. Any account

[4] San Angelo, Texas, *Standard-Times*, December 30, 1945, p. 14, col. 2.
[5] El Paso *Evening Post*, October 29, 1929, p. 1, cols. 1–8.

of the Big Lake oil discovery must revolve about the work of venturesome wildcatters. One of these was Rupert P. Ricker, University of Texas law graduate, former army officer, and Big Lake practicing attorney.

At the end of World War I, Ricker, wearing the double bars of an army captain, returned home to find Reagan County suffering from a drought. He was told that his was one of a few Texas counties in which there was no drilling for oil, although the Ranger oil fever had fairly well spread over the whole of West Texas. Ricker believed that here was his opportunity, that oil was somewhere in this vast region. A study of Dr. John Udden's recent report to the University of Texas Board of Regents further convinced him. Udden had stated that along the crest of the region's "buried unconformity" there were natural chances "for the accumulations of oil and gas."

Oil might be in Reagan County, reasoned Ricker. With the help of P. G. Stokes and other men of Big Spring, he therefore leased 431,360 acres of land in Reagan, Irion, Crockett, and Upton counties—all owned by the University of Texas.[6]

State law allowed Ricker only thirty days from the date of his filing on the land to pay the ten cents an acre rental. He did not have the $43,136 necessary to meet this payment; but fortunately, Frank Pickrell, one of Ricker's former army sergeants, and Haymon Krupp of El Paso came to Big Lake inquiring about a large drilling block, and took over Ricker's leases, paying him a nominal sum above the regular acreage rental. Then Dr. Hugh Tucker, their geologist, selected the site of the first well, the No. 1 Santa Rita, within a stone's throw and north of the Orient Railroad, fifteen miles west of Big Lake and within the city limits of present Texon.[7]

Pickrell managed the new enterprise and served as vice-president of the company, the Texon Oil and Land Company, which

---

[6] The Big Lake oil field was north of the present town of Texon, ten miles west of Big Lake, and on a solid block of land comprising sixty-eight sections, or 43,520 acres of land owned in fee by the University of Texas. But in October, 1923, the Big Lake Oil Company acquired sixteen sections of this lease from Pickrell and his associates.—Interview with Chas. E. Beyers at Texon, May 27, 1946, who also furnished the author other materials. See also Martin W. Schwettman, *Santa Rita*.

[7] *Oil Weekly*, Vol. XXIX, No. 10 (June 2, 1923), 25.

was launched only after clever financing and promotion, and Krupp became its president.

Pickrell employed Carl G. Cromwell as driller. Cromwell and his wife moved to a shack near the well site, and the well was spudded in. Since the country was lonely, Cromwell found it difficult to keep laborers. He first employed Crawford Stillwagon as tool dresser, but he did not stay long. Then he hired Will Hale, and he, too, left shortly. But a third man, Dee Locklin, stayed with Cromwell until the well was finished. Cromwell also occasionally employed cowboys—Bus Barfield, Claude Lyle, Charlie and Jeff Hickok, Jim Schooler, and Jess Kuykendall, among others.

On Monday, May 28, 1923, Editor M. A. Wilson of the Big Lake *News* telephoned the San Angelo *Standard* that the Santa Rita well on the Ollie Parker ranch had blown in at six o'clock that morning, spraying the prairie for about eleven minutes. It smeared the immediate vicinity for 250 yards north of the well with an estimated ten to fifteen barrels of crude oil. On the next day the *Standard* reported that the well was estimated as a 200-barrel producer and that on Monday morning the tremendous gas pressure coming from it had hurled the slush bucket high in the air and that mud and oil had spouted fifty to sixty feet over the top of the derrick. On May 31, the *Standard* reported further that 300 people were at the well on Wednesday night, mostly from near-by West Texas towns, and that both Gulf and Texas company scouts were on hand.

No doubt this spectacular well, ninety miles southwest of Mitchell County's Westbrook oil field, was an example of hazardous but successful wildcatting. Credit for its discovery should go to Frank Pickrell; to Hugh H. Tucker, geologist who made the Santa Rita location; to Carl Cromwell, the driller who managed this wildcat test; and to Rupert P. Ricker, who had faith enough in Dr. Udden's report to lease the land.

Other developments followed quickly. On March 1, 1925, there were seventeen producing oil wells from the shallow Texon formation, with a daily yield of 11,500 barrels of crude oil. And by January 1 of the next year, there were seventy-four wells with a daily yield of 32,000 barrels. Peak production was reached on August 31, 1925, with more than 40,000 barrels. The total gross output from Big Lake by January 1, 1926, had reached 10,060,330 barrels. The

oil tested 39 degrees Baumé and came from a depth of approximately 3,000 feet.[8] Seven months later, Big Lake's 107 wells had produced a cumulative total of 16,000,000 barrels.[9]

As was often the case with a new wildcat field, storage and
transportation presented mounting problems. For a time the Orient
Railroad transported all of Big Lake oil. But the field's rapidly growing output and the spread of production made necessary a more
adequate outlet.

Marland,[10] seventy-eight miles west of San Angelo on the Orient
Railroad, became an important oil-shipping center, to which, by
May, 1926, pipe lines funneled Reagan County's 30,000 barrels of
crude oil daily from 103 producing wells. Here was the western
terminus of the Humble Pipe Line Company; and here sat, like
giant, squat toadstools, sixteen reservoirs of 80,000-barrel capacity,
into which Reagan County's oil was emptied by gathering lines. A
powerful pumping plant, equipped with huge engines, started
Gulfward through Humble's eight-inch pipe line a constant stream
of oil on its 500-mile journey, or to loading racks on the Orient.

The first segment of Humble's pipe line ran from Marland via
San Angelo to Comyn, Comanche County, 195 miles away; and
from there through the main trunk line the remaining 300 miles to
the Gulf Coast. The western extension of this line was completed
in the spring of 1925 at a cost of $2,500,000 and was later looped for
an additional $750,000, thereby increasing its capacity from 20,000
to 30,000 barrels of crude oil daily.

This great underground carrier was supplemented by other
pipe lines in handling Reagan County's oil output. The Reagan
County Purchasing Company, by means of a gathering system of
small pipe lines, daily brought 33,500 barrels of oil through a twenty-mile line to Marland; and the Marland Pipe Line Company built
another, a six-inch line, to extend southward from Marland to the
Powell field in northern Crockett County. The Orient moved a
trainload a day, delivering it to the Santa Fe at San Angelo; and,

[8] E. H. Sellards and Leroy T. Patton, "The Subsurface Geology of the Big Lake
Oil Field," in Oil Weekly, Vol. XLII, No. 6 (July 30, 1926), 72; Paul Wagner, "Big
Lake Leading Texas Fields in Per Well Per Day Average," in National Petroleum
News, Vol. XVIII, No. 3 (January 20, 1926), 100.

[9] Oil Weekly, Vol. XLII, No. 6 (July 30, 1926), 68.

[10] A pumping station now known as Kemper.

before adequate pipe-line facilities were available, these two roads shipped, on the average, three trainloads of oil every twenty-four hours.

A golden harvest began to pour into the University of Texas coffers by 1926. By August of that year, the total revenues received from Reagan County's 194,560 acres, in leases and royalties, amounted to $3,855,689. The June receipts alone from the Big Lake Oil Company reached $169,475, and from the Texon Oil and Land Company, $86,938. By December, the total receipts had increased to $4,985,742, with the same two oil companies contributing the major share.[11]

Small wonder the press predicted that the University of Texas would become the nation's richest university. In Crane County, the University owned 63,000 acres of land; in Upton County, 77,000 acres; and in Andrews County, 294,000—all of which geologists said were in line with the eastern New Mexico Maljamar field and possible oil-producing territory. Already Winkler County's 53,120 acres of oil-producing land, which will be discussed shortly, was running approximately $245,000 monthly.

This was not all. In Pecos County, the University of Texas owned 184,960 acres; in Crockett County, 356,480 acres; in Ward County, 86,640 acres; in Loving County, 22,400 acres; in Hudspeth County, 453,120 acres; in Irion County, 22,720 acres; in Martin County, 14,080 acres; in Schleicher County, 47,600 acres; in Culberson County, 46,800 acres; and in Terrell County, 61,400 acres. A part of these vast holdings were thought to be potential oil lands.[12]

West Texas wildcatting was widespread after the Santa Rita well blew in,[13] with press notices of discovery after discovery breaking into the columns of the San Angelo *Standard*, the El Paso *Evening Post*, and other surrounding city newspapers. Crockett County led off on June 8, 1925, when the World Oil Company opened the World-Powell field. Shortly Loving County claimed the first high-gravity, sweet-oil production in West Texas, when the Pecos Valley

11 "University Royalties," in *Oil Weekly*, Vol. XLII, No. 7 (August 6, 1926), 88; "Texas University Royalties," in *ibid.*, Vol. XLIV, No. 2 (December 31, 1926), 26.
12 *Oil Weekly*, Vol. XLIV, No. 4 (January 14, 1927), 57.
13 H. H. King, "Big Lake Field Responsible for Wildcat Drilling in Western Texas," in *Oil Weekly*, Vol. XLII, No. 6 (July 30, 1926), 68; *ibid.*, Vol. LXXXVI, No. 6 (July 19, 1937), 32–37.

Permian Basin Discoveries

Petroleum Company's No. 1 J. J. Wheat well made initially 25 barrels of 38–40-gravity oil daily from 4,272 feet. By August 1, 1929, this field was owned by Lockhart and Company, whose fourteen wells had a daily average yield of 716 barrels and a cumulative recovery of almost 200,000 barrels from a proven 1,240 acres.

Upton County had the first oil field discovered west of Big Lake, September 20, 1925, with its L. P. Johnson–George B. McCamey and Marland's No. 1 M. L. Baker well, soon to be owned by the Republic Production Company. Its initial yield was seventy barrels of 27–30-gravity oil from 2,161–2,200 feet. Quickly this field overlapped into Crane County, and on February 24, 1926, the Independent and Luther Turman and Joe C. Maxwell *et al.'s* No. 1 Len Taylor well (H. T. Sapp Survey), in Crane County, produced an initial 140 barrels of 28–30-gravity oil from 2,038–2,045 feet. These two producing areas, shortly to be considered one,[14] yielded on August 1, 1929, from their 266 wells a daily average of 9,512 barrels of crude, with a total cumulative recovery of 16,000,000 barrels.

Howard County, too, was added to West Texas' oil-producing counties in 1925 by the Fred Hyer *et al.* No. 1 Clay well. Its initial daily average was fifty barrels of 31–32-gravity oil from horizons at 1,542–1,562 feet, and from 1,780–1,794 feet. The Chalk pool in Howard County was opened on April 18 of the next year by Owens-Sloan *et al.'s* No. 1-A Chalk well, making seventy barrels of 31–32-gravity oil from 1,578–1,583 feet; and deeper production was found in the same county by the Roberts pool at 2,956–2,968 feet. Magnolia's No. 1 Dora Roberts made this important find on October 24, 1927. Earlier, however, three small pools were found by Choate-Henshaw *et al.'s* No. 1 McDaniel; by Lockhart and Company's No. 1 Scott and the Marland-Texon No. 1 Harding.

Marland and Texon, in March, 1927, gave Glasscock County a field on the W. R. Settles ranch, and the World Oil Company, two years later, drilled another on the L. S. McDowell ranch. Producing areas in Howard and Glasscock counties overlapped like those in Crane and Upton counties.

But to turn again to West Texas in 1926 with its two fabulous "black Golcondas," the Winkler and Pecos counties' Hendricks and Yates fields, the most sensational finds in all West Texas. R. A.

[14] *Ibid.*, 36.

291

Westbrook and Company brought in the discovery well on the T. G. Hendricks ranch.[15] Drilling had been hard to promote, and it was necessary for the lease block to be subdivided into ten-acre tracts and sold to a number of companies and individuals, all of whom were subsequently forced to develop their holdings to protect their leases from drainage and water encroachment—much the same story as in many other fields.

Hendricks developed so fast and built up such an enormous output that by 1928 it had become West Texas' most important oil field, even though the Texas Railroad Commission prorated it to 150,000–175,000 barrels of crude oil daily. The field's potential reached 2,-750,000 barrels daily on May 4, 1928.[16]

In July, 1927, a Winkler extension came when the Llano Oil Company drilled in the Scarborough pool,[17] eight miles north of the Hendricks field; and another in 1928 when Gibson and Johnson and Kessler and Logan opened the Leck area, three miles west of the Scarborough wells. On August 1, Winkler County's 615 wells yielded daily almost 150,000 barrels of crude oil and had a record of 95,574,158 barrels of cumulative production from depths ranging from 2,850 to around 3,150 feet.

But Yates was truly "Queen of the Pecos," and of all West Texas, for that matter. Production was found by the Mid-Kansas and Transcontinental Oil Company's wildcat well near the Pecos River, in Pecos County, on the I. G. Yates ranch.

This "Beyond the Pecos" discovery well was in a canyon or a dry arroyo, which at rare intervals became a flowing stream and emptied its muddy water into the Pecos River, two miles to the north, thirty miles south of Rankin, and the same distance southwest of Big Lake.[18] Either side of the Pecos was a gulley-corrugated flat bottom, with impressive but barren and lonely rock-rimmed mesa walls, chrome, yellow, and red, shielding, like desert guardi-

[15] The No. 1 Hendricks had been announced as "making a flow of 25 barrels" as early as July 22, 1926. See *Oil and Gas Journal*, Vol. XXV (July 22, 1926), 37.

[16] Two Fort Worth wildcatters, Sid Richardson and Amon G. Carter, were among Hendricks' most active operators, the latter discovering the rich Ellenburger sand in 1936.

[17] In S1, Block C-22, Public School Land, about ten miles north of the Hendricks field.

[18] San Angelo *Morning Times*, October 28, 1936, p. 1, col. 5.

ans, the valley below from the fierce winds of the upland. Coyotes, rattlesnakes, and occasionally pronghorns and deer, were the region's inhabitants until ranchmen, impelled by a restless urge and a quest for water and grass, drove their herds thither.

Ira G. Yates was among these pioneer cattlemen. On June 1, 1915, Yates had bought 16,640 acres of ranch land from T. F. Hickock and his wife, at the price of $41,600; and two years later, a second tract of 25,000,000 square varas at $13,284. Smaller tracts were added in 1921 and 1922.[19] Little did he expect that his investment would be repaid many times over. Certainly, his cattle had yielded small returns. The land was poor, and the price of cattle grew ever more discouraging. But the friendly Yates ranch house was opened to all comers, and the "Big Red Barn" fed more than one half-starved horse.

Yates could hardly appreciate the import of the findings of Jack Hogan, district geologist of the Transcontinental Company, incorporated in a report to his superiors, which led directly to the drilling of the first well. "The best apparent location for a test well," he had stated, "would be the northwest portion of the vacancy and a half mile due west of the southwest corner of section 60."[20]

Yates' lease money would have been regarded as a godsend had there been no other benefits, for at this time a few hundred dollars in hard cash seemed great wealth to many a Pecos County ranchman. But this unexpected income was small compared with the other riches that were to come his way.

The Mid-Kansas and Transcontinental Oil Company's No. 1 Yates well on a huge domal-type anticline that was plainly visible on the surface,[21] blew in on the ranchman's birthday. That is, while the well was actually shut down on October 28, 1926, the date of its discovery, Yates was not notified of the oil strike until about one o'clock the next morning—which was the twenty-ninth, his birthday. And what a birthday occasion! It was reported to be a $10,000,-

[19] For these several purchases, see Deed Records, Vol. 32, p. 599 and Vol. 40, p. 325, Pecos County, Fort Stockton, Texas.—Courtesy J. Noble Boydston, County Clerk.

[20] San Angelo *Morning Times*, October 28, 1936, p. 1, col. 5. For Transcontinental's lease, see Deed Records, Vol. 27, pp. 522, 525, 538, Pecos County, Pecos, Texas.

[21] R. V. Hennen and R. J. Metcalf, "Yates Oil Pools, Pecos County, Texas," in *Bulletin of the American Association of Petroleum Geologists*, Vol. XIII, No. 12 (December, 1929).

Oil! Titan of the Southwest

000 to $15,000,000 present,[22] a 70,824-barrel producer in a class with the famous Lucas gusher. Oil came right from the bed of the dry arroyo a short distance south of his ranch house.

A decade later to a day, the San Angelo *Morning Times* carried Yates' own story of the occasion. "Men from the well came to my house, about six miles away," he related, "at about one o'clock the morning of the 29th. They told me they had brought in an oil well. I went back to bed and slept until my regular getting-up time. My son, John, and I, got up about 5 o'clock, made coffee, had breakfast, and then drove on up to the well.

"We talked to the men, looked the thing over, stood around a while and then about seven or eight o'clock there was an awful rumbling down in the well. I said, 'John, we'd better get away from here, something is coming out of there pretty soon.' We drove about a half a mile away, around to a place where we could get a good view of the well.

"In a little bit the oil came from the well with a rush, throwing small rocks out of the hole along with the gas and oil. It made a lot of noise and smeared the hillside for several hundred yards with oil. We did not know much about oil but we knew we had something.

"The news spread to McCamey and Rankin and was soon telephoned to Fort Stockton, San Angelo, Ozona, Sonora, Big Lake and Texon. In a little while you could see the clouds of dust set up by motor cars as the people came to the well to see what had really taken place. Excitement was pretty high, but John and I tried to keep cool.

"I had not expected oil at any such shallow depth [1,004 feet]
• and the information I had was that oil from shallow wells was short-life production—a sort of flash in the pan. I said to John, 'Son we will sell enough leases while the excitement is running high to pay

[22] A metal marker at the well carries this legend: "The Ohio Oil Company I. G. Yates Well No. 1-A. Location 2,900 F.W. of SW. Corner of SE. 60, Block I. and G. N. Survey. Elevation 2,399 feet. Commenced October 5, 1926. Top lime 990 feet. Completed October 28, 1926. Total depth 1,004 feet. Drilled deeper April 6 to April 15, 1927, from 1,004 feet to 1,032 feet. Production increased from 450 barrels to 2,200 barrels per 24 hours. Drilled August 8 to August 18, 1928, from 1,032 to 1,150 feet. Total depth 1,150 feet. Production increased to 2,951 barrels per hour. January 1, 1929 test 3,036 barrels per hour."

all the debts we owe, and then if they still keep buying we will sell a little more while the buying lasts.' "

There was no lack of buyers. "I stayed on the ranch until about twelve o'clock of the 29th selling leases," said Yates. "By the time we had left the ranch for San Angelo a little after midnight, I had sold about $180,000 worth of leases. Not a single man who bought a lease from me that night has even taken one dollar on a single lease purchased at that time."

Singularly enough, a San Angelo news item of December 24, 1926,[23] played up two significant developments—the Southern Crude Oil Purchasing Company's wildcat oil producer on the T. G. Hendrick's ranch in Winkler County and the Mid-Kansas and Transcontinental Oil Company's No. 1 Yates well, yielding 390 barrels of 29.5-gravity oil daily.[24] By this time Humble had contracted to run the Yates oil, and was building a 55,000-barrel steel tank on Yates' ranch, with a pipe-line connection to its main line at Mc-Camey. Mid-Kansas and Transcontinental[25] had started their sec-

---

[23] *Oil Weekly,* Vol. XLIV, No. 1 (December 24, 1926), 29.

[24] Benedum and Trees of Pittsburgh controlled the Transcontinental. Later they sold it to a group of speculators headed by Amos Beaty, who consolidated it with the Ohio Oil Company, which also owned the Mid-Kansas.—San Angelo *Standard-Times,* May 28, 1933, Sec. 3, p. 24, cols. 3, 4, 5, and 6.

The sun-scorched hills and plains of West Texas had given Benedum and Trees their pot of gold. Both Mike Benedum and Joe Trees were indefatigable wildcatters. The former as a young man went into the oil business in western Pennsylvania and West Virginia as a land man for one of the Standard of New Jersey subsidiaries. Trees graduated from the Indiana Normal School in 1892 and from the University of Pittsburgh in 1895, and began oil production in Pennsylvania, West Virginia, and Indiana oil fields during his vacations. Then the two men became partners, doing wildcatting for the Standard of Indiana, and later for their own company, Benedum and Trees. Their wildcatting trail led through Texas, Oklahoma, the Northwest, Mexico, Romania, Russia, and the Pacific Coast; but it was in West Texas that they made their richest strikes. They controlled a half-interest in the Reagan County field in 1923 and almost that much of the Yates field in 1926.

[25] *National Petroleum News,* Vol. XVIII, No. 52 (December 27, 1926), 27. With the purchase of the Mid-Kansas Oil and Gas Company, the Ohio Oil Company entered the Mid-Continent area in 1916. Mid-Kansas had held important leases in the Augusta pool, in Butler County; and later, additional leases in Butler, Greenwood, and Cowley counties. During World War I, the Ohio Oil Company entered Texas, through its subsidiary the Mid-Kansas Oil and Gas Company, by a one-half interest in 31,873.36 acres of leases in the Ranger field. Then, in 1924, Ohio entered the Permian Basin, acquiring a 10,000-acre lease block in Pecos County from the Transcontinental Oil Company, and two years later brought in the Yates field discovery well. Ohio began operations in Oklahoma by securing a lease in Seminole County, bringing in its first well in June, 1924. In 1923 the company began operations at Burbank, Shidler, Pawhuska, Avant, and Hominy. Meanwhile, it had en-

ond Yates test 537 feet due west of the discovery well; and Kimberlin and Frank Pickrell were to sink another southeast of the No. 1 Yates, near the center of Section 55.

Meanwhile, the Yates ranch was being swamped by a daily inflow of people, whom the hospitable ranchman did his best to accommodate. He transformed his red barn into a rooming house by putting in beaverboard partitions, cots, and other fixtures. Before Iraan had made its municipal bow to tin-hatted visitors, Yates' "Red Barn" was the only lodging possible for the oilmen.[26]

Major companies moved into both the Hendricks and Yates fields soon after each was discovered. By 1928 fifteen companies were producing oil at Yates and twenty held acreage. Eighteen days after the No. 1 Hendricks well was brought in, an oil trade journal announced a "Million Dollars Paid for Leases Around Winkler Wildcat," stating that the Southern Crude Oil Purchasing Company had taken over the Westbrook discovery well and 1,440 acres of checkerboarded leases throughout the original block for $510,-000.[27] Humble acquired 1,580 acres in six separate tracts for $224,-000, and Roxana had purchased 880 acres for $225,000. The same companies entered the Yates field about the same time, paying from fifteen to fifty dollars for numbers of tracts.[28]

Yates quickly became the wonder field of the nation. Its second well was gauged as a daily 3,440-barrel producer from about the same depth, and on the fourth day after it blew in, flowed 3,380 barrels of 30-degree gravity oil through a pipe line into a 55,000-barrel steel tank on a near-by hillside.[29] And the No. 2 Yates gauged 6,650 barrels daily by March 1. In June, 1927, the Mid-Kansas and Transcontinental added their fourth producer, flowing 2,200 barrels

---

tered Louisiana, at Haynesville (April 23, 1921); Arkansas, in the Stephens field (October, 1922), Champagnolle (May, 1925), and Lisbon (December, 1925); and New Mexico, at Artesia (May, 1924), Hobbs (December, 1929), Monument and Hardy (1936).

[26] H. P. Courtney, of the Standard Oil Company of Texas, in an interview granted the author, September 20, 1947, stated that the original purchase price of the Yates ranch was about twenty-five cents an acre. He added that after the barn was converted into a rooming house, it was given a sheet-iron roof and painted red.

[27] *Oil Weekly*, Vol. XLIII, No. 10 (November 26, 1926), 28. The Southern Crude Oil Purchasing Company also built a twenty-mile six-inch pipe line from the Hendricks field to the Texas and Pacific Railroad.—*National Petroleum News*, Vol. XVIII, No. 48 (December 1, 1926), 64.

[28] *Ibid.*, No. 47 (November 24, 1926), 48.

of oil in its first four hours and raising the field's output from 25,000 to 30,000 barrels daily. This was the shallowest producing well in the entire West Texas district.

By July 1, 1928, 207 Yates wells had been completed with a combined daily potential of 2,500,000 barrels of crude oil, which increased within a year to a potential open flow of more than 4,500,-000 barrels a day for 306 wells. By October 29, 1929, it could indeed be said that Pecos County alone had astonished the oil world, then having five separate pools, in an area formerly considered by many as the "graveyard of the wildcatter." Two of its pools had been opened in recent months. So prolific was the Yates field's output that the Texas Railroad Commission was forced to restrict production to 130,000 barrels a day.

At that time Yates consisted of 20,000 proven acres, which some geologists believed would yield 40,000 barrels to the acre, or 640,-000,000 barrels. Here were huge wells that could flow upward of 100,000 barrels a day natural potential, with one well acclaimed to be the greatest producer in the country. This was the No. 3 Bob Reid, owned by the Standard Oil Company of Texas, which reached a potential rating of almost 170,000 barrels a day.[30] Within a year after the No. 1 Yates was discovered, sixty-nine wells in this field had an estimated flow of 365 barrels a well per hour. By 1942, Yates' 572 wells had produced about 260,000,000 barrels of crude oil and had an estimated reserve of 407,944,000 barrels. Moreover, 90 per cent of its wells still flow, although the field was discovered more than two decades ago.

Until October 1, 1927, the enormous Yates oil output was without pipe-line connection, except for the Illinois Pipe Line Company's small line connecting with a loading rack at McCamey. But the Humble Pipe Line Company was hurriedly building into West Texas, connecting with its terminal at Ingleside, near Corpus Christi, and proposed to market 30,000 barrels of Yates oil a day

[29] "Three West Texas Counties Have Big Flush Wells," in *Oil Weekly*, Vol. XLIV, No. 9 (February 18, 1927), 67. National drilling machines (cable tool) were used in most of the Yates drilling. In 1929, says Harry Wiess, "West Texas production equalled 45 per cent of the total for Texas."—Mimeographed copy, "Oil Development in the Permian Basin," address before annual meeting of the Permian Basin Association, Odessa, Texas, June 21, 1940.

[30] H. H. King, "West Texas-New Mexico District Again Is Booming," in *Oil Weekly*, Vol. LXXXVI, No. 6 (July 19, 1937), 32–37.

when its line was completed. Yet this would provide only a small outlet for the prolific Yates oil field.

Proration was necessary if disaster were to be averted. On August 18, 1927, W. S. Farish, president of the Humble Oil and Refining Company, invited the Yates field producers to Houston to consider a plan that would permit Humble to buy ratably 30,000 barrels of oil a day and that proposed to leave in the ground the oil for which there was no market outlet. He explained the urgency of such an agreement, asserting that Yates' production was already in excess of an outlet; that when the Humble pipe line was completed by October 1, it could handle only 30,000 barrels a day; that the Yates oil had a sulphur content which would cause tankage corrosion and therefore great loss if the producers sought to store excess oil; and that a ratable taking of oil, until a long-range plan could be inaugurated, would prevent great waste and operator losses.

The Houston meeting accomplished little, but a second meeting was held at Fort Worth on September 2, at which a committee, headed by W. A. Moncrief, was asked to present a proration plan. Six days later the committee was named, and a tentative operator agreement was drawn up. The plan was successful. By October 1, 1927, voluntary proration was put into effect, at which time there were "23 producing wells with a 24-hour potential of 172,000 barrels to be allocated to a 300,000 barrel per day outlet."

West Texas Oil Output, September, 1927[31]

Pool	Present Potential Production	Oct. 1	Nov. 1	Dec. 1	Estimated Ultimate Recovery
Yates	86,000	156,000	236,000	323,000	255,000,000
Church & Fields	93,000	100,000	100,000	100,000	55,000,000
Gulf McElroy	25,000	46,000	40,000	35,000	100,000,000
McCamey	20,000	20,000	20,000	20,000	54,000,000
Hendricks	16,000	56,000	86,000	116,000	135,000,000
Totals	240,000	378,000	482,000	594,000	599,000,000

In addition, B. C. Clardy was employed as Yates field umpire to supervise voluntary control rules and regulations that prorated the

[31] San Angelo *Morning Times*, October 28, 1936, p. 1, c. 6.

pipe-line outlet on the basis of well potentials. The new program immediately started indiscriminate drilling to increase the volume of each operator's supply. On January 1, of the next year, therefore, the plan was changed to prorate by proven acreage, each operator being apportioned that percentage of outlet which his acreage bore to the whole.

On July 1, 1928, the enforcement of proration was transferred to the Texas Railroad Commission. Then the Commission issued its first order for the Yates field, based on both potential and acreage, with the field divided approximately into 100-acre units. Any lease smaller than a unit was entitled to full participation under certain regulations.

Later, Farish explained this significant innovation. "Twenty-five per cent of the pipe line outlet was divided equally among all the producing units, and 75 per cent according to the average potential of the unit [that is, the total potential of the unit divided by the number of wells of the unit]. It was required that each unit produce oil allocated to it, and offset wells on neighboring leases were required to produce ratably in accordance with their potentials."[32]

This program was launched by the field umpire appointed by the Commission, under the supervision of an advisory committee made up of one representative from each lease owner. Yates was the second Texas oil field to be prorated by the Commission—Hendricks had been the first, by an order made effective on May 5, 1928.

Shortly after the Railroad Commission prorated the field, Yates was given an adequate pipe-line outlet. The Texas–New Mexico Company entered the field with a twelve-inch line, the Gulf with an eight-inch line, and Shell with a six-inch line.

The Hendricks field was given a top allowable of 150,000 barrels, from a daily potential of 521,597 barrels until the Commission could perfect its proration regulations. A number of hearings were necessary before final controls were adopted.[33]

Exploration and wildcatting at Big Lake took on added momentum after the Hendricks and Yates oil discoveries. In 1926, Ector

[32] *Ibid.*
[33] Hearings were held on March 10, April 13, and April 24, 1928, before the Hendricks order was issued.

Oil! Titan of the Southwest

County shared the spotlight with Winkler and Pecos counties when J. S. Cosden, Inc., found oil on the W. E. Connell land. But Crane and Upton counties' Church-Fields and Gulf-McElroy oil pools were among this year's major discoveries. On April 8, Church and Fields' No. 1 University well made 190 barrels of oil from a lime formation at 3,040 feet; and on July 22 the Gulf Oil Corporation completed its No. 1 McElroy, a 600-barrel oiler, at 2,750 feet. These two important wells, four miles apart, were soon found to be in one major field, which, by October, 1927, produced daily 117,000 barrels of oil.[34]

The next two years brought other fields. Geologists and wild-catters entered Crockett, Loving, Mitchell, Reagan, Terrell, Upton, Glasscock, Howard, Irion, Pecos, and Ward counties, doing intensive work in the last five counties named. A few oil strikes followed. Reagan County gained a pool with its Skelly–Utah Southern Oil Company's No. 1 University well, on February 6, 1926, and Irion County had its first oil well on March 24, 1928, with the P. E. Hill No. 1 Horney well for an initial ten barrels a day at 1,270 feet. Pecos County, too, added another field in December when the Pecos Valley Company completed its No. 1 Fee for 185 barrels of oil.

Ward County had its first production on November 2, 1928, with its No. 1 Hazlett well, of the Shipley pool, now in the South Ward field; and deeper production was reached at Big Lake, on November 30, 1928, at 8,525 feet, increasing considerably this field's daily output.

In 1929, Andrews County claimed a discovery with its Deep Rock Oil Company *et al.'s* No. 1 Ogden well, a 200-barrel producer at 4,305 feet; and Ector County added still another pool in the Penwell area, in November, by the R. R. Penn No. 1 Kloh well, for 365 barrels a day. Ward County also claimed oil in the same year when the Gulf Production Company completed its No. 4 O'Brien well, on April 12, for a daily 1,500-barrel yield, a find that led to rapid expansion of the field.[35]

By 1936, Permian Basin production extended into twenty-one West Texas counties, opening fields of major proportions, and

[34] *Petroleum Development and Technology, 1927,* 626.

[35] For a detailed county-by-county production report see mimeographed papers, "West Texas, 1933," and "West Texas Development and Production Statistics for 1935," authorship and place not given.

spread into southeastern New Mexico, including Lea, Eddy, and Chaves counties. New Mexico had previously added oil areas in Eddy and San Juan counties, but refineries and limited tank-car shipments had absorbed this output.

New Mexico's commercial development and production of oil dates from the opening of the Artesia field, in Eddy County, in 1924. Geologists paid little attention to Lea County, perhaps feeling that surface conditions gave no promise of a deep-seated structure favorable to an oil horizon.

However, the finding of the three sensational West Texas fields of Big Lake, Hendricks, and Yates stimulated a revival of interest in southeastern New Mexico. Extensive surveys were made to find out whether or not the Permian Basin's north-south trend extended into southeastern New Mexico. Then drilling followed, which in 1927 uncovered a well of 90,000,000 cubic feet of gas a day by the Texas Production Company in its No. 1 Rhodes at Jal, in Lea County.

Already, Eddy County claimed New Mexico's first oil well. Its Artesia oil field,[36] fourteen miles southeast of the town of Artesia, had been mapped earlier by V. H. McNutt, of Tulsa. The discovery well,[37] on a block of leases held by Flynn, Welch, and Yates, was a small producer when completed in August, 1923. The second well made 2,500,000 cubic feet of gas daily from 2,085 feet. A group organized as the Picher Oil Company from Joplin, Missouri, and Picher, Oklahoma, drilled another near-by small producer. But the Twin-Lakes well[38] made 250 barrels daily and started the field toward rapid development. Within two years its two hundred wells had produced 2,000,000 barrels of oil.[39]

Major companies immediately entered this area. The Texas, Prairie, Midwest, Roxana, Ohio, Humble, Empire, Skelly, Amerada, and Sinclair took up government permits, comprising approximately 2,560 acres each, carrying certain drilling requirements.

Independent operators also were present, the Maljamar Oil and

[36] *Structure of Typical American Oil Fields*, I, 113–14; Circular No. 4, New Mexico School of Mines, January 1, 1931, 2–4.

[37] In S31-T18S-R28E.

[38] In S28-T18S-R28E.

[39] "Extensive Wildcat Campaign Started in New Mexico," in *Oil Weekly*, Vol. XLIV, No. 7 (February 4, 1927), 29.

Gas Corporation, that had opened the Maljamar field, the Mid-Continent Oil Company of Los Angeles, Danciger Oil and Refining Company, E. M. Treat and Company, Snowden-McSweeney Company, Cap Rock Oil and Gas Corporation, Dexter and Blair Exploration Company, the Sentinel Oil Company, Inglefield, Bridges and McDonald, and McNeal—all taking up large blocks of leases.

The Maljamar Oil and Gas Corporation, headed by William Mitchell of New York, had opened the Maljamar field in Lea County, in 1924. The first well was on the Baish permit[40] approximately twenty-five miles east of the Artesia field. At 2,300 feet the well picked up oil, but when it was drilled to 4,132 feet, it made a 115-barrel-a-day producer. By the opening of 1927 the Maljamar Corporation had three producing wells out of three drilled; the Skelly Oil Company, one, five miles to the west; and the Ohio Oil Company, another which linked the two areas. Promptly the Illinois Pipe Line Company prepared to lay a line having a capacity of 5,000 barrels daily to the Maljamar field.

Hobbs, a cattle market and irrigation-farming center, was founded in 1907 by James Hobbs, a Texan, and until oil was discovered in 1927, was still small. A geophysical survey, with both magnetometer and torsion balance, conducted by the Midwest Refining Company (among others) indicated that there was a structural high near Hobbs, then many miles from the nearest railroad and even without adequate highway connections.[41]

On October 12, 1927, the Midwest spudded in what was to be Hobbs' discovery well.[42] The well showed both oil and gas at several levels, but in June, 1928, at a depth of 4,065 feet it was completed as a 200-barrel oil well of 32.50-degree Baumé test.[43] The well was then drilled still deeper, to 4,214 feet, where it tested 700 barrels of oil a day, and at 4,245 feet sulphur water almost ruined it. But it was plugged back to 4,215 feet for a final production of a little more than 100 barrels daily.

Several other wells were soon started, among which, on June 10, 1929, the Humble Oil and Refining Company spudded its No. 1

40 In S21-T17S-R32E.

41 Circular No. 4, 2–3.

42 Near the NE corner, S9-T19S-R38E.

43 Circular No. 4, 2–3; *New Mexico, A Guide to the Colorful State* (American Guide Series), 400.

Permian Basin Discoveries

Bowers permit[44] more than three miles to the northwest of the Midwest well. This well, at 4,106 feet, proved to be Hobbs' first large producer, having 12,000,000 cubic feet of gas at 2,820 feet, 438 barrels of oil at 3,368 feet, 50,000,000 cubic feet of gas at 3,684 feet, and 9,720 barrels of oil at 4,106 feet.

Obviously, this well prompted a rapid development campaign within the new area, in which over twenty oil companies, mostly majors, were active. The Texas and New Mexico Railroad connecting Lovington, Hobbs, Eunice, and Jal with Monahans on the Texas-Pacific Railroad in western Texas was soon built, as were the Atlantic, Humble, and Shell eight-inch pipe lines.

Hobbs boomed. In 1930 its population reached approximately 12,000. The town became an oil-field supply center, with new banks, mercantile houses, and other businesses.

In January, 1931, Hobbs' productive area was extended a mile to the east by Midwest's No. 29 Turner well, in the Hobbs townsite. It made 19,182 barrels of oil in a twenty-four-hour test, from a depth of 4,175 feet, before it had fully cleaned itself of drilling water. This townsite discovery not only extended the field eastward but opened a prolific part of the field. Midwest controlled 160 acres, in the southwestern part of Section 34, on which the well was located; but Amerada had an offset quarter on the east, and Skelly, Shell, and Landreth companies had tracts in the north half of Section 34.

In 1931 it was stated authoritatively that "with more than 130 wells completed, showing a rated potential of over 1,000,000 barrels a day," the limits of the Hobbs field were fixed by edge wells at only a few points. Up to January 1, 1931, Hobbs had produced and marketed nearly 7,000,000 barrels of oil.[45] An executive committee for proration purposes fixed the Hobbs potential production for the last half of January, 1931, at 1,081,411 barrels of oil a day from 137 wells on 122 units. By the end of 1941, Hobbs had 265 wells with a productive 10,080 acres of land.

Within an oil empire so vast lies much of the nation's black treasure. From January 27, 1930, to July 28, 1937—or for approximately eight years—forty-seven new oil pools were found, including the extensive Slaughter field (April 6, 1937) and Wasson (June 19,

[44] In S30-T18S-R38E.
[45] Circular No. 4, 4.

1937). And substantial new production was found in twenty-two others, including the discovery of deeper oil horizons and the expansion of old fields.

With West Texas oil expansion came a network of gathering and trunk pipe lines. Much of the oil went by pipe line to distant refineries. Among these market and refinery outlets were: a ten-inch line from McCamey to Oklahoma; one twelve-inch and three ten-inch lines to the Gulf Coast; one ten-inch and three eight-inch lines to North Texas trunk-line junctions; one eight-inch line to a Southwest Texas junction with a coastal trunk line; and an eight-inch line to El Paso.

Distant refineries processed the most of West Texas' crude oil, but regional refineries handled 60,300 barrels of it. In 1940, West Texas refineries included the Areo Gas Refining Company at Fort Stockton; the Col-Tex Refining Company at Colorado City; the Concho Refining Company and the Paramount Refining Company at San Angelo; the Cosden Petroleum Company and the Howard County Refining Company at Big Spring; the Mertzon Refining Company at Mertzon; the Standard Oil Company of Texas and The Texas Company at El Paso; the Farmers Refinery at Lubbock; the Western Refining Company at Pecos; and the Wickett Refining Company at Wickett. In addition, there were other refineries in New Mexico.

The Permian Basin's cumulative oil output at the close of 1941 was 1,499,351,000 barrels, with West Texas making 1,195,073,000 barrels. Moreover, in this area of Texas, there were known crude reserves of 2,564,831,000 barrels with 14,296 wells and 376,321 producing acres.

The Slaughter and Wasson fields had the largest acreages of the newer finds. Slaughter, covering parts of Cochran, Hockley, and Terry counties, had 52,000 outlined acres of production. At the close of 1941 it had produced approximately 6,500,000 barrels of crude oil from 849 wells, with 97 per cent flowing. Wasson, centering upon the Gaines-Yoakum County line, had 58,000 proven acres. From 1936 to 1941 it had produced 33,000,000 barrels of crude from 1,311 wells, 95 per cent of which had a natural flow; and its estimated reserve was 415,000,000 barrels of oil.[46]

New Mexico figures for 1941 are equally impressive, especially when it is remembered that the state's annual output did not exceed 2,000,000 barrels of oil until 1930, when Hobbs made headlines. But presently the production trend extended from the Jal field via Cooper, South Eunice, Eunice, and Monument areas. The vast Eunice-Monument region was only a short distance south of Hobbs. This combined area had a cumulative production of 104,-475,575 barrels of oil from 1,078 producers, and the structure's reserves were estimated at 257,844,000 barrels.

Hobbs, the first major field in the state, passed the 100,000,000-barrel mark in production by the end of 1941, producing from 265 wells on 10,080 acres.

A detailed narrative of the immense Permian Basin oil development, from the Westbrook field discovery in 1920 to the present time, can hardly be encompassed in this chapter. The region's producing zone is larger than some of the American states. Today one may travel northward, by well-paved highways, from one rich oil field to another, from Ozona, in Crockett County, Texas, via Big Lake, McCamey, Crane, Odessa, Andrews, Seminole, to Morton, in Cochran County, Texas—approximately 275 miles—and not be out of a potential oil-producing region. Or one may go westward from the Cedar Lake field, in Gaines County for 140 miles, to the western limits of New Mexico's oil-producing zone, at its widest depth.

[46] H. H. King and Gilbert M. Wilson, "West Texas-New Mexico Permian Basin," in *Oil Weekly*, Vol. CV, No. 9 (May 4, 1942), 29.

XXII

Fabulous East Texas

A DECADE after Steve Owens opened the Permian Basin's great oil reservoir with his No. 1 Abrams well in a mesquite flat at Westbrook, "Dad" Joiner accomplished just as notable a feat by drilling his No. 3 Daisy Bradford well a short distance from Overton, in East Texas. He had, indeed, discovered the Texas "Black Giant."

Following the opening of the Mexia and Powell oil fields in the early nineteen twenties and the exploitation of the Mexia fault zone, extensive exploration was made of the areas both to the east and to the west. In 1915, F. Julius Fohs and James H. Gardner recommended to Snowden and McSweeney a test well near Kilgore. Had it been drilled, this well would have opened the East Texas field. Snowden and McSweeney, in turn, arranged with Roxana to make the test. But Roxana's president, Van Waterschoot van der Gracht, insisted on a site one and one-quarter miles farther east, and the well was dry.[1]

In June, 1927, a seismograph crew of the Geophysical Research Corporation, in the employ of the Pure Oil Company, found a favorable oil structure at Van, in Van Zandt County; and on October 14, 1929, Pure developed there an important oil field. The No. 1 Jarman, making 146 barrels of crude oil hourly, was the discovery well.[2] Then the Pure, Sun, Shell, Texas, and Humble companies unitized their leases and developed the new field in an orderly manner. Although Van's production was pinched to a daily average below 50,000 barrels,[3] by 1932 it had produced more than 15,000,000 barrels of crude oil.

[1] F. Julius Fohs, "Notes," MS, March 12, 1948.

306

Fabulous East Texas

While oilmen's interests were riveted on Van, the No. 3 Daisy Bradford well, about fifty miles to the southeast, opened an area so vast that it startled the oil world.

For many years East Texans had been interested in their region's oil possibilities, even before the Van field was opened. And the finding of near-by fields—at Mexia, Powell, Wortham, and Nigger Creek—seemed only to spur them on in their efforts to find it.

"We have plenty of oil, if only we can find it," East Texas wild-catters had often said. Then, at last, they found it. In 1919, Oklahoma City speculators McFarland, Smith, and Glover had come to East Texas, studied the country, and returned home with contracts for twelve thousand acres of Rusk County land, which later they sold at a profit to an Oklahoma City lease syndicate.

But there were a few hundred acres in Rusk County that they had overlooked, and C. M. ("Dad") Joiner of Ardmore, Oklahoma, quickly picked them up. Most of his leases were in the southern part of the county, between the towns of Overton and Henderson.[4]

This area had gently rolling hills, covered with pine, oak, and gum, interspersed with pastures and farms. Here for nearly a century a quiet, rural folk had lived, for the most part in poverty, raising cotton, sweet potatoes, and corn. Only an occasional community gin or sawmill gave promise of the present-day industrialization sweeping that country.

Joiner's geologist, Dr. A. D. Lloyd, studied his leases to select a drilling site for the first well, and marked a spot about two miles northwest of where the first well was actually drilled, on the Bradford farm.

All East Texas watched, with great expectancy, this Joiner test. The region had suffered from poor crops during 1929 and 1930, in the latter year because of an unprecedented drought. Then came the Great Depression with its added hardships. In the past, farmers had supplemented their income from cotton by engaging in dairy

[2] R. A. Liddle, "Petroleum Development in East Texas and Along the Balcones Fault Zones, 1927," in *Petroleum Development and Technology, 1927*, 630.

[3] James McIntyre, "East Texas Depressed Whole Industry," in *Oil and Gas Journal*, Vol. XXX, No. 37 (January 28, 1932), 56. The Dallas *Morning News*, October 11, 1930, p. 12, c. 4, reported 27,500 barrels. The Anderson-Gogelson and Van Oil Company's No. 1 Mrs. Ella York well was estimated to have a daily potential of 65,000 barrels.—*Ibid.*

[4] Harry Harter, *East Texas Oil Parade*, 46.

farming and poultry raising, and in producing truck crops and fruit. Now they must sell on a poor market, and many farmers were unable to pay their debts. An oil field, therefore, might pull East Texas out of an economic bog.[5]

Preliminary work was pushed about the No. 1 Daisy Bradford well site, as men, women, and children of the neighborhood watched. First, several wagons, each pulled by six to eight laboring mules and loaded with heavy equipment (the engine, boiler, and pumps), turned off the dirt road and crossed the unmarked pasture to the spot where the derrick was to be set up. At the same time laborers cut down large pine trees and hewed them into derrick timbers, and then raised the pyramid-shaped, framelike derrick above the treetops.

There the wagons were unloaded and sent back to shipping points for other equipment. And in a few days the grass about the site was littered with rotary equipment, piping, iron boilers, tongs, spools of rope, and other necessary materials.

The head driller, Ed C. Laster, and his crew lost no time. They dug a slush pit for the well's cuttings, installed their mud-hog pumps to supply the hollow drill stem with its necessary heavy fluid, built pipe racks level with the derrick floor, and set the rust-covered steam drilling engine on its foundation. Next, they connected the draw works with the rotary table and located the boilers about seventy-five yards from the rig, for which they then dug a water pit.

The towering derrick was completed by putting on the crown block. It was equipped with a sheave and pulleys for steel cables to support the heavy traveling block and elevators. Sheave cables were attached to an engine-operated drum, and the drill pipe was lifted by the traveling block and placed over the rotary table. On the "business end" of the drill stem was to be fixed a bit, a fish-tail, diamond, or rock bit, depending on the kind of formation encountered as the hole was deepened.

When everything was ready, the well was spudded in. This was an interesting occasion, for the onlookers hoped that East Texas was entering a new era. The drill stem was now ready to bore into Rusk County's iron-colored soil.

[5] Dallas *Morning News*, February 4, 1931, p. 4, cols. 4–5.

Fabulous East Texas

No doubt enthusiasm was dampened when Joiner's No. 1 and No. 2 Daisy Bradford wells were abandoned because of mechanical difficulties. But people were yet interested and watched daily the drilling of the third well. Laster and his crew, most of whom were East Texans, kept doggedly on, although more than one visiting oilman thought that there was little chance of finding oil.

Joiner had financial as well as mechanical difficulties. He sold a little more than 1,000 acres of his leases to his friends at the rate of $25 for a one-acre interest in syndicate holdings, with a pro rata share in the No. 3 Daisy Bradford well, estimated at $75,000. He organized three syndicates, each of which was also given an interest in the well being drilled. No doubt this and other financial expedients enabled him to complete the well.

October 2 was a gala day. Approximately 8,000 people assembled on the Bradford farm to watch Laster drill through a cement plug in the well. There had been a showing of oil late in September, but they had waited until now for the "drilling-in" moment. The drill had reached the Woodbine sand at 3,536 feet; and when it penetrated to 3,592 feet,[6] Laster cemented his six and five-eights–inch casing and inserted a five and three-sixteenths–inch perforated liner. As the crowd milled about or sat on the ground watching the derrick floor, vendors sold soda-pop and peanuts.

For hour after hour Laster and his crew ran the bailer without a trace of oil. Late on Wednesday evening the crowd dispersed, but on the following morning the expectant watchers were on hand again, only to be disappointed for a second day. It was not until Friday night, October 3, that the well blew in, throwing a spray of gas and oil over the crown block. Here was a tense moment. Joiner, pale with excitement, leaned for support against the derrick; and the watching throng roared a hilarious shout.

The Dallas *Morning News* of October 6, 1930, evidently regarded Joiner's well as unimportant, for it relegated the news of it to the Sports Section. But it did supply important details about the discovery. It stated that the well was still flowing by heads Saturday night, heading at two-hour intervals. The well ran fifty-two barrels in seventeen minutes and was estimated as being capable

[6] *Bulletin of the American Association of Petroleum Geologists,* Vol. XVII (January–December, 1933), Part II, 761.

of a daily production of 5,600 barrels,[7] from the Woodbine sand at 3,592 feet.

By the following Saturday people from all sections rushed to the new field. Experienced writers sought futilely to describe this human avalanche. A Henderson observer told of seeing a string of automobiles miles long on the Henderson-Tyler highway. The entire distance from Henderson to the new well, about seven miles, was crowded to such an extent that cars could make only four to six miles an hour.[8]

There was brisk trading in leases and royalties. Properties that could have been bought a few days previously for ten dollars an acre now were sold for eight hundred to one thousand dollars.[9]

A forest of yellow-pine derricks soon appeared, like a picket fence around Joinerville, the oil field's new boom town. By Sunday, journalists, lease buyers, oil scouts, and scores of other persons swarmed over its yet grass-covered streets. Cafés, grocery stores, gasoline stations, confectioneries, rooming houses, and a maze of shacks were being built as fast as lumber could be hauled in. Excited people milled about, and the *News* reported "big deals."

Tyler, Kilgore, Longview, Gladewater, Henderson, and Overton also caught the oil fever, and their streets, too, were alive with people ready to invest in leases and royalties or to set up business houses.

The East Texas oil field expanded from and finally consolidated about three key wells—the No. 3 Daisy Bradford; the No. 1 Lou Della Crim, twelve miles north of Joiner's discovery well, near Kilgore; and the No. 1 Lathrop, about four miles west of Longview and a shorter distance from Gladewater.[10]

By the end of the year, Deep Rock's No. 1 Ashby well, one mile west of Joiner's producer, was the first of several East Texas well completions. It showed even greater pressure and volume than the No. 3 Daisy Bradford and tended to prove that the main oil forma-

[7] Actually the well flowed 226 barrels of oil in 24 hours. *Ibid.*, Vol. XV (January–December, 1931), Part II, 843.

[8] Dallas *Morning News*, Monday, October 6, 1930, pt. 1, p. 8, col. 2.

[9] *Ibid.*, Sunday, October 5, 1930, p. 13, col. 3.

[10] P. W. McFarland, "East Texas Oil Field," in *Bulletin of the American Association of Petroleum Geologists*, Vol. XV (January–December, 1931), Part II, 843. By the spring of 1931, it seemed probable that an enormous new field had been discovered, a probability that grew into a certainty a few months later.

tion was west of the discovery well. Had Joiner's third well been a quarter of a mile farther east, it would have missed production.[11]

On November 5, leases jumped to $250 cash and $500 in oil because of a new showing of oil and gas in the Arkansas Gas and Fuel Corporation's well, about three-quarters of a mile southeast of the discovery well. Buying and selling again gained momentum three weeks later when the No. 1 Ashby blew a solid black stream of oil 135 feet from the derrick; and once more highway traffic was quickly congested.

A Henderson report of February 9, 1931, stated that four pipe lines—the Panola, Rusk County, Inland Waterways, and Petroleum Marketing companies'—had been completed from the Joiner field to loading racks near Henderson. And a second news item a week later revealed that Magnolia was building a ten-inch pipe line to connect with this company's line from Arkansas south to Neches, Texas.[12]

Meanwhile, Joiner decided to sell a part of his holdings. He had seen other fields mushroom and fade; East Texas might do the same, even though the Ashby well had great possibilities. Toward the end of November he sold 4,000 acres of his Rusk County leases to L. H. Hunt of El Dorado, Arkansas, for more than $1,250,000. Several Dallas businessmen—A. V. Lane, F. S. Davis, J. T. Cook, J. H. Shelton, and others—shared in the sale.[13] Joiner retained two 4,000-acre blocks, one south and one northeast of the No. 3 Daisy Bradford.

Still the dizzy pace of drilling went on. Three months later, there rose about the Joiner discovery well a "veritable forest of derricks," following the southward trend of production.

But it was the sensational Crim well that brought major-company scouts and land men to East Texas. The Stroube and Stroube No. 1 Frederick, 600 feet north of Joiner's No. 3, blew in on December 2, throwing oil twenty feet over the top of its 120-foot derrick,

[11] When fully developed, the East Texas field was found to be on the west flank of the Sabine Uplift, where the normal regional dip was westward. It embraces a large stratigraphic trap along an old shore line where the Woodbine formation pinches out between the Austin chalk above and the Georgetown of the Lower Cretaceous below. See "Major Oil Fields of the United States," MS in E. DeGolyer's Library, Continental Building, Dallas, Texas.

[12] Dallas *Morning News*, February 10, 1931, p. 21, col. 6; *ibid.*, February 17, 1931, p. 19, cols. 2–3.

[13] *Ibid.*, November 30, 1930, p. 5, col. 6 (Editorial section).

but it proved only that East Texas was a major field. The Crim well indicated that the field was of huge proportions.

Ed W. Bateman of Fort Worth had acquired a Kilgore lease belonging to the Crim family. On December 17 the Dallas *Morning News* reported that his first test, the No. 1 Della Lou Crim well, cored ten and one-half feet of oil and gas sand (also the Woodbine) at 3,650 feet; and eleven days later announced that on the previous day (Sunday) it had broken loose under a tremendous gas pressure for an estimated 22,000 barrels of crude oil daily.[14] Two 1,000-barrel tanks were filled with oil in an hour's time through a four-inch lead line; but William E. ("Checkbook Bill") Cain, contractor on the well, brought it under perfect control, marking his sixth discovery well.

Once more leases sold at fabulous rates, with Humble, Gulf, and Shell acquiring properties at fancy prices. Within a few weeks twenty-one derricks could be counted from one spot in the field, and builders had put others up that could not be seen. Several organizations were hauling lumber and material to locations.

Kilgore, a town of 1,000 people, was expected to have 8,000 to 10,000 population within the next few months. On Monday its streets were filled with strangers. Land men, oil scouts, and speculators were the first to arrive, but only as a vanguard of the eager crowds a few weeks later. As seen by W. R. Smith, president of the Oriental Oil Company of Dallas, Kilgore was the "most seething, wildly excited, and booming oil boom town" he had ever gazed upon. "This beats them all," he said. "I would judge there are between 1,500 and 2,000 carpenters at work in this little Gregg County town. Shacks are springing up everywhere like mushrooms. . . . The sidings are filled up with unloaded freight cars, the roads are choked with traffic, and there is literally standing room only in the town itself."[15] Roy Laird, businessman, had announced that he would build three new brick structures in the immediate future; the telephone company was putting in a new switchboard; a telegraph office was under construction; and an oil exchange and a hotel were planned.[16]

[14] One authority says that the No. 1 Crim had an initial production of 10,000 barrels a day. See "Major Oil Fields of the United States," MS, *loc. cit.*

[15] Dallas *Morning News*, February 19, 1931, p. 22, col. 5.

[16] *Ibid.*, December 30, 1930, p. 13, col. 2.

Keystone field, Andrews County, Texas

Discovery well in Hobbs, New Mexico, field

East Texas discovery well, 1930—No. 3 Daisy Bradford,
near Henderson, Texas. C. M. ("Dad") Joiner, left, is
shaking hands with A. D. Lloyd, geologist

Dallas Morning News

First well in the city of Kilgore, Texas (J. A. Knowles
Fee)

photograph by Knight Studio
Mayor Roy H. Laird, Kilgore

Fabulous East Texas

By the latter part of February, 1931, Humble had purchased for $2,100,000 the lease on which the Crim well was found and then started the erection of derricks at intervals of 150 feet along the boundary of the block. At that time fully half a hundred rigs had risen, although by dirt road this area was three and one-half miles from Kilgore. So rough was the terrain that it was not uncommon for operators to leave their loaded trucks by the roadside and employ broad-tired wagons, pulled by four, six, and even nine teams, to haul their equipment to new locations.[17]

Longview wanted a part of Kilgore's prosperity. As yet the field was undefined, and Longview had hopes that it would come its way. Its chamber of commerce offered $10,000 for the first well in Longview's trade territory. The J. E. Farrel, W. A. Moncrief, and Arkansas Fuel Oil Company's No. 1 J. K. Lathrop well, in the William Robinson survey, about fifteen miles due north of the Crim well and six miles northwest of Longview, won the $10,000. The award was given to the drillers, Foster and Jeffries.[18]

A week before the well was completed, a saturated core taken from it created intense excitement. Telegraph and telephone wires hummed at night; and by daylight fast cars whizzed in from El Dorado, Tulsa, Wichita Falls, Fort Worth, Dallas, Houston, and other oil centers, following all-night drives, while trains and busses discharged their human cargoes.

Longview's hotel lobbies, sidewalks, streets, two local banks, and the Gregg County courthouse were alive with people, mostly strangers, while at night hotels and rooming houses had proof of the old adage, "as thick as three in a bed." There was scarcely standing room at the Gregg Hotel. Its manager, J. T. Harris, said that he had been able to provide only a small percentage of the accommodations requested.

The county clerk employed a corps of deputies and abstractors to help with land transactions; and lawyers and stenographers overran the courthouse. County maps were almost as common as handkerchiefs, and probably used more.

Natives and old settlers also felt the oil-field excitement. They

[17] *Ibid.*, February 21, 1931, p. 20, cols. 3–4.
[18] By the close of 1931, the Joiner, Kilgore, and Longview areas produced 107,727,912 barrels of oil, or a daily average of 295,145 barrels. McIntyre, *loc. cit.*

313

engaged in lease trading, assumed the oilman's garb of laced boots, riding breeches, and soft leather jackets; and they learned such technical terms as "commercial lease," "royalty acre," and "saturated core."

Oil money brought new life to Longview. By February its population had grown from 5,025[19] to approximately 10,000 since the beginning of the year. Secretary M. D. Abernathy of the Chamber of Commerce reported on February 6, 1931, that his organization had found rooms, apartments, and houses for no fewer than 15,000 persons within the preceding four weeks. Among other improvements were a sixty-four-room addition to the Gregg Hotel and new space for the First National Bank (by using its basement for safe-deposit vaults).

Major oil companies added new installations, such as the Humble Pipe Line Company warehouse on the outskirts of town. Gulf, Humble, and Magnolia opened offices in Longview, having purchased extensive acreages.

Meanwhile, near-by leasing was lively. B. A. Skipper, a Longview real-estate operator, a short time before the Lathrop well was completed, sold a ten-acre tract near the well for $750. When the big gusher assured this area of a great field, he offered the lease-holder $25,000 for the ten acres, only to be told that the lease was not for sale.[20]

From the Bradford-Crim-Lathrop line, oil development rapidly spread throughout Rusk and Gregg counties and over into Smith and Upshur counties. There was a common belief in East Texas that the three oil-producing areas would not and could not join. This was expressed repeatedly for two or three months. But the Guy Lewis *et al.* No. 1 Cook well, in the Jones-Jordan Survey, was drilled four and one-half miles west of the No. 3 Daisy Bradford well, extending the field into Smith County. On March 30, 1931, it flowed 137 barrels in thirty-three minutes through a three-fourths-inch choke, reaching the top of the pay sand at 3,672 feet. The

[19] The Census of 1930.

[20] The Arkansas Fuel Oil Company bought the interests of Moncrief and associates in the No. 1 Lathrop well, half-interest in 96 acres surrounding it, and half-interest in about 2,400 additional acres for a consideration of $3,500,000. Terms of the sale were $500,000 in cash, $500,000 in six months at 6 per cent interest and $2,000,000 in oil.

Fabulous East Texas

Mudge Oil Company's No. 1 Richardson, four miles northwest of the Lathrop well, on May 5, 1931, carried production northward into Upshur County,[21] flowing 274 barrels in two hours through a 42/64-inch choke; and by the spring of 1931 it seemed probable that a vast field had been found. A few months later this probability had become a certainty. Oil discoveries had defined a producing zone thirty-six miles long and from three to seven and one-half miles wide, with an approximate area of 92,000 square miles.

During the first few weeks after the Joiner discovery, there were on the average seven well completions every two weeks, and during the next twenty-four, the number soared to seventy-three. By December 31, 1931, East Texas had 3,732 wells completed, and in the next year, 5,652.

This situation, of course, led to overproduction. As early as February, 1931, East Texas was divided on the question of prorating its giant oil field. Some land- and royalty-holders feared that proration would imperil their new-found source of income; but an actual check on Gregg and Rusk County operators showed that a majority of them favored curtailment.[22]

Two proration meetings were held in Tyler on Thursday, February 4. The first, representing lease, land, and royalty owners and small producers, formed a permanent organization, and named a committee of twenty-five men to promote their interests. After their meeting adjourned, the proration advisory committee for Rusk and Gregg counties met and urged the Railroad Commission to hold a proration hearing soon.

The permanent organization growing out of the first meeting, the East Texas Lease, Royalty and Producers Association was set up with Judge C. L. Brachfield of Henderson, president; W. B. Hamilton of Wichita Falls, vice-president; and Carl Estes of Tyler, secretary-treasurer. Proration was heatedly debated. Hamilton urged orderly development. "West Texas is for proration," he said. "We ask for it as Texans. . . . If you permit just anyone to take your market outlet, you'll have anarchy among operators; you will wit-

[21] Lucile Silvey Beard, "The History of the East Texas Oil Field," (unpublished Master of Arts thesis, Hardin-Simmons University, Abilene, Texas, June, 1938), 42; Frederic H. Lahee, "The East Texas Oil Field," in *Petroleum Development and Technology, 1932*, 270.

[22] *Petroleum Reporter*, Vol. II, No. 9 (December, 1930), 28.

ness men taking the law into their own hands." This prophecy soon came true. J. F. Donohue supported Hamilton's point of view, as did Jake Hamon of Ardmore, Oklahoma. "It's the only sensible way to exist properly," Hamon said. It seemed to him a question of "getting 25 cents or less per barrel of oil or $1 per barrel."[23] But Dr. A. D. Lloyd and others felt that proration was unnecessary.

On April 20, 1931, Guy A. Blount of Nacogdoches, Texas, then president of the East Texas Chamber of Commerce, supported conservation and the Texas Railroad Commission's orders in his annual convention address.[24] And on August 6, East Texas operators met in Tyler to discuss a general field shutdown. At a second meeting a week later, several hundred operators favored a shutdown and appointed a committee to confer with Governor Sterling.

Experienced operators had watched with alarm the rapidly ascending scale of well completions. Early in 1931 the Railroad Commission had warned against overproduction, explaining that East Texas, with its oil outlet, its high-grade oil,[25] and its area divided into hundreds of ownerships, could bring disaster to the whole oil industry unless production were controlled.

But local interests were too diverse for common agreements. Operators ranged from leaseholders of a few acres to those with many thousand acres. Some operators promoted rapid development and quick monetary returns, while major companies and far-sighted independents cautioned against overdevelopment and glutting the market.

The Texas Railroad Commission, composed of Pat Neff (chairman), C. V. Terrell, and Lon A. Smith, sought to promote orderly development. Yet the production problem was difficult to solve.

One of the present commissioners, E. O. Thompson, thus sums up the growing East Texas problem: "It was not until the epochal discovery of the East Texas field in September, 1930, that the real science of modern conservation began to crystalize. . . . The vast size of the field, underlying more than two hundred square miles, and its incomprehensible capacity, quickly upset the world's economic and price structure of petroleum."[26]

[23] Dallas *Morning News,* February 6, 1931, p. 1, col. 5, and p. 4, cols. 3–4.
[24] Henderson, Texas, *Daily Times,* February 17, 1932, p. 16.
[25] East Texas Oil had a paraffin base and an average A.P.I. gravity of 39 de-

Fabulous East Texas

The first hinge upon which the science and philosophy of Texas conservation swung was the law of March 27, 1929, to be implemented by the Railroad Commission. But "unfortunately," thinks R. E. Hardwicke, "the Railroad Commission waited until the spring of 1931 before undertaking to bring the field under control, and such delay increased complications."[27]

In April, 1931, after due hearings, the Commission issued an order allowing 70,000 barrels of oil for the East Texas field, to be gradually increased to 100,000 barrels until the movement of new well completions was stabilized. By this time, however, the field had increased its daily output to 140,000 barrels of oil. Then the Commission increased its allowable to 90,000 barrels, its order providing a 15,000-barrel increase each fifteen days for a ninety-day period. During the preceding week, however, production again climbed, this time to 340,000 barrels daily.

East Texas operators had been drilling and producing oil much as they pleased. Although the May allowable for many wells was in excess of 1,000 barrels of oil a day, there was a storm of protest over the Commission's declared intention of enforcing its ruling. Many of the operators ignored it; others brought injunction suits.

In view of this unprecedented oil-output increase, it is small wonder that East Texas became a state proving ground for experimental laws and methods. The pathway of control was tortuous. As one law was cast aside, a new one was enacted; as one regulation was invalidated, a new one was drawn up; and as one weakness was remedied, a new one was found.[28]

When the Joiner well was discovered in October, 1930, high-grade oil was bringing $1.10; but early in the next year the new field's rapid expansion and overproduction drove the price down to twenty-five cents. In April four major companies sought to help matters by posting a top price of sixty-seven cents for East Texas oil; but they withdrew it when certain other producers ignored

grees.—*Bulletin of the American Association of Petroleum Geologists,* Vol. XV (January–December), Part II, 487.

[26] Manuscript copy, "Railroad Commission of Texas," which Colonel Thompson furnished the author. Although the oil sand was penetrated in September, the Joiner well did not produce until October 3, 1930.

[27] R. E. Hardwicke, "Legal History of Conservation of Oil in Texas," in *Legal History of Conservation of Oil and Gas,* 229.

[28] Beard *op. cit.,* 55; Hardwicke, *loc. cit.,* 228 ff.

317

Oil! Titan of the Southwest

proration regulations and ran "hot oil" with reckless abandon. Then the price of crude oil tumbled to ten cents a barrel.

No doubt the field's daily output of 360,000 barrels of oil from 1,000 wells by June 1 was a contributory cause of the market's demoralization. Yet the Commission's daily allowable was 160,000 barrels.

East Texas resisted a reduction of its oil output desperately, says Commissioner Thompson, "and through the pressure of powerful interests the legislature was persuaded to curb the authority of the Commission by expressly forbidding the use of market demand as a gauge of the operators." Dozens of suits and injunctions against the Railroad Commission nullified its orders. "The field was in a cut-throat war of frenzied production. The mad race brought Gargantuan expansion."[29]

The California fields, Greater Seminole, Oklahoma City, and West Texas were deluging the market with additional oil floods. By August 1 the Mid-Continent's price had fallen from $1.07 for high-gravity oil to an average of twenty-two cents a barrel. Because of this market decline the Texas Railroad Commission's proration plan alarmed harassed producers operating on a shoe string, who must produce oil to the limit to maintain sufficient income to pay supply houses for drilling materials and meet other costs.

At a Commission hearing in June, 1931, engineers and geologists testified that East Texas could produce 400,000 barrels of oil daily without causing physical waste; but they warned that a higher rate of withdrawal would imperil the field's reservoir energy and bring premature waterflooding. Acting upon this expert opinion, the Commission fixed the daily maximum withdrawals of East Texas oil at 400,000 barrels.

East Texas operators again took recourse to the federal courts to stop proration. The well-known Macmillan case was most decisive. The Macmillans had brought suit to restrain the Commission from applying its orders to their properties in the East Texas field on the ground that its orders were price-fixing and not designed to prevent physical waste. Hearings were held before a three-judge western Texas district court (DuVall West, Joseph C. Hutcheson, Jr., and Randolph Bryant), on June 24, 1931; and a month later a

29 Thompson MS.

318

decision in favor of the Macmillans was handed down. The court declared the Commission's orders had no reasonable relation to physical waste but were based on market demand, and were designed for, and had the effect of, fixing prices and preventing economic waste. This was contrary to a previous state law stating that "waste" was not to be "construed to mean economic waste."[30]

Governor Ross S. Sterling, formerly president of the Humble Oil and Refining Company, who a short time previously had called the legislature into session to strengthen the authority of the Commission, now accepted the court's decision and declared that he would veto any bill carrying a market-demand basis for the Commission's orders.

No doubt Sterling's warning and the court's opinion in the Macmillan case influenced the final passage of a state law on August 12, 1931, prohibiting every conceivable kind of physical waste, but not economic waste. In fact, the Commission was not to prohibit the storage of oil except for the prevention of physical waste.[31]

Conservation had unquestionably received a setback through the court's ruling and the new state law. East Texas oil production was appreciably stepped up in spite of the Railroad Commission's efforts to prevent it. Yet the ground was cleared for a new policy of state control.

Governor W. H. Murray of Oklahoma had also been confronted by overproduction and a market decline and had declared martial law and closed down Oklahoma oil fields. He had demanded one dollar oil. Sterling now decided to pursue a similar policy.

Meanwhile, major companies and independents with considerable lease holdings in East Texas had sought to educate other land- and lease-holders in sound field maintenance principles. They had kept before East Texans the findings of scientists, who urged that excess well completions and overproduction would shorten the life of the field—a condition that would be equally unfortunate for lease and royalty owners.

Formerly East Texans had given very little thought to deple-

[30] Alfred MacMillan *et al. vs.* Railroad Commission of Texas, 41 F. (2d) 400 (W. D. Tex., July 28, 1931).
[31] *General and Special Laws of the State of Texas,* Acts of the Forty-Second Legislature, First called Session, 1931, p. 46; Hardwicke, *loc. cit.,* 231–32.

tion. But when at last they realized that their field was in imminent peril, they turned angrily on outlaw producers, threatening to dynamite their tanks and pipe lines and to set their wells on fire. Indeed, all the evils of an angry community uproar were in East Texas, with threats of rioting and disorder.

On August 15, 1931, Sterling ordered the shutting down of all gas and oil wells in Upshur, Gregg, Rusk, and Smith counties, and sent the National Guard under General Jacob F. Wolters to take charge of the oil field. (The East Texas oil field had hit a production peak of 848,398 barrels of crude oil daily!) Two days later state troops established a large military camp at "Proration Hill," near Kilgore.[32] Wolters had been called away from his duties as chief counsel for The Texas Company to assume command. Immediately, the troops took charge of the field, and Wolters' various orders were issued and published, including General Order No. 4, completely shutting down all crude and gas wells.[33]

Armed troops patrolling the East Texas oil field had a sobering effect on operators flouting the Railroad Commission's orders. Regulations were now enforced. Later, on September 18, the allowable on each East Texas well was only 185 barrels of oil, and on October 13, 165 barrels.[34]

Governor Sterling was both commended and condemned for his resort to martial law; but an overwhelming majority of the letters, telegrams, petitions, and resolutions which soon poured into his office supported his action. In answer to those who criticized his policy, on March 23, 1932, Sterling stated that while martial law was declared primarily to conserve the state's natural resources, State Auditor Moore Lynn had presented him with figures proving that the state had profited to the extent of more than $1,600,000[35] in production taxes.

The governor called attention to another advantage gained by

[32] The Kilgore Chamber of Commerce had invited Adjutant General M. M. Sterling to establish National Guard headquarters at Kilgore. Kilgore Chamber of Commerce, Roy Laird, president, to M. M. Sterling, adjutant general, Austin, Texas, 1931, August 15, P. M. 231, in Martial Law—East Texas, Corres., 1931, No. 370.8, Adjutant General's files.

[33] See Adjutant General's files. Also Beard, op. cit., 64; Harter, op. cit., 110.

[34] Petroleum Development and Technology, 1932, 82.

[35] In file marked "Martial Law—East Texas," No. 370–8, G. O. and S. O., Grand Jury Proceedings, Misc., 1931–32, Adjutant General's Office, Austin, Texas.

military control. Crude oil advanced from twenty-four cents in the week ending August 21, to sixty-seven cents in the week ending March 12, 1932, and to eighty-two cents as an average price in the week ending November 2 and for the remainder of the year. Most of the small operators and royalty owners who earlier objected to any curtailment of drilling or production, now supported proration when they could get more money for less oil and still retain part of their product in the ground.

But irreconcilable operators and opponents of the Commission's orders again appealed to the federal courts. On October 13, 1931, an oil firm sought to restrain the Railroad Commission, the Attorney General, and Wolters from enforcing orders limiting the East Texas field's oil output; and a federal judge issued a temporary restraining order. Thereupon Sterling supplanted the Commission's orders with his own in order to reduce the field's allowable.

Sterling's summary action literally lifted crude-oil prices at the point of the bayonet. A few weeks later, however, this proration gain was offset by a federal court decision in the Constantin case, on December 12, 1932. The three-judge court ruled that martial law could be invoked only when there was actual insurrection or the menacing threat of one, and that neither condition had existed in East Texas in August, 1931.[36]

In view of this decision, Sterling did not continue the use of state troops to enforce the Commission's orders, but he maintained them in the field to act as ordinary peace officers. Nevertheless, rebellious operators continued to ignore proration regulations.

Pat M. Neff resigned from the Railroad Commission in the spring of 1932, and Governor Sterling appointed Ernest O. Thompson to take his place. Thompson now became and remained a conspicuous champion for conservation.

In June, 1932, the East Texas field's daily allowable was fixed at 325,000 barrels of oil. Yet "hot-oil" operators ran daily an excess of 100,000 to 350,000 barrels, and oil thieves added to illegal consumption. It was alleged that a large amount of oil was stolen from five Gladewater townsite wells, one of which was the property of the First Baptist Church. These thefts brought 213 indictments

[36] Sterling vs. Constantin, 287, U. S., 378.

against eighteen men, but actual proof was difficult and convictions were few.[37]

Much "hot oil" was secretly run to small topping and skimming plants, even though there were five or six better refineries in the field. The state collected no gasoline tax on this oil, for the outlaw plants kept no records. Criminals openly defied the law. Every kind of subterfuge was employed—"hot-oil" running, "forged tenders and telegrams, tenders obtained illegally on truck loads of water, perforated and gateless valves, and lockstops that flowed when apparently closed, and secret pipe lines and bypasses."

Frequently, Railroad Commission officials were turned away from refineries and installations with shotguns and threats of violence. In one instance, a state gauger found that a steel stairway had been cut down from a storage tank so that he could not measure its contents; and in another, an investigator located a switch controlling a "hot-oil" pipe line, hidden behind a bathtub in an operator's home.

Such subterfuge made extremely difficult the Commission's work of controlling the East Texas oil field. And the field's vast expanse, covered by many thousands of wells, pipe lines, refineries, and other installations, only added to its burdens.

To correct these and other overproduction evils, on November 12, the legislature at last approved a Market Demand Law, a second hinge, according to Thompson, upon which Texas conservation was to swing. This law enabled the Railroad Commission to prorate production in keeping with the market demand and thus maintain a reasonable price level. In months to follow, the Commission used its power under this law to weld a strong proration policy.

Federal agents helped the Commission's field men. In September, 1933, to enforce the "Code of Fair Competition for the Petroleum Industry," they established their headquarters at Tyler, Texas. For a time there was little change. Reliable figures for the closing months of this year showed that "hot-oil" operators were still running from sixty to seventy thousand barrels of illegal oil. Nor did the federal court's "Panama case" decision help matters. By it, federal investigators were denied access to complainant refineries or their records.

[37] *Petroleum Reporter,* Vol. IV, No. 3 (June, 1932), 5.

Fabulous East Texas

Texas countered with a new legislative enactment giving ample inspecting powers to the Railroad Commission and strengthening the Attorney General's authority to prosecute violators of the Commission's orders. Likewise, federal authorities were given the right to inspect refineries when the federal Congress imposed a tax on all oil produced in the United States.

The Texas legislature further helped the Railroad Commission. In February, 1934, it enacted House Bill No. 99, a refinery control bill, requiring all state refineries to report the source of oil which they processed. At the time of this enactment there were sixty refineries in East Texas, only four of which, it was said, submitted the reports required by the Railroad Commission. It was also charged that they were processing daily approximately 60,000 barrels of oil while the Commission's allowable for the wells supplying them was but 18,000 barrels.[38] East Texas refiners bitterly opposed House Bill 99 and staged a demonstration at Austin to influence Governor Miriam Ferguson against signing it, but in this they failed.

These refiners complained that they could not compete with the major companies in obtaining crude oil. But after the enactment of House Bill 99, the majors offered to allocate 5 per cent of their own East Texas output to them. Reluctantly, the independents accepted the offer. Some of them, however, closed down. Where formerly they had paid a "hot-oil" rate, now they could compete neither with the regular price nor with their competitors' better quality product.

Finally, too, the Railroad Commission was upheld by a three-judge federal-court ruling, on May 26, 1933. In April the Commission had based its proration order on a well's potential, to be determined by key wells. The court decision upheld this order, and injunction suits were no longer common.

Moreover, beginning with the Commission's order of April 22, 1933, the East Texas field's allowable was fixed relatively high. That between May 1 and December 1, including new wells, was approximately 700,000 barrels a day.

After this, "hot-oil" runners were less active, particularly since now they could be prosecuted under the N.I.R.A. and the Petroleum Code. Moreover, a new state law became effective on September

[38] Harter, *op. cit.*, 129.

1, 1933, making it a felony to by-pass or produce oil in violation of the Railroad Commission's orders. The Railroad Commission's "State Tender Board" began passing on crude-oil tenders on June 27, 1934.[39] Then six months later, on December 25, the legislature presented the Commission with a real Christmas gift, a law to stop the shipment of illegally produced crude oil and its products.

A "Federal Tender Board" also held its first hearing at Kilgore on October 25, 1934, under authority of Subsection 9(c) of the N.I.R.A.; but the United States Supreme Court declared N.I.R.A. unconstitutional on January 7, 1935. Fifteen days later, however, the Connally "Hot Oil" Act made possible a new Federal Tender Board, which began its work on March 1 of the next year.

On June 20, 1935, L. C. E. Bignell wrote that there were yet seventy-nine refineries in the East Texas oil field but that a number were shut down because of a lack of cheap oil. He believed that this was evidence of the effectiveness of state and federal control; that federal and state officials were checking daily tank-car and truck movements; and that 98 per cent of all oil produced passed the inspection of their tender boards.[40]

By 1935, East Texas had 17,650 wells spaced over 120,000 acres, of which more than 700 wells were within the Kilgore townsite, several being found on a single lot in some instances. Experts variously estimated that from $100,000,000, to $150,000,000[41] had been thrown away in this mad grab for riches, for competent oilmen believed that half as many wells could have drained the field properly.[42]

Early East Texas drilling had taught oilmen an important lesson. Water contact was made 3,320 feet below sea level and Mexia experience had shown that minimum penetration of the oil formation was best. In the East Texas field the thickness of the sand ranged from a few inches to two or three feet along the east edge of the

[39] C. A. Warner, *Texas Oil and Gas Since 1543*, 176.

[40] "East Texas Oil Field Insured of Long Life By Good Engineering," in *Oil and Gas Journal*, Vol. XXXIV, No. 5 (June 20, 1935), 11.

[41] The Tyler *Courier Times* of April 15, 1938, p. 6, estimated the total drilling cost at $293,000,000.

[42] Kenneth Culp Davis and York Y. Wilburn, "Administrative Control of Oil Production in Texas," in *Texas Law Review*, Vol. XXII, No. 2 (February, 1944), 154–55.

field to an average of forty feet in the fairway, or the field's richest part. In either case too deep a penetration encountered water. Still, in 1935, between forty and fifty wells that had produced water upon being drilled in had also produced in excess of 50,000 barrels of oil.

Engineers and geologists soon discovered that, in part, water drive was the source of energy moving the oil to the wells. And as reckless drilling and overproduction went unrestrained, there was not only a perceptible lessening of the reservoir's energy but also a rapid water encroachment from the west, flooding many of the edge wells.

From March 10 to July 12, 1933, while East Texas was producing at the rate of 900,000 barrels daily, the field's pressure dropped from 1,370 pounds per square inch to 1,220 pounds, or approximately 1.2 pounds a day. This rate of depletion would have brought the field to 1,000 pounds (the artificial lift stage) by January, 1934. But the Commission ordered occasional temporary shutdowns, lowered the field's allowable, and regulated the recycling of water, so that by January, 1939, the pressure was still 1,107 pounds per square inch. Yet the field had produced 1,400,000,000 barrels of oil and 19,600 of the field's 25,600 wells were still flowing.[43]

Drilling presently extended beyond the limits of the main East Texas field. By 1935 this wildcat movement meant the completion of 205 wells, most of which were dry. Among these were the Gulf Production Company's No. 1 Royal-Davey well in the Camp Hill field, in Anderson County, Texas; and the Tidewater-Seaboard No. A-21 well in this area. Both made considerable gas and distillate. Then Peveto *et al.* drilled the discovery well at Talco, in the northwestern part of Titus County. This well pumped 552 barrels of oil on a twenty-four hour gauge. Three other wells were also completed as test wells, thus proving another field.[44]

Fabulous East Texas continued to maintain its dizzy rate of development. A break in the crude-oil market during the first eight months of 1933 slowed down well completions to only 934; but one-dollar oil during this year's last four months increased it to 1,342

[43] Ernest O. Thompson, MS, "An Administrator's View on Proration."
[44] *Bulletin of the American Association of Petroleum Geologists*, Vol. XX (January–December, 1936), Part II, 975–79.

wells, with a year's total of 11,891 wells. With the maintenance of fair prices, 3,616 new wells were drilled in 1934 and 4,000 during the next year. From its discovery in the fall of 1930 up to 1944, East Texas had produced 2,104,173,790 barrels of crude oil, twice as much as any other field in the history of the United States.

XXIII

Finding New Horizons

IN OIL PROSPECTING the last two decades have been characterized by the discovery of deep oil horizons, horizons which disclosed different subsurface patterns that were beyond the reach of Southwestern pioneer drillers with their primitive equipment. Modern science has unlocked these subterranean treasure chambers.

The early twentieth-century oilman could hardly conceive of the radical methods soon to transform Southwestern oil operations. For example, the airplane enabled geologists to make aerial maps revealing structural faults and details not apparent from ground surveys. Science evolved new prospector gadgets—the torsion balance and gravimeter to measure gravitational attraction, the seismograph to gauge the depth to the reflecting beds, and the magnetometer to register sensitive pencilings of the direction and intensity of the earth's magnetic field. These instruments now used to find deep oil zones represent a decided advance in prospecting— a long distance from the early twentieth-century soothsayer's predictions, the divining rod, and the ouija board.

Engineers and manufacturers improved the rotary rigs and techniques necessary for deep exploration, far beyond the reach of early-day drilling practices. Rotary derricks of better steel were built higher and sturdier than those used by early Gulf Coast drillers, with drill pipe of greater tensile strength. By the nineteen thirties drillers were using a 122-foot steel derrick, twenty-four feet square at its base and about five feet at the top. Designers made better drill bits—the fish-tail, with hard surfacing, the cone and roller, to meet all kinds of drilling conditions and for all sizes of holes, and several other patented kinds—all to drill deep, straight

327

rotary holes economically. Mud fluids, with heavy barite and hematite compounds, weighing as much as 135 pounds per cubic foot, enabled the rotary driller to hold back a high pressure in the hole and to prevent blowouts and the premature coming-in of the well. All these and other revolutionary innovations of the last two decades have made profitable the oilman's search for deep horizons.

In 1930, Southwestern oil wells had an average depth of 3,000 feet; in 1940, of 3,900 feet; and in 1945, of 4,300 feet. Deep drilling for hidden oil traps had become the order of the day.

The discovery and early development of the reasonably shallow East Texas field, with all its major predecessors, rounded out the broad base upon which the Southwestern oil industry is to grow during the present decade. By the nineteen forties great shallow fields had risen and declined—Glenn Pool, Cushing, and Healdton in Oklahoma; Electra, Burkburnett, Ranger, and Mexia in Texas; Jennings and Caddo in Louisiana; Eldorado and Augusta in Kansas; and El Dorado and Smackover in Arkansas. Each in its day had been the mecca of Southwestern oilmen, but now each had become a stripper field, a reminder to the industry of unscientific early-day operations.

The discovery of fabulous East Texas had added a third giant producing area[1] to Texas' oil lands (although it is in one field), but by no means the last major field. Formerly, as one great field had declined in production and the Eastern press and official Washington reports had "viewed with alarm" an approaching oil shortage, another great field had been discovered. One who scans daily newspaper pages of the last four decades will become impressed with these recurrent pessimistic forecasts, forecasts that are strikingly similar to those of today. But just as often they have been discredited by new discoveries of rich fields.

A steadily rising oil market, from $0.97 per barrel in 1935 to $1.22 in 1945 stimulated intensive operations. All oils were in demand—fuel oil, motor fuel, distillate fuel oil, residual fuel oil, kerosene, and lubricants. Both dealers and consumers had overstocked by 1939 to meet an anticipated war demand, and during the early nineteen forties a rapidly increasing domestic need more than offset this overstock.

[1] The other two were the Panhandle and West Texas (or the Permian Basin).

Finding New Horizons

After the discovery of the East Texas oil field, wildcatters carried deep drilling to every nook and corner of the vast Southwest at enormous cost, as evidenced by the increasing number of dry holes. Yet there were also oil discoveries, too many of them to follow field by field in a study of this scope. But, in contrast to the early-day unskilled prospectors for oil, a majority of those who now went out were highly trained geologists, geophysicists, and engineers.

Texas, which produced 45 per cent of the nation's petroleum in 1945, furnishes convincing proof of the rapid rise of the Southwestern oil industry. By 1947 this state was producing 2,200,000 barrels of oil daily. In 1930, its production was 290,457,000 barrels of oil; in 1940, it had increased its output 100 per cent; and within the next four years, 50 per cent more. In 1945 there was drilling, land under lease, or other oil activity in every Texas county; and production, either gas or oil, was found in 174 of the 254 counties.

The Gulf Coast was the second oldest oil-producing district of Texas. By 1940 it had reached an annual output of 122,000,000 barrels of petroleum, having more than doubled its production within five years, and production climbed to 253,000,000 barrels within the next five years.[2] Humble (through 1946) became the greatest salt-dome field, having a cumulative production of 130,753,923 barrels of crude oil as compared with 128,215,936 for Spindletop. Such formerly great fields as Batson, Goose Creek, Sour Lake, and Spindletop were now fully developed and less productive, so that new fields were primarily responsible for upholding the state's oil production. Conroe, situated in Montgomery County, was its latest major field.

Conroe was discovered on December 13, 1931, when George Strake's No. 1 South Texas Development Company well, six and one-half miles southeast of the town of Conroe, came in for an initial daily 15,000,000 cubic feet of gas and some distillate. For several months geologists and operators doubted that this discovery was of great importance. Not until the drilling of Strake's second well, a 900-barrel producer, and the Heep Oil Corporation *et al.'s* No. 1 Freeman, both important, did they realize that Conroe had great possibilities. Then majors and independents alike rushed in to claim their share of a rich harvest. By the end of 1938, Conroe had

[2] Bureau of Mines, *Minerals Yearbook Review of 1940,* 966.

produced 77,063,000 barrels of crude oil, although its output fell to about 9,200,000 barrels in the next year.

Each major oil discovery intensified exploration, and men with the seismograph and torsion balance sought out every likely structure. Fifty-seven oil, gas, and distillate fields in the Gulf Coast district represented the prospectors' harvest from the date of the Conroe discovery until 1938. Six of these fields were found in 1932, four in 1933, seven in 1934, eight in 1935, eighteen in 1936, and sixteen in 1937. Their ascending scale indicates the gathering momentum of geophysical exploration.

Three of these fields, Old Ocean, Hastings, and Anahuac, were later listed among the nation's leading oil fields. Old Ocean, in Brazoria County, was found on November 8, 1934, by the Harrison and Abercrombie and Atlatl Royalty Corporation No. 1 Bernard River Development Company well, which made 500 barrels of oil a day at 8,651 feet. But drillers with bigger rigs and better equipment than those who labored at early-day Spindletop or Sour Lake sought deeper pay sands; and in later years seven additional oil zones, from 9,800 to 10,600 feet, were found.

The Hastings field, in Brazoria and Galveston counties, was discovered on December 23 of the same year and within three years was developed by more than 450 wells. The Anahuac field, in Chambers County, was found on March 16, 1935, when the Humble Oil and Refining Company's No. 1 Middleton well struck the pay sand. Development started slowly but grew steadily, and by January 1, 1938, the field's cumulative production was more than 7,000,000 barrels of crude oil.

In most districts there were occasional recessions. The close of the decade of the thirties showed a slight decrease in production for South Texas, a district that had come up fast in oil output in the preceding ten years. Its total production for 1939 was 55,105,506 barrels. This oil-producing region was large, a total of 168 fields in Webb, Nueces, Jim Wells, Brooks, Jim Hogg, Starr, Duval, Cleburg, Zapata, McMullen, Willacy, San Patricio, and Hidalgo counties. By 1940 these fields had a composite cumulative production of more than 270,000,000 barrels of petroleum.[3]

[3] Petroleum Division, A.I.M.E., *Petroleum Development and Technology, 1940,* 458, 461–76.

Finding New Horizons

Routine drilling in South Texas had also declined, but a number of new discoveries kept oilmen's interest high; and leasing and royalty trading were widespread. The chief oil activity was along the Frio-Vicksburg trend in Jim Wells, Brooks, Hidalgo, and Starr counties and the Cockfield zone in Duval County. Among this region's new fields were Reynolds and Ben Bolt in Jim Wells County, and Chiltipin, Muralla, Sejita, and Southland in Duval County. In the nineteen forties this area steadily developed, going from an output of 32,018,000 barrels of crude oil in 1941 to 48,477,000 in 1945.

Back across the state, in North Texas, operators had a successful year (1939), with a 40,000,000-barrel output, 3,000,000 barrels more than in the preceding year. And in 1940 the total rose 371,000 barrels more. This sent prospectors and wildcatters out from such towns as Wichita Falls, Abilene, and Fort Worth in search of new fields, independents vying with major company scouts for a chance at hidden wealth. K.M.A (Kemp-Munger-Allen) had reached its peak; but a new field, the Hull-Silk, a 1938 discovery, made up for K-M-A's decline.[4] Clay, Cooke, and Montague counties led in this area's discoveries for 1939. New fields for 1940 were the Bonita and Ringgold fields in Montague County and the Fargo field in Wilbarger County. In 1945, North Texas produced 12,764,000 barrels of crude oil.

North Central Texas had no new Ranger, Breckenridge, or Desdemona. This region's production had so declined that statisticians listed it with North Texas. Yet there was prospecting along its western border. Some drilling was on the Palo Pinto trend in Jones and Shackleford counties, and the Griffin and Guitar pools in Jones County were active. Also in Jones County, a deeper horizon, the Hope, proved productive.

Farther west, the Permian Basin has recently claimed Texas primacy, producing 564,300 barrels daily in 1947. Even the late nineteen thirties and early nineteen forties found this area alive

[4] In 1939 John F. O'Donohoe, then president of the North Texas Oil and Gas Association, led in the organization of the K-M-A Pressure Maintenance Association to inaugurate a retarded recovery program and gas reinjection at the K-M-A field. Eighty operators entered the agreement. The first results of pressure maintenance were satisfactory. Ultimate oil recovery promises to be considerable.—*Oil Weekly,* Vol. CV, No. 5 (April 6, 1942), 22.

with activity. On every main highway one met men wearing tin hats and oil-stained clothes, some in automobiles, some in trucks loaded with casing or oil-field equipment, and others attached to seismograph crews. Within a few years after the discovery of oil fields here and there, new towns, refineries, pumping stations, and other installations had sprung up like magic on the prairies. They were the by-products of a new regional economy.

During 1938 and 1939 alone, 3,895 Permian Basin wells were completed, with the ratio of dry holes to producing wells running about 1 to 9. In 1938, Ector County led in drilling, with 622 new oil wells, and 485 additional ones in 1939; operations also slowed down in Howard and Winkler counties in the same year. The largest gain in 1939 was in Yoakum County, where 350 oil wells were completed in the Denver-Wasson area. The Basin's oil output in this year made a new record of 79,493,000 barrels, an 8,000,000-barrel increase over the previous year. From 1941 to 1945, West Texas gradually stepped up its crude-oil production, from 92,907,000 to 175,727,000 barrels.

The Panhandle produced one-third as much oil as the Permian Basin in 1939, with an increase a little short of 1,000,000 barrels over 1938. In addition, from 1941 to 1945 the Panhandle counties increased their production from 27,831,000 to 31,726,000 barrels. But Panhandle's wealth was more varied. In 1939 pipe lines, natural-gasoline plants, and carbon-black industries put to commercial use 815,305,931,000 cubic feet of gas. Forty-two natural-gasoline plants extracted more than 295,000,000 gallons of natural gasoline, and thirty-one carbon-black plants, 420,000,000 pounds of carbon black.[5] In addition, there were many billions of cubic feet of gas yet vented to the air.

Within the eastern Texas oil-producing region in 1939 there were forty-seven oil and gas fields, the ranking fields being East Texas, Talco, and Rodessa (the Texas portion). East Texas produced approximately 140,000,000 barrels of crude oil, and the other two fields 20,000,000 more in 1939. The East Texas oil field showed little variation in its oil production during the nineteen forties, having an oil output of 132,486,000 barrels in 1941 and 131,315,000 in

[5] *Petroleum Development and Technology, 1940,* 455.

1945. Under rigid curtailment, in 1940 it produced 141,023,000 barrels of crude oil in comparison with 144,615,000 barrels in 1939.

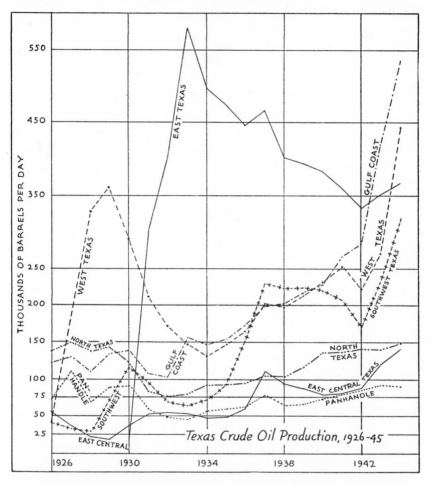

Texas Crude Oil Production, 1926-45

The Hawkins oil field in southeastern Wood County, about seventeen miles southeast of Tyler, had been mapped during 1930 by E. A. Wendlandt of the Humble Oil and Refining Company. During the early part of 1935 this company moved a core-drill unit into the area and made seven tests to the Navarro group, thus proving the structure. Then the lease block was materially enlarged, and drilling was started. Prior to the beginning of the Humble well, Bobby Manziel, an independent operator, had drilled the discovery well, his No. 1 Frank Morrison, on the northwest flank of the Hawkins structure, on December 20, 1940. This well pumped 124 barrels of eighteen-degree gravity black oil and 290 barrels of salt water in twenty-four hours, from the Woodbine sand at 4,963 feet. The field was developed rapidly. By 1941, 243 oil wells and 9 dry holes had been drilled, with a cumulative production at the end of the year of almost 1,500,000 barrels of crude oil.[6]

Kansas was thought to have reached its peak of oil production in 1918, during the heyday of Augusta and Eldorado. But the same movement of wildcatting, new field discoveries, and intensive development during the nineteen thirties that had swept other parts of the Southwest gave the state new prosperity. The closing year of this decade brought it an oil output of more than 60,703,000 barrels from 19,669 wells, an increase of more than 15,000,000 barrels over the previous peak year, 1918.

Although in 1939 there were fewer Kansas oil wells completed than in 1938, the potential production of these wells was 1,500,000 barrels, an increase of more than 200,000 barrels over the output of the 1938 completions. New pools included Van Patton, in Norton County; Bow Creek, in Phillips County; Pospishel and Kruckenberg, in western Barton County; Darien and Hittle, in Cowley County; and Barnholdt, in Rice and McPherson counties.[7]

But Kansas' limit in oil output was not yet reached. In 1941 it gained the high place of 83,000,000 barrels from 21,838 wells, an increase of nearly 18,000,000 barrels over 1940 production. Then in 1944 it reached its all-time peak of 106,178,000 barrels of crude oil. In 1941 new fields had brought back the boom days of Augusta and Eldorado. The Trapp field in Russell and Barton counties stood at the head of the list, with a yield of 7,500,000 barrels of oil; Silica, of Rice and Barton counties, ranked second with 7,000,000 barrels; and the Bemis-Shutts pool, in Ellis County, third with 4,800,000 barrels. Two other fields, Burnett in Ellis County, and Zenith, in

[6] E. A. Wendlandt, T. H. Shelby, Jr., and John S. Bell, "Hawkins Field, Wood County, Texas," in *Bulletin of the American Association of Petroleum Geologists,* Vol. XXX, No. 11 (November, 1946), 1831–33.

[7] Edward A. Koester and Robert F. Meyer, "Development in North Mid-Continent in 1939," *ibid.,* Vol. XXIV, No. 6 (June, 1940), 995, 997–1003; W. A. Ver Wiebe, "Kansas Oil and Gas during 1939," in *Petroleum Development and Technology, 1940,* 290–91.

Stafford County, were also important. Developments in central and western Kansas had carried this state to its new oil-production peak. In western Kansas alone, more than 1,600 test wells were drilled, 1,186 of which were oil producers, 34 gas, and 415 dry holes.[8]

South of Kansas, both prospectors and operators restudied Oklahoma. Oklahoma's record for 1939 showed declining production bolstered by strenuous efforts to find new oil fields or new horizons in old fields. The daily average oil output had receded more than 20 per cent in two years. Drilling activity had increased slightly, with 1,921 well completions. Of these, 1,097 were oil wells with a potential of 408,000 barrels, 162 were gas wells with an initial flow of 688,000,000 cubic feet of gas, and 662 were dry holes.

A program of working over old fields yielded some good results. In the Oklahoma City field there was considerable reconditioning and plugging back to shallower oil and gas horizons. Fourteen oil wells with an initial average of 490 barrels of crude oil and one well with 1,200,000 cubic feet of gas were the fruits of this activity. Also in the Milroy and Fox pools, wells were plugged back from the Ordovician to the Hunton horizons with profit; and several small producing areas were opened in the Greater Seminole section.

A summary of drilling operations in Oklahoma during 1939 shows that forty-four wildcat wells were drilled in half as many counties. The Ramsey field, in Payne County, held first place, with 140,000 barrels of oil from twenty successful completions, although since its discovery on January 12, 1938, this field had a sharp drop in output. A Greater Seminole field, St. Louis, in Pottawatomie County, also came up with a surprising 11,302,000 barrels of oil, only 305,000 short of its peak production in 1930. Cement, in Caddo County, was also a good producer, with forty-four wells averaging an initial 1,250 barrels of oil daily. Billings, in Noble County, also improved, having three wells with a combined yield of 7,878 barrels of crude oil from the Wilcox sand.

Since the flush production days of El Dorado and Smackover, Arkansas had experienced a period of declining oil yield. Particularly during the first seven years of the nineteen thirties Arkansas seemed to have had its best days. At Schuler, Union County, on

[8] Walter A. Ver Wiebe, "Exploration for Oil and Gas in Western Kansas during 1941," in State Geological Survey of Kansas *Bull. No. 42*, 8 ff.

Oil! Titan of the Southwest

March 18, 1937, the Phillips Petroleum Company and the Lion Oil Refining Company opened an oil pool in lenticular sands at better than 5,500 feet. But this pool was small, and only fourteen wells were completed in it during 1937. This sand (Morgan) proved to be productive in an area of about 640 acres. But the gas from the sands was soon dissipated, and the wells declined rapidly in output.

Then came a change. In September, 1937, the E. M. Jones Marine Oil Company No. 1 fee well, a 1,500-barrel producer at 7,615 feet in the Jones sand, opened a new Schuler oil horizon. By January 1, 1942, Schuler had expanded into a 4,000-acre field, was unitized, and had 146 wells. Unitization was highly successful. The decline in its reservoir pressure was arrested and the recovery of oil from the Jones sand greatly increased. A second important discovery was made at Schuler when on October 22, 1937, the Lion Oil and Refining Company and Phillips Petroleum Company's No. 1-A Morgan well struck the deep Reynolds oil zone at 7,683 feet for an initial daily production of 720 barrels of condensate. By June 1, 1939, this second zone's productive area had been defined by fifteen producing wells and approximately 1,000 acres.

Prospecting in southwestern Arkansas continued throughout 1937, and the Buckner field, near the town of Buckner, Columbia County, was discovered on November 30, 1937, by the Standard Oil Company of Louisiana's No. 1 McKean well at 7,309 feet. The well was plugged back from a salt-water zone at 7,280 feet to 7,258 feet, where it was completed as a 122-barrel-an-hour oil well.

Then the Kerr-Lynn Oil Company's No. 1-A J. M. Barnett well (later purchased by the Atlantic Refining Company) opened the Magnolia field,[9] on March 5, 1938, when it tapped the oolitic zone of the Smackover limestone at 7,740 feet for 302 barrels of oil. By January 1, 1943, the Magnolia field, with 116 wells drilled on approximately 4,600 acres, was the largest Arkansas producing petroleum reservoir in the Smackover limestone.

Other 1938 deep-zone discoveries in southwestern Arkansas were the two Columbia County fields of Village (May 20) and

[9] "Report of Investigations, Magnolia Oil Field, Columbia County, Arkansas," R. I. 3720, mimeographed (co-operative report prepared by the Bureau of Mines, United States Department of the Interior, and the Arkansas Oil and Gas Commission, September, 1943), 12.

General view of Cement, Oklahoma, a town that has
had four oil booms in its history

photograph by Corsini
Standard Oil Company (N. J.)

Abandoned farmhouse and oil-well derricks, West
Edmond, Oklahoma

photograph by Corsini
Standard Oil Company (N. J.)

Wrapping the Big Inch

Laying the Big Inch

Finding New Horizons

Atlanta (December 8), both from the oolitic zone of the Smackover limestone; and in 1939 another field, Lewisville (April 25) was found in Columbia County, producing from the Smackover level. During 1940 there were other fields—Nick Springs, Union County; Fouke, Miller County; and McKamie, Lafayette County.[10]

Arkansas had its peak production of 77,398,000 barrels of crude oil in 1925. In 1936 it produced only 10,469,000 barrels; but in 1947 it recovered a part of its lost ground with an annual 29,609,000 barrels.[11]

Geophysical prospecting made possible these deep-zone fields. During 1939 there were twenty seismograph, three gravimeter, one magnetometer, one soil-analysis and one electromagnetic crews at work in Arkansas. As a result, twelve wildcat tests were drilled to the Smackover limestone, of which two found production, opening the Big Creek and Dorcheat fields in Columbia County.[12] The Standard Oil Company of Louisiana completed its No. 1 Petty Stave Lumber Company well in the former field, on December 23, 1939, as a distillate well at 7,999 feet; and the Dorcheat field was opened by the Atlantic Refining Company's No. 1 Pine Woods Lumber Company well on September 2, 1939.[13]

In the same year the oil production from the Gulf Coast and the northern district combined to give Louisiana 93,646,000 barrels of crude oil. North Louisiana had 278 oil-well completions, 83 gas wells, and 160 dry holes from its drilling activity; while the Gulf Coast had 42 oil wells and 6 dry holes. In northern Louisiana, the important production increases were in the Cotton Valley and Shreveport fields, with Homer, Sligo, and Zwolle making light

[10] For excellent historical summaries of each of these fields see George H. Fancher and Donald K. MacKay, *Secondary Recovery of Petroleum in Arkansas—A Survey* (report to the 56 General Assembly of the state of Arkansas under the auspices of the Arkansas Oil and Gas Commission), 27 ff. See also "Report of Investigations. Survey of Crude Oil of the Producing Fields of Arkansas," R. I. 3486, January, 1940, mimeographed (co-operative report prepared by the Bureau of Mines, United States Department of the Interior, and the Arkansas Geological Survey), 11–12.

[11] Figures supplied the author by Mr. Warren Baker, editor of *World Oil*, June 14, 1948.

[12] Warren B. Weeks and John Purzer, "Developments in Southern Arkansas and Northern Louisiana during 1939," in *Bulletin of the American Association of Petroleum Geologists*, Vol. XXIV, No. 6 (June, 1940), 1093.

[13] Warren B. Weeks, "Oil and Gas in South Arkansas in 1939," in *Petroleum Development and Technology, 1940*, 243–47; Arkansas Oil and Gas Commission, *Midyear 1940 Survey of the Oil and Gas Industry in Arkansas*, 57 ff.

gains, and with the greatest decreases occurring in the Lisbon and Rodessa fields.

Prospecting crews sought for oil in every part of southern Louisiana, even penetrating the cypress forests and swamplands, trudging through steamy jungles and enduring mosquito attacks. Here the most important new discoveries were the Eola field, Avoyelles Parish, and the Paradis field, St. Charles Parish. The former went on production in January, 1939. Sid Richardson, of Fort Worth, Texas, drilled Eola's first well on the Hass Investment Company's property and hit the pay sand a little below 8,500 feet. Within the year the field had forty-two commercial producers and six dry holes. The Texas Company–Louisiana Land and Exploration Company's No. 1 Paradis well, in St. Charles Parish, just west of New Orleans, also found production in a thick sand. Other discoveries were the Chalkley field (1938) and Grand Lake (1939), in the Cameron Parish, but only Chalkley later proved to be a large producer.

Yet Louisiana's oil output was considerable. In the biennium of 1938–39, its crude-oil output was 188,065,393 barrels; and in the biennium of 1940–41, it increased about 15 per cent[14] with thirty-eight counties listed in the producing column in 1940. In 1947, Louisiana reached a peak production of 159,276,000 barrels of crude oil.

New Mexico was the newest Southwestern oil state. Its 1940 oil yield came almost wholly from the Permian Basin, of which West Texas was the larger part. For several years it had been the sixth ranking state in production, then was surpassed by Illinois, and in 1939 ranked seventh. During 1939 six new fields were discovered: three in Lea County, two in Eddy County, and one in Chaves County. In this year more than 2,700,000 barrels of crude oil were produced in Eddy and 33,600,000 barrels in Lea County, with an inconsiderable production in northwestern New Mexico. Six hundred and fifty-nine wells were drilled in the state, of which 565 were oil wells, 15 gas, 6 carbon-dioxide–gas wells, and 73 dry holes.[15] New Mexico's peak oil production came in 1947 when it reached 40,-971,000 barrels.

[14] *Fifteenth Biennial Report, Department of Conservation, State of Louisiana, 1940–1941*, 205–206.

[15] A. Andreas, "Oil and Gas Development in New Mexico in 1939," in *Petroleum Technology, 1940*, 342–46.

Finding New Horizons

The American petroleum industry entered the 1940 decade handicapped by a world war, which brought a material decline in exports. The loss of European markets, the strict rationing of oil products throughout most of the world outside the Western Hemisphere, and the availability of Asian and South American oil to Great Britain and her allies posed a difficult overproduction problem for American operators.

But before a solution could be found, swift-moving events brought the answer. On December 7, 1941, the Japanese made a sneak attack on Pearl Harbor and the United States found herself at war. Immediately, the nation's oil became strategic material of extraordinary significance, and every effort was made to keep production and supply at a high level.

Upon the outbreak of war, the United States' oil industry had an impressive record. It had reached a peak production of 1,595,000,-000 barrels of crude; and it employed over 1,000,000 workers, to whom it paid annually approximately $1,500,000,000, and it paid to the state and the nation another $1,350,000,000 in taxes. But this was not enough. The federal government asked for greater accomplishments; and under the impetus of war, the oil industry swept forward to spectacular gains, as will be seen later in this volume.

On the eve of conflict, the Southwestern states (Arkansas, Louisiana, Kansas, Oklahoma, New Mexico, and Texas) were fully prepared to assume their burden of production; they yielded the major share of the nation's oil, or 925,320,000 barrels of its 1,595,-000,000 barrels of crude oil.[16]

Texas alone produced 1,343,350 barrels of crude oil daily. During the early war years, Conroe, Hastings, Saxet, Seeligson, and Withers-Magnet, along the Gulf Coast, had good records. Wasson, Slaughter-Dean, and Yates fields of West Texas were also good producers; and in eastern Texas, the East Texas, Talco, and Hawkins fields kept up production.

Proportionately, the other five states kept stride with Texas. Kansas reached its all-time high oil output in 1941 with 83,000,000 barrels of crude oil; and once sluggish Arkansas yielded a respectable 26,327,000 barrels, with a noticeable output from its new Midway field in Lafayette County. Louisiana was more productive, with

[16] Bureau of Mines, *Minerals Yearbook, 1942,* 1036.

Oil! Titan of the Southwest

115,908,000 barrels of oil. In its Gulf Coast area, Ville Platte maintained first place, and the Chalkley field in Cameron Parish and the Paradis field in St. Charles Parish showed to good advantage. Ville Platte's twenty-seven completed wells had an average initial daily production of 417 barrels. Haynesville, Olla, Little Creek, and Nebo, in northern Louisiana, substantially raised this area's oil output.

In 1941, New Mexico had reached a crude-oil production of 39,-660,000 barrels. The Monument field held first place, with neighboring Eunice second, although the two fields are separate only in a technical sense and the entire area is actually the Monument-Eunice field. By 1942 the greatest drilling activity was in the Square Lake pool of Eddy County, with ninety-two completed wells averaging daily 179 barrels of oil.

Oklahoma's 1941 production was 154,702,000 barrels of crude. Such major producing areas as Oklahoma City, Greater Seminole, and the Osage country were declining; but new production elsewhere, as in Pottawatomie County, at Apache in Caddo County, the Pauls Valley field, the Watchorn field in Pawnee County, and the Ardmore field in Carter County, kept this state's oil yield high.

Throughout the war years, 1941 to 1945, this pattern of proportional oil production with only minor fluctuations was maintained by these six Southwestern states. (There was one notable exception: in 1943, Kansas oil production soared to 106,178,000 barrels.) Each year the demands of our armed forces called for more crude-oil products than in the preceding year, and just as often the oil industry put forth extra effort to meet the demand, strained and tested as never before in history. For example, early in 1945 the nation's oil production started with a daily 4,700,000 barrels, then climbed until it reached a high of nearly 5,000,000 barrels in August, decreased after V-J Day, on September 2, and finally seemed to reach a reconversion plateau of about 4,500,000 barrels by the end of the year.

Throughout the hectic war years, Texas continued its gigantic output, producing almost twice as much oil as second place California. But its 1945 net increase of 7,000,000 barrels of crude over 1944 was not evenly distributed. West Texas and the lower Gulf Coast increased their crude-oil output by 13,000,000 barrels and

Finding New Horizons

7,000,000 barrels respectively; while East Texas, the upper Gulf Coast, the Panhandle, and South Texas decreased.

The discovery and development of the West Edmond field was the most significant event in Oklahoma's oil history during the war years. Ace Gutowsky initiated early development in this field. He claimed that the West Edmond structure had been made known by "doodle-bug" exploration. When he was convinced that it had a favorable oil structure, he acquired considerable acreage[17] west of the Oklahoma City, Britton, and Edmond fields. Here he proposed to test his belief.

Oil-company land men and independent promoters would not support Gutowsky's proposal to drill a test well, although he actively sought their help; neither could he secure sufficient geological or geophysical data to sell enough of his acreage to finance his own well. Fortunately, however, he enlisted the aid of B. D. Bourland of San Antonio, who helped him to gain the support of the Fox brothers and Herbert Schmitz of Chicago. The new associates agreed to drill a well to 7,350 feet, at which depth Gutowsky expected to reach the Wilcox sand.

Thus it was that the No. 1 Wagner[18] was spudded in on January 2, 1943; and on the following April 28, Gutowsky confounded his critics and amply justified his course, for at approximately 6,950 feet the rotary bit struck the rich Hunton zone. In a twenty-four-hour period the well flowed through a 9/32-inch choke 522 barrels of 41-degree gravity oil. Oil then streamed by natural flow through a perforated liner.

In its annual report of 1943, the Bureau of Mines listed West Edmond as a field under active development, with eleven large wells producing from the Hunton limestone at a depth of almost 7,000 feet. And in the next year, it reported that Oklahoma's long decline in production was reversed, when its fields yielded 124,616,-000 barrels of crude oil, an increase of approximately 1,500,000 barrels over the previous year. "The greatest addition of new oil,"

[17] In the southwest part of T14N-R4W, the southeast part of T14N-R5W, and the northwest part of T13N-R4W.

[18] In the NW NW SW of Sec. 32, T14N-R4W, Oklahoma County. E. G. Dahlgren and Dan O. Howard, "The West Edmond Oil Field of Oklahoma," a reprint from *Mining and Metallurgy*, Vol. XXVI, No. 468 (December, 1945), Section One, 607–10, supplied the author by Mr. Dahlgren of the Interstate Oil Compact Commission, Oklahoma City.

ran the report, "was from West Edmond," which rapidly expanded into a major field, producing 7,752,000 barrels.[19] Here the greatest concentration of rotary rigs in the world were boring down into West Edmond's red earth, and the field's oil output was creating a $500,000 pay roll and a major housing headache for the once again oil-booming Oklahoma capital. Pauls Valley, Cumberland, Cement, and the Glenn Pool–Sapulpa area (where secondary recovery operations had been inaugurated) were also given favorable mention.

West Edmond presently had an adequate pipe-line outlet. The Cimarron Valley Pipe Line Company was first in the field, transporting West Edmond crude oil to the Champlin refinery at Enid, Oklahoma. The Phillips Petroleum Company and the Sohio Petroleum Company[20] built a joint line to the new field from the former's pipe-line station east of Oklahoma City; and there were other lines— to the Denver Producing and Refining Company refinery east of West Edmond and the Peppers Refining Company natural-gasoline plant built in the field; and residue gas from these two refineries was made available to the Oklahoma Natural Gas Company and the Cities Service Gas Company.[21]

In 1945, Oklahoma gained third place in oil production with an annual increase of 16,000,000 barrels, passing Louisiana at least temporarily. West Edmond made this possible. But Louisiana, now in fourth place, increased its yield 2,000,000 barrels, with the Gulf Coast area increasing its lead over northern Louisiana.

Kansas and Illinois maintained fifth and sixth places respectively, both states failing to keep up their 1944 production records; and New Mexico scarcely retained seventh place, because of a 2,000,000-barrel loss from its 1944 oil output. Arkansas trailed in ninth place, its oil yield dropping off 1,000,000 barrels.

War demands had brought the United States petroleum indus-

[19] Bureau of Mines, *Minerals Yearbook, 1943*, 1089–1090; *ibid, 1945*, 1095. In 1945, West Edmond was fourth in rank among America's leading oil fields. See *Petroleum Facts and Figures* (Eighth edition), 57.

[20] The Standard Oil Company of Ohio became an independent company in 1911, after a federal court decision forced the dissolution of Standard Oil. At present its trade name "Sohio" is as familiar in Southwestern Oil fields as in refining and marketing areas. Moreover, Sohio now owns 2,605 miles of crude-oil pipe line and 254 miles of gasoline pipe line; 1,180 miles of pipe line owned by other companies are utilized in part by Sohio; and it also has title to river tugboats and barges.

[21] E. G. Dahlgren and Dan O. Howard, *loc. cit.*

Finding New Horizons

try to a production of 1,711,000,000 barrels in 1945, 22 per cent above its prewar peak. The Southwestern states (Arkansas, Kansas, Louisiana, Oklahoma, New Mexico, and Texas) produced 1,186,-026,000 barrels of this total. It is significant, too, that the nation's all-time, cumulative oil production was 31,000,000,000 barrels; the Southwestern states', 20,000,000,000 barrels, or approximately 66 per cent of the whole.

XXIV

Oil at War

THE ACCOUNT of the role played by the American petroleum industry during both World War I and World War II is very largely the story of Southwestern oil. When we took part in the first war, in 1917, the states of Kansas, Louisiana, Oklahoma, and Texas produced more than 60 per cent of the nation's crude oil; and when we entered World War II, in 1941, with Arkansas and New Mexico added, 70 per cent.

Such an account also revolves about great Southwestern oil fields. As the Kaiser's juggernaut was gaining momentum in Europe, between June, 1914, and April, 1915, the Cushing, Oklahoma, field had reached a maximum daily production of some 300,000 barrels of high-grade petroleum, over one-third of the country's entire output.[1] No doubt this gave the German war lords grave concern, for this high-grade oil would be made available to their enemies. Twenty-four years later, when Hitler thrust his mechanized war machine into Poland, East Texas was the Southwest's great oil producer.

In fact, on the outbreak of World War I, Germany's first military move was southward, toward the Romanian oil fields, a move which had all the logic of war behind it. These fields she occupied in 1916 and for a time operated the oil wells. Shortly, however, the Allies destroyed a majority of the producing wells, pipe lines, and refineries, thereby preventing Germany from using much of this oil for war purposes.

At this time Russia had considerable oil, but the Central Powers

[1] H. A. Garfield, "Final Report of the U. S. Fuel Administration, 1917–1919 (Washington, 1921)," MS, incl. Requa's "Report of the Oil Division," 282, in Records of the United States Fuel Administration, Executive Office, Tray 146, Division of Natural Resources Records, National Archives, Washington.

344

prevented her from shipping it through the Dardanelles to her allies; and the present oil fields of the Near East—Iran, Iraq, and Arabia, which in 1940 yielded more than 122,000,000 barrels of crude oil—were then not in commercial production, although the Egyptian oil field of Hurghada supplied the British fleet in the eastern Mediterranean during World War I.

Oil was not so essential during World War I as it was in World War II. Europe's consumption of petroleum products on the eve of that war was only 55,000,000 barrels; but immediately prior to World War II, it had grown to 275,000,000 barrels. In 1914, at the beginning of the first European conflict, the motorization of that continent had only begun. Motor transport was in its infancy—witness the rush of French reinforcements in taxicabs to Joffre's hard-pressed army in the first battle of the Marne. A large part of the war materials and supplies at that time was carried to the various fronts in horse- and mule-drawn vehicles.

Before the end of the war, however, armies were becoming mechanized, which in turn called for an ever increasing quantity of petroleum products. Marshal Ferdinand Foch had warned that the Allies would lose the war if the United States did not keep up its oil supply. Trucks, tanks (developed during the war), airplanes, and ships were using millions of barrels of oil. By 1918 the United States government had officially recognized the importance of oil; in January, President Woodrow Wilson had appointed Mark L. Requa as head of an oil division of the Fuel Administration.

Our memories would be short indeed were we to forget the American petroleum industry's contributions to the winning of World War I. In 1918, after the Armistice, Viscount Curzon made his significant tribute to the oil industry, which was quoted earlier: "The Allies floated to victory on a wave of oil."

This was a striking figure of speech, and it was, at least in part, true, as shown by General Ludendorff's admission that it was chiefly insufficient oil reserves that had forced the German General Staff to sue for peace in November, 1918. American tankers were able to keep the Allies supplied with petroleum, in spite of German submarines; while through the Allies' preventive measures, every foreign oil supply was denied the Germans.

In World War II, the role of petroleum was even more vital, as

345

explained by H. C. Wiess, president of the Humble Oil and Refining Company: "Oil is needed to fuel the ships, planes, tanks, and trucks that move supplies, carry the bombs, and provide the tremendous striking power that is so essential in modern war. Oil is also used to produce toluene for explosives, as a raw material for synthetic rubber and chemicals, and for many other purposes."[2]

Prior to the Nipponese attack on Pearl Harbor, Japan imported from the Western Hemisphere more than 85 per cent of her oil. With the outbreak of war, of course, she was denied American oil, and without any other adequate supply, her warships and airplanes were eventually immobilized.

An old military axiom that "war is won by the nation with the greatest resources" is sound, both for manufactured goods and for raw materials. Bob Allen properly assessed the value of manufactured products in 1942, when he said, "By the cruel nature of things this is a war of machines."[3] Axis leaders had thought so, too, and before the war had amassed vast quantities of airplanes, tanks, trucks, mechanized equipment, and ammunition; but they had not appraised sufficiently their limited supply of raw materials, which were just as essential. Many of the raw materials must be imported, thus making it important for England, France, and the United States to keep Germany from getting them.

It is equally clear that oil was one of a very few indispensable commodities. The effectiveness of all branches of the armed forces during World War II rested to a large extent on the adequacy of petroleum products—gasoline, fuel oil, and lubricants.[4] Any one of the major powers could send out an air fleet greater in number than all the planes that fought on all fronts in World War I; and each could put into the field an army that was moved by trucks with fully motorized equipment. Both of these armed services would require huge quantities of oil, the consumption of which would jump at once to a wartime maximum.

[2] "Interpretation of Petroleum Development," Wiess' mimeographed copy, supplied the author, along with other materials, by the Humble Oil and Refining Company, Houston.

[3] Robert E. Allen (director of the Production Division, Office of the Petroleum Co-ordinator), "Oil's Role in a War of Machines," in *World Petroleum,* Vol. XIII, No. 2 (February, 1942), 22.

[4] "A Historical Record of the Committee on Production of the Petroleum Industry War Council Appointed by the Petroleum Administrator for War," MS, in PAW,

Oil at War

Because of petroleum's growing importance, in the fall of 1938 an Englishman estimated Europe's war needs.[5] He said that the world's yearly wartime oil consumption was 275,000,000 tons. Germany's yearly wartime requirements would reach 12,650,000 tons (twice her peacetime use), half of which would consist of Diesel oil plus 1,500,000 tons of aviation fuel. Germany had gone far ahead of other nations in the utilization of Diesels, the majority of her commercial vehicles and a large percentage of her planes being fitted with Diesel engines.

German scientists and war lords had evidently studied their oil needs carefully, for they knew that they must have motor power. Their available oil would include 475,000 tons from Germany, 35,-000 tons from Austria, and 18,000 tons from Czechoslovakia; and in addition, a possible 7,150,000 tons from Romania and 401,000 tons from Poland. This would give them a total of 8,179,000 tons.

Italian peacetime consumption amounted to 1,830,000 metric tons, and it was assumed that her war demand would equal twice that amount. Yet Italy had an indigenous production of only 15,000 tons and could expect 90,000 tons from Albania. So, together, Germany and Italy, requiring a total of 16,310,000 tons in wartime, would have available at best only 8,284,000 tons.

Outside of conquest, from which German strategists must have expected to gain a great quantity, the Axis powers could count on little oil from imports. England and her allies, on the other hand, could look to the Americas—the United States and Mexico in North America; and Venezuela, Colombia, Peru, and Ecuador in South America—to supply their needs. Also, the Allies would have to keep Germany out of a third oil-producing area, out of those countries clustering around the eastern end of the Mediterranean—Romania, the Soviet Union and Iraq.

At this time the oil output of the United States was estimated at around 173,000,000 tons, and that of Mexico and the exporting South American countries at 92,200,000 tons. But the Allied nations needed an additional 37,000,000 tons, or a 14 per cent increase in

Historical Records, File "Appendix, Misc.," etc., file now being accessioned by the National Resources Records Division, National Archives, from the Department of the Interior records.

[5] "War's Effect on Petroleum Trade," in *World Petroleum*, Vol. IX, No. 10 (October, 1938), 33 ff.

the North and South American production. This would necessitate a daily yield of 4,000,000 barrels in the United States against her July output of 3,329,000 barrels; and the war demands on the other American nations would be proportional.

Watching anxiously the gathering war clouds and seeing the approaching storm about to break over the United States, President Franklin D. Roosevelt, on May 27, 1941, declared the existence of an unlimited national emergency and called upon all citizens and industry to put forth an all-out effort for national defense.[6] The next day Roosevelt appointed Secretary of the Interior Harold L. Ickes as petroleum co-ordinator for national defense and directed him to unify the various phases of the oil industry to meet the emergency.[7]

Ickes began his gigantic task, working through the Office of Petroleum Co-ordinator; but by Executive Order No. 9276, on December 2, 1942,[8] the Petroleum Administration for War was created and Secretary Ickes was named petroleum administrator. Previously, on June 4, 1941, he had selected Ralph K. Davies of the Standard Oil Company of California to serve as deputy co-ordinator, who now became deputy petroleum administrator.[9]

By the end of July, 1941, the Washington administrative units were substantially organized. The main functional units included divisions of production, refining, transportation, marketing, conservation, foreign, and research and information, each to supervise those petroleum-industry operations indicated by its title.[10] Each division was set up to meet a critical need, and it is difficult to say which served most effectively. Certainly it can be said that the division of supply and transportation, particularly under the period of Jubal Parten's directorship, gained widest popular acclaim.

[6] PAW Historical Records, Appendix, Foreign Operations Committee, Petroleum Industry War Council, Technical Advisory Committee, MS, Misc., Natural Resources Records Division, National Archives.

[7] Broadcasts, Speeches, 6–1–41/6–30–42, PAW, *idem.*

[8] *Ibid.;* John W. Frey and H. Chandler Ide, *A History of the Petroleum Administration for War, 1941–1945,* Appendix 7, Exhibit 2, 375–76.

[9] Francis T. Bourne, "Putting PAW to Bed, or the Record Retirement Program of PAW," in *American Archivist,* Vol. IX, No. 2 (April, 1946), 136–37. It should be added, too, that PAW (Petroleum Administration for War) was not a division of the Department of the Interior but an independent agency.

[10] *Ibid.*

Yet the promotion of production, foreign supply, and distribution and refining were also quite important.

To supplement and make effective the work of these units, close co-operation between the government and the oil operators was needed. To this end Co-ordinator Ickes called a meeting of industry representatives in Washington on June 19, 1941. There a unified government-industry co-operative program was agreed upon. Five districts were created, two of which (Nos. 2 and 3) included the Southwestern states. Each district had a general committee and a number of functional committees, composed of representatives of the petroleum industry and of production, refining, transportation, and marketing, together with local regional subcommittees, designed to promote defense efforts.[11]

On November 29, 1941, Co-ordinator Ickes appointed seventy-eight leaders from all branches of the industry to the Petroleum Industry Council for National Defense, later renamed the Petroleum Industry War Council, to serve as an advisory body in formulating policies and programs for the nation's domestic and wartime requirements, and to assist OPC (Office of Petroleum Co-ordinator) in mobilizing resources and securing the co-operation of the petroleum industry in carrying out plans.

In addition to the PIWC (Petroleum Industry War Council), a Foreign Operations Committee was also created, with headquarters in New York. It was to advise OPC concerning foreign oil policies.

Thus, by the beginning of 1943, a comprehensive organization had been set up to solve one of the nation's major problems. This government-industry administration moved forward to assume its responsibilities, generally recognized as critical and heavy. The complete fulfillment of the requirements of the military forces, after all, was the main responsibility of PAW, as Ickes explained to Wisconsin oilmen. "This is a war of machines and of ships and of airplanes powered by oil," he said. "In short this is an *oil war*. The side, which, by interrupting the flow of petroleum products to the enemy, and which at the same time can supply its own tanks, its mechanized guns, its fighting ships, and its airplanes with gasoline,

[11] For the names of persons appointed to this council, see Frey and Ide, *op. cit.,* 327; for other committees, 327–49.

and lubricants, and fuel oils of the proper kind at the time required, and in the right places is the side which will eventually win this world-wide conflict."[12]

So long as the German juggernaut was adequately fueled, it remained invincible in Europe and Africa, but without oil it was impotent. This was demonstrated by the sudden collapse of Rommel's *Afrika Korps* when the German fuel supply lines were cut. Rommel's mechanized army was immobilized. And Germany's subsequent military collapse in Europe was attributed to the same cause; its *Luftwaffe* and *Panzer* divisions, mobile artillery and infantry, and trucks were as useless as so much junk.

Without underestimating the part played by the atomic bomb in ending the Japanese war, it should be remembered that even before the first bomb was dropped, the Japanese position from a military point of view was hopeless. Japan's loss of fuel supplies for its navy and air forces deprived her of maintaining the mobility necessary to ward off Allied attacks. General McArthur's island-hopping left stranded well-trained and eager-to-fight Japanese armies; so without oil to power it, the Nipponese Army was forced to surrender without entering a major test of military strength.

To fight a two-front war, the United States was handicapped as never before. Fortunately, however, we had sufficient oil. Whereas our maximum oil output in World War I was approximately 1,000,-000 barrels a day, the peak production during World War II reached 5,000,000 barrels a day, an oil yield that was necessary to meet the needs of the rapidly expanding armed and mechanized forces.

This is best seen in Germany's experience. The invasion of Russia had cost the Germans 21,000,000 barrels of oil; the Axis powers had used yearly 255,000,000 barrels of oil; and Hitler's forty-five days' blitz of Europe had required 12,000,000 barrels of oil, equal to the amount of all oil stores captured.

PAW's efforts to promote production, supply, transportation, and refining to meet war demands were vitally aided by the Southwestern oil industry. Each area of petroleum need required extraordinary accomplishment.

Wartime prospecting and drilling were quite beyond peacetime

[12] An address of January 21, 1943, in PAW, Broadcasts, Speeches, 7-1-42/12-21-43, Natural Resources Records Division, National Archives.

experience. From 1941 to 1944 geophysical crews, increasing in number from 259 in 1941 to 430 in 1944, ranged far and wide; and, during the same period, drillers completed 13,880 wildcat wells and discovered 915 fields. PAW had set the drilling stakes at 4,000 wildcat wells in 1942, 4,500 in 1943, and 5,000 in 1944, representing increases of 23 per cent, 38 per cent, and 53 per cent over the 1941 record,[13] but 380 below the three-year accomplishment.

The Southwest's own prospecting, drilling, and production achievements were recounted in the preceding chapter. The nation's fields discovered since Pearl Harbor accounted for a yield of 400,000 barrels of oil a day; and the total United States oil output of the war period reached 5,800,000,000 barrels, or one-fifth of all we had produced up to that time.

Crude-oil production in the United States during the war years reflected the operators' hearty response to PAW appeals for more oil. The output in 1941 was 1,400,000,000 barrels, and in 1945 it reached 1,700,000,000 barrels. Even the nation's stripper wells contributed their share. Congress enacted its stripper-well subsidy law on August 1, 1944, providing for federal payments of thirty-five cents a barrel for crude oil from fields with an average production per well of fewer than five barrels daily; and of twenty cents a barrel for fields averaging as many as seven barrels but fewer than nine barrels daily per well.

The hardest objectives to reach, for both the nation and the industry, were in transportation and refining. Enormous demands for oil supplies, far beyond those of prewar days, accentuated these problems.

Before the war, more than 95 per cent of the 1,400,000 barrels of oil consumed daily by the seventeen Eastern states was shipped to market by tanker over 1,500 miles of open water, from the Gulf Coast, California, and the Caribbean;[14] and vast quantities were sent to England and France to meet their war-born needs. During the spring of 1941, to meet urgent war requirements, Great Britain called upon the United States for eighty tankers.[15] (German sub-

[13] "History of the Production Division, Petroleum Administration for War, 1941–45" (November 15, 1945), MS, PAW, S-200, Box 452, Item 4, *idem.*

[14] Ickes' address before the Central Motor Freight Association, Chicago, June 11, 1942, in PAW, Broadcasts, Speeches, 6–1–41/6–30–42, *idem.*

[15] Bureau of Mines, *Minerals Yearbook, 1943,* 1071; Richard J. Gonzalez, "War-

marines had taken a toll of 182 tankers carrying oil to the RAF and British armies.) The United States government supplied Britain's need and asked Southwestern operators to use tank cars to carry oil to the Eastern seaboard.

The oil operators complied. By October they had increased their west-to-east tank-car shipments from a mere trickle to over 140,000 barrels a day.[16] At that time, Ickes said later, this was regarded as a great achievement, but it was found to be only an appetizer, a sort of *hors d'oeuvre*.[17] By the first week in February, 1942, tank-car shipments eastward passed the 200,000-barrel-a-day mark; by March, 400,000 barrels a day; by mid-May, 700,000 barrels a day; and by the first of June, 800,000 barrels a day.

Rationing of gasoline helped to control domestic demand. The Office of Price Administration required ration stamps of the users of various kinds of vehicles—passenger cars, motorcycles, commercial cars, and trucks. Passenger-car rations were of three types, indicated by A, B, and C coupons. All passenger cars except those used commercially were originally restricted to A coupons, with B and C coupons given for supplemental driving in connection with certain essential occupations and war needs.

Yet the Eastern seaboard oil shortage remained acute; and tank-car shipments by no means met the west-to-east transportation demand.[18] At the outbreak of war the United States was consuming 175,000,000 gallons of petroleum products every twenty-four hours, or about five quarts for every man, woman, and child—and a large part of our population was distributed along the Atlantic seaboard. This meant that huge quantities of oil must move from the wells to the refineries, from the refineries to large ocean barges and pipe-line terminals, from these places to intermediate bulk stations, and from bulk stations to Eastern service stations.

This heavy oil movement had been a perennial problem for the

---

time Changes in Petroleum Industry," in *Bulletin of the American Association of Petroleum Geologists*, Vol. XXVII (January–December, 1943), Part II, 977.

16 "Oil and War," address of the Hon. Harold L. Ickes before the Baltimore Advertising Club, on Wednesday, September 16, 1942, in PAW, Broadcasts, Speeches, 6–1–41/6–30–42, Natural Resources Records Division, National Archives.

17 Address by Ickes before Central Motor Freight Association, Chicago, Thursday, June 11, 1942, as cited.

18 "Tank Car Movement of Oil," in *World Petroleum*, Vol. XIV, No. 1 (January, 1943), 32.

oil industry even in peacetime; in war, it assumed colossal and vital importance. The armed services required enough oil to power a two-ocean navy, a rapidly expanding air force (at the rate of 1,000 units per month),[19] and a highly mobile army, or more than 65 per cent of all exports for war purposes.

Thus, at the height of the German submarine attacks, Co-ordinator Ickes put the problem of replacing tankers by overland shipments in the hands of a standing committee of oil executives.[20] In March, 1942, W. Alton Jones, chairman of this committee, called a meeting of seventy pipe-liners at Tulsa, Oklahoma, to plan their part of the program. For three days and nights these men worked on their problems, and out of this meeting came a recommendation for comprehensive pipe-line projects, which will be described shortly.

The army's consumption of petroleum grew alarmingly. Deputy Co-ordinator Davies had found a picture-article in a current magazine showing on four pages fifty-seven different army vehicles. Forty-seven of these were gasoline- or oil-powered and nine were trailers drawn by oil-fueled units. In the war then raging, he said, "1,500,000 American soldiers would ride to battle in 300,000 vehicles."[21] By August, 1942, two gallons of gasoline were required each day for every soldier in action; or the daily delivery of 9,000,000 gallons of gasoline.[22] W. R. Boyd, Jr., said that each of General Montgomery's tanks chasing Rommel in Africa required the exclusive service of a 1,000-gallon gasoline truck; and that one thousand two-engine Allied bombers ranging only four hundred miles into

[19] Robert E. Wilson (consultant, Petroleum Unit, Office of Production Management), "Petroleum and the War," in *Bulletin of the American Association of Petroleum Geologists*, Vol. XXV, No. 7 (July, 1941), 1264.

[20] Members of this committee were: W. Alton Jones, president of Cities Service; Charles S. Jones, president of the Richfield Oil Company; Burton W. Musser, director of the Utah Oil and Refining Company; E. S. Seubert, president of the Standard Oil Company (Indiana); and H. C. Wiess, president of the Humble Oil and Refining Company.

[21] Ralph K. Davies (deputy petroleum co-ordinator), "Oil and the War," in *World Petroleum*, Vol. XIII, No. 1 (January, 1942), 28.

[22] Address of Ernest O. Thompson, Texas Railroad Commission, at Midland, Texas, August 27, 1942, before Senator Hatch and members of the United States Senate Public Land Committee. In PAW, S-200, Box 416, Texas General, 4400–13, Natural Resources Records Division, National Archives.

Oil! Titan of the Southwest

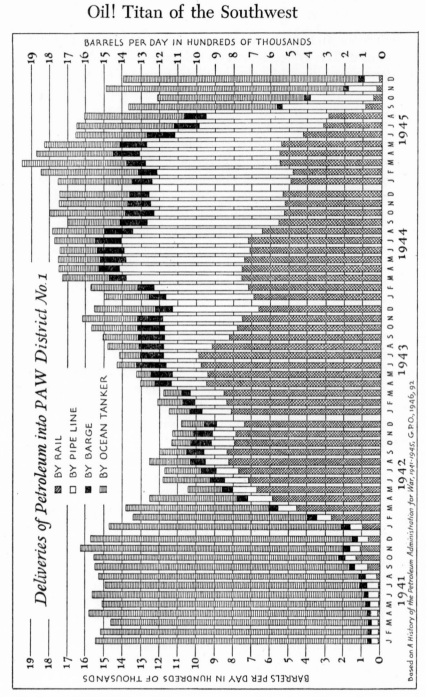

Deliveries of Petroleum into PAW District No. 1

BARRELS PER DAY IN HUNDREDS OF THOUSANDS

BARRELS PER DAY IN HUNDREDS OF THOUSANDS

☒ BY RAIL
☐ BY PIPE LINE
▥ BY BARGE
▤ BY OCEAN TANKER

1941 1942 1943 1944 1945

Based on A History of the Petroleum Administration for War, 1941-1945, G.P.O., 1946, 92

Europe from England, used more than 400,000 gallons of aviation gasoline.[23]

German war leaders saw that it was imperative, if they were to win the war, to prevent Great Britain and her allies from getting American oil. Thus, by the spring of 1942, German submarines were waging a deadly campaign against American tankers transporting oil from the Caribbean area and the Texas-Louisiana Gulf Coast to the Atlantic seaboard and to Europe. For a time observers of the Gulf and Atlantic coasts could hear shattering torpedo explosions and see tankers enveloped in smoke and flame. By March, submarine "wolf-packs" ranged off the American coast, in the Caribbean and around Cape Hatteras, and ploughed the high seas in search of their oil-carrying prey. For many months they wrought great destruction. Daily tanker crude shipments from the Gulf Coast to the East Coast declined from about 1,200,000 barrels plus 225,000 barrels of other imports during the spring of 1941 to about 100,000 barrels in January, 1943.[24] The total number of United States tankers dropped from 389 in 1942 to 366 in 1943.

Before the end of 1944, however, the United States Navy had countered effectively; and American shipyards had increased the launching of more, and, to some extent, bigger and better tankers. These countermeasures brought improvement to our seagoing transportation; by 1944, American tankers in service had increased to 556, and by the next year, to 780.

Railroads and trucks were also making their contributions. In the spring of 1941 tank cars moved only 5,000 barrels of oil daily to the Eastern states; but by July, 1942, they had increased their carrying to 800,000 barrels daily, and by July, 1943, to about 1,-000,000 barrels.[25] Yet tankers and railroads combined could not meet the growing military and Eastern-seaboard petroleum needs, despite the fact that gasoline was rationed and civilian transportation greatly curtailed.

At the Tulsa meeting, previously mentioned, the pipe-liners had found their own means of transportation becoming increasingly

[23] William R. Boyd, Jr., "Oil Industry Moves Deeper into War," in *World Petroleum*, Vol. XIV, No. 1 (January, 1943), 22.

[24] Bureau of Mines, *Minerals Yearbook, 1943*, 1071.

[25] Gonzalez, *loc. cit.*, 976.

important. In 1940 there was a total of 94,384 miles of crude-oil pipe lines in the United States, 59,909 miles of it in Southwestern trunk lines and gathering lines; and in 1941 the total of national pipe lines increased by 13,966 miles, the Southwest sharing proportionately in this increase.[26] Through these lines, by planned schedule, moved silently 1,300,000,000 barrels of crude oil and almost 100,000,000 barrels of gasoline, with an estimated value of $1,500,000,000 and $200,000,000 respectively. The domestic consumption of gasoline along the Atlantic seaboard in 1942 rose to a daily peak of 823,000 barrels.

But all the tankers, railroads, trucks, and pipe lines then in service could not handle the oil needed on the Atlantic Coast, despite all improvement measures. Barge transportation had been increased, the use of tank trucks expanded and confined to short hauls, steel drums had been used to transport kerosene in box cars, and tank cars had been pooled and their loading and unloading time cut. Still the crisis was acute. As early as July, 1940, Secretary of the Interior Ickes had seen a rising west-to-east oil-transportation problem and had called the attention of President Roosevelt to it, suggesting the building of a large-dimension pipe line. The matter was not pressed, and nothing was done.

After Ickes had been named petroleum co-ordinator, he was pleased to see his pipe-line proposal activated. An industry committee, made up of executives from eleven companies doing 85 per cent of the oil business in the East, was named to restudy west-to-east major pipe-line needs.[27] These oilmen chose W. Alton Jones, president of Cities Service, as their chairman, and set up an engineering committee headed by Wallace R. Finney of the Standard Oil Company of New Jersey to make a preliminary study of the economics, design, specifications, and aerial surveys of proposed pipe-line routes. The committee of executives accepted the engineers' report and on September 8, 1941, incorporated in Dela-

[26] *Petroleum Facts and Figures* (Eighth edition), 141; Leven, *op. cit.*, 503.

[27] Members of this committee were: W. Alton Jones, Cities Service; John A. Brown and Brewster Jennings, Socony-Vacuum; Robert H. Colley, Atlantic; J. Frank Drake, Gulf; Alexander Frazier, Shell; Ralph W. Gallagher and Eugene Holman, Standard Oil Company (New Jersey); B. I. Graves, Tide Water; Harry T. Klein, The Texas Company; J. Edgar Pew, Sun; Harry F. Sinclair, Sinclair; and Robert E. Wilson, Standard Oil Company (Indiana).

ware two companies—National Defense Pipelines, Inc., and Emergency Pipelines, Inc.—to build and to own privately a west-to-east twenty-four-inch crude-oil line and a twenty-inch refined-oil line.

The plan was approved by Co-ordinator Ickes and Secretary of Commerce Jesse H. Jones, but SPAB (the Supplies and Priorities Allication Board), concluding that the required critical building and installation materials could better be employed in meeting other national defense needs, refused to grant necessary priorities.

Later, after the United States entered the conflict, Co-ordinator Ickes again requested a consideration of the oil executives' original application, and again SPAB turned it down, on February 24, 1942. But Ickes and the oil-company executives continued to promote their plan. Then followed frequent conferences between oil company representatives, Congressional committees, various governmental agencies, and army and navy officials, out of which, almost a year later, finally came the War Production Board's approval for the release of 137,500 tons of steel for the construction of the first segment of the pipe line, from Longview, Texas, to Norris City, Illinois.[28] The Reconstruction Finance Corporation was to make available the necessary funds for the work through the Defense Plant Corporation.

Meanwhile, the eleven oil companies—Cities Service, Standard Oil of New Jersey, Atlantic, Sun, Gulf, Texas, Socony-Vacuum,[29] Consolidated, Shell, Tidewater, and Pan American—reorganized Emergency Pipelines as the War Emergency Pipelines, Inc., a nonprofit organization.[30]

On June 26, 1942, the Defense Plant Corporation executed a con-

[28] Wallace R. Finney, "The 'Big Inch' Pipe Line," in *Petroleum Engineer*, Vol. XV, No. 4 (January, 1944), 185.

[29] The Standard Oil Company of New York acquired a controlling interest in the Magnolia Petroleum Company in 1918 and complete ownership in 1925. Thus Magnolia became a part of the present Socony-Vacuum Oil Company, Incorporated, when the Standard Oil Company of New York merged with the Vacuum Oil Company in 1931. Most of Socony-Vacuum's oil production comes from the properties of Magnolia in Texas, Oklahoma, Louisiana, Kansas, and Illinois, and from those of another subsidiary, the General Petroleum Corporation, in California. In 1946, Socony-Vacuum had 10,668 producing wells in the United States and 10,000,000 acres leased for future oil and gas development. It has fifteen refineries within easy access of American markets.

[30] Frey and Ide, *op. cit.*, 108. The building of the line was ultimately financed by the Reconstruction Finance Corporation at a cost of about $76,000,000.

tract with the new pipe-line company, and plans were announced for starting the work.[31] The main section of the line, of twenty-four-inch pipe, was to extend from Longview, Texas, to Phoenixville, Pennsylvania, a distance of 1,254.7 miles; and from Phoenixville a twenty-inch line of 85.73 miles was to run on to Linden, New Jersey, where it was to enter a delivery system of the various refineries in the New York area. A second branch line of pipe, ranging from twenty-inch to fourteen-inch, was to reach refineries in the Philadelphia area.[32] Construction offices were established at Little Rock, Arkansas, on July 3, and the first trainload of pipe was shipped two weeks later from mill to construction site.

Burt Hull of The Texas Company, dean of the old-time pipe-liners, was chosen as the Big-Inch building boss.[33] The construction of the Big Inch was a tremendous task requiring consummate skill, speed, and long hours of laborious effort. Men of technical skill and experience must be employed, vast quantities of materials transported to various points along the right of way, and steamy swamps and high mountains crossed.

On June 23, 1942, Hull put fifteen surveying parties at work to stake out a right-of-way for the Big Inch toward Norris City, Illinois, 531 miles from Longview, Texas, the starting point. At the same time WEP (War Emergency Pipelines) ordered for the already agreed-upon eight construction sections, many kinds of materials—for pumping stations, storage tanks, loading racks, and other installations, including pipe, transformers, motors, pumps, fittings, railroad trackage, and such raw materials as steel, brass, copper, and aluminum.

Close behind the surveyors came gangs of workmen with ax, saw, dynamite, and torch to clear a fifty-foot right-of-way; and these were followed in turn by contractors and field bosses with gangs of workmen—graders, muckers, night men, blacksmiths, stabbers, clamp men, pick-and-shovel men, welders, and other skilled workers.

[31] *House Report, No. 685,* 77 Cong., 1 sess., p. 3.

[32] Finney, *loc. cit.,* 185.

[33] Interview with Burt E. Hull, Texas Pipe Line Company, Houston, Texas, February 27, 1946; Charles Morrow Wilson, *Oil Across the World,* 157. War Emergency President W. Alton Jones described Hull as the world's best pipe-liner. See " 'Big Inch' in Operation," in *World Petroleum,* Vol. XIV, No. 1 (January, 1942), 39.

Oil at War

Already, on July 15, at Washington, contractors had signed cost-plus-fixed-fee agreements.[34] Federal officials urged these contractors to drive their men every hour of the day until the work was completed. This was done. The first pipe was laid on August 3, 1942, the schedule calling for the delivery of five miles of pipe line a day, but presently the hard-working crews were laying nine miles a day.

Assisting the men were huge oil-powered monsters—one to plow a trench more than two feet wide and six feet deep; another to handle the two-ton joints of pipe; another to cover the pipe in the ditch; and still others for work beyond the strength of human hands. Pipe-liners had to rebuild or redesign trucks, tractors, and winches and provide heavier plows and bigger wheels for ditching machines.

Men and engines worked as a team, the huge ditchers, like waddling monstrous turtles, plowing mile after mile of deep trenches for the twenty-four-inch pipe, over hills, through the swamps of Arkansas, across Missouri and southern Illinois, across rivers and over mountains, until the task was done. Arkansas and Mississippi river floods washed away sections of the pipe, but repairs were hastily made and the work went on.[35]

Complementary installations were necessary. At Longview and at Norris City, thirty-one steel storage tanks were built from old tankage that was cut down, shipped, and set up again; and at Norris City over a mile of three loading racks was erected, requiring the building of seven miles of railway tracks. By November 1, pumping-station sites were acquired and work was delayed. But by much shifting of materials and substitute arrangements, alternate pumping stations were finally made ready for filling the line.

Hull and his men worked at top speed. Every hour saved might hasten the end of the war and make the difference between life and death for many American soldiers. Hour after hour, in rain, sleet, and snow, and through muck and flood waters, they labored. At

[34] "History of the Transportation Division," Petroleum Administration for War, Historical Files, Misc., Department of the Interior, now being accessioned by the Natural Resources Records Division, National Archives.

[35] River and large creek crossings were difficult and required separate contracts. Ditchers moved through swampland, as much as fifteen miles on a stretch, roaring and plunging; and tractors followed over corduroyed roads to deliver two-ton joints of pipe to the workmen.

last, on December 31, at midnight, their initial task was done: Crude oil was turned into the twenty-four-inch line at Longview, preceded by a fifty-mile-long slug of water under high pressure to test the line. But the welders had done their job well: there were no leaks.[36]

The first oil arrived at Norris City on February 19, 1943;[37] and trains of tank cars, standing at the seven-mile-long racks, were soon loaded for consignment to Eastern refineries.

Six pumping stations were completed by March 25, giving the Big Inch a carrying capacity of 190,000 barrels a day; and by April 9 all stations were completed and were pumping from Longview a steady flow of 200,000 barrels of crude oil a day.

West Texas crude also entered the Big Inch at Longview on June 16, 1943, thereby starting the flow from this huge producing area also. From February 19 to June 30, a total of 21,000,000 barrels of Western crude oil was delivered at Norris City, and then was moved by train to Eastern refineries by the fastest schedule possible. Norris City's tank-car loading reached a peak of 1,250 cars a day, enough for sixteen to eighteen trains.

Following the completion of the Longview-to-Norris City part of the Big Inch, surveying parties were sent to stake out the next segment of the line, from Norris City to Phoenixville, Pennsylvania, 722 miles away. Construction plans divided the 722 miles of twenty-four-inch and 100 miles of twenty-inch branch lines into eighteen sections, each up to sixty-five miles in length. The twenty-four-inch line was to be laid to a point near Phoenixville. There it branched with two twenty-inch lines to refinery centers, one to Philadelphia and the other to New York.

Crossing the Susquehanna River delayed for one month the completion of the twenty-four inch line from Norris City to Phoenixville. But the crossing was finally made and the whole line welded into a single long pipe line in the unbelievably short period of 350 days, a remarkable demonstration of engineering and construction skill.[38]

[36] "History of the Transportation Division," *loc. cit.;* " 'Big Inch' in Operation," *loc. cit.*

[37] Bureau of Mines, *Minerals Yearbook, 1943,* 1066.

[38] "History of the Transportation Division," *loc. cit.*

Night operations on the Carter No. 1 W. D. Lamar well,
McClain County, Oklahoma

An industry that does not sleep—Esso Standard Oil
Company Baton Rouge refinery

Standard Oil Company (N. J.)

Aerial view, The Texas Company Port Neches refinery

The Texas Company

Oil at War

Phoenixville received its first crude oil on August 14, 1943, delivered to the Sinclair and Sun refineries; and Linden, New Jersey, received its first crude oil six days later. By September 24 the line from Norris City east had a capacity of 225,000 barrels a day with nine stations in service, but operations were reduced to 175,000 barrels a day, because at that time deliveries could be made only to the Philadelphia area. It was not until two months later that the line was in full operation.

When completed, the Big Inch, a gigantic gullet of steel, was serviced by twenty-six main-line pumping stations, spaced about fifty-three miles apart between Longview, Texas, and Linden, New Jersey. In the line were 3,836,000 barrels of oil constantly moving eastward. Each pumping station was equipped with three main sixteen-inch by twelve-inch single-stage centrifugal pumps making 8,750 revolutions a minute at 630 feet head, each pump producing approximately 240 pounds of pressure. Fifteen public utilities supplied power through many miles of transmission lines to the large electric motors. The 1,254 miles of this twenty-four-inch line required approximately 358,000 tons of oil-pipe steel, in addition to the steel used for the building of fifty-one storage tanks, mostly of 80,000 barrels capacity, at Longview, Norris City, Phoenixville Junction, and Linden, with an aggregate capacity of 3,955,000 barrels.[39]

The story of the building of the Big Inch was repeated in that of the Little Big Inch, the twenty-inch refined-oil-products line, first to run from the Beaumont-Houston refining area, via Norris City, to Seymour, Indiana, to a tank-car loading rack; and later, thence east, paralleling the Big Inch, a total distance of 1,475 miles from Beaumont, Texas, to Linden, New Jersey.[40]

The first section of the Little Big Inch from Beaumont and Houston to Seymour, Indiana, required 160,000 tons of steel, about 2,200 tons of other critical materials, and 53,000 connected horsepower for its forty-one motors and pumps. Actual work started on this line's western leg on April 23, 1943, and the last pipe of its eastern segment was laid on the following October 8. For the first segment,

[39] Frey and Ide, *op. cit.*, 431.
[40] For an interesting article on the purposes and plans for the twenty-inch pipe line, see "'Little Big Inch,'" in *World Petroleum*, Vol. XIV, No. 1 (January, 1934), 42.

Oil! Titan of the Southwest

SPAB allocated 173,750 tons of steel, at an estimated cost of $44,-000,000, to be financed through the Defense Plant Corporation.

From Norris City the line extended another 639 miles to Linden, New Jersey, making a total distance of 1,633 miles of main line, with several sizes of smaller feeder and distribution lines and with the cost proportionately the same as in the building of the first segment.

The final weld was made on this last part of the Little Big Inch on December 2, 1943, and a period of testing and mending breaks and leaks followed, so that it was not until January 26, 1944, that a slug of about 125,000 barrels of gasoline, followed by heating oil, entered the western end of the line. The initial operations were at the rate of 120,000 barrels a day. Little Big Inch carried seven grades of refined products, in batches ranging from 250,000 to 1,-300,000 barrels. Its peak day oil carriage was 239,844 barrels, more than 72 per cent of which was for military use.[41]

During the war, nearly 390,000,000 barrels of crude oil and re-fined-oil products passed from the West to the Atlantic seaboard through the Big Inch and Little Big Inch gullets to meet the maximum needs of the armed forces and civilian consumers. By November, 1945, when both pipe lines were at last emptied of their oil loads and turned over to the War Assets Administration for disposition, they had fully justified the faith of their designers.

But these two gigantic construction achievements represented only a part of the pipe-line program drawn up at the Tulsa meeting and the later projects planned by PAW in March, 1942. Thousands of miles of shorter lines and lines of smaller dimensions were also built during the war period. By the end of 1941 three lines—the Plantation, the Southeastern, and the Portland-Montreal—were completed; and over 11,000 miles of other pipe lines were built, reversed, or converted to crude-oil use. In all, PAW authorized thirty-five major projects, thirty-three of which were completed, to facilitate a wartime northward and eastward flow of oil and oil products, at a total cost of $88,311,143.[42] But a detailed account of these would extend this chapter unnecessarily.

An increase in refinery products was another major wartime

[41] *Ibid.*, 434 ff.; Bureau of Mines, *Minerals Yearbook, 1943*, 1072.

[42] *Ibid.*, 1071; Frey and Ide, *op. cit.*, 417. The government financed these in the amount of $161,447,483, and private industry, $126,863,660.

necessity, and in meeting it, the refiners' contribution to the final victory of Allied arms was enormous and decisive.

During 1941 the United States refineries processed an average of 3,861,000 barrels of crude oil daily, from which came about 40,-000 barrels a day of 100-octane gasoline, 1,983,000 barrels of other gasoline, and proportionate quantities of kerosene, Diesel oil, fuel oils, and other products.

In 1945, Deputy Petroleum Administrator Davies estimated that refinery daily crude runs at home and abroad were 5,071,000 barrels, or 31 per cent greater than the prewar high, and that the production of 100-octane gasoline had increased over 1,600 per cent. For the war period, almost one billion dollars' worth of new refinery facilities had been built in the United States and more than one fourth of that amount had been spent for refinery expansion in other lands.[43]

But this is in summary; a fuller account is necessary. The expansion of refinery facilities to produce 100/130-octane aviation gasoline had been spectacular, production rising from 49,000 barrels daily in 1941 to a peak of 701,000 barrels daily in April, 1945.[44] Aviation fuel meant fighting power for bombers, pursuit planes, and war planes of all types; and that, of course, meant gasoline with an octane rating of 100 or higher. Nothing less would give army and navy fliers a fair fighting chance in the sky battles then being fought. "More 100-octane!" was the constant military plea. "More and more and more!"

On August 26, 1945, Secretary of the Interior Ickes said that when the Petroleum Administration for War began its work in 1942, it was believed that the armed forces would require only 40,000 barrels of 100-octane gasoline a day. Later he asked the refiners to raise this amount to 80,000 barrels a day, again, to 120,000 barrels, and then to 200,000 barrels. At the end of 1944 the output of 100/130-octane gasoline from United States sources reached 484,-

---

[43] "A Valediction," an address by Deputy Petroleum Administrator Ralph K. Davies before the Twenty-first Annual Meeting of the American Petroleum Institute, Chicago, Illinois, November 14, 1945, in PAW, Broadcasts, Speeches, 1-1-44/——, Division of natural Resources Records, National Archives.

[44] Bureau of Mines, *Minerals Yearbook, 1945,* 1105.

000 barrels a day.[45] "We never ceased to pace the armed forces," Ickes later added, "as well as to supply them, until the day, only a few months ago, when we were actually producing 625,000 barrels a day of high octane gasoline."[46]

Fortunately, United States refiners, at Baton Rouge, along the Louisiana-Texas Gulf Coast, elsewhere in the Southwest, and in the East, had long been in training for such an emergency. But, as E. DeGolyer, assistant deputy petroleum administrator for war, pointed out in the spring of 1943, "Rapidly mounting needs for . . . 100-octane and 91-octane gasolines—for toluene, for the butadiene constituent of synthetic rubber, for greatly improved aviation and Diesel lubricants, and for numerous specialty products—chemicals to cutting oils—have revolutionized the refining industry and embarked us upon a construction program intended to supplement our already great refining industry."[47]

Before World War II, American refiners had developed methods and processes for isolating the constituents of high-test aviation fuel and combining these with high-grade blending stocks and tetraethyl lead to produce 100-octane gasoline. Although there was little demand for such a high-test gasoline at that time, the knowledge gained regarding these high blending agents had been usefully applied in raising the antiknock rating of commercial gasoline. And, upon the outbreak of war, research that had been devoted to this subject put the refiners in a position to expand their facilities and supply the military demand.

So, in the year 1942, PAW's Refining Division, directed by Wright W. Gary of the M. W. Kellogg Company, had inaugurated its 100-octane program: A survey was under way to determine the capacity and potential increases from existing plants; a $150,000,-000 plant expansion was either being planned or under construction; SPAB had granted Co-ordinator Ickes' request for A-1-A ratings on all new 100-octane projects; large oil companies had

[45] "History of the Refining Division . . .," p. B-7, in PAW, Refining Division, Box 2131, Natural Resources Records Division, National Archives.

[46] Address by the Hon. Harold L. Ickes, Secretary of the Interior, speaking in lieu of Drew Pearson on the latter's radio broadcast over the American Broadcasting Company's network at 7:00 P.M., E.W.T., August 26, 1945, in PAW, Broadcasts, Speeches, 7-1-42/12-21-43, Natural Resources Records Division, National Archives.

[47] "War Demands More Oil," in World Petroleum, Vol. XIV, No. 3 (March, 1943), 26.

agreed to make refining processes available to others at low cost; and the leaders of the industry were working wholeheartedly with Co-ordinator Ickes, Director Gary, and the National Petroleum Council for National Defense, to meet military petroleum demands.[48]

At times, refining techniques improved so fast as to make plants obsolete almost before they were put into operation. Progress came in catalytic cracking, cyclization, super-fractionation, and de-sulphurization. Simply stated, catalytic cracking depended on a foreign substance, a catalyst, that modified chemical reaction by causing certain elements to join or to separate without itself entering into the reaction. Thermal cracking produced a gasoline high in olefin content, whereas catalytic cracking operations gave products high in aromatics and isoparaffins—hydrocarbons that served excellently as base stock for aviation gasoline.[49]

By 1943 the production of aromatic hydrocarbons from naphthas by catalytic cyclization or hydroforming had received considerable attention.[50] Aviation gasoline was PAW's prime objective, as is seen in the fact that by 1943 thirty-two new plants were supplying 100-octane gasoline and forty more were scheduled for completion early in 1944.

In 1945 the United States refiners could justly boast of supplying the armed forces with all their war needs for 100-octane gasoline. "Without question," said the Army-Navy Petroleum Board, this was one "of the great industrial accomplishments in the history of the warfare." But 100-octane gasoline was only one vital petroleum product. The United Nations also needed 91-, 87-, and 73-octane gasoline for pilot training; 80-octane for trucks, tanks, and other motorized ground equipment; Diesel fuel for marines and landing boats; lubricants for all vehicles and planes; asphalt for roads and runways; butadiene for synthetic rubber; toluene for TNT; jellied gasoline for flame-throwers; smoke for the army and

[48] "Primary Objective: Maximum Production of 100-octane Fuel," *ibid.*, Vol. XIII, No. 1 (January, 1942), 28.

[49] *Minerals Yearbook, 1943,* 1122. Improvement in catalysts progressed with refinery equipment. Early catalysts were natural or treated clays, but by 1943 synthetic catalysts were being introduced to emphasize such qualities as greater porosity, a greater yield of aromatics and other high-octane gasoline, longer life, and freedom from deposition of coke. The bead catalyst was among those announced in 1943.

[50] Elementary aromatics are benzene, toluene, and xylenes.

navy's screening movements; petroleum coke for aluminum; and wax for packaging. It was also necessary for the refiners to supply our own domestic requirements. As for the refiners' war attainments, they increased the daily crude-oil runs to stills from 3,861,-000 barrels in 1941 to 5,001,000 barrels in 1945; they boosted the daily 100-octane gasoline production from 40,000 barrels in 1940 to 514,000 barrels in 1945; and they also met the principal civilian requirements.

The refineries also produced synthetic rubber for the nation at a time when it seemed that half our automobiles would become tireless. After Japan's conquest of the East Indies had cut off the United States raw rubber supply, American rubber stocks were frozen, automobile tires rationed, and scrap rubber collected for future use.[51]

Also to help ease a threatened transportation paralysis, President Roosevelt's special committee, headed by Bernard M. Baruch and assisted by technical advisers, presented a workable plan for the manufacture of synthetic rubber at oil refineries, where the principal source of butadiene rubber was produced in high-boiling petroleum fractions and by catalytic dehydrogenation of butylene.

The Baruch committee's plan was accepted, and a comprehensive government–oil-refinery industry was launched, under Rubber Director Jeffers. By November, 1942, the Defense Plant Corporation had given contracts to sixty-seven plants to manufacture rubber and its components, at a cost of approximately one-half billion dollars. However, by 1943, only four units were actively engaged in supplying most of the required butadiene rubber.[52] The butadiene rubber supply was sufficient for every vital need, and in mid-1944 Jeffers resigned, since synthetic rubber production had reached a rate of 836,000 tons a year, a colossal amount in comparison with prewar rubber imports ranging from 550,000 to 650,000 tons a year.

The refinery of 1941–45 had come a long way from the early

[51] The production of civilian automobiles was stopped and the automobile industry was converted to the making of tanks, guns mounts, airplanes, airplane parts, engines, and other war matériel.

[52] Walter Miller, "Review of Refining Engineering for 1942," in *Petroleum Development and Technology, 1943*, CLI, 593–94; "History of the Refining Division," *loc. cit.*

twentieth century "cheese box" and "tea kettle," whose major product was kerosene for lamps and stoves. The refinery of 1941 was a vast and awesome assemblage of roaring furnaces, cat crackers, towering stills, pumps, and labyrinths of piping; and sometimes it sprawled over thousands of acres. In fact, it made profitable every activity of the oilman—prospecting, drilling, producing, and pipe lining.

Indeed, petroleum was America's major contribution to the winning of the war. On November 10, 1945, the joint chiefs of staff of the Army-Navy Petroleum Board recognized this fact in a letter to Deputy Petroleum Administrator Ralph K. Davies, referring to the industry's "superb contribution made to the victory of the United States by providing in full and on time the vast flood of petroleum products required by the Armed Forces during World War II. . . . No Government agency and no branch of American industry achieved a prouder war record," the citation continued, an "outstanding . . . contribution to the victory of the United Nations."[53]

[53] Quoted in Deputy Petroleum Administrator Ralph K. Davies "Valediction," as previously cited.

XXV

Oil Conservation and Control

I N EACH SOUTHWESTERN STATE, conservation controls and the mounting influence of the Interstate Conservation Commission have been strong incentives for increased oil production and at the same time for the protection of oil and gas reserves.

State legislatures and control agencies have fashioned conservation mechanisms to prevent waste and to keep pace with improvement. The necessity for control arises from a paradox. Production greatly below a field's maximum possible output rate will in the end bring the maximum recovery of oil; yet each operator, to protect his own interests, seeks to produce as rapidly as possible. The "rule of capture" allows a surface owner to produce all the oil he can drain from wells on his own property, which, in turn, prompts neighboring leaseholders to drill offset wells to protect their interests. This unfortunate rivalry leads to overproduction, which inevitably causes waste.[1]

State and federal regulations were designed to curb overproduction and to protect oil reservoirs. "Modern conservation practices," said the late J. C. Hunter, " . . . date from the realization that an oil reservoir is a physical unit and may be controlled as a unit."[2] Southwestern states base their control regulations—for drilling and the production of oil, the procurement of drilling permits, the plugging of abandoned wells, and the filing of official inspection reports with

[1] "Administrative Regulation of Petroleum Production," in *Harvard Law Review*, Vol. LIX (1945–46), 1142. See also Robert E. Hardwicke's excellent analysis of "The Rule of Capture and its Implications as Applied to Oil and Gas," a reprint of an address delivered before the Section of Mineral Law, American Bar Association, at its annual meeting in Los Angeles, California, July 15 and 16, 1935.

[2] J. C. Hunter, "Conservation of Oil and Gas," reprint from *Interstate Oil Compact Quarterly* for July, 1944, 9.

Oil Conservation and Control

a central state office—on the same principles. Conservation enactments of state legislatures are generally shaped to prevent waste, which all the Southwestern states broadly define as physical waste of oil or gas, including the dissipation of reservoir energy, and "economic waste," or producing oil in excess of market demand or outlet.

It has been seen that conservation measures were adopted in individual states as the necessity for control in the different fields became apparent. Since these regulations were forerunners and gradually became an integral part of a broader movement to solve interstate problems, it is necessary here to recount briefly the evolution of controls in the various states.

Kansas' first oil and gas legislation came as early as 1889, providing for the inspection of all petroleum products before they were offered for sale for illuminating purposes; but the first oil-field control law was passed in 1891, requiring the casing of oil and gas wells and a method of plugging them when abandoned.[3] Other oil- and gas-field control laws were adopted in 1901, 1905, and 1920, the last governing the shooting and acidizing of oil wells. Another law passed in 1920 regulated drilling.[4] The state legislature, however, did not provide legal proration until March 15, 1931.

Oklahoma's legislative enactment in 1913[5] providing for ratable production from natural gas reservoirs was its first state law relating to either oil or gas, and two years later a law was passed defining crude-oil waste, limiting crude production, and initiating proration. These laws, however, established only the broad base upon which state policy was built. Madcap operations and profligate waste, as at Burbank, Tonkawa, Garber, Greater Seminole, and Oklahoma City, were required to bring the operators' voluntary, and then state, control. It was not until April 10, 1933, that the legislature buttressed the Corporation Commission's orders with definitive regulations, when the Corporation Commission was in-

[3] *Report of the State Oil Inspector of the State of Kansas, January 1, 1891 to December 31, 1892,* 3 ff.; *General Statutes of Kansas, 1935,* Sections 55–115 and 55–116.

[4] *General Statutes,* 1935, Sections 55–110 and 55–111.

[5] "Protracted Struggle for Conservation Brought to Focus by Federal Code," in *The Petroleum Industry, 1859–1934* (published by *Oil and Gas Journal-Oil City Derrick*), 260.

vested with full power to prescribe rules and regulations and to issue orders for the prevention of the defined wastes.[6]

Texas also moved slowly with its oil-field control policy. The Corsicana field felt the mild restrictions of the state law of March 29, 1899.[7] Next came the amendatory enactments of 1905, 1913, and 1917. Although dealing primarily with pipe lines as common carriers, the law of 1917 also contained general provisions concerning waste. In 1917, too, the state constitution was amended, providing that "the conservation and development of all the natural resources of this state are each and all hereby declared public rights and duties and the legislature shall pass all such laws as may be appropriate thereto." Two years later the legislature enacted another law defining and prohibiting the waste of oil and gas and conferring broad regulatory power upon the Texas Railroad Commission.[8]

The unexampled waste of oil in the nineteen twenties and the early nineteen thirties, together with a market slump, prompted the legislature to exercise its rights under the 1917 constitutional amendment by enacting a Market Demand Law on November 12, 1932, after its Common Purchaser Act of March, 1930, and the Anti-Market-Demand Act of August, 1931, had proved faulty.[9] Then a second victory was won for the conservationists when in 1932 the state courts in the Danciger case (Danciger Oil and Refining Company vs. R. R. Comm. 49 SW [2nd] 837) upheld the authority of the Railroad Commission to limit production to current market demand in order to prevent waste and non-ratable takings.

Oil-producing states have named control agencies to implement their oil and gas conservation laws. At present Congress recognizes these and the federal courts generally support them. Federal courts

[6] W. P. Z. German, "Legal History of Conservation of Oil and Gas in Oklahoma," in *Legal History of Conservation of Oil and Gas*, 198. This book is hereafter cited as *Legal History*.

[7] Wallace E. Pratt, "The Basis of Proration in Texas," in *Bulletin of the American Association of Petroleum Geologists*, Vol. XXIII, No. 9 (September, 1939), 1314.

[8] *Oil and Gas Conservation Law and Rules and Regulations for the Conservation of Crude Oil and Natural Gas* (Oil and Gas Circular No. 11—Revised, Railroad Commission of Texas, Austin, July 1, 1920).

[9] In February, 1934, a federal district court finally upheld a Railroad Commission's order limiting the East Texas field's oil production to a reasonable market demand for oil from that field, thus recognizing this state's "economic waste" regulation.—Robert E. Hardwicke, "Legal History of Conservation of Oil in Texas," in *Legal History*, 214 ff.

rest the right of the state to control and prorate production on the grounds of the conservation of natural resources and the adjustment of correlative rights of adjoining landowners;[10] and state courts, by various interpretations of statutes, fall in line.

Litigation, controversy, violations of official "orders," and oil-field irregularities continued to harass state oil control during the thirties. Although state laws, rules, and regulations had been promulgated, it was not until the early nineteen forties that state enforcement was seated firmly in the saddle; but there are oil-field problems yet to solve and harmful practices to correct.

Kansas and Oklahoma vest control of oil fields and production in their corporation commissions; Texas, in its Railroad Commission. These three states were oil-producing pioneers and gave regulatory authority to agencies originally created for other purposes. Arkansas, Louisiana (also an early producer), and New Mexico, on the other hand, provided their control mechanisms later. The Arkansas Oil and Gas Commission regulates oil production in that state. In Louisiana, the control agency is called the Department of Conservation, Minerals Division; and in New Mexico, the Oil Conservation Commission. Regardless of differences in titles, procedures are much the same in all the states. Each group of officials holds hearings, requires bottom-hole pressure surveys and gas-oil ratio tests, investigates production, tests gas and oil wells, conducts certain kinds of research, and, in addition, supervises drilling, proration, and well-spacing.

Arkansas attempted to enforce conservation under several state laws, particularly in 1923, 1927, and 1933, before it passed its thoroughgoing enactment of 1939, basing its restrictions of oil and gas production on past experience.[11] The Louisiana legislature enacted a law that has met its every need—a law described by H. W. Bell as the most comprehensive ever to be written, although Louisiana's record of oil-field control is not better than that of any other Southwestern state. Governor Sam H. Jones approved the measure on July 12, 1940.[12] The bill recognizes conservation principles and

[10] "Administrative Regulation of Petroleum Production," in *Harvard Law Review*, Vol. LIX (1945–46), 1143.

[11] W. Henry Rector, "Legal History of Conservation . . . in Arkansas," in *Legal History of Conservation of Oil and Gas*, 22, 23.

[12] *A Survey of the Administration of Oil and Gas Conservation Laws . . .* (a re-

371

contains checks, balances, and controls growing out of oil-field experience. The Interstate Oil Compact Commission's legal committee drafted a proposed comprehensive oil and gas conservation law in 1940, which was revised in 1942 and 1946, embodying the best features of all the conservation laws.

In February, 1940, President J. C. Hunter of the Mid-Continent Oil and Gas Association told a House committee that "the record of achievement in the conservation of oil and gas is nothing short of remarkable. . . . One by one the states have enacted reasonably adequate conservation laws; these laws and the administrative regulations thereunder have been reviewed by the courts and their validity and limits established."[13] Congress has also generally supported state-control mechanisms in three ways: by its efforts to supplement or to support state regulations, by providing federal supervision over its own oil-producing lands, and by enacting temporary, over-all controls.

The federal government's oil-production control was brief. In December, 1924, President Calvin Coolidge startled the oil world with his statement, "It is evident that the present method of capturing oil is wasteful to an alarming degree."[14] He went on to say that the oil industry might work out its problems on the basis of the simple law of supply and demand were it not for the fact that the industry's welfare was so "intimately linked with the industrial prosperity and safety of the whole people." He believed that the time had come for government and industry to join forces to work out this problem, and appointed the Federal Oil Conservation Board, composed of the secretaries of the Interior, War, Navy, and Commerce, facetiously called "Coolidge's Four Wise Men."

The American Petroleum Institute accepted Coolidge's invitation to co-operate by naming a committee of seven oilmen, headed by Amos L. Beaty,[15] to recommend federal and state legislation for

print from the Interstate Oil Compact Commission's *Quarterly Bulletin*, Vol. II, No. 4 [December, 1943]), 21; Louisiana Department of Conservation, *Louisiana Oil and Gas Conservation Law*, Act 157, of 1940.

[13] *Petroleum Investigation, Hearing Before a Sub-committee on Interstate and Foreign Commerce, House of Representatives, Sixty-seventh Congress, Third Section on H. Res. 290 and H. R. 7372,* Part 4, 1959.

[14] "Protracted Struggle for Conservation . . . ," *loc. cit.*, 260.

[15] Other members of the committee were Messrs. Veasey, Ames, Townes, Weil, Byles, and Proctor.

Oil Conservation and Control

operator agreements and overproduction legislation. Presently this committee drew up a proposed enactment for each of the states of California, Oklahoma, and Texas, believing that these three states could accomplish the purposes sought by both the government and the industry. The proposed bill sanctioned agreements by "operators and others" to diminish or postpone crude-oil production when transportation facilities were inadequate or production exceeded consumption.[16] Beyond this recommendation, little progress was made in oil conservation.

Oilmen accepted with some reserve the Coolidge Oil Board and its recommendations; and when the Hoover administration ended, there were doubts that his own similar board would be continued.[17] However, the new president, Franklin D. Roosevelt, was still interested in the oil problem. His successful sponsorship of the National Recovery Act was followed by the naming of Harold L. Ickes as petroleum administrator. The President set up a new committee, appointing three men to represent the government, and asked the oil industry to appoint twelve other members. The new body, the Planning and Co-ordination Committee, was to advise the Petroleum Administration.

[16] "Protracted Struggle for Conservation . . . ," loc. cit., 260.

[17] President Hoover called an oil-conservation congress to assemble at the Broadmoor Hotel, Colorado Springs, on June 10, 1929, to consider the problem of overproduction. Federal officials present favored interstate action to solve this problem and hinted at federal control if this were not done. In the afternoon session, Wirt Franklin of Ardmore, Oklahoma, delivered an address opposing this idea and keynoting the independents' point of view by demanding "American markets for crude oil . . . for American producers of crude oil." Next day independent producers met at the Antlers Hotel and organized the Independent Petroleum Association of America with Franklin as its first president. It immediately launched a fight on foreign oil importation, and Congress met its demands two years later by enacting an excise tax of twenty-one cents a barrel on imported crude oil and two and one-half cents a barrel on gasoline.

In later years the IPAA (Independent Petroleum Association of America) was a staunch champion of the independent producer's rights and interests. Its presidents have been: Wirt Franklin, Ardmore, Oklahoma, 1926–35; Charles F. Roeser, Fort Worth, Texas, 1935–39; Frank Buttram, Oklahoma City, Oklahoma, 1939–43; Ralph T. Zook, Bradford, Pennsylvania, 1943–45; B. A. Hardey, Shreveport, Louisiana, 1945–47; and Merle Becker, St. Louis, Missouri, 1947– still serving. Each oil-producing state (Texas, Louisiana, Arkansas, Oklahoma, Colorado, Montana, Kansas, and New Mexico) was given an executive vice-president at the Colorado Springs meeting. H. B. Fell (executive vice-president of IPAA) furnished the author with the minutes of the Colorado Springs organization meeting of June 11, 1929, and with other documents relating to IPAA's founding, growth, and work.

Oil! Titan of the Southwest

This committee accomplished little more than the Coolidge board. It considered fixing a code price for crude oil at 18.5 times the price of gasoline, but prolonged discussions in the Planning and Co-ordination Committee and throughout the industry caused the proposal to be dropped. Next, it sponsored a marketing and purchasing agreement within the industry, but this idea was finally elbowed aside in favor of a plan to have the companies buy excess East Texas gasoline, if the producers would abstain from overproduction. This proposal likewise failed. Oil operators did not like to have Washington "swivel-chair experts" tell them what to do.

Throughout the life of these two committees, Southwestern oilmen objected to every trend toward federal control of their industry. The Petroleum Administrator had promoted a federal control bill (the Thomas-Disney bill). But Texas opposition in the House and Senate and lack of time at the close of the session caused its defeat. Then a House committee was named to investigate the necessity for such a move.

Although under NRA, and through the Petroleum Code, the federal government exercised wide but temporary control over oil production, no similar peacetime effort has since been made, despite repeated suggestions in Congressional committee hearings for such supervision. Yet the Petroleum Conservation Division of the Department of the Interior, charged with the enforcement of the Connally Act through a system of tender boards and permits, has been accepted by the oil industry and has rendered valuable aid to state conservation.

Meanwhile, working independently, certain oilmen had proposed two co-operative conservation plans. Unitization was the first, a plan suggested by H. L. Doherty at a meeting of the American Petroleum Institute at Fort Worth, Texas, in 1924, although it was his idea that the federal government should control. Unitization, as defined by a Mid-Continent Oil and Gas Association committee, means that divided interests in an oil and gas pool containing a number of tracts of land be converted into the area's undivided interests, "where the owner of the oil or gas rights in an individual tract (or tracts) of land surrenders his exclusive ownership thereof in return for an assignment to him of an undivided interest in the oil and gas rights of the pool as a whole." The purpose was "to develop

374

and operate the area as one property or unit through the instrumentality of a common agent, trustee, or committee and thus avoid unnecessary competitive drilling, waste of gas and duplication of effort and secure greater recovery of oil at less cost."[18]

Unitization had already been tried. In a committee report from the American Institute of Mining Engineers, Petroleum Division, presented at its annual meeting in New York in February, 1930, it was shown that approximately 185 unitization projects were already in successful operation in the United States and foreign countries. And still more recently, the unit concept has increased in favor among oilmen.

The second proposal related to interstate action. Southwestern oilmen had repeatedly suggested this procedure to state officials. And governors of the oil-producing states met again and again after 1931 to work out an oil-compact agreement.[19] On February 28, 1931, the governors of Texas, New Mexico, Kansas, and Oklahoma met in Fort Worth and agreed to the naming of a "Governors' Committee," later known as the Oil States' Advisory Committee. In the following spring four other meetings were held, and at Austin on May 3 and 4, a tentative draft of a Uniform Legislative Act for Conservation and Interstate Compact was approved. After further meetings, the proposed measure was presented to Congress, but it failed to pass. Then through other meetings in 1932, 1933, and 1934 the objectionable features of earlier compact proposals were eliminated. After discussing the proposed compact with President Roosevelt early in 1933, Colonel Ernest O. Thompson called a meeting in Washington of the governors of all the oil-producing states to form a compact. The meeting was held, but no decision was reached. The passage of the National Recovery Act in June, 1933, and the adoption of the Code of Fair Competition for the Petroleum Industry temporarily shelved the compact movement.

Then in December, 1934, Chairman William P. Cole, Jr.'s subcommittee of the House Committee on Interstate and Foreign Commerce suggested that "A state compact . . . is the solution of

---

[18] "Protracted Struggle for Conservation . . . ," *loc. cit.*, 260.

[19] Claude Barrow says that a critic of unitization refused to recognize its paternity, saying that it is like the Chinese orphan found in Central America by O'Henry, which "had no mother but was conceived by a father who killed himself in infancy." —Claude Barrow, "Compact-1, The Oklahoma City Oil Field."

those problems of petroleum production" of interstate scope, and recommended that Congress enact no federal-control legislation until state governors had been given a chance to work out such a plan.[20]

In answer from the Secretary of the Interior came this assertion: "Interstate compacts have been tried over and over again and they have failed. . . . I disapprove."[21]

Nevertheless, E. W. Marland and others sponsoring the compact lost no time acting on the Cole Committee's suggestion, in meetings at Marland's home in Ponca City, on December 3, 1934, and on January 3, 1935. Indeed, an "interstate compact" was written into Marland's platform for the Oklahoma governorship in 1934. At last, during the 1935 sessions, the states of California, Illinois, Kansas, New Mexico, Oklahoma, and Texas approved the compact. By 1945 seventeen states had agreed to it; and at present twenty states are members, with Georgia as an associate member. Congress added its endorsement by Public Resolution No. 64, on August 27, 1935, after it had previously failed to approve a House Resolution setting up a Federal Petroleum Administrative Board.

The one purpose of the compact is found in Article II of the "Text of the Compact": "The purpose of this Compact is to conserve oil and gas by the prevention of physical waste thereof from any cause."[22]

The Compact Commission, now serving twenty-one member states, seeks to accomplish its purpose in several ways. Among other activities, it prepares, recommends, and distributes the best forms of oil and gas conservation laws, and rules and regulations for the information of governors, legislatures, state control officials, and the industry; it gathers and disseminates engineering and other scientific information; it conducts an educational program on conservation through the columns of newspapers and magazines and by public addresses, motion pictures, and forums; and it encourages each state to adopt efficient rules and regulations for a comprehensive oil and gas conservation program.

[20] "The Interstate Oil Compact Commission," in *Rocky Mountain Petroleum Yearbook* (1945), 91.

[21] Quoted in Barrow, "Compact-8," *loc. cit.*

[22] Pamphlet, *The Interstate Compact to Conserve Oil and Gas*, 11.

Digging up pipes used in running "hot oil"

Cattle pasture near a row of derricks laid out on a forty-
acre spacing plan, West Edmond field, Oklahoma

photograph by Corsini
Standard Oil Company (N. J.)

"Christmas tree" over casing head of Carter L. Whistler
No. 2, West Edmond, Oklahoma

photograph by Corsini
Standard Oil Company (N. J.)

Oil Conservation and Control

One oil expert has said that the Interstate Compact has dramatized not only the fact of state sovereignty, but also its need and sufficiency. The willingness of the individual state to follow the Commission's lead and to work harmoniously with other states for conservation, apparently proves that federal control is unnecessary.[23]

[23] "The Interstate Oil Compact Commission," *loc. cit.*, 92–93.

XXVI

An Era of Specialization

THE OIL INDUSTRY of the Southwest has emerged from the shadows of World War II as one of America's most highly specialized businesses. Its every department—prospecting, drilling, production, refining, and marketing—has felt the impact of change.

Never before in Southwestern industrial experience has science been given a freer hand in the shaping of an enterprise. At present, chemistry, engineering, and geology help to solve the oil industry's intricate and multiple problems; research laboratories of the major companies employ many full-time, highly trained scientists; and there is a growing number of consulting chemists, engineers, and geologists. Both national and regional trade journals help to promote the new movement and serve as media supplying oilmen with news and feature articles concerning the most recent scientific improvements and innovations in their several fields.[1]

---

[1] The *National Petroleum News* has been and is now the leading general oil-industry trade journal on a national front. It was founded in February, 1909, by Warren C. Platt, a Cleveland newspaper reporter, who thus sought to champion the rights and interests of complaining independent refiners against the competitive practices of the Standard Oil Company. A short time later, however, Platt recognized a broader field of service—of reporting accurately and promptly the general developments in the fast growing oil industry. During World War I the *News* was changed from a monthly to a weekly (in December, 1917) to keep pace with the industry's news tempo. Platt also published more specialized trade periodicals.

The *Petroleum Engineer,* founded in October, 1929, represented a more specialized field. It sought to provide men engaged in the petroleum industry with current factual and technical and semitechnical information, in 1929 emphasizing the necessity for higher rotating speeds in drilling and carrying an article on electrical well logging, a technique not yet used in United States oil fields.

The Southwest also has its own general oil trade journals, the *Oil and Gas Journal* and *World Oil.* The *Oil and Gas Journal,* founded in 1910 by Patrick C. Boyle, grew out of a semimonthly publication known as the *Oil Investors' Journal.* Boyle estab-

An Era of Specialization

This accent on science has been influential in accelerating oil production. For the first seven years of the present decade, the Southwest's oil output, with slight year-to-year fluctuations, has gradually increased, from 884,000,000 barrels in 1940 to 1,334,196,-000 barrels in 1947. Only specialization and scientific techniques, coupled with fairly strict state control, could have made this possible. And this improvement has been made in spite of the public's clamor for more oil, occasional "oil shortage" news releases from Washington, and frequent suggestions of federal control to avert an oil-supply breakdown.

Two unexpected factors during 1945 caused oil consumption to go far beyond reasonable expectations: an unprecedented increase in the number of automobiles, causing additional heavy demands for gasoline and lubricants; and the widespread substitution of oil burners for coal burners in homes and business houses, in some instances in areas adjacent to coal fields. Moreover, other oil products, from "fly-flit" to synthetic rubber, have established a varied market. It should also be mentioned that at the same time gas burners and furnaces were being installed in the Southwest.

In 1945 the total United States demand for all oils, 1,952,000,000 barrels, was 22 per cent above the prewar peak of 1941.[2] This represented a gain of 73,000,000 barrels over the previous year, including an increase of 7.1 per cent for motor fuel, 7 per cent for kerosene, 2.9 per cent for distillate fuel, and 2.7 per cent for lubricating oils. The total demand for residual fuel oil rose from 524,000,000 barrels in 1944 to 535,000,000 in 1945.

These increased demands of 1945, when added to normal consumption, strained every department of the oil industry. But spe-

lished his new publication in Tulsa, Oklahoma, as a weekly, and a short time later branch offices were set up at Houston and Fort Worth, Texas, at Shreveport, Louisiana, at Los Angeles, California, at Casper, Wyoming, and at Toledo, Ohio. Six years later, in September, the *Gulf Coast Oil News* also appeared. In 1918, under the editorship of Ray L. Dudley, a well-trained newsman, it changed its name to the *Oil Weekly*, and still later, in 1947, to *World Oil*. The present editor of the *Oil and Gas Journal* is C. O. Willson, and of *World Oil*, Warren L. Baker. Both editors represent the finest traditions of their profession. Indeed, both national and regional publications have grown in popularity primarily because of their editors' policies of timely and complete news-coverage and dependable feature articles. Their publishers also supply each division of the industry with specialized information either through special editions or publications or both.

[2] *Minerals Yearbook of the United States, 1945, Part II, Nonmetals,* 1042.

379

cialized methods in prospecting, in drilling, in production, and in refining enabled the industry to fill every need.

New geophysical prospecting techniques are commonly employed in present-day operations to supplement geological surveys. Deep horizons are not always indicated by surface structure. Geophysicists must find them so that their oil-bearing zones may be tapped. This calls for the employment of either the seismograph, the magnetometer, or the gravity meter, the choice of instruments depending on cost, desire for speed, and, to some extent, the kind of structure to be surveyed.

The Interstate Compact Commission's report of December, 1947, reveals the importance of this kind of prospecting. It lists 529 geophysical and core-drilling crews searching for oil- and gas-bearing traps on the last day of the year. Of these, 372 geophysical crews and 18 core-drilling crews were at work in the Southwest. Southern Louisiana was the scene of greatest activity, having 80 geophysical crews, and Southwest Texas was next with 57 crews. Then came Oklahoma with 52, East Texas with 22, Arkansas with 18, New Mexico with 15, and Kansas with 11.[3]

Intensive work of this sort brought results. During the postwar period of a drilling-equipment shortage, there was a rise in United States well completions, which, in fact, brought the industry back to a normal level. During 1946 a total of 30,840 wells were completed, an increase of 3,700 over the previous year, of which 19,179 were producers. Texas led in the total number of new wells drilled, with Louisiana second and Oklahoma third. Then in 1947, 33,646 wells of all kinds were completed, an increase of 9 per cent over the previous year and the largest number since 1937.

The drilling of wildcat wells, merely one phase of a company's operations, demonstrates the great risk and advancing cost involved in today's oil business. The increasing depth of wells is seen by comparing the 21,990 wells completed in 1942 at an average depth of 3,088 feet with the 33,646 wells five years later at an average depth of 3,365 feet. A large percentage of these wells were dry holes. In 1946, 1,591 wells were drilled in one Southwestern state, of which only 281, or 16.55 per cent, made producers. In 1947 there

[3] *Statistical Bulletin,* Vol. II, No. 10 (Interstate Oil Compact Commission, January 15, 1948), 14.

were 3,736 exploratory test wells drilled in the Southwest, of which 2,905 were dry.[4] Yet each well was drilled at a staggering cost. The drilling of a well 3,000 feet deep often costs $3.50 a foot; one at 8,000 feet, $8.00 a foot; and at 12,000 feet, from $20.00 to $55.00 a foot, or even more.

Proof of increasing drilling costs is provided by the records of one Texas company. In 1937 it completed its wells with an average expenditure of $22,000 each, and ten years later, of $86,000.[5] In 1947 its dry-hole costs amounted to $17,000,000 for 130 wells.

In 1947 the average depth of wells was slightly under the record of 3,469 feet per well drilled in 1945, but enough over the 1946 average to indicate a definite trend toward deeper drilling. The deepest drilling in 1947 was in Louisiana, with the average at 5,241 feet per well; and the shallowest wells were in Oklahoma, with an average of 3,077 feet.[6] The other four states of the Southwest in this year ranged between these extremes. The greatest depth ever reached was by the Superior Oil Company's Weller 51–11 well, a wildcat test in Caddo County, Oklahoma, that reached 17,823 feet (almost three and one-half miles) and was completed as a dry hole. The total 1947 oil-well footage drilled was greater than 110,000,000 feet, more than 18,000 miles of hole, or nearly three times the diameter of the earth.

Southwestern drilling has been scientific in both machinery and methods. Recently, new drilling techniques have appeared from a backlog of drawing-board and laboratory ideas that accumulated during the war.

Among these was a new use of "directional drilling" in marine operations, by which special tools are used in conjunction with regular rotary rigs to drill "directional" branches from the main vertical well bore (by turbine bit and electric drill).[7] This tech-

[4] Cecil Smith, "Wildcat Drilling Highest Despite Handicaps," in *World Oil,* Vol. CXXVII, No. 11 (Yearbook, February, 1948), 140.

[5] "Drilling Costs Rise Sharply in Ten Years," in *World Oil,* Vol. CXXVIII, No. 1 (May, 1948), 53.

[6] J. E. Kastrop, "Drilling Technology Progress," in *World Oil,* Vol. CXXVII, No. 11 (Yearbook, 1947), 120–22.

[7] For an example of the revolutionary changes that came in the construction of drilling rigs, see Leigh S. McCaslin, Jr., "Many Heavy Rig Features in New Portable Rig for Shallow-Well Drilling," in *Oil and Gas Journal,* Vol. XLVI, No. 52 (April 29, 1948), 124.

nique is used to economize in marine drilling from a single plat-form, to tap large reserves lying below the shallow Gulf Coast waters. It was recently employed in connection with the sensa-tional Kerr-McGee Oil Industries[8]–Phillips Petroleum Company–Stanolind Oil and Gas Company project to drill their first offshore producer. Their No. 1 well, ten and one-half miles from the Lou-isiana shore, off Terrebonne Parish, promises extensive marine operations. This technique also embraces the construction of a drilling platform to stand the shock of wave action and the build-ing of a barge (a floating dock) to accommodate the enormous amount of equipment.[9]

Other improvements have come in oil-well surveying (radioac-tivity logging), wire-line measurements, the improvement of drill-ing fluids, the diamond-core bit, reverse circulation, metals, and tools for cutting and fishing, automatic control of rotary rigs, and portable electric rigs. All of these became realities only after engi-neers, chemists, and physicists spent long hours over their drawing boards and in their experimental laboratories.

Crude-oil and natural-gasoline production was also stimulated by scientific research, production reaching nearly 2,000,000,000 barrels in 1947. Of this amount, the Southwest produced 1,428,-572,000 barrels, the Texas output alone being 881,808,000. Lou-isiana, Oklahoma, Kansas, Arkansas, and New Mexico accounted, in order, for the remaining amount.

[8] Kerr-McGee Oil Industries, Incorporated, had its beginning in the Anderson-Kerr Drilling Company, previously mentioned. In 1936, Anderson sold his interest and the two firm names of Anderson-Kerr Drilling Company and A and K Petroleum Corporation were changed to Kerlyn Oil Company and Kerr-Lynn and Company. Partners in Kerr-Lynn and Company (which owned 95 per cent of Kerlyn Oil Com-pany) included Kerr, Robert Lynn, Dean A. McGee, T. M. Kerr, T. W. Fentem, and Dean Terrill. In August, 1942, Kerr-Lynn and Company assets were sold to Kerlyn Oil Company and Lynn sold out (Kerr-Lynn had nine rigs at this time). In January, 1946, the present name of Kerr-McGee Oil Industries, Incorporated, was adopted. Kerr-McGee has built up oil and gas production to a monthly volume of $250,000 and has rigs running in Wyoming, Colorado, Utah, Oklahoma, Texas Panhandle, West and East Texas, North Louisiana, and the Gulf Coast.—D. A. McGee to C. C. Rister, April 6, 1948.

[9] By January, 1948, at least twenty companies were aggressively engaged in exploring and drilling this offshore area. There were twenty-eight reflection seismo-graph crews and two gravity-meter units at work.—Manuscript copy, "Offshore Drill-ing Development," written for the A. P. I. District Meeting in San Antonio, April 16, 1948, and furnished the author by Mr. D. A. McGee, executive vice-president, Kerr-McGee Oil Industries.

An Era of Specialization

Each Southwestern state bettered its output of the previous year: New Mexico, by 11.6 per cent; Arkansas, by 6 per cent; Kansas, by 8.3 per cent; and Oklahoma by 4.6 per cent, reversing its slight drop of the previous year and resuming its slow climb started in 1944.

In 1947 the 110 major oil fields, each having an ultimate output of at least 100,000,000 barrels, produced nearly 50 per cent of the nation's oil. Of these fields, sixty-eight are in the Southwest: fifteen in Oklahoma, three in Kansas, two in Arkansas, six in Louisiana, four in New Mexico, and thirty-eight in Texas.[10]

Past accomplishments indicate that other major oil accumulations may yet be found. In 1942 the Fullerton field in West Texas was discovered; in 1943, the Cranfield and Heidelberg fields of Mississippi, and the West Edmond field of Oklahoma; and in 1944, the Delhi–Big Lake field in Louisiana and the T-X-L field of West Texas. The Benedum-Slick field near Midland, Texas, and the Cross Roads field in Northeastern Lea County, New Mexico, are among the latest discoveries which promise to become major fields.

Science also revolutionized refining. Samuel Kier's petroleum and refining experiments during the eighteen forties were an earnest of one of the greatest research and development programs ever launched by an American industry. The ultimate result has been the present-day modern, giant refinery. Every modern refinery represents hundreds of improvements and intricate processes making standardized perfection. From it may issue as many as 5,400 petroleum by-products, which add to the comfort and convenience of the United States citizen and assist in maintaining his high standard of living.[11] It would be difficult to imagine American life without petroleum products.

As in other divisions of the industry, so each annual report in refining brings record-breaking totals. In 1945, American refineries processed an all-time high of 774,460,000 barrels of gasoline, or more than 50,000,000 barrels above the output of the previous year. Crude runs to stills moved from 1,666,000,000 barrels in 1944 to

[10] Herndon David, "110 Major Fields Produced Nearly 50 Per Cent of Oil in 1947," in *Oil and Gas Journal*, Vol. XLVI, No. 39 (Review and Forecast Number, January 29, 1948), 168–69.

[11] Frank Carlson, "Federal Control Threatens Oil Industry," in *World Oil*, Vol. CXXVII, No. 11 (Yearbook, 1948), 100.

Oil! Titan of the Southwest

1,720,000,000 barrels in the next year, although for the first eight months of the year the war was still being fought. During the last four months of 1945, the total quantity of aviation gasoline, including components, transferred to other and now peacetime products, were abnormally large, reaching 57 per cent as compared with 3 per cent for the first eight months of the year.

Since 1945, both oil production and demand have steadily increased. Crude-oil production in the United States increased about 32.4 per cent from 1941 to 1947, and natural gasoline and light petroleum gases jumped more than 60 per cent, because of the increased refining of liquefied petroleum gases. The 1947 output of light petroleum gases was 167 per cent greater than in 1941. The 1947 gasoline output (including straight-run, cracked, and natural blended) totaled 814,150,000 barrels or 2,231,000 barrels daily, 8.8 per cent more than in 1946.

Active Refineries in the Southwestern States, 1928[12]

	No. Refineries	Barrels Daily Crude Oil Capacity	Cracking Capacity
Arkansas	6	53,000	21,150
Kansas	18	201,900	139,450
Louisiana	13	420,100	244,300
New Mexico	8	15,750	5,850
Oklahoma	25	260,200	147,950
Texas	81	1,733,850	1,068,000
Total for Southwestern States	151	2,684,800	1,626,700
Total for United States	369	5,969,525	3,752,220

There were seven million more automobiles in use in 1947 than in 1944.[13] This increase, due in part to a higher per capita income and more leisure time for car owners, and in part to after-the-war replacements, naturally influenced gasoline consumption to a

[12] "North American Operating Refineries, Their Capacities and Locations," in the Oil and Gas Journal, Vol. XLVI, No. 48 (April 1, 1948), 227.

[13] Text of Governor Beauford Jester's speech delivered at the LaSalle Hotel, Chicago, Illinois, on May 6, 1948, before the Interstate Oil Compact Commission, which Governor Jester kindly furnished the author.

Halliburton cement outfit, Tonkawa, Oklahoma, 1923

Seismograph charge near Huntsville, Texas

THE SEISMOGRAPH
EAVESDROPPING ON MOTHER NATURE

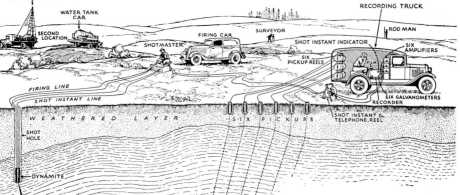

Long used for recording and measuring earthquakes, the seismograph has in recent years played an extremely important part in oil exploration. It is the most accurate method now known to science for mapping sub-surface formations and structures.

A charge of dynamite is exploded in shot holes, drilled at selected locations, and the resulting seismic waves travel downward through the earth until they reach the underlying hard formations. Reflected by these structures, they are picked up at the surface by sensitive receiving sets. The time interval between the explosion and the appearance of the reflected seismic waves is accurately measured to one-thousandth of a second by means of a specially calibrated tuning-fork.

The entire operation is repeated until sufficient information is collected to permit the making of highly accurate profile maps of the underlying geological structure.

The Shield, *Phillips Petroleum Company, June, 1937*

An Era of Specialization

marked degree. Motor-car gasoline requirements increased more than 77,000 barrels daily from 1941 to 1947, almost one-third of which was the result of the greater number of passenger cars in operation and two-thirds to meet the additional mileage following abandonment of rationing.

The 1947 demand for Diesel fuel was also significant, rising 158 per cent above that of 1941. Almost 100 per cent more mechanized equipment, including tractors (which used gasoline), was used on farms than in 1941. Among the many industrial users of the Diesel engine on a wide scale are the nation's railroads, which increased Diesel oil purchases 42 per cent from 1946 to 1947. This signified a change from coal and oil-burning locomotives to Diesel engines. The rivalry of air travel with motor and rail transportation gave added impetus to experiments with and final acceptance of this type of engine. Diesel engines in service on railroads in 1947 were twenty-two times greater than in 1937.[14]

Crude-oil production and runs to stills in 1947 were not far apart; the daily crude-oil output totaled 5,085,000 barrels, and runs to stills, 5,075,000 barrels, of which the Texas and Louisiana Gulf Coast processed 1,581,441 barrels. But the industry's chief concern was the problem of manufacturing enough gas oil and distillate fuel oil to satisfy demands. Since 1941 the output of distillate fuel oil, including heating oil, necessarily has been increased more than that of other products. By adjusting upward the amount of distillate fuels taken from crude runs to stills, refiners of 1947 produced almost one-third of a billion barrels. Even this record-breaking output of distillate fuel oils could not satisfy the demand, and stocks at the end of the year were 8,539,000 barrels less than those of the previous year.[15]

Almost one-half the nation's 369 refineries, and the output of more than one-third of their products, are concentrated in the Southwest, the Gulf Coast having fifty in 1948, of which thirty-eight are in Texas, eight in Louisiana, one in Mississippi and two in Alabama, with a total daily capacity of 1,833,450 barrels. The

[14] "Demand for Petroleum and Products Will Average 6,152,000 Bbl. Daily," in *Oil and Gas Journal*, Vol. XLVI, No. 39 (Review and Forecast Number, January 29, 1948), 179.

[15] *World Oil*, Vol. CXXVII, No. 11 (Yearbook Forecast Issue, February, 1948), 192.

Oil! Titan of the Southwest

Texas-Louisiana Gulf Coast is the site of eight of the nation's fifteen major refineries, each with a daily capacity of 100,000 or more barrels—the Gulf and Texas companies at Port Arthur, the Humble at Baytown, the Esso Standard Oil at Baton Rouge, the Cities Service at Lake Charles, the Magnolia at Beaumont, the Pan American at Texas City, and the Shell at Houston. Each refinery is the focus of railroads and pipe lines daily feeding large quantities of crude oil into storage tanks for processing. And ocean-going tankers and coastwise and canal barges slip in and out of port with their holds laden with valuable cargoes.

By day the modern refinery with its maze of large and small pipes, each filled with oil, gas, or water; its tall catalytic crackers, fractionating towers, and stills; and its glowing furnaces, some generating more heat than the fiery furnace of ancient Hebrew days; and its hundreds of tin-hatted men—carpenters, compounders, electricians, firemen, machinists, pipe-fitters, pump men, still men, treaters, and others[16]—engaged in their various tasks, such as checking, testing, watching dials, and conducting laboratory experiments—all tend to create a sense of the unreal. At night, too, the hissing of steam, the drumming of the giant "cat" crackers, the leaping flares ribboning the sky with fire, and the winking of innumerable electric lights tell of an industry that does not sleep.

These Cities of Steel not only power and lubricate America's machines on our highways and railroads and in factories and shops, but also stimulate growth in neighboring towns and cities. Houston is an example, with its near-by Humble refinery at Baytown, and its smaller Sinclair, Texas Company, Shell, Crown Central, Eastern States, and Maritime oil plants, which have helped it to grow into a great industrial metropolis.

The Texas refineries are concentrated in three areas: Beaumont-Port Arthur, Houston–Texas City, and Corpus Christi. These three centers account for 80 per cent of the Gulf Coast's refined oil.

The Beaumont–Port Arthur area has its Texas Company, Gulf, Magnolia, and Atlantic refineries, processing daily approximately one-half million barrels of crude oil; and, with many millions of

[16] For the several classes, see United States Department of Labor, Bureau of Labor Statistics, Division of Wage Analysis, pamphlet, *Earnings in Southwestern Petroleum Industry, April, 1943, Bull. No. 762, 27.*

dollars invested in complementary plants, it rivals Houston in potential industrial greatness. Both Beaumont and Houston are inland cities, but both support heavy Gulf Coast and overseas commerce, Beaumont with its Neches-Sabine Waterway and Houston with its Ship Canal. Both cities receive daily many thousands of barrels of crude oil, from Arkansas and Louisiana fields, from the far-off Mid-Continent area, from North Texas, from the Panhandle, from the Permian Basin country of western Texas and New Mexico, and from East Texas.

The two large Louisiana refineries, at Baton Rouge and Lake Charles, have similar shipping advantages. Here, as elsewhere, two decades of refinery improvements, 1926 to 1946, have wrought marked changes to supply a growing market. During this twenty-year period many grades of petroleum products have been made. Today, "tailor-made" gasoline is a far cry from the "virgin" naphtha sold in 1926.

Refinery changes at Baton Rouge during the first decade of this twenty-year period are typical of those in other major Southwestern plants. Here during the nineteen-thirties were installed thermal cracking units to secure high-octane gasoline; gas-absorption plants to recover light fractions, which previously had been lost; crude pipe stills for improved fractionating; a hydrogenation process to improve the quality of lubricating oil fractions; a phenol-treating process to extract undesirable oil components from lubricating oil fractions; and methods of barisol dewaxing and propane deasphalting and dewaxing.

Then came the early nineteen-forties, the war, and its demands. Like other big plants, Baton Rouge added new units—for an alkylation process to convert gaseous fractions into high-octane alkylate; for perbunan and butyl rubber; for steam cracking; for fluid catalytic cracking; for making alcohol from cracked gasses; and for an isomerization process to convert normal butane into isobutane needed for the manufacture of aviation gasoline.[17]

After the war, the United States oil industry inaugurated for 1947–48 a capital expenditure of $4,000,000,000, of which 22.1 per

[17] Manuscript copy, "Baton Rouge Refinery." This and other data were furnished the author by Mr. W. B. Cotten, Jr., Public Relations Department, Standard Oil Company (N. J.), Baton Rouge, Louisiana.

cent, or almost $1,000,000,000, was earmarked for refinery improvements. A part of these expenditures have been, and will yet be, made for replacements of worn-out installations, but a major share will be used to procure new catalytic cracking units to substitute for thermal cracking to meet the increasing demand for high-octane gasoline.

Two vacuum pipe stills of 18,500- and 14,500-barrel capacity, an atmospheric still of 58,000-barrel capacity, additional wax and lubricating manufacturing facilities, a new lube dewaxing plant, a light-ends recovery unit with a daily capacity of 20,000,000 cubic feet, and a 4,000-barrel polymerization unit are now under construction at Baton Rouge.

The new Cities Service refinery at Lake Charles was built as a war measure at an estimated cost of $76,000,000. Three giant catalytic cracking units form its heart. It also has such familiar units as a treating plant, and straight-run fractionating, alkylation, deasphalting-desalting, and topping. It has emerged from the war period one of the Southwest's most modern refineries. At present, Cities Service and Continental also have a major lube plant under construction at Lake Charles.

. Mid-1948 found the Beaumont–Port Arthur refining area engaged in a comprehensive construction program. The Texas Company is building facilities to increase its capacities by about 2,500 barrels daily of finished oils, including lube and wax-manufacturing equipment, all at a cost of $15,000,000.[18] The Gulf Oil Corporation has just completed or has under construction three topping and vacuum units and a catalytic desulphurization plant.[19] And at Beaumont, the Magnolia Petroleum Company is building dewaxing, solvent-extraction, and vacuum units, and a crude still.[20]

In the Houston–Texas City area more than $70,000,000 had been earmarked for construction by June, 1948. The Humble Oil and Refining Company plant at Baytown had completed or under construction a $20,000,000 building program. From its beginning in 1919 until January, 1948, this refinery's crude runs to stills exceeded

[18] Dahl M. Duff, "Gulf Coast Refining," in *Oil and Gas Journal*, Vol. XLVII, No. 8 (June 24, 1948), 228.

[19] R. B. Tuttle, "Expansion Under Way Will Boost Crude Charging Capacity to 6,000,000 Bbl. Daily," *ibid.*, Vol. XLVI, No. 48 (April, 1948), 178.

[20] Duff, *loc. cit.*, 223.

An Era of Specialization

1,054,000,000 barrels. At present the plant is processing about 245,-000 barrels daily.

Dahl N. Duff classifies the Humble Refinery as the largest in the United States, although comparisons are difficult. Certainly it ranks among the leaders. It has a new 400-foot dock under construction on the ship canal at Baytown, so that the refinery will soon have facilities for loading ten vessels at one time. It has recently completed a new lube dewaxing plant and is planning a second phenol lube plant and a fourth pipe still.[21] It has installed facilities to recover and handle 2,000 barrels daily of propane to help meet the increased demand for liquefied petroleum gases, and it produced for the first time in 1947, and sold as a new raw material for chemical manufacturing, commercial quantities of cyclohexane. Humble is also constructing at Baytown a new central shop building where most of the plant maintenance work will be done.

In the same area, two other major refineries, Shell and Sinclair, are also engaged in extensive building. Shell has started a $50,000,-000 construction program at its adjacent Chemical Corporation plant and is spending $33,000,000 in a lube plant. It also has under construction additional power-plant facilities to cost $7,500,000, a $500,000 wax plant, and it has completed (in June, 1948) a $1,000,-000 control laboratory. Sinclair is engaged in a $35,000,000 building program which includes a grease house, barrel works, and a new lube plant.

At Corpus Christi the Southwestern Oil and Refining Company, a small refinery, is constructing a catalytic reformer and polymerization unit. At present it is a skimming plant of 18,000-barrel capacity.

Many operators of small refineries, especially of 10,000-barrel capacity or less, not having the capital to buy improved or new units, are being forced out of business. Even during the period 1940 to 1946, the total number of such refineries decreased from 363 to 252.

Those refineries that survived sought within the bounds of their means to keep step with larger competitors, and many succeeded. At El Dorado, Arkansas, T. H. Barton had pioneered with the Lion Oil Company. This company now showed the way with a modern

[21] *Loc. cit.;* MS, "History of Baytown Refinery," furnished the author by Mr. W. N. Finnegan, Jr., Humble Oil and Refining Company, Houston, Texas.

plant of 22,000-barrel capacity. After the war, to keep stride with its big competitors, Lion installed a thermofor catalytic cracking unit at a cost of $1,500,000, and operated a government-owned chemical plant for the making of anhydrous ammonia, aqua ammonia, solid ammonium nitrate fertilizer, and ammonium nitrate solutions. In addition, the refinery produced aviation and automotive gasolines, lubricants, tractor fuel, kerosene, asphalts, butadiene, road oil, fuel oil, and butane, and propane liquid petroleum gases.[22]

The Root Petroleum Company also operated an El Dorado refinery of 20,000-barrel capacity to compete for Arkansas' crude oil. Then there were smaller Arkansas refineries: the Berry Asphalt Company at Stephens, the Harry H. Cross Company at Smackover, and the McMillan Petroleum Company at Norphlet. At present, the state's total refinery crude-oil capacity is 53,200 barrels and its cracking capacity, 21,150 barrels.

Kansas and Oklahoma also have creditable refinery records,[23] although without 100,000-barrel-capacity plants. In Kansas there are eighteen refineries with a total crude-oil capacity of 201,900 barrels and a daily cracking capacity of 139,450 barrels, ranging in size from the small 1,000-barrel Chanute Refining Company plant to the Phillips Petroleum 36,000-barrel refinery at Kansas City. Other refinery towns are Wichita, McPherson, Coffeyville, Phillipsburg, Arkansas City, Shallow Water, Eldorado, Augusta, Neodesha, and Potwin, with such major operators represented as Phillips, Sinclair, Skelly, Socony-Vacuum, and Standard Oil (Indiana).

Oklahoma has twenty-five refineries, with Tulsa and Ponca City as the two leading refining cities. In West Tulsa, south of the Arkansas River from Tulsa proper, is the Mid-Continent Petroleum's 45,-000-barrel-capacity plant, and The Texas Company's 21,000-barrel refinery. At the growing town of Ponca City, Continental Oil's 33,-000-barrel-capacity plant has a good record. Other Oklahoma refinery centers are Stroud, Cyril, Barnsdall, Grandfield, Ardmore, Enid (Champlin refinery of 18,000 barrels capacity), Cushing, Edmond, Wynnewood, Cleveland, Oklahoma City, Okmulgee, Duncan, Sand Springs, Allen, Drumright, and Bristow. The crude-oil

[22] Manuscript copy, "Lion Oil Company." This and other data was furnished the author by the Lion Oil Company, El Dorado, Arkansas.
[23] "North American Operating Refineries," *loc. cit.*, 228, 230.

capacity of Oklahoma refineries is 260,200 barrels and their cracking capacity, 147,950 barrels.

But much crude oil has moved and still moves by tanker, tank car, and pipe line to refineries outside the Southwest, to the Sun and Sinclair refineries at Marcus Hook and the Atlantic and Gulf at Philadelphia; to Standard Oil's (New Jersey) at Linden and Bayonne and Tidewater's at Bayonne, New Jersey; and to other plants in the Eastern states, in Illinois, Indiana, and Ohio. Each of these refineries has also been mechanically transformed to meet modern demands.

Yet future demands will cause other changes. With scientists predicting 500,000 products by synthesizing natural and refinery gases, almost unbelievable developments are yet possible. The average citizen is only vaguely aware of breath-taking miracles now being performed with hydrocarbon molecules of gas and oil. Of course, he is familiar with synthetic rubber; but he has yet to learn of vastly superior paints, textiles, plastics, cosmetics, medicines, fertilizers, and chemicals in limitless numbers promised by scientists working in laboratories and manufacturing plants.

XXVII

The Impacts of Petroleum

AT BEAUMONT, TEXAS, on the site of the famous Spindletop gusher, rises a monument commemorating the oilman's proud record of forty years. On one side of it is this inscription: "Petroleum has revolutionized industry and transportation; it has created untold wealth, built cities, furnished employment for hundreds of thousands and contributed billions in taxes to support institutions of government. In a brief span of years, it has altered man's way of life throughout the world."

These claims are substantiated by national and state records, by federal and state officials closely associated with the oil industry, and by the common daily activities of our own lives. What is said about the nation's petroleum industry is to a large extent also a tribute to the Southwestern industry, for at the beginning of 1947 this region produced approximately 70 per cent of the nation's crude oil.

The Southwestern oil industry is today engaged in rapidly changing and varying activities—several thousand oil fields, each with its forest of derricks, some active and others inactive, but all, with installations, representing many billions of dollars; a maze of 65,000 miles of crude-oil pipe lines, and other thousands of miles of products lines, great and small, crossing and crisscrossing farms, ranches, hills, and valleys, silently funneling day and night several hundred thousand barrels of crude oil, with barges, trucks, tank cars, and tankers transporting other thousands; and 151 refineries pouring out daily a wide variety of petroleum products to supply a waiting world.

Indeed, oil, Southwestern oil for the most part, has become industrial America's lifeblood, without which our fast-moving econ-

The Impacts of Petroleum

omy would be paralyzed. This is true in a literal sense. "There are no substitutes for petroleum lubricants, without which the machine age could not exist,"[1] and none for gasoline and Diesel oil.

The impacts of petroleum are not so generally recognized as those of gold and silver. The California gold strike of 1848 started an immigrant stampede, bringing tens of thousands of argonauts from the East to the West, by overland trails and the sea. Thousands of settlers poured into California, and later, into Arizona, Nevada, Montana, Colorado, and other mineral-bearing areas of the Far West. Small hamlets like San Francisco grew into cities within a few years, hundreds of new communities were established, new industries were started, and states and territories were carved from the public domain.

But the actual value of the gold and silver taken from all our Western mines was not too impressive. W. Jett Lauck presents figures, indeed, to show that all the gold and silver mined in the world from 1493 to 1875 was worth only $15,375,753,000, a sum not equal to the amount spent in the miners' quest for these metals.[2] Crude oil produced in the United States since 1859, not counting refinery oil products, at posted field prices has been worth approximately four times that amount.

The average United States history textbook treats adequately the influence of mining upon an evolving Western life, but neglects petroleum, which has had a far stronger impact both on the nation's, and more particularly on the Southwest's, economy and way of life. The value of this region's petroleum and petroleum products during 1948 alone is greater than all the gold and silver mined in the United States since early colonial days.

Including its annual wage payments to employees, the petroleum industry each year makes a total cash contribution of $4,000,-000,000 to the national economy. Of this, $200,000,000 is paid to landowners in the form of royalties, bonuses, and lease rentals; $875,000,000 to other industries for equipment, supplies, and services; $260,000,000 to railroads; and $1,300,000,000 in federal, state,

[1] Statement of Russell B. Brown at a *Hearing Before a Sub-committee of the Committee on Interstate and Foreign Commerce, House of Representatives, Seventy-sixth Congress, Third Session on H. Res. 290 and H. R. 7372 . . . February 19, 20, 21, 22, 26 and 27, 1940*, Part IV, 1877.

[2] *Causes of the Panic of 1893*, 16.

and local taxes. In addition, oil companies provide worker benefits by their social security plans, started in the eighteen-eighties and now among the most liberal in the United States.

Petroleum production shares in this contribution, although its operating cost has been heavy. W. Alton Jones recently estimated that $102,000,000,000 have been invested in the discovery and production of oil. At posted field prices, all the crude oil recovered up to 1947 had a gross value of $61,000,000,000, leaving a debit balance of $41,000,000,000, which approximately represents the value of known oil and gas reserves yet in the ground.[3]

In addition to prospecting and producing costs, the oil industry has been forced to make heavy equipment investments, more so than any other industry except the railroads. In 1943, thirty of the leading American companies doing two-thirds of the oil business spent $925,000,000 for properties, plants, and equipment, generally within the limits of or adjacent to Southwestern metropolitan areas.[4] In 1947, the oil industry spent $2,000,000,000 to expand and improve its facilities, and the value of its total gross plant and equipment investments reached $18,000,000,000,[5] again, many of them in the Southwest.

The petroleum industry is paying annually large sums of money in taxes to the nation and to the oil-producing states. It pays more taxes than any other industry and probably more than any other two or three. For the two decades prior to 1940, petroleum's annual tax bill increased from $132,250,000 to $1,500,000,000; and by 1940, it paid to 161,144 federal, state, and local taxing jurisdictions, approximately $1.00 out of every $8.00 these agencies received. Its net earnings for 1945, after subtracting depreciation costs, taxes, interest, and other charges, amounted to $747,700,000. Petroleum taxes for this year were $1,902,037,000, or 254.4 per cent of its net earnings.[6] In Texas alone during 1945 the petroleum industry paid more than $74,000,000 in taxes.[7]

[3] Text of address by W. Alton Jones, president of Cities Service Company, before the Interstate Compact Commission at Oklahoma City, on December 4, 1947.

[4] Leonard M. Fanning (ed.), *Our Oil Resources*, 271.

[5] *New York Times*, Sunday, April 4, 1948, Sec. 3, p. 1; Dallas *Morning News*, March 26, 1948.

[6] *Petroleum Facts and Figures* (Eighth edition), 176.

[7] Commissioner E. O. Thompson to C. C. Rister, February 10, 1947.

The Impacts of Petroleum

In 1945, federal motor-fuel taxes reached $778,605,000, of which the six Southwestern oil-producing states collected $113,037,000. The average federal gasoline tax per motor vehicle, counting excise taxes, was $23.18; the average state gasoline tax and registration fee, $50.17; and the combined average for the two, $63.35.[8]

A large part of petroleum's taxes has been used to build hard-surfaced highways. In 1926 automobile owners paid $1,000,000,000 of the total American road costs.[9] Motorists paid taxes on the average of 2.38 cents per gallon of gasoline, on almost 8,000,000,000 gallons, or a total of $187,603,231, and they paid other taxes in the form of vehicle registration and license fees amounting to $288,-282,352. These two sums are significant, for about 95 per cent of the first and 93 per cent of the second went to the building and maintenance of highways. And if to these figures are added the special taxes on busses and trucks, property taxes on automobiles, taxes paid by the petroleum and the automobile manufacturers, a total of more than $1,200,000,000 may be accounted for. This meant that the people who bought, operated, and manufactured motor cars, and who produced, bought, and burned gasoline, were more than paying the bill for good roads.

Following out this early trend, a large portion of the 1945 composite tax bill of the Southwest went for highway construction and maintenance. On November 5, 1946, Texas adopted a constitutional amendment requiring that taxes on motor fuels, lubricants, and motor-vehicle registration fees, with certain exceptions, should be used for highway construction, maintenance, and administration.[10] For this purpose in that year the state collected more than $30,000,-000. Arkansas spends on its highways the money collected from its gasoline tax, amounting to $17,978,717.15 in the tax year 1947–48.[11]

Since the discovery of the first Spindletop gusher in 1901, oil's impacts on Texas have been decisive, just as Texas oil has been decisive in the nation's economy. A Texas authority recently stated that the bringing in of the Spindletop oil field "and the succession of discoveries that have followed have done more than anything

[8] *Petroleum Facts and Figures* (Eighth edition), 176.
[9] *Ibid.*, (First edition), 189.
[10] Sec. 7-a, Art. VIII.
[11] State Treasurer J. Vance Clayton to C. C. Rister, June 18, 1948.

else to send Texas hurriedly along the path of industrialization."[12]

Texas had extensive oil wealth for industrialization. The North Texas Oil and Gas Association has shown that in 1930 the state's oil industry spent $666,446,000, exclusive of gasoline taxes, or $698,-654,000 including gasoline taxes.[13] The average annual value of all Texas farm crops for the preceding decade, according to United States Department of Agriculture estimates, had been $687,000,000.

Through such large expenditures in Texas, oil has promoted a better standard of living in the state. "Texas, economically and culturally would have been a quarter century behind its present point of progress had there been no petroleum,"[14] declares one expert.

Despite the allegations of some writers and analysts, most of the Texas oil income stays largely in Texas. Dividends paid by oil companies ordinarily are moderate.[15] This means that the bulk of the money spent stays in the oil-producing country or where oil operations are being carried on.

Eugene Holman, president of the Standard Oil Company of New Jersey, explains that "one out of every six of those who live in the state [Texas] depends directly or indirectly on the petroleum industry for a livelihood," a statement that is supported by statistics.[16] For example, in 1947, 189,000 Texans worked in the petrole-

[12] *Texas Almanac, 1927–1948* (published by Dallas *Morning News*), 109.

[13] Quoted in *Texas Weekly,* December 5, 1931, p. 11.

[14] *Texas Almanac, 1945–1946,* 238.

[15] *Petroleum Facts and Figures* (Eighth edition), 196. It is stated in this volume that from 1923 to 1946 the average rate of return on the net worth of the petroleum industry was 6.7 per cent; on manufacturing, 8.5 per cent; and on all industry, 7 per cent.

[16] Holman has been recognized for his progressive industrial ideas and his forthright expressions of a belief that business executives should administer their responsibilities with the broad public interest constantly in view. No doubt the fact that he was reared and trained in the rugged school of an oil field's hard knocks, ran the gamut of grueling experience both in the Southwest and abroad, and then rose to the pinnacle of oildom success has made his career good copy for journalists.

After attending Simmons College and the University of Texas, Holman began his professional career with an exploration party sent to Cuba by The Texas Company in 1917. Then came World War I and Holman's enlistment in the army, where he served as an aerial photographer. After his discharge in 1919, he joined the United States Geological Survey and went on a field trip to Texas. There he caught the eye of the Humble Oil and Refining Company's brilliant chief geologist, Wallace E. Pratt, and was taken into that company in 1919. He was conspicuously successful in the booming North Central Texas fields and rose rapidly in the company, becoming

um industry and received more than $580,000,000 in wages and salaries. In the same year, this Texas industry was paying in wages and salaries, lease rentals, bonuses, and royalty, for equipment and supplies, for contract drilling, geophysical prospecting, in state and local taxes, in federal taxes, in interest on borrowed capital, and for other investments the enormous sum of $2,253,181,000. Indeed, says Beauford Jester, the Texas governor, "the entire economy of Texas and its citizens is injured by anything which injures the domestic oil industry in this state."

Texas Petroleum Industry Expenditures[17]
For the Year 1947

Wages and salaries	$ 580,344,000
Leases, bonuses, and royalty payments	331,738,000
Intangible drilling and development costs	258,963,000
Equipment and supplies	433,352,000
State and local taxes	133,385,000
All other expenditures	515,399,000
Total expenditures	$2,253,181,000

Certainly, thousands of Texans in every part of the state who have received lease and royalty payments have tangible proof that much of the oil industry's earnings remains in Texas. By 1944, there was prospecting, drilling, and leasing in every county, and oil

superintendent of the Louisiana-Arkansas division in 1923 and succeeding Pratt as Humble's chief geologist when Pratt moved up in the organization.

In 1929, Holman went to New York as a junior executive officer of the Jersey company and presently was made chief executive of two Venezuelan companies (the Creole Petroleum Corporation and the Lago Petroleum Corporation). In the next eight years Standard's Venezuelan properties became its most valuable foreign possessions, supplying two-thirds of its entire foreign production. In 1940, Holman was elected a director of the Standard Oil Company (New Jersey), two years later a vice-president, and in 1944 president. Since then he has been generally ranked as one of America's leading business executives.

[17] *Texas Oil and Gas, 1948,* 9. Address of Eugene Holman, president of Standard Oil Company (New Jersey) before the Institute of Latin-American Studies of the University of Texas, April 12, 1946. He further showed that within ten years after the discovery of the Spindletop oil field in 1901, Texas manufacturing increased 200 per cent.

In 1947, 1,500,000 workers were employed by the United States oil industry, and a total of 11,000,000 people were dependent directly or indirectly on oildom's payroll.

production in 155 of the 254 counties, and in 172 counties three years later. Texas land under lease for oil and gas in 1947 comprised 58,000,000 acres, more than the combined areas of Massachusetts, Connecticut, New Hampshire, Vermont, Rhode Island, Delaware, New Jersey, Maryland, West Virginia, and the District of Columbia. Rentals and bonuses and oil and gas royalties paid Texas landowners approximately, $331,738,000.

Texas education has also received its share of oil wealth. The oil industry during 1947 paid into the Permanent School Fund, in lease rentals, bonuses, and oil and gas royalties, $7,051,984, and to the Permanent University School Fund $6,739,767; and the combined cumulative total of all payments through 1947 was $115,078,-329. Its total tax payments to education reached $73,445,630 in the school year 1947–48, or 33.8 per cent of all school taxes.

Tax Revenue for Texas Education[18]
1947–48 School Year

	All Texas taxpayers pay:	Petroleum industry pays:
From Local Sources (ad valorem taxes):		
Common Schools	$ 14,566,035	$ 4,740,146
Independent School Districts	70,141,500	21,170,097
Rural High Schools	1,677,331	545,804
From State Funds:		
Per Capita Apportionment	$ 83,155,802	$26,609,857
Equalization Aid	15,829,024	7,123,061
Textbooks	4,702,840	1,504,909
Vocational Education	1,443,424	649,541
Deaf and Blind Schools	558,734	251,430
Dept. of Education (Administration)	1,595,513	717,981
Higher Education	23,730,219	10,132,804
	$217,400,422	$73,445,630
Per cent paid by Oil and Gas	33.8	

In each of the other Southwestern oil-producing states, oil's con-

[18] *Texas Oil and Gas, 1948,* 19.

tributions have been proportionately much the same as in Texas. In Oklahoma, since 1906, oil fields have been as so many employment centers. By 1940 more than 57,000 persons out of a state population of 2,336,000 were gainfully employed by the oil and gas industry. From statehood, in November, 1907, to 1943, the Oklahoma oil industry paid enough gross production taxes to buy one-sixth of all property in the state at its assessed value in 1942. The more than $200,000,000 gross production taxes on oil and gas would build, furnish, and equip Oklahoma's public school system twice over and equal almost four times its common school fund.[19] In one year, 1939, the Oklahoma Tax Commission credited the oil industry with 55 to 60 per cent of all corporation income taxes collected.

The present worth of Louisiana's oil and gas is estimated at one billion dollars, based on $356,000,000 for production, $300,000,000 in by-products, a pay roll of $180,000,000, and $164,000,000 for all other benefits. The petroleum industry pays more than one-half of the state's taxes, the severance tax alone being approximately $18,-020,805.91 during the fiscal year ending in June, 1947. The industry also pays directly or indirectly the entire cost of education in the state. In the present fiscal year, Louisiana has a budget of slightly less than $44,000,000 for education, and the oil and gas industry will pay about $60,000,000 to the state in taxes (estimated yield of severance and gas-gathering tax).[20]

Of oil's other influences on the Southwest, its effect on cities has been most noticeable. Beaumont is the first Texas city that oil money built. Since 1901 it has become the center of a vast industrial area, including Port Arthur, the refining center. Small wonder! It claims the support of thirty-four Gulf Coast oil fields and approximately 1,943 producing wells; and on its Sabine-Neches waterway are situated three of the world's largest refineries, with a total daily capacity of 365,000 barrels. Twenty pipe lines daily feed into these refineries their many thousands of barrels of crude oil, from the fields in Texas, Louisiana, Oklahoma, Arkansas, and Kansas.[21]

[19] *Oil and Gas in Oklahoma*, 36–37.

[20] Arthur R. Carmody, Chairman, Mid-Continent Oil and Gas Association, Louisiana-Arkansas Division, to C. C. Rister, November 9, 1948 (with data). Also data from Mrs. W. D. Chew, Shreveport, Louisiana, to C. C. Rister, October 15, 1948.

[21] In Beaumont the Jefferson County Courthouse is a striking architectual memorial to the early-day oilman.

Oil! Titan of the Southwest

Early salt-dome oil money also poured into Houston. After the opening of near-by oil fields, the city quickly spread beyond its 1900 limits and absorbed suburban communities. By 1939, the Houston seaport was surpassed only by New York and Philadelphia in shipping tonnage, its canal feeding into the Gulf a gross 28,156,-757 tons of shipping, an all-time high for a Texas port. And, like Beaumont, Houston became the center of a prolific oil-producing area—a 600-mile radius including over one-half of the world's total supply of oil, with Conroe, Hastings, Anahuac, Friendswood, and Thompson fields having reserves estimated at 1,750,000,000 barrels.

The wealth created directly or indirectly by money from oil and hydrocarbon products has made possible leading business structures in Houston. Among these are the Gulf, Niels Esperson, Shell, Sterling, Petroleum, Humble, Texas Company, and Mellie Esperson buildings, ranging in height from thirteen to thirty-seven stories. All were built with oil money. And the twenty-story, $21,000,000 Shamrock Hotel, now nearing completion, is backed by oilman Glenn H. McCarthy.

North Texas' "twin cities" of Dallas and Fort Worth have also benefited from oil wealth. By 1945, Dallas claimed to be the "new oil capital" of 365,000 people. It was North Texas' leading commercial, jobbing, wholesaling, retailing, and financial center, the home of the Eleventh District Federal Reserve Bank, and the headquarters of a number of major oil and machinery companies. Among the several hundred firms representing various phases of the petroleum industry were oil producers, refiners, and marketers, natural-gas producers and marketers, pipe-line companies, lease and royalty companies, oil-well supply companies, drilling contractors, consulting geologists, petroleum engineers, and geophysicists. Dallas's perennial support was the giant East Texas oil field, and, in addition, a short distance southeast and south of the city are the older fields of Powell, Mexia, and Wortham. Oil money has built a large portion of Dallas's industries, its cultural institutions, and its homes. By 1945 it had become a worthy rival of Tulsa and Houston for the favors of the oil world.

Fort Worth, "where the West begins," is Dallas's close neighbor and industrial competitor. With a population of 220,000, it has survived near-by oil-field depressions while other towns have risen,

Analytical laboratory of oil refinery on Texas Gulf Coast

The Texas Company

W. H. Bryant No. 3 Poe well in Round Top pool near Hamlin, Texas. In the picture is A. G. Hudgens, superintendent for Moutray-Moore Drilling Company, Abilene, Texas

W. C. Russell

Tulsa, Indian Territory, 1889

photograph by The Howards
Tulsa Chamber of Commerce

Tulsa today

photograph by Graif's
Tulsa Chamber of Commerce

The Impacts of Petroleum

then leveled off or fallen. To the west, Ranger, Desdemona, and Breckenridge have seen their best days as great oil fields, and many of their promoters have pulled stakes and gone elsewhere, although the towns proper have continued to grow. But Fort Worth attracted oil-field operators and specialists, men who now are prominent citizens of the city. Here, too, over the doors of tall buildings are the names of oilmen, and adjacent to the town are refineries, oil-field-equipment manufacturing plants, and allied industries.

It is hardly necessary to repeat that oil accounts for the growth and prosperity of other Texas towns. Former mayors W. B. Hamilton and Walter Cline, themselves experienced oilmen, say that Wichita Falls was built by oil money. Amarillo's growth was coincident with that of the great Panhandle oil- and gas-producing area; and Midland, Odessa, and Kermit, Texas, and Hobbs, New Mexico, with the expansion of the Permian Basin oil fields. Since 1944 this West Texas–New Mexico oil-producing area has experienced the most rapid development of any territory in the United States. This growth in oil production brought immediate prosperity to West Texas towns and communities. In April, 1948, West Texas produced an all-time peak of 678,600 barrels of crude oil a day.[22]

But Odessa, Kermit, and Hobbs come nearest to being 100 per cent oil towns. Kermit is an enthusiastic young city built entirely by Permian Basin oil wealth, and in each of the leading towns in this area are magnificent school buildings, business houses, and churches.

In East Texas, Tyler, Longview, and Kilgore are notable. Unquestionably, Tyler is the East Texas oil capital and consequently a thriving industrial center, but it is hardly more prosperous than Longview and Kilgore. At Longview one finds a progressive chamber of commerce, factories, and an airport that would do credit to a city many times its size.

Tulsa is Oklahoma's largest city built primarily by petroleum, and of all the cities in the principal oil region of the United States it, by its character and spirit, can best claim the position of primacy. It was a rural village in 1901 when the Red Fork oil discovery literally caused a new "Oklahoma run." Added impetus to its growth came

[22] Statistical data furnished the author by Editor Warren Baker of *World Oil*, June 14, 1948.

with the development of the rich Glenn Pool, Cushing, Drumright, and Osage oil fields. By 1920 this former Creek Indian town had blossomed into a young oil city of 70,000 people, and by 1945 to a metropolis of 175,000. In January, 1948, its metropolitan area supported a population of 256,430. More than 700 firms located in Tulsa supply the specialty needs of companies engaged in oil production and marketing. Fifteen oil companies during 1947 spent more than $300,000,000 there for equipment and supplies. Tulsa, the home of the International Petroleum Exposition, proudly claims that it is the oil capital of the Mid-Continent area. And its towering buildings—the Philtower, the Stanolind (formerly the Philcade), the Kennedy, the Cosden, the National Bank of Tulsa, the First National Bank, the Sinclair, the Mid-Continent, and the Skelly buildings, and fine hotels—together with beautiful schools, churches, homes, and parks, lend weight to this claim.[23]

Similarly, Oklahoma City felt the impact of petroleum. In 1925 its population was 120,458. Then came I.T.I.O.'s No. 1 Oklahoma City discovery six miles south of town, the Mary Sudik, and other gushers, and by 1930 Oklahoma City was off to a whirlwind growth. In 1930 its population was 189,389; in 1936, 201,400. The Great Depression could not stop it. During 1930–31 a $15,000,000-building campaign was launched, with two thirty-three-story buildings —the First National Bank and Trust Company and the graceful Ramsey Tower—and the thirty-two-story Skirvin Tower Hotel giving the city an imposing sky line.

Other Oklahoma oil towns, such as Bartlesville with its tall Phillips and Cities Service buildings; Ponca City, trim and modern, with its refineries and industries; Enid, northern Oklahoma's trade center, with its Champlin refinery; Ardmore, the center of southern Oklahoma's oil business; Duncan, with its thriving Halliburton Oil Well Cementing Company; and Seminole, which has survived the shock of Greater Seminole's decline—all are still growing oil towns.

By 1940, Oklahoma had 57,000 residents directly engaged in the oil and gas industry and 25 per cent more in allied industries, with a pay roll of upward of $100,000,000; and in Kansas, 60,000 men

[23] John H. Barhydt, assistant general manager, Tulsa Chamber of Commerce, to C. C. Rister, June 25, 1948; and Ben Matkin, director, public relations, Tulsa Chamber of Commerce, to Rister, November 29, 1948.

were similarly employed, with a pay roll of more than $75,000,000.

Elsewhere in the Southwest there are prominent oil centers; in Kansas, Wichita;[24] in Louisiana, Baton Rouge, Homer, and Shreveport; and in Arkansas, El Dorado. Each of these has new public and business buildings, machine shops, and oil-supply houses.

It is generally recognized that petroleum production and refining have caused population increases in Tulsa, Oklahoma City, Houston, Dallas, and Baton Rouge; but the fact that smaller towns have been equally influenced is often overlooked. El Dorado, Arkansas, increased in population 322 per cent from 1920 to 1930; Monroe, Louisiana, 150 per cent; Wewoka, Oklahoma, 584 per cent; and Breckenridge, Texas, 310 per cent. Even Ranger, Desdemona, and Burkburnett, once great oil-field boom towns that oil-field observers and writers again and again consigned to oblivion, have staged comebacks and have become better towns than before oil was discovered; and the same statement can be made about Smackover, Arkansas, Rodessa, Louisiana, and Augusta and Eldorado, Kansas.

The Southwest also has its oil-field ghost towns, although not so many as in the mining areas. As a rule oil-field ghost towns resulted from failure of an oil field, or from rapid decline in production, or occasionally because of the discovery of an adjacent and more prolific field. Near Pershing, Oklahoma, in the nineteen-twenties oil production quickly declined and left the town with little to support it; and, farther north, at Burbank, the oil-producing trend was away from town, making possible other boom towns and leaving Burbank isolated. Similarly, to Ragtown, in the Healdton oil field, the passing of flush production and the field's decline brought oblivion.

Even in the nineteen forties oil-boom towns changed to ghost towns. White City is a conspicuous example. The site of this town, fifteen miles northwest of Lamesa, Texas, on the northeast side of Cedar Lake, or *Sabinas Laguna,* as the early-day Spaniards called it, had almost a century before been the rendezvous of New Mexican

---

[24] "Oil is very important in our municipal life," writes Bliss Isely. "At last count 773 firms in Wichita are engaged in some phase of the oil business."—Isley to C. C. Rister, July 8, 1948.

traders and wild Indians. Then, when oil was discovered here in 1939, a town was quickly built.

Detailed seismograph work had led the Stanolind Oil and Gas Company to drill its No. 1 Rayner well,[25] to a total depth of 4,830 feet and then plug back to 4,770 feet, where the well was "shot," acidized, and completed for a daily 1,279 barrels of crude oil, on a gas lift through a one-inch choke. Then derricks quickly rose above the sand dunes and the field promised major production. The bringing in of good oil producers quickened the tempo of speculation and the making of investments.

Bill and Gus White caught the boom spirit and platted and promoted a supply town. Streets were laid off, lots were sold, and a shanty town of groceries, a filling station, cafés, rooming houses, a power house, a lumber yard, a theater, and a hotel presently harbored oil-field derrick men, drillers, firemen, maintenance men, pumpers, roustabouts, tool dressers, and truck drivers.

The workers called their town "White City" in honor of its sponsors, since already Texas had a Cedar Lake. Presently, however, exploratory drilling defined the field as a minor producer, and citizens and wildcatters of once-buoyant faith moved to Lamesa, to Midland, to Hobbs, or to other prosperous Permian Basin towns.

It is a fact that the petroleum industry stimulated a rise in population more often than it left ghost towns. Census returns furnish conclusive proof. It was not until after 1903 that Oklahoma had its most noticeable influx of oilmen from Pennsylvania, Ohio, West Virginia, New York, and Indiana—prospectors, producers, refiners, and supply men, alighting in large numbers from trains at Bartlesville, Tulsa, Muskogee, Nowata, Sapulpa, and Claremore, to spend a few days talking with informed natives and then driving into the country in buckboards or other conveyances to locate a site for a well, a refinery, or a pipe-line right-of-way. These new arrivals, with others who came "to take a plunge," swelled Oklahoma's population.

In 1910 there were fifteen Oklahoma oil-producing counties whose population had increased 25 per cent in three years, while the non-oil counties had gained 15 per cent. Ten years later there

[25] Dana M. Secor, W. C. Fritz, and W. W. West, "Development in West Texas and Southeastern New Mexico During 1939," in *Bulletin of the American Association of Petroleum Geologists,* Vol. XXIV, No. 6 (June, 1940), 1038.

The Impacts of Petroleum

were 25 oil-producing counties, whose population had increased 29.5 per cent since 1910 in comparison with 12.6 per cent for the remainder of the state. And by the end of the next decade the oil-producing counties had increased in population 30.7 per cent over 1920, while the non-producing counties had declined slightly.[26] In 1940, Oklahoma's forty-one oil-producing counties had a population of 1,629,395 as compared with thirty-six non-producing counties with only 707,039 persons. From 1940 to 1945, Oklahoma's population as a whole declined slightly.

In 469 counties and parishes of Arkansas, Louisiana, Oklahoma, and Texas from 1920 to 1930, there was an increase in population amounting to 1,934,606, nearly 47.3 of which was in the 88 oil-producing counties. Since that time these gains for the most part have been held and other new producing areas have experienced similar advances.

No doubt, Southwestern oil's most important single contribution to higher education is the $64,965,576 in bonuses, leases, and royalties paid by 1948 to the University of Texas on this institution's vast holdings of West Texas land. One-third of this amount is awarded the Texas Agricultural and Mechanical College because it is nominally a part of the University. Today, the University of Texas is one of the most heavily endowed state schools in the nation.

In addition to these several general impacts, personal gifts from oilmen have stimulated the Southwest's cultural and economic growth. As a result, well distributed over the area are churches, hospitals, art centers, libraries, stadia, and other civic enterprises, made possible, either in part or wholly, by such gifts. Almost every important municipal or sectarian college or university has received liberal donations, either as an endowment or to construct a much needed building. And other gifts have been made for more general causes, as to promote the Boy Scouts or to further a community's land-conservation enterprise.

No doubt, petroleum will continue to implement Southwestern progress. The petroleum industry has climbed out of early-day over-production, low markets, and oil-field chaos and waste, into a well-organized and scientifically equipped business. Both major com-

[26] See federal census returns, 1910, 1920, and 1930; pamphlet, *Oil and Gas in Oklahoma*, 58.

panies and the so-called independents[27] have closely integrated and streamlined their organizations to make profits despite large expenditures and possible losses.

To meet the increasing demands for crude oil, old petroleum reservoirs are being depleted, and new ones must be found to keep up production. But new reservoirs are hard to find, and up-to-date and expensive methods of prospecting and wildcatting are necessary. (This includes large-scale block leasing rather than checkerboarding as earlier employed.) Nevertheless, present-day prospectors and wildcatters are active. Driving over highways between the Arkansas and the Río Grande, or between the Rockies and the muddy Mississippi, one sees frequent and unmistakable evidences of this activity—colored streamers on barbed-wire fences, the ribbons of seismograph crews; here and there, the small core-drill derricks; and, at intervals also, silhouetting Southwestern skies, towering oil derricks, which at night, with twinkling lights, bear witness of an ever expanding industry.

Today, the petroleum industry is the product of American enterprise. True, it is hedged by federal and state law, but only to promote conservation and the welfare of small business and the long-term interest of the public. Otherwise it employs its own business methods and goes its own way. It is unlikely that such an industry, composed of some 34,000 companies and employing approximately 1,500,000 workers, can become monopolistic, as was forecast in Theodore Roosevelt's day.

This history of a half-century proves the Southwestern oil industry's right to assume a major role in the nation's industrial tomorrow. With alert leaders who are trained in an exacting school of experience, rising from day laborers to company executives, and with trained scientists, technicians, and field workers making up its personnel, it is prepared to meet the challenge of the future.

[27] An "independent," said Wirt Franklin addressing the Oil Conservation Conference at Colorado Springs on June 10, 1928, is "a misnomer, because there is no class engaged in productive enterprise more dependent than the small oil producer." A copy of this address was furnished the author by Mr. H. B. Fell, executive vice-president, Independent Petroleum Association of America, Tulsa, Oklahoma.

Appendix

Crude-oil Production of Important New Mexico Fields
(thousands of barrels)

Year	Artesia	Hobbs	Eunice	Lea County	Monument
1925	748	-----	-----	-----	-----
1926	1,016	-----	-----	2	-----
1927	582	-----	-----	39	-----
1928	410	-----	-----	69	-----
1929	323	‡	-----	‡899	-----
1930	261	6,525	-----	2,782	-----
1931	426	12,788	-----	1,490	-----
1932	480	10,237	-----	1,345	-----
1933	596	11,543	¶	¶1,609	¶
1934	898	12,628	¶	¶2,962	¶
1935	867	11,276	¶	¶7,970	¶
1936	1,056	9,169	¶	¶16,592	¶
1937	2,000	7,300	¶	¶29,166	¶
1938	2,216	5,040	8,966	¶27,882	9,451
1939	§255	4,401	7,863	**	8,206
1940	§267	3,785	6,561	**	6,887
1941	§157	3,686	6,658	**	6,960
1942	§203	2,928	5,242	**	6,698
1943	*173	3,780	6,498	**	7,190
1944	*159	4,120	6,470	**	7,570
1945	†366	3,874	5,707	**	7,139
1946	†156	∅3,569	∅5,094	**	∅6,565
1947	†130	∅3,562	∅4,792	**	∅6,541

‡ Hobbs included in Lea.
¶ Lea includes Eunice and Monument.
** Production given by the fields in county.

All figures taken from *Mineral Resources, Part II, Nonmetals* (published by U.S.G.S., 1882–1924; and by the Bureau of Mines under the same title, 1924–31, and as *Minerals Yearbook,* 1931–45) except the following: § *Oil Weekly,* Vol. XCVI, No. 8 (January 29, 1940); Vol. CIV, No. 8 (January 26, 1942); and Vol. CVIII, No. 8 (February 1, 1943); ∅ *Oil and Gas Journal,* Vol. XLVI, No. 39 (January 29, 1948); † *Yearbook* (National Oil Scouts and Landmen's Association), Vol. XVI (1946), and Vol. XVIII (1948); * *Petroleum Development and Technology* (A. I. M. E.), 1944 and 1945.

407

Crude-oil Production of Important Arkansas Fields
(thousands of barrels)

Year	Champagnolle	El Dorado	Magnolia	Rodessa	Schuler	Smackover	Stephens	Urbana
1921	—	10,473	—	—	—	—	—	—
1922	—	10,592	—	—	—	2,107	13	—
1923	—	5,830	—	—	—	30,048	732	—
1924	—	4,760	—	—	—	40,000	818	—
1925	—	4,247	—	—	—	72,144	673	—
1926	—	2,722	—	—	—	52,063	607	—
1927	—	2,433	—	—	—	35,201	499	—
1928	3,522	2,456	—	—	—	24,569	416	—
1929	2,651	1,987	—	—	—	18,991	363	—
1930	1,486	1,424	—	—	—	15,405	319	236
1931	944	1,186	—	—	—	11,504	272	322
1932	623	1,182	—	—	—	9,510	213	146
1933	488	1,231	—	—	—	8,882	127	499
1934	486	991	—	—	—	7,916	210	826
1935	872	862	—	—	—	7,368	212	793
1936	900	811	—	—	—	7,126	214	651
1937	522	747	—	1,252	1,153	6,751	205	446
1938	452	708	68	2,317	6,359	6,406	198	422
1939	566	630	3,639	1,358	6,430	5,945	196	381
1940	581	591	7,383	711	6,547	5,500	196	468
1941	332	534	7,121	497	6,005	5,351	251	837
1942	273	497	6,364	366	5,913	4,907	614	985
1943	* 247	449	6,041	* 213	5,520	4,458	1,485	§ 1,058
1944	* 235	416	5,592	* 196	4,733	4,280	1,828	§ 1,019
1945	† 247	402	4,951	† 227	4,563	4,146	2,035	§ 817
1946	† 221	ø 386	ø 4,683	† 207	ø 4,312	ø 4,070	ø 1,880	†§ 299
1947	† 231	ø 382	ø 4,643	† 207	ø 3,939	ø 3,954	ø 1,461	†§ 290

§ Includes New London.

All figures taken from *Mineral Resources, Part II, Nonmetals* (published by U.S.G.S., 1882–1924; and by the Bureau of Mines, under the same title, 1924–31, and as *Minerals Yearbook*, 1931–45), except the following: * *Petroleum Development and Technology* (A.I.M.E.), 1944 and 1945; ø *Oil and Gas Journal*, Vol. XLVI, No. 39 (January 29, 1948); † *Yearbook* (National Oil Scouts and Landmen's Association), Vol. XVI (1946) and Vol. XVIII (1948).

Appendix

Kansas Crude-oil Production by Important Counties and Fields, 1925–48.*
(thousands of barrels)

Year	BARTON CO. Silica-Raymond	BUTLER CO. Eldorado	ELLIS CO. Bemis-Walters	McPHERSON CO. Ritz-Canton	RENO CO. Burton	RICE CO. Chase-Campbell	RUSSELL CO. Trapp-Sellens
1925	---	2,397	---	---	---	---	†1,336
1926	---	2,406	---	---	---	---	†1,858
1927	---	2,759	---	---	---	---	†1,026
1928	---	2,620	---	†287	---	---	†1,304
1929	---	2,598	---	1,189	---	---	†1,288
1930	---	2,414	—	—	—	---	†1,329
1931	---	2,245	†238	3,553	—	†451	†1,109
1932	---	1,979	ø†298	4,902	†326	ø†858	ø†933
1933	†144	1,817	†225	6,627	†623	†1,936	†1,067
1934	†446	1,974	†167	4,644	‡2,333	1,701	†2,548
1935	†738	3,920	†167	2,974	7,439	4,934	†4,146
1936	1,195	3,508	†758	2,346	5,248	ø3,489	747
1937	7,618	3,340	2,184	1,872	5,384	3,591	3,780
1938	5,534	3,023	2,826	1,650	3,521	2,127	3,393
1939	5,000	2,710	2,881	1,753	3,187	2,256	4,255
1940	5,763	2,651	3,419	1,373	2,625	2,338	5,481
1941	7,615	2,597	4,866	1,366	2,539	2,746	7,577
1942	9,063	2,498	5,847	1,145	2,101	3,379	9,726
1943	9,825	‡2,433	6,720	960	1,740	3,750	10,840
1944	7,834	ø2,530	5,268	864	1,525	3,702	9,347
1945	6,422	ø2,628	5,507	742	1,351	3,076	10,631
1946	ø5,691	ø2,618	ø5,305	ø721	ø1,209	ø2,766	ø11,042
1947	ø5,783	ø2,764	ø6,057	ø657	ø1,073	ø2,644	ø11,371

* Figures prior to 1925 not available.
† Production figures are listed by counties, as indicated by †, until one field gains importance, after which the production of this field is reported.
All figures taken from *Mineral Resources, Part II, Nonmetals* (published by the Bureau of Mines, 1925-31, and as *Minerals Yearbook*, 1931-45), except the following: ‡ *Petroleum Development and Technology* (A.I.M.E.), 1944; ø *Oil and Gas Journal*, Vol. XXXI, No. 36 (January 26, 1933); Vol. XXXV, No. 37 (January 28, 1937); Vol. XLV, No. 38 (January 25, 1947); and Vol. XLVI, No. 39 (January 29, 1948).

Crude-oil Production of Important Oklahoma Fields

(thousands of barrels)

Year	Burbank	Bowlegs	Carr City	Cushing a	Earlsboro	Fitts	Garber	Glenn Pool	Healdton	Hewitt	Oklahoma City	Little River	St. Louis-Pearson	Seminole City	Tonkawa	West Edmond
1907								19,927								
1908								20,494								
1909								18,947								
1910								19,237								
1911								13,880								
1912								10,496								
1913								9,470								
1914				21,945				8,677	b2,868							
1915				49,080				5,994	b4,819							
1916				39,911				7,282	b13,601							
1917				26,740				7,906	b18,354							
1918				20,993				5,388	b15,695							
1919				c				c	c							
1920	†20,396			c				c	c	7,426						
1921	†20,848			c				c	c	13,095					2,482	
1922	$24,134			$10,190			†1,849	c	$7,711	10,690					28,003	
1923	$31,969			$9,883				c	$5,800	8,695					22,414	
1924	†30,806			†8,743				†f3,596	†6,039	6,905					22,722	
1925	19,955			8,025			7,684	3,284	5,576	5,315						
1926	16,353			7,621			10,920	3,204	5,501	4,202				e11,227	13,867	
1927	15,266			6,942	†36,885		†5,293	2,903	5,448	3,539		5,144	d813	e135,951	7,747	
1928	12,060			6,521	$33,396		†2,943	2,289	5,069	3,338		24,804	d21,235	e105,728	4,878	
1929	7,436		†3,309	5,988	$25,599		†1,974	2,448	4,599	2,953	101	28,743	d30,816	e101,392	3,518	
1930	5,717		†3,280	4,980	†23,398		†1,639	2,373	4,209	2,501	8,710	17,348	d11,567	e66,217	2,432	

Year																	
1931	4,566	4,392	4,262	4,656	g5,539	-----	†1,293	1,938	4,025	2,146	44,823	g7,422	7,278	4,370	1,992	-----
1932	3,974	4,200	4,252	4,349	4,648	-----	†1,066	1,428	3,881	2,045	33,398	6,391	6,674	3,960	1,837	-----
1933	3,516	3,918	†2,749	5,414	4,514	-----	†1,006	1,770	3,639	1,903	66,834	6,311	7,908	3,932	†1,675	-----
1934	5,685	3,761	2,039	5,044	3,888	329	†898	1,936	3,386	1,818	60,834	5,371	8,084	3,779	†1,387	-----
1935	3,102	3,845	2,003	4,738	7,414	6,901	†789	†1,904	3,397	†1,716	53,386	5,587	8,365	4,062	†1,226	-----
1936	2,827	4,335	2,216	4,129	6,601	19,908	†733	†1,726	3,436	†1,638	51,232	5,068	8,543	3,810	†1,016	-----
1937	2,871	4,178	1,973	3,908	5,596	30,977	†761	†1,566	3,654	§1,587	54,776	4,222	7,528	3,428	†868	-----
1938	2,814	3,200	1,294	3,848	3,751	16,655	†723	†1,488	3,401	1,400	38,796	3,040	7,766	2,842	†759	-----
1939	2,689	2,678	922	3,446	3,590	9,120	†657	†1,430	3,236	1,362	35,728	2,865	11,303	2,618	†678	-----
1940	2,838	2,464	840	3,353	3,730	6,246	§627	§1,241	3,177	1,778	35,970	2,875	9,331	2,501	623	-----
1941	3,282	2,134	791	3,223	3,757	4,223	§620	1,483	3,086	4,860	32,184	2,705	6,997	2,243	632	-----
1942	3,356	1,900	662	3,069	3,718	3,050	§611	1,527	2,827	3,304	26,484	2,333	5,687	2,854	593	-----
1943	3,251	1,721	602	2,991	3,253	2,489	*615	1,856	2,618	2,382	20,338	1,931	3,828	2,555	512	322
1944	3,140	1,525	555	2,940	2,495	2,150	*629	2,245	2,515	2,055	16,295	1,741	2,690	2,240	411	7,752
1945	3,128	1,250	514	2,814	1,737	1,701	ø601	2,359	2,423	1,084	12,968	1,492	1,703	1,990	385	26,548
1946	†2,927	†1,169	†456	†2,792	†716	†1,518	†549	†2,418	†2,438	†1,698	†10,693	†1,159	†1,500	†1,307	†396	†23,565
1947	†2,615	†1,172	†405	†2,839	†616	†1,287	†506	†2,568	†2,431	†1,672	†9,670	†1,432	†1,356	†1,271	†374	†14,936

a Includes Shamrock from 1925 to 1947.

b Includes Wheeler.

c Figures not available.

d Pearson only.

e Includes Earlsboro.

f Includes Sapulpa.

g Bureau of Mines lists East Earlsboro separately for these years: 1931, 5,197; 1932, 4,912; 1933, 5,798; and 1934, 3,792. Little River shows a decrease from 1930 to 1931 because East Little River is listed separately.

All figures taken from *Mineral Resources, Part II, Nonmetals* (published by U.S.G.S., 1882–1924; and by the Bureau of Mines, under the same title, 1924–31, and as *Minerals Yearbook,* 1931–

45), except the following: * *Petroleum Development and Technology* (A.I.M.E.), 1944 and 1945; § *Oil Weekly,* Vol. XXXII, No. 4 (January 19, 1924); Vol. LVI, No. 7 (January 31, 1930); Vol. CIV, No. 8 (January 26, 1942); and Vol. CVIII, No. 8 (February 1, 1943); † *Oil and Gas Journal,* Vol. XX, No. 35 (January 27, 1922); Vol. XXIII, No. 36 (January 29, 1923); Vol. XXIX, No. 37 (January 29, 1931); Vol. XXXV, No. 37 (January 28, 1937); Vol. XXXVI, No. 37 (January 27, 1938); Vol. XXXVII, No. 37 (January 26, 1939); Vol. XXXVIII, No. 37 (January 25, 1940); Vol. XLV, No. 37 (January 26, 1947); Vol. XLVI, No. 39 (January 29, 1948); and *Yearbook* (National Oil Scouts and Landmen's Association), Vol. XVI (1946).

Crude-oil Production in Southwestern States, by Years*

(In thousands of barrels)

Year	Arkansas	Kansas	Louisiana	New Mexico	Oklahoma	Texas
1889	—	1	—	—	—	—
1890	—	1	—	—	—	—
1891	—	1	—	—	—	—
1892	—	5	—	—	—	—
1893	—	18	—	—	—	—
1894	—	40	—	—	—	—
1895	—	44	—	—	—	—
1896	—	114	—	—	—	1
1897	—	81	—	—	1	66
1898	—	72	—	—	—	546
1899	—	70	—	—	—	669
1900	—	75	—	—	6	836
1901	—	179	—	—	10	4,394
1902	—	332	549	—	37	18,084
1903	—	932	918	—	139	17,956
1904	—	4,251	2,959	—	1,367	22,241
1905	—	3,750	8,910	—	8,264	28,136
1906	—	3,627	9,077	—	18,091	12,568
1907	—	2,410	5,000	—	43,524	12,323
1908	—	1,801	5,789	—	45,799	11,207
1909	—	1,264	3,060	—	47,859	9,534
1910	—	1,128	6,841	—	52,029	8,899
1911	—	1,279	10,721	—	56,069	9,526
1912	—	1,593	9,263	—	51,427	11,735
1913	—	2,375	12,499	—	63,579	15,010
1914	—	3,104	14,309	—	73,632	20,068
1915	—	2,823	18,192	—	97,915	24,943
1916	—	8,738	15,248	—	107,072	27,645
1917	—	36,536	11,392	—	107,508	32,413
1918	—	45,451	16,043	—	103,347	38,750
1919	—	33,048	17,188	—	86,911	79,366
1920	—	39,005	35,714	—	106,206	96,868

Year						
1921	10,473	36,456	27,103	——	114,634	106,166
1922	12,712	31,766	35,376	——	149,571	118,684
1923	36,610	28,250	24,919	——	160,929	131,023
1924	46,028	28,836	21,124	98	173,538	134,522
1925	77,398	38,357	20,272	1,060	176,768	144,648
1926	58,332	41,498	23,201	1,666	179,195	166,916
1927	40,005	41,069	22,818	1,226	277,775	217,389
1928	32,096	38,596	21,847	943	249,857	257,320
1929	24,917	42,813	20,554	1,830	255,004	296,876
1930	19,702	41,638	23,272	10,189	216,486	290,457
1931	14,791	37,018	21,804	15,227	180,574	332,437
1932	12,051	34,848	21,807	12,455	153,244	312,478
1933	11,686	41,976	25,168	14,116	182,251	402,609
1934	11,182	46,482	32,869	16,864	180,107	381,516
1935	11,008	54,843	50,330	20,483	185,288	392,666
1936	10,469	58,317	80,491	27,223	206,555	427,411
1937	11,764	70,761	90,924	38,854	228,839	510,318
1938	18,180	60,064	95,208	35,759	174,994	475,850
1939	21,238	60,703	93,646	37,637	159,913	483,528
1940	25,775	66,139	103,584	39,129	156,164	493,209
1941	26,327	83,242	115,908	39,569	154,702	505,572
1942	26,628	97,636	115,785	31,544	140,690	483,097
1943	27,600	106,178	123,592	38,896	123,152	594,343
1944	29,418	98,762	129,645	39,555	124,616	746,699
1945	28,613	96,415	131,051	37,351	139,299	754,710
1946	28,375	97,218	143,303	36,860	134,497	760,505
1947	29,609	105,072	159,276	40,971	141,325	817,987
Totals	702,987	1,779,101	1,978,549	539,505	5,790,759	11,242,720

* *World Oil*, Vol. CXXVII, No. 11 (Yearbook, February, 1948), 167–68. See also *Petroleum Facts and Figures* (Eighth edition), 55; *Oil and Gas Journal*, Vol. XLVI, No. 39 (January 29, 1948), 166; *Minerals Yearbook*, 1944 (Bureau of Mines, 1946), 1078. The *Statistical Bulletin* (Interstate Oil Compact), Vol. III, No. 1 (April 15, 1948), 9, gives the following daily average crude-oil production, January, 1948: for the Southwestern states, 3,709,700 (Bureau of Mines) and 3,747,450 (A.P.I.), and for the United States, a total of 5,283,300 (Bureau of Mines) and 5,323,437 (A.P.I.). The total cumulative oil production of the United States, 1857–1947 is above 35,000,000,000 barrels, of which the Southwest's contribution is 22,000,000,000 barrels.

Crude-oil Production of Important Louisiana Fields
(thousands of barrels)

Year	Anse-la-Butte	Boscoe	Caddo	Cotton Valley	DeSoto	Golden Meadows	Haynes-ville	Homer	Iowa	Jennings	LaFitte	Red River	Rodessa	Urania	Vinton
1902	—	—	—	—	—	—	—	—	—	549	—	—	—	—	—
1903	—	—	—	—	—	—	—	—	—	893	—	—	—	—	—
1904	—	—	—	—	—	—	—	—	—	2,906	—	—	—	—	—
1905	9	—	—	—	—	—	—	—	—	8,891	—	—	—	—	—
1906	25	—	3	—	—	—	—	—	—	9,025	—	—	—	—	—
1907	60	—	50	—	—	—	—	—	—	4,896	—	—	—	—	—
1908	146	—	500	—	—	—	—	—	—	6,119	—	—	—	—	—
1909	38	—	1,029	—	—	—	—	—	—	1,967	—	—	—	—	—
1910	44	—	5,091	—	—	—	—	—	—	1,625	—	—	—	—	27
1911	62	—	6,996	—	—	—	—	—	—	1,180	—	—	—	—	2,454
1912	25	—	7,178	—	—	—	—	—	—	1,105	—	—	—	—	933
1913	7	—	9,782	—	b3,835	—	—	—	—	791	—	—	—	—	1,889
1914	19	—	7,572	—	1,797	—	—	—	—	412	—	402	—	—	1,465
1915	21	—	6,472	—	—	—	—	—	—	435	—	6,802	—	—	1,234
1916	13	—	5,464	—	1,657	—	—	—	—	517	—	4,691	—	—	1,640
1917	5	—	5,484	—	1,371	—	—	—	—	399	—	1,665	—	—	1,595
1918	a3	—	11,144	—	1,066	—	—	—	—	369	—	1,045	—	—	1,839
1919	d	—	a8,700	—	a1,200	—	—	a2,000	—	347	—	a2,900	—	—	1,592
1920	d	—	6,336	—	c5,923	—	—	21,508	—	232	—	c	—	—	1,333
1921	47	—	5,342	—	719	—	3,161	13,030	—	254	—	2,844	—	—	1,379
1922	36	—	4,498	—	531	—	19,939	5,673	—	191	—	1,778	—	—	1,395
1923	18	—	4,178	—	429	—	10,496	3,581	—	204	—	1,207	—	—	2,071
1924	12	—	4,319	1,211	353	—	6,720	2,837	—	213	—	1,231	—	—	1,968
1925	17	—	4,067	3,348	305	—	4,604	2,296	—	278	—	1,074	—	10	2,274

414

Year															
1926	17	—	4,749	2,914	321	—	3,328	2,033	—	342	—	1,037	—	3,669	2,215
1927	17	—	5,789	1,968	541	—	2,600	1,785	—	299	—	1,070	—	3,321	1,786
1928	16	—	4,798	1,731	463	—	2,150	1,548	—	250	—	1,109	—	2,487	1,569
1929	14	—	4,589	1,040	276	—	1,806	1,405	—	515	—	987	—	2,155	1,484
1930	9	—	4,120	880	247	—	1,743	1,278	—	495	—	838	—	1,976	1,768
1931	12	—	3,054	509	192	—	1,902	1,083	—	169	—	713	—	1,448	1,940
1932	11	—	2,486	353	469	—	1,534	1,021	489	332	—	257	—	1,208	1,514
1933	d	—	2,248	307	411	—	1,402	991	3,396	400	—	190	—	883	1,302
1934	d	1,036	2,200	290	398	—	1,379	980	5,300	444	—	145	—	1,077	1,168
1935	d	6,356	2,630	233	ec517	—	1,266	977	7,363	686	635	e	1,364	1,062	906
1936	d	4,661	2,554	207	ec502	—	1,216	950	6,626	754	2,709	e	19,220	1,060	650
1937	d	3,020	2,353	1,151	ec538	—	1,143	932	6,383	2,996	4,136	e	18,050	1,085	470
1938	74	2,085	2,659	3,527	ec499	—	1,107	952	5,641	7,537	5,862	e	13,443	1,003	472
1939	24	1,737	2,663	4,384	ec412	739	1,064	988	4,436	8,119	4,745	e	9,042	974	d
1940	380	1,718	2,912	5,189	ec371	4,074	987	1,041	3,475	5,505	4,602	e	6,859	869	306
1941	1,446	1,494	3,077	3,459	ec365	4,814	956	1,033	3,400	4,991	4,523	e	5,212	832	323
1942	2,235	1,395	2,694	1,953	ec355	4,124	4,621	1,060	2,506	4,402	3,750	e	4,100	778	369
1943	2,191	1,094	2,421	1,532	ec307	3,606	5,368	1,067	2,928	3,416	4,688	d	3,462	739	661
1944	2,620	1,046	1,950	724	e332	2,796	3,816	1,019	3,309	2,840	4,452	d	2,930	678	1,942
1945	2,481	1,000	1,910	388	e384	2,494	2,356	976	2,731	2,442	4,139	d	2,515	632	2,703
1946	e2,441	e1,007	e1,897	e2,671	fc331	e1,433	e2,936	e944	e2,497	e2,443	e4,383	e	e2,025	e601	e3,359
1947	e2,422	e944	e2,332	e2,980	fc273	e2,649	e3,099	e915	e2,429	e1,823	e4,350	e	e1,714	e644	e3,673

a U.S.G.S. estimate.

b Includes Sabine.

c Red River included in DeSoto.

d Included in unclassified reports only.

All figures taken from *Mineral Resources, Part II, Nonmetals* (published by U.S.G.S., 1882–1924; and the Bureau of Mines under the same title, 1924–31; and as *Minerals Yearbook*, 1931–45), except the following: e *Oil and Gas Journal*, Vol. XXXIV, No. 37 (January 30, 1936); Vol. XXXV, No. 37 (January 28, 1937); Vol. XL, No. 38 (January 29, 1942); Vol. XLI, No. 38 (January 28, 1943); Vol. XLII, No. 38 (January 27, 1944); Vol. XLIII, No. 38 (January 27, 1945); Vol. XLIV, No. 38 (January 26, 1946); Vol. XLV, No. 38 (January 26, 1947); and Vol. XLVI, No. 39 (January 29, 1948); f *Yearbook* (National Oil Scouts and Landmen's Association), Vol. XVIII (1948).

Glossary

Air-lift: to produce oil from a well by jetting compressed air into the oil column at the base of the well tubing.

Alidade: a straight edge, with attachments for sighting, used with a plane table. The simplest form, the open-sight alidade, is essentially a ruler with hinged standards mounted on each end, one of the standards carrying a slot for sighting and the other a wire for alignment on the target. The telescopic alidade is essentially a telescope mounted on a ruler. It usually carries a vertical arc, with or without a vernier, for measuring vertical angles. The telescope includes the usual wires for sighting on target and leveling, as well as stadia wires for measuring distances.

Allowable: that quantity of oil, determined on the basis of the well's potential output, which state proration permits to be produced daily.

Anticline: an upfolded structure or rock fold in which oil is often trapped in limestone or sandstone formations.

Asphalt: a natural solid or viscous chemical compound of partially oxidized hydrocarbons, usually dark brown or black in color.

Asphalt base: a term loosely and often erroneously used to describe a petroleum which yields substantial amounts of asphalt upon distillation or evaporation as distinguished from petroleum which yields chiefly paraffin under similar treatment. Many so-called asphalt-base oils also yield paraffin.

Baumé: a scientist named Baumé devised a gravity measurement for oil consisting of a slender tube with a weighted bulb on the lower end and with numbered graduations known as degrees. It is similar to the filling-station operator's tester by which he determines the antifreeze liquid in your radiator. It is largely replaced now by the A.P.I. scale which differs from it very slightly.

Big Inch: a twenty-four-inch crude-oil pipe line built during World War II to transport Southwestern crude oil to the Eastern seaboard refineries.

416

Glossary

Bitumen: a mixture of native hydrocarbons.

Blanket lease: a lease of a large area, often embracing the holdings or interests of many persons, e.g., the Foster Osage lease.

Blow out: an explosion of gas under high pressure within a well which often blows out a huge surface cavity, as occurred at El Dorado and Smackover, Arkansas.

Cable-tool rig: a drilling rig using a cable suspended from its crown block to lift and drop the drilling tools, as in churning.

Carbon black: a black residue, as lampblack, which collects on the walls of a furnace where natural gas with a little air is burned.

Casing: a large pipe inserted into a well bore to act as a permanent wall to prevent earth caving, seepage of water, or both. Usually cement holds this pipe fast to the earth.

Casing head: that part of a well casing protruding above the surface of the ground.

Casing-head gasoline: a highly volatile gasoline derived from the "wet gas" of a well, presumably taken from the well's casing head.

Catalytic cracker: a huge steel drum in which a foreign substance called a catalyst breaks down the hydrocarbon molecules while they are heated to a high temperature preparatory to their rearrangement into new and different molecules. When a particular oil is subjected to a certain temperature and pressure, a certain cracking takes place, making certain products.

Choke: a "flow bean" or a heavy steel nipple inserted into the flow pipe to reduce its cross-sectional area and thus regulate the well's oil flow.

Christmas tree: the assembly of valves and fittings on a well's tubing and casing, above the surface of the ground, to control the well's oil yield. The term "Christmas tree" is used to denote this installation's expansive, distinctive array of well fittings.

Closure: the vertical distance between the anticlinal crest and the highest point at the base of the fold.

Coal oil: a term variously applied to liquid products of coal, sometimes to crude petroleum, and most generally to kerosene derived from crude oil.

Control head: a heavy fitting that screws on the innermost casing top of a well.

Copé: Spanish explorers who visited the Texas coast in 1543 found an asphaltic substance floating on water which they called "*copé*."

Core: a sample "plug" taken from a rock stratum of a well by means of a core drill. These plugs are studied to determine their oil saturation and porosity.

417

Core drill: a hollow drill stem used to extract a core from any formation encountered in drilling.

Crown block: a wooden or steel frame at the top of the derrick from which are mounted vertical grooved pulley wheels (the "sheaves").

Crude oil: unrefined petroleum.

Cuttings: the rock particles ground by the bit at the bottom of the well and which are brought to the surface by bailing or rotary mud circulation.

Derrick: a square, open, wooden or steel tower, ordinarily from seventy to more than one hundred feet high and from twenty to twenty-eight feet square at the base and from five to seven feet at the top.

Directional drilling: the practice of slanting a hole from the straight course first taken (a) by "whipstocking" (putting a beveled bar of steel in the bottom of a hole at a point where the driller desires to angle the hole off of its straight course); or (b) by using a "knuckle-joint" drilling tool to accomplish the same purpose. Some Gulf Coast salt-dome traps of oil have been reached this way more easily than by drilling a straight course and offshore oil formations have been tapped by oil wells drilled on the adjacent shore.

Distillate (also *"condensate"*): that liquid which is produced from a well by cooling the produced gas in much the same manner as dew is condensed into a liquid from the air when it is cooled.

Doodle bug: a prospecting instrument similar to the "divining rod" or "dowsing rod" or "witching stick" used during the last century to find oil or water. The term is used today somewhat derisively to include all complicated prospecting instruments.

Downthrow: a geological term used to describe a side of a fault that has slipped down relative to the other side.

Drive head: a circular steel coupling-like tool, used to protect a coupling from drive-clamp damage.

Dry gas: a gas that does not contain easily separated gasoline.

Dry hole: a completed well that does not produce oil or gas.

Duster: a completed well that does not produce oil or gas.

Electric logging: the determination and recording of certain electrical characteristics of formations through which a well is drilled. The most commonly used form records the self-potential and resistivity. Self-potential is generally interpreted as an index to the porosity of the formations logged, while resistivity is generally interpreted as giving a clue to their fluid content.

Fault: a formation fracture along which there has been a relative slipping of the walls. The slipping of a sandstone or limestone formation below

418

Glossary

an impervious formation sometimes creates an oil fault trap.

Fishtail bit: a wedge-shaped bit divided like a fishtail, the two points of which are bent in opposite directions like an augur.

Flush production: that period of the life of a well when oil is brought to the surface by gas pressure or natural flow.

Fractionating tower: a "bubble tower" or vertical steel cylinder varying from 2 to 25 feet in diameter and 40 to 120 feet in height. This tower is partitioned with perforated trays so as to take off oil fractions of heated oil passing upward through the tower in the order of their volatility, the lightest fraction, of course, escaping from the uppermost tray.

Gas-oil ratio: that proportion of gas (expressed in cubic feet) to oil (measured in barrels) produced by a well or wells in a field.

Gusher: a well from which oil flows spontaneously under a strong gas or water, or gas and water, drive.

Heavy oil: oil of low Baumé gravity, from about 30 degrees down.

Hot oil: oil which the operator surreptitiously or secretly runs from a well or tank to sell in violation of proration regulations. The operator ordinarily has secret underground pipes and connections.

Hydrogenation: when, within a refinery installation, hydrocarbons are being subjected to a high temperature, while simultaneously free hydrogen is being introduced, the atomic groupings of the hydrocarbons resulting from the cracking unite with the hydrogen atoms introduced and combine into smaller molecules of the lighter hydrocarbons.

Lens: a lentil or sedimentary bed that pinches out or "lens out" in all directions.

Light oil: an oil with a high Baumé gravity, ranging from about 30 degrees upward.

Little Big Inch: a twenty-inch oil products pipe line built during World War II to transport oil products to the Eastern seaboard ports and cities.

Loading rack: a loading platform with oil pipes and hoses at the side of a railroad track for loading oil into tank cars.

Magnetometer: a geophysical instrument used to measure the variation and intensity, both horizontal and vertical, of the earth's magnetic field.

Marsh gas: methane (CH_4), the chief constituent of natural gas. It also often results from the decay of swamp plants.

Mud pump: rotary rig pumps used to force a mud fluid into the bottom of a well and through the drill pipe back to the surface to remove the cuttings made by the drill, to keep the bit cool, to prevent the sides of the well from caving, and to prevent a high-pressure formation from causing damage by blowing the drilling equipment from the well.

Multiple drilling: the drilling of two or more wells from one location of a drilling rig by slant holes to reach two or more horizons, or by use of a whipstock to drain one formation at widely separated points.

Offset well: a well on one lease drilled to offset a well on an adjacent lease to capture the leaseholder's rightful part of oil in the common oil zone before it "migrates" to the neighboring well.

Oil horizon: a sandstone, limestone, or other rock stratum saturated with oil.

Oil sand: any oil-saturated subsurface stratum of rock.

Oil shale: shales high in organic content which yield liquid hydrocarbons upon retorting.

Outcrop: a surface exposure of bed rock.

Paraffin base: a paraffin-base oil yields a paraffin residue on evaporation or distillation, in contrast to an oil which yields asphalt.

Perforate: to perforate a casing is to lower a "gun" or mechanical instrument loaded with cartridges into a well and discharge it at a desired depth to perforate the casing for the seeping of the formation's oil into the casing.

Pipe still: an important refinery installation, in which crude oil is vaporized while passing through a series of pipes.

Plant table: a small board mounted on a tripod by means of a swivel or ball-and-socket joint and used for mapping a surface geological structure.

Plugged: the closing of a "dry" well or a "duster" or a well that has ceased to produce by inserting a solid "plug" of metal or concrete in it.

Plugged back: a drilling technique of placing an effective plug between lower water-bearing formations and the stratum to be tested, or from which oil is to be derived.

Polymerization: the application of heat to hydrocarbons in a refinery installation to cause the hydrocarbon molecules to combine into larger ones.

Pool: an underground accumulation of oil in a single and separate reservoir (ordinarily a porous sandstone or limestone). In a real sense, oil is not found in subsurface pools or lakes as formerly believed.

Popping of gas: the "flaring," burning, or wasting of gas at a well head.

Potential: the estimated oil yield of a well. Under proration only a minor portion of potential output is ordinarily allowed.

Glossary

Prospecting: the quest for an oil structure. During early decades of American oil history "water-witching" (see "doodle bug") and other unscientific methods were used to search for oil. In 1910, geological methods were applied, and in more recent times, both geological and geophysical (seismograph, torsion balance, magnetometer, etc.).

Red Beds: Sedimentary formations of predominantly red color. The Permian and Triassic of western Mid-Continent fit this definition and are generally referred to as "the Red Beds."

Reservoir pressure: the pressure within a well caused by gas, or gas and water, which furnishes the energy to bring the oil to the well.

Rig irons: steel parts and fittings that go into or on the derrick.

Rock oil: petroleum derived from a rock formation, as sandstone or limestone, a term commonly used up to 1900 but seldom heard since.

Rotary bit: a cutting device at the end of a drill pipe rotated by an engine-powered table on the rig floor. Rotary bits are of many shapes and designs, from the simple fishtail bits to the cones or rollers which revolve as the tool turns.

Royalty: a percentage of oil or its cash equivalent paid to the land or royalty owner by the leaseholder when oil is produced on the property.

Salt dome: salt plugs found along the Texas-Louisiana Gulf Coast that during past geological ages have pushed upward through other formations toward the surface, often providing traps for oil in the rocks above and at the sides.

Samson post: a huge upright timber near a cable-tool well on which is balanced a "walking beam." It is used only in cable-tool drilling.

Scouting: seeking information regarding exploration and development of oil areas.

Seismograph: an instrument for recording the speed of transmission of shock waves through the earth at different points. Such shock waves are generated by setting off dynamite charges.

Shackle-rod system: a method of pumping several wells on one lease by means of small rods (called shackle rods) extending from the wells to a central pumping house, and connected to the wells in such a way as to carry the power of the central pump to each well.

Sheaves: vertical-grooved pulley-wheels which are built into the crown block, over which run three steel cables: the "casing line," the "sand line" for bailing the well, and the "drilling line."

Shooter: one who makes his living by the hazardous occupation of "shooting" or exploding nitroglycerin in wells to shatter a producing sand and thus improve its oil yield.

Shooting: the discharge of nitroglycerin in the bottom of a well.

421

Oil! Titan of the Southwest

Skimming: In the refining process, lighter fractions of oil are taken off ("skimmed"), leaving heavier products in an unfractioned residuum.

Slush bucket: a hollow cylinder used to draw sludge from the bottom of a well.

Slush pit: a surface pond near the derrick used to receive sludge from a well during drilling.

Sour gas: a gas with appreciable sulphur content.

Spudding in: the beginning of a well by the use of a "spudding bit" attached to a jerk line suspended from the derrick's crown block.

Still: a steel drum tower at a refinery in which crude oil yields hydrocarbon vapors.

String of tools: tools used in drilling.

Stripper well: a well that has already yielded most of its oil and produces a few barrels of oil and water each day by pumping.

Sweet gas: a non-sulphurous gas.

Syncline: a rock structure in which the rocks are down folded, the opposite of an anticline.

Tank farm: an area embracing a collection of steel or wooden oil-storage tanks.

Tongs: large pipe wrenches commonly used in pipe-line construction.

Tool dresser: a "toolie" or "tool dresser" is a cable-tool driller's right-hand man, who helps to dress or reshape a worn bit by heating and hammering it with a sixteen-pound sledge.

Tool pusher: one who has charge of rig builders and a drilling crew, and sometimes superintends the work at two or more wells.

Topping: a refinery technique employed to secure complete fractional distillation except a heavy residuum. The term is sometimes used in a more narrow sense to mean the taking off of the lighter fractions of oil.

Torsion balance: an instrument that measures minute differences in the gravitational attraction of the earth at different places.

Traveling block: a huge pulley suspended from a sheave from the crown block of a rotary derrick and used in drilling.

Upthrow side: that side of a fault which appears to have been raised relative to the other side, the downthrow.

Walking beam: a timber used in cable-tool drilling, so balanced on a Samson post as to teeter up and down to aid in drilling.

Well log: a driller's detailed record of the formations encountered in the drilling of a well.

Wet gas: a gas that contains easily separated gasoline.

Wildcatter: an oil operator who leases and drills for oil in unproven territory.

Bibliography

A LARGE PERCENTAGE of the materials used in this narrative is more technical than historical. But occasionally technical papers contain historical nuggets, e.g., a contemporary account of a prospecting device, a new drilling technique, or a refining process. Frequently, too, they have historical sketches of oil-field development—when and where the discovery well blew in, the drilling of other wells, growing production, and detailed field operations, ordinarily carried in the first few paragraphs or under such sub-captions as "History of the Field," "Development of the Field," or other suggestive titles. General trade journals cover a wider range of subjects, including rapid changes in community life with oil discovery and a new oil field's boom spirit. From these several publications I have sought to garner all choice bits of information.

The use of bibliographical guides is indispensable in the study of any division of the petroleum industry. Among those particularly useful in a history of Southwestern petroleum are: E. DeGolyer and Harold Vance, *Bibliography on the Petroleum Industry, Bulletin No. 83*, Agricultural and Mechanical College of Texas, Fourth Series, Vol. XV, No. 11 (September, 1944); Robert E. Hardwicke, *Petroleum and Natural Gas Bibliography* (Austin, 1937); Clarence P. Dunbar and Lucile M. Dunbar, *A Selected List of Periodicals, Serials, and Books Dealing with Petroleum* . . . (Department of Conservation, Louisiana, New Orleans, January, 1939); and Alan G. Skelton and Martha B. Skelton, *A Bibliography of Oklahoma Oil and Gas Pools*, Oklahoma Geological Survey *Bulletin No. 63* (Norman, 1942).

A full catalog of the materials used in this narrative would be far too extensive for our needs here. Rather, I list those manuscript and printed materials that were of greatest use in the shaping of this book.

MANUSCRIPTS

The National Archives, Washington, D. C., house extensive bodies of manuscripts in seven divisional files related to the petroleum industry.

Oil! Titan of the Southwest

The Bureau of Mines and the United States Geological Survey records, in the Division of Natural Resources Records, contain large units of letters, reports, charts, photographs, and maps covering principally the last three decades. Records of the Department of the Navy ("Secretary's Office General Correspondence, Correspondence Files"; and "Correspondence of the Bureau of Engineering, Relative to Oil Fuel, Lands and Reservations, 1911–1924") contain year-by-year figures on production and estimates of field potentials. Records of the Federal Oil Conservation Board and of the United States Fuel Administration, in the Division of Natural Resources Records (covering the period of World War I), are equally broad in their subject catalogs but much less limited in point of time, as their titles indicate.

Two other bodies of materials in the Division of Natural Resources Records were also fruitful in this study. The "Narrative Reports, Osage Agency Report, 1910–1923," in the Records of the Office of Indian Affairs, contained papers on the Osage leasing problem, oil discovery, and oil-field activity. Finally, the records of the Petroleum Administration for War are voluminous and cover such subjects as prospecting, production, transportation, and refining during the period of World War II. I also found maps of Southwestern oil-producing states and areas in the Division of Maps and Charts.

State and county records, showing state legislation, oil-field control, and land transactions, were equally helpful. State official correspondence, e.g., miscellaneous records of the adjutants general, tax commissions, and state police were examined. County Clerk deed volumes, showing lease patterns, company and independent operator activity, furnish important local data.

Typical of lengthy single manuscript narratives of great value in my writing of this book are: a history of the Mid-Continent oil fields by Mr. H. T. Galey, Caracas, Venezuela, lent to me by Mr. Rush Greenslade, vice-president, Gulf Oil Corporation, Gypsy Division, at Tulsa; the John W. Flenner manuscript "History of Petroleum" and "Chronology of Events Leading and Pertaining to the Discovery of Oil at Red Fork, Indian Territory (Sue A. Bland No. 1 well), June 25, 1901," both in the files of the Mid-Continent Oil and Gas Association, at Tulsa; and the Claude V. Barrow history of the Oklahoma City oil field, in Mr. Barrow's private collection.

I have examined other private collections of oil-field materials. Among these are the correspondence of J. C. Heydrick, about the Red Fork oil field, now the property of L. C. Heydrick, Wichita Falls, Texas; papers relating to early Texas oil fields, in Mr. Lou Kemp's collection, Houston,

Bibliography

Texas; correspondence relating to early oilmen and fields, in Mr. E. De-Golyer's library, Dallas, Texas; Indian papers in Miss Muriel Wright's collection, Oklahoma City; and the correspondence of Dr. Charles N. Gould, Norman, Oklahoma, regarding Panhandle oil and gas discoveries. Equally useful have been the papers and minute book of the Gladys City Oil Company, Beaumont, Texas, relating to early-day oil developments near Beaumont, Texas. And such state collections as the manuscripts division, the Kansas State Historical library (a few papers and scrapbooks) at Topeka; the Oklahoma Historical Library (the Barde papers and Indian Archives) at Oklahoma City; and the Texas State Archives (papers of the state adjutant general), Austin, Texas, were also important.

Other gleanings were from manuscripts, some important and others relatively immaterial, found in various places. These papers ranged from one piece to ten or fifteen pieces. Those of greatest value, together with the names of their custodians, follow: manuscripts and photographs relating to early Eastern and Southwestern oil fields, Mr. Thomas M. Galey, Owensboro, Kentucky; a scrapbook of letters, telegrams, and other materials relating to El Dorado and Smackover, Arkansas, oil fields, Mrs. Mamie Smith McCurry, El Dorado, Arkansas; a manuscript portraying El Dorado as a boom town, Miss Ann H. Cardell, El Dorado, Arkansas; a manuscript on the early-day Neodesha oil-field discovery, Mr. E. A. Warren, Neodesha, Kansas; materials on the building and early operations of the Neodesha refinery, Mr. E. A. Metcalf, Neodesha, Kansas; a register of Northwestern Louisiana oil development, Mr. A. R. Carmody, Shreveport, Louisiana; contemporary data and photographs on Jennings and South Louisiana oil fields, Mr. W. Scott Heywood, Jennings, Louisiana; a manuscript and photographs showing the early Jennings oil-field development, Miss Alice Mosher, Jennings, Louisiana.

W. E. Campbell's letter of February 2, 1907, about Glenn Pool, Mr. R. B. Campbell, Colorado Springs, Colorado; James M. Payne letter, dated September 7, 1847, Grant Foreman, Muskogee, Oklahoma; original Edwin B. Foster lease, dated March 16, 1896, files of Osage Indian Reservation, Pawhuska, Oklahoma; a longhand contract for the drilling of an Abilene, Texas, well in 1885, and a folder of other materials, Mr. Henry Sales, Jr., Abilene, Texas; contemporary account of the No. 1 Clayco well completion at Electra, and photographs, Mr. Ben Donnell, Wichita Falls, Texas; a manuscript relating to the Electra oil discovery, Mrs. N. D. Cooper, Electra, Texas; a manuscript relating to the Brownwood oil-well discovery, Mrs. J. D. Sandefer, Sr., Abilene, Texas; a letter about post–Civil War Gulf Coast oil development, Mr. Chilton O'Brien, Beaumont, Texas; a letter regarding the Merriman oil field, Rev. W. T. Hamor,

425

Oil! Titan of the Southwest

Abilene, Texas; the Hog Creek Oil Company Minute Book, J. R. Palmer, Stephensville, Texas; a bound volume including Sour Lake and Saratoga oil leases and other papers, John Hamman, Houston, Texas; and a scrapbook of letters, etc., on Mexia oil field, Blake Smith Jr., Mexia, Texas.

PRINTED DOCUMENTS

a. Federal

Federal documents devote a large amount of space to the oil industry, but I found two studies of special value in connection with this narrative. The first is Charles B. Eliot's *Petroleum Industry of the Gulf Southwest* (U. S. Department of Commerce, Bureau of Foreign Commerce, Domestic Commerce Series, No. 44, Washington, 1931) covering production and refining. And the second is H. C. Miller and Ben E. Lindsly's "Report on Petroleum Production and Development," in *Hearings before a Subcommittee of the Committee on Interstate and Foreign Commerce, House of Representatives, Seventy-third Congress (Recess) on H. Res. 441 (Printed Herein), September 17, 18, 19, 20, 21, and 22, 1934* (Washington, 1934), Part II, 1087–1306, carrying such subjects as "Exploration and Prospecting," "Development," "Production of Oil," "Unit Operation," and "Proration."

Other federal documents of secondary importance are: *Tenth Census of the United States, Special Reports on Petroleum, Coke and Building Stones* (Washington, 1884), X, 26; *Report on the Commissioner of Corporations on the Petroleum Industry, Part II (Prices and Profits)* (Washington, 1907); Raymond S. Blatchley, "Waste of Oil and Gas in the Mid-Continent Fields" in Department of the Interior, Bureau of Mines, *Technical Paper 45* (Washington, 1913); Department of the Interior, *Request of Oil Lessees Holding Leases in the Osage Reservation for the Amendment of the Regulations of the Secretary of the Interior Applicable Thereto in Certain Particulars* (Tulsa, *circa* 1917); *Osage Reservation Oklahoma, Structure Maps,* United States Geological Survey *Bulletin No. 686* (Washington, 1922); H. C. Fowler, *Accidents in the Petroleum Industry of Oklahoma, 1915–1924* (U. S. Department of Commerce, Bureau of Mines, Washington, 1928); *Report of the Federal Trade Commission on Panhandle Crude Petroleum, February 3, 1928* (Washington, 1928); Gustave Wade, "Mechanical Equipment Used in the Drilling and Production of Oil and Gas Wells in Oklahoma City Field," U. S. Department of the Interior, Bureau of Mines, *Technical Paper No. 561* (Washington, 1934); U. S. Department of the Interior, Petroleum Administrative Board, *Preliminary Report on a Survey of Crude Petroleum, Cost of*

Bibliography

Production for the Years, 1931–1933 and Comparison with Years, 1927–1930 (Washington, 1934); U. S. Department of the Interior, *Report on the Cost of Producing Crude Petroleum* (Washington, 1936), 1–13; U. S. Department of the Interior, Petroleum Administrative Board, *Operation of the New Pool Plans of Orderly Development* . . . (Washington, 1936).

Hearings before the Temporary National Economic Committee . . . *Seventy-Sixth Congress, Second Session, Pursuant to Public Resolution, No. 113 (Seventy-fifth Congress)* . . . *Petroleum Industry, Part XIV–A, September 25, 1939* (Washington, 1940), 9697, 7730–37, 7719–30; *ibid., Part XVII, Section IV, October 17, 18, 19, 20, 23, 24, and 25, 1939* (Washington, 1940), conservation, 9512–15, unit operation, 9522–56; *ibid., February 19, 20, 21, 22, 26, and 27, 1940*, 1429–65, 1477–97, efficiency of petroleum production in Texas, Louisiana, and New Mexico, 1627–46, 1647–67; G. R. Hopkins, *Economic Paper 20, Petroleum Statistics, 1935–38* (U. S. Department of the Interior, Bureau of Mines, Washington, 1940); Bureau of Mines, *Crude Petroleum and Petroleum Products* (Washington, 1941); *Hearings Before a Special Committee Investigating Petroleum Resources* . . . *Seventy-ninth Congress, First Session, Pursuant to S. Res. 36 (Extending S. Res. 253, Seventy-eighth Congress), A Resolution Providing for an Investigation with Respect to Petroleum Resources in Relation to the National Welfare, October 3 and 4, 1945* (Washington, 1946), 12–14 ff.; *Message from the President of the United States to the Two Houses of Congress at the Commencement of the First Session of the Third Congress (House Ex. Doc. No. 1, 1 sess.);* Carl H. Beal, "The Decline and Ultimate Production of Oil Wells, with Notes on the Valuation of Oil Properties," Department of the Interior, Bureau of Mines *Bulletin 177, Petroleum Technology 51* (Washington, 1919); U. S. G. S., *Mineral Resources of the United States, Part II, Nonmetals* (Washington, 1882–1924); Bureau of Mines, *Mineral Resources of the United States* (Washington, 1924–31); Bureau of Mines, *Minerals Yearbook* (and *Statistical Appendix*) (Washington, 1932–45). Among the serial documents are: "Production Technology and Uses of Petroleum and Its Products," *House Misc. Doc. No. 42,* 47 Cong., 2 sess., Part X, 1–319; "Conservation of Oil and Gas" in *House Report No. 1585,* 72 Cong., 1 sess.

Articles of value in bulletins of the United States Geological Survey are numerous. Among these I found the following of practical use: George I. Adams, "Oil and Gas Fields of the Western Interior and Northern Texas Coal Measures and of the Upper Cretaceous and Tertiary of the Western Gulf Coast," in *Bulletin No. 184* (Washington, 1901); C. W. Hayes and William Kennedy, "Oil Fields of the Texas-Louisiana Gulf

427

Oil! Titan of the Southwest

Coastal Plain," in *Bulletin No. 212* (Washington, 1903); G. I. Adams, Erasmus Haworth, and W. R. Crane, "Economic Geology of the Iola Quadrangle, Kansas," in *Bulletin No. 238* (Washington, 1904); G. B. Richardson, "Salt, Gypsum and Petroleum in Trans-Pecos Texas," in *Bulletin No. 260* (Washington, 1905), 573–85; Joseph A. Taff and Millard K. Shaler, "Notes on the Geology of the Muscogee Oil Fields, Indian Territory," in *Bulletin No. 260* (Washington, 1905), 441–45; Frank C. Shrader and Erasmus Haworth, "Oil and Gas of the Independence Quadrangle, Kansas," in *Bulletin No. 260* (Washington, 1905), 446–58; N. M. Fenneman, "Oil Fields of the Texas-Louisiana Gulf Coast," in *Bulletin No. 260* (Washington, 1905), 459–67; N. M. Fenneman, "Oil Fields of the Texas-Louisiana Gulf Coastal Plain," in *Bulletin No. 282* (Washington, 1906); Frank C. Schrader and Erasmus Haworth, "Economic Geology of the Independence Quadrangle, Kansas," in *Bulletin No. 296* (Washington, 1906); David T. Day, "The Petroleum Resources of the United States," in *Bulletin No. 394* (Washington, 1909), 30–50; G. D. Harris, "Oil and Gas in Louisiana, with a Brief Summary of The Occurrence in Adjacent States," in *Bulletin No. 429* (Washington, 1910).

Robert H. Wood, "Oil and Gas Development in North-Central Oklahoma," in *Bulletin No. 531-B* (Washington, 1913), 27–53; Carl D. Smith, "The Glenn Oil and Gas Pool and Vicinity, Oklahoma," in *Bulletin No. 541-B* (Washington, 1914), 34–48; G. C. Matson, "The Caddo Oil and Gas Field, Louisiana and Texas," in *Bulletin No. 619* (Washington, 1916); C. H. Wegemann and K. C. Heald, "The Healdton Oil Field, Carter County, Oklahoma," in *Bulletin No. 621-B* (Washington, 1916), 13–30; C. H. Wegemann and K. C. Heald, "A Reconnaissance in Palo Pinto County, Texas, with Special Reference to Oil and Gas," in *Bulletin No. 621-E* (Washington, 1916), 51–59; Wegemann, Heald, and R. W. Howell, "The Lawton Oil and Gas Field, Oklahoma," in *Bulletin No. 621-G* (Washington, 1916), 71–85; A. E. Fath, "An Anticlinal Fold Near Billings, Noble County, Oklahoma," in *Bulletin No. 641-E* (Washington, 1917), 121–38; K. C. Heald, "The Oil and Gas Geology of the Foraker Quadrangle, Osage County, Oklahoma," in *Bulletin No. 641-B* (Washington, 1917), 17–47; C. H. Beal, "Geologic Structure in the Cushing Oil and Gas Field, Oklahoma, and Its Relation to the Oil, Gas, and Water," in *Bulletin No. 658* (Washington, 1917); A. E. Fath, "Structure of the Northern Part of the Bristow Quadrangle, Creek County, Oklahoma, With Reference to Petroleum and Natural Gas," in *Bulletin No. 661-B* (Washington, 1918), 69–99.

George C. Matson and Oliver B. Hopkins, "The Corsicana Oil and Gas Field, Texas," in *Bulletin No. 661-F* (Washington, 1918), 211–52;

Bibliography

K. C. Heald and Kirtley E. Mather, "Structure and Oil and Gas Resources of the Osage Reservation, Oklahoma," in *Bulletin No. 686-M* (Washington, 1919); K. C. Heald, "Geologic Structure of the Northwestern Part of the Pawhuska Quadrangle, Oklahoma," in *Bulletin No. 691-C* (Washington, 1919), 57–100; H. D. Miser and A. H. Purdue, "Asphalt Deposits and Oil Conditions in Southwestern Arkansas," in *Bulletin No. 691-J* (Washington, 1919), 271–92; D. E. Winchester, "Geology of Alamosa Creek Valley, Socorro County, New Mexico, With Special Reference to the Occurrence of Oil and Gas," in *Bulletin No. 716-A* (Washington, 1921), 1–15; Frank Reeves, "Geology of the Cement Oil Field, Caddo County, Oklahoma," in *Bulletin No. 726-B* (Washington, 1922), 41–85; N. H. Darton, "Geologic Structure of Parts of New Mexico," in *Bulletin No. 726-E* (Washington, 1922), 173–275; Clarence S. Ross, "The Lacasa Area, Ranger District, North-Central Texas," in *Bulletin No. 726-G* (Washington, 1922), 303–14; Carroll E. Dobbin, "Geology of the Wiles Area, Ranger District, Texas," in *Bulletin No. 736-C* (Washington, 1923), 55–69; Frank Reeves, "Geology of the Ranger Oil Field, Texas," in *Bulletin No. 736-E* (Washington, 1923), 111–70; and W. W. Rubey, "Progress Report on a Subsurface Study of the Pershing Oil and Gas Field, Osage County, Oklahoma," in *Bulletin No. 751-B* (Washington, 1925), 23–70.

b. State Documents

Arkansas Oil and Gas Commission, annual reports to 1948; Jim G. Ferguson (commissioner of mines, manufactures, and agriculture), *Outlines of Geology, Soils and Minerals of the State of Arkansas* (Little Rock, 1920); H. W. Bell and J. B. Kerr, *The El Dorado, Arkansas Oil and Gas Field . . .* (published jointly by United States Bureau of Mines, the United States Geological Survey, the University of Arkansas, and the State Bureau of Mines, Manufacturing, and Agriculture, Little Rock, 1922); Jim G. Ferguson (commissioner of mines, manufactures, and agriculture, state of Arkansas), *Minerals in Arkansas* (Little Rock, 1922); H. W. Bell, S. P. Haury, and R. B. Kelly, *Preliminary Report on the Eastern Part of the Smackover, Arkansas Oil and Gas Field* (published by Arkansas State Bureau of Mines, Manufactures, and Agriculture, Little Rock, *circa* 1924); Arkansas Oil and Gas Commission, *General Rules and Regulations Relating to Oil and Gas, Order 2–39* (El Dorado, March, 1939); *Discussion of Petroleum Development in Arkansas* (prepared for the Arkansas State Planning Board through the facilities of the Arkansas Oil and Gas Commission, El Dorado, 1940); Arkansas Oil and Gas Commission, *Arkansas Oil and Gas, Statistical Bulletin* (El Dorado,

Oil! Titan of the Southwest

1944); and George H. Fancher and Donald K. MacKay, *Secondary Recovery of Petroleum in Arkansas—A Survey* (a report to the Fifty-sixth General Assembly of the state of Arkansas under the auspices of the Arkansas Oil and Gas Commission, El Dorado, 1946).

Kansas Corporation Commission, annual reports to 1948; *First Annual Report of the State Oil Inspector of the State of Kansas . . .* (Topeka, 1891); *Report of the State Inspector of Oils . . .* (Topeka, 1893); University Geological Survey of Kansas, *Special Report on Oil and Gas* (Topeka, 1908), IX; Raymond C. Moore and Winthrop P. Haynes, *Oil and Gas Resources of Kansas,* State Geological Survey of Kansas *Bulletin No. 3,* (Topeka, 1917); A. E. Fath, *Geology of the El Dorado Oil and Gas Field, ibid., Bulletin No. 7,* (Lawrence, 1922); L. W. Kesler, *Oil and Gas Resources of Kansas in 1927, ibid., Mineral Resources Circular 1, Bulletin No. 11* (Topeka, June 1, 1928); Kenneth K. Landes and Raymond P. Keroher, *Geology and Oil and Gas Resources of Logan, Gove, and Trego Counties, Kansas, ibid., Mineral Resources Circular No. 11,* XL (1939); Walter A. Ver Wiebe, *Western Kansas Oil and Gas Developments During 1938, ibid., Mineral Resources Circular No. 13* (April 15, 1939); Walter A. Ver Wiebe, *Exploration for Oil and Gas in Western Kansas during 1941, ibid., Bulletin No. 42* (Topeka, 1942); *ibid., 1942, Bulletin No. 48* (Lawrence, 1948); *ibid., 1943, Bulletin No. 54* (Lawrence, 1944); *ibid., 1944, Bulletin No. 56* (Lawrence, 1945); John Mark Jewett and George E. Abernathy, *Oil and Gas in Eastern Kansas, ibid., Bulletin No. 57* (July, 1945); and Walter A. Ver Wiebe, *Exploration for Oil and Gas in Western Kansas During 1945, ibid., Bulletin No. 62* (Lawrence, 1946).

Louisiana, Department of Conservation, Minerals Division, biennial reports up to 1948. Other Louisiana items listed chronologically are: Gilbert D. Harris and A. C. Veatch, *A Preliminary Report on the Geology of Louisiana, Part V, Geology and Agriculture,* State Geological Survey Report for 1899 (Baton Rouge, *circa* 1899); other Minerals Division publications are: W. W. Scott and B. K. Stroud, "The Haynesville Oil Field," in *Bulletin No. 11* (Baton Rouge, 1922); *Conservation Laws of Louisiana Applying to Oil and Gas, Corrected to January 1, 1928* (New Orleans, *circa* 1928); *General Bulletin, Handbook* (New Orleans, 1933); *Louisiana Oil and Gas Conservation Law, Act 157, of 1940* (New Orleans, *circa* 1940); and *Special Minerals Bulletin No. 1* (Baton Rouge, 1942).

New Mexico's printed sources on oil and gas production are not so extensive as those of other Southwestern states, since development here has come in recent years. Publications of the New Mexico Oil Conservation Commission, however, are of prime importance. In addition, these

Bibliography

other state items were examined: Robert W. Ellis, *Oil and Gas in New Mexico in 1923*, University of New Mexico, Whole No. 112, Geological Series 3, *Bulletin No. 5* (Albuquerque, May, 1923); E. H. Wells, *An Outline of the Mineral Resources of New Mexico*, New Mexico School of Mines, Bureau of Mines and Mineral Resources, Circular No. 1 (Socorro, September 1, 1930), 1; E. H. Wells, *The Hobbs Field and Other Oil and Gas Areas*, Preliminary Report, *Circular No. 4* (January, 1931), 2–5, 12–14, 15–18; Dean E. Winchester, *The Oil and Gas Resources of New Mexico*, State Bureau of Mines and Mineral Resources, *Bulletin No. 9* (Socorro, 1933), 139–80; University of New Mexico Geological Series, V, No. 3, *Bulletin, Whole No. 343* (May 1, 1939) (papers presented at New Mexico oil conference); "Future Oil Possibilities of New Mexico," State Bureau of Mines and Mineral Resources, *Circular No. 12* (reprint from *Oil and Gas Journal*, February 2, 1946), 6; and *Annual Statistical Report of the Lea County Operators Committee* (Hobbs, New Mexico, 1947).

The expansion of the Oklahoma oil-producing area and oil-field control are covered by the Oklahoma Corporation Commission, annual reports to 1948. Brief references to petroleum are found in the reports of the Governor of Oklahoma to the Secretary of the Interior (Washington, 1899); *ibid.*, 1900; *ibid.*, 1904; and *ibid.*, 1906. The numerous bulletins of the Oklahoma Geological Survey also have year-by-year reports on oil production, such as Charles N. Gould, L. L. Hutchison, and Gaylord Nelson, *Preliminary Report on the Mineral Resources of Oklahoma* (Norman, November, 1908); L. L. Hutchison, "Oil and Gas," *Bulletin No. 1* (Norman, 1908); *Preliminary Report on the Rock Asphalt, Asphaltite, Petroleum and Natural Gas in Oklahoma, Bulletin No. 2* (Norman, 1911); D. W. Ohern, *Director's Biennial Report to the Governor of Oklahoma, 1912, Mineral Production of Oklahoma from 1901 to 1911, Bulletin No. 15, Parts I and II* (Norman, 1912); Frank Buttram, *The Cushing Oil and Gas Field, Oklahoma, Bulletin No. 18* (Norman, 1914); *Petroleum and Natural Gas in Oklahoma, Bulletin No. 19* (Norman, 1915); A. I. Levorsen, *Oil and Gas in Oklahoma, Geology of Seminole County, Bulletin No. 40-BB* (Norman, March, 1928); *Oil and Gas in Oklahoma, Bulletin No. 40* (3 vols., Norman, July, 1928); A. Travis, *Oil and Gas in Oklahoma, Oklahoma County, Bulletin No. 40-SS* (Norman, May, 1939).

Reports of the Texas Railroad Commission, Oil and Gas Division, up to 1948. Other miscellaneous state publications are: E. T. Dumble, "Mineral Oil," in *Second Annual Report of the Geological Survey of Texas, 1890* (Austin, 1891); William Battle Phillips, *Texas Petroleum, Bulletin No. 5*, University of Texas, Mineral Survey *Bulletin No. 1* (July,

Oil! Titan of the Southwest

1900), 1–9; William Battle Phillips, *The Fuels Used in Texas,* Bureau of Economic Geology and Technology, *Bulletin No. 307* (Austin, 1913); Railroad Commission of Texas, *Oil and Gas Circular No. 10, An Act Regulating Pipe Lines Together with Rules and Regulations* (Austin, circa 1919); *ibid., Oil and Gas Circular No. 11—Revised, Oil and Gas Conservation Law and Rules and Regulations for the Conservation of Crude Oil and Natural Gas* (Austin, 1920); *ibid., New Oil Fields, Discovered in Texas, During 1937* (Austin, 1937); *ibid., Report on the Rodessa Oil Field* (Engineering Department of the Railroad Commission, December 15, 1937); *Texas Oil and Gas Conservation Laws . . .* (mimeographed, Austin, February 5, 1937); Railroad Commission of Texas annual reports on the Panhandle Oil and Gas Field, 1937, 1938, 1939 (Austin); *ibid., Texas Oil and Gas Conservation Laws . . .* (Austin, 1940); and *Texas Mineral Resources,* University of Texas Publication, No. 4301 (August, 1946).

NEWSPAPERS

Regional newspapers, contemporary with neighboring oil-field development, present aspects of oil history—community prosperity, town building, and thriving business enterprises—not found elsewhere. General contemporary accounts (often day by day), too numerous to itemize here, have appeared in such metropolitan newspapers as the Kansas City *Times* (the Mid-Continent area), Topeka *Commonwealth* (particularly Kansas oil fields); Tulsa *World* and *Tribune* (Mid-Continent oil fields and especially Oklahoma); Oklahoma City *Daily Oklahoman* and *Times* (Oklahoma fields); Wichita Falls, Texas, *Times* (on Electra, Burkburnett, and North Texas); the Amarillo, Texas, *Globe* and *News* (the Panhandle oil and gas fields); the San Angelo, Texas, *Standard Times* and *Morning Times* (Permian Basin oil fields); Fort Worth, Texas, *Star-Telegram* and *Record* (West Texas oil fields); Dallas *Herald* and *Morning News;* Houston *Post* (general Texas oil news); Galveston *News* (Gulf Coast oil news); New Orleans *Picayune* (southern Louisiana oil fields); and Shreveport *Journal* (Northern Louisiana and Arkansas oil fields).

Other single-item oil-field accounts are listed chronologically. Oil wells near Nacogdoches, in *South-Western,* September 12, 1866; Texas as an oil region, in *Flake's Weekly Bulletin,* Galveston, Texas, May 23, 1866; tar spring near Paola, Kansas, in *Kansas Daily State Record,* Topeka, December 22, 1870; oil near Ness post office, in Dodge City *Times,* June 15, 1878; oil in western Oklahoma Territory, in Woodward *Jeffersonian,* April 26, 1895; oil at Sour Lake, Texas, in Houston *Morning Star,* February 23, 1898; oil near Ardmore, Oklahoma, in El Reno *News,* Sep-

Bibliography

tember 14, 1899; oil well east of Oklahoma City, in *Cherokee Messenger* (Cherokee, Woods County), March 31, 1901; on Spindletop and Beaumont enterprises, oil edition, Beaumont *Daily Enterprise,* January 10, 1901, and August 20, 1901; oil at Red Fork, in Tulsa *Democrat,* August 16, 1901; "Early Days at Sour Lake", Houston *Post-Dispatch,* July 15, 1903; near-by oil field, oil edition, *Weekly Examiner,* Bartlesville, Indian Territory, December 26, 1903; Cushing field, Guymon *Herald,* February 6, 1913; Cushing oil field, Kingfisher *Weekly Star and Free Press,* April 24, 1913; oil wells at Cushing field, Guymon *Herald,* September 11, 1913; oil land sale at Cushing oil field, in Blackwell *Times-Record,* January 17, 1918; Cushing oil-field reports, *ibid.,* September 4, 1919; the No. 1 Rogers well and development of the Mexia oil field, in Mexia *Evening News,* November 20, 22, 23, 24, 26, and 29, and December 3, 9, 1920, and January 3, 5, 8, 17, February 4, 12, and May 9, 1921; oil wells at Garber, in Blackwell *Morning Tribune,* September 20, 1928; oil drilling in Payne County, *ibid.,* April 25, 1929; oil and gas at Burbank, *ibid.,* March 25, 1931; "Taken From Our Files," in Burkburnett *Star,* June 17, 1932; oil production in the Burbank Field, Blackwell *Morning Tribune,* September 17, 1932; Sinclair-Prairie Oil Company at Garber, *ibid.,* October 12, 1932; "Records Indicate Indians Need Help," in Muskogee *Phoenix,* Muskogee, Oklahoma, February 5, 1939; gas well at Ponca City, in Ponca City *News,* September 10, 1939; Electra oil field celebration, in Electra *News,* March 28, 1946.

Books

There is no dependable objective history of the petroleum industry, either of the nation as a whole or of the Southwest. For the most part, books on petroleum production are either technical, professional, or highly colored popular accounts, with only fragments of information for the historian. The following selected list, however, includes those volumes that contain general state summaries, statistical tables, maps, and sketches of oil-producing areas and fields.

General: Frederick Law Olmsted, *A Journey Through Texas . . .* (New York, 1857); *Derrick's Hand-Book of Petroleum* (4 vols., Oil City, Pa., 1898–1919), indispensable for early-day operators, and brief mention of Southwestern production; Edward Gaylord Bourne (ed.), *Narratives of the Career of Hernando de Soto . . .* (2 vols., New York, 1904); Raymond Foss Bacon and William Allen Hamor, *The American Petroleum Industry* (2 vols., New York, 1916), relating to large petroleum companies in Vol. I, 260–70, Oklahoma petroleum and the principles of cracking, Vol. II, 554 ff.; Roswell H. Johnson, *Legal and Economic Fac-*

Oil! Titan of the Southwest

tors in the Conservation of Oil and Gas (Washington, 1917); J. C. Yancey, *Why and Where Oil Is Found* (n.p., 1919), a popular account about North Texas prospecting, producing, and oil-field promotion; Victor Ross, *The Evolution of the Oil Industry* (Garden City, New York, 1920), on drilling and drilling terms; Captain J. H. Thompson and Sir Boverton Redwood, *Handbook of Petroleum* (revised and added to by Major A. Cooper-Key, London, 1922), 35–50, explanation of terms, steam engine, boiler, bull-wheel, sand reel, etc.; V. R. Garfias, *Petroleum Resources of the World* (New York, 1923), 14–17, including the Mid-Continent area; Isaac F. Marcosson, *The Black Golconda* (New York, 1924), generally, the Southwestern oil industry; Victor E. Kulp, *Cases on Oil and Gas* (St. Paul, 1942); Ernest Raymond Lilley, *The Oil Industry, Production, Transportation, Resources, Refining, Marketing* (New York, 1925), 212–24, Mid-Continent area and Texas.

Ray C. Capes, *The Oil Royalty Analyzed* (Tulsa, 1929), an informal explanation; *Structure of Typical American Oil Fields* (2 vols., Chicago, 1929), both volumes carry sketches of each Southwestern state's oil fields; Leonard M. Logan, *The Stabilization of the Petroleum Industry* (Norman, 1930), chaps. III and IV, problems of production and proration; Ralph Arnold and William J. Kemnitzer, *Petroleum in the United States and Possessions* (New York and London, 1931), chaps. V, VII, VIII, X, oil production in the Mid-Continent area, the Gulf Coast, elsewhere in Texas and New Mexico; Granville Cubage, *Oil, A Handbook for Reference: A Study of Lloyd Oil Corporation of Fort Worth, Texas* (Fort Worth, 1931), a popular explanation of the oilman's terms and techniques; Edward Petty, *Developments in the Petroleum Refining Industry as Related to Overproduction of Crude Oil* (Norman, 1931); John W. Leonard *et al.*, *Romance of American Petroleum and Gas* (2 vols., New York, n.d.), II, chap. VIII, North Central Texas, 213–20, Mid-Continent area; Northcutt Ely, *The Oil and Gas Conservation Statutes* (Washington, 1933).

Wilbur F. Cloud, *Petroleum Production* (Norman, 1937), technical but excellent coverage of oil-field development, oil-well care, pumping, and repressuring; *Legal History of Conservation of Oil and Gas* (a symposium, published by the Section of Mineral Law of the American Bar Association, Chicago, December, 1938); Max W. Ball, *This Fascinating Oil Business* (Indianapolis, 1940), a brilliant explanation of the oilman's techniques, machines, and procedures; Ronald Shuman, *The Petroleum Industry, An Economic Survey* (Norman, 1940), general discussion of production and refining; J. Paul Getty, *History of the Oil Business of George F. and J. Paul Getty, 1903–1939* (n.p., 1941), 37–38; Gerald

Bibliography

Forbes, *Flush Production* . . . (Norman, 1942), in the Gulf Southwest; Leonard M. Fanning, *Our Oil Resources* (New York and London, 1945); John Floherty, *Flowing Gold, The Romance of Oil* (Philadelphia and New York, 1945), a readable popular account, including such subjects as the Big Inch, oil at war, and refining; D. Thomas Curtin, *Men, Oil and War* (Chicago, 1946), the petroleum industry in the Middle West during World War II; Charles Morrow Wilson, *Oil Across the World* (New York, London, and Toronto, 1946), on pipe-lining; *Oil for Victory* (by editors of *Look,* New York and London, 1946), pictorial history of the importance of petroleum during World War II; Walace Hawkins, *El Sal del Rey* (Austin, 1947); and *Petroleum Facts and Figures* (American Petroleum Institute, Baltimore and New York, 1928–47).

Arkansas: John P. ("Slim") Jones, *Ten Years in the Oil Fields* (El Dorado, Arkansas, *circa* 1926); W. C. Spooner, *Oil and Gas Geology of the Gulf Coastal Plain in Arkansas, Bulletin No. 2* (Little Rock, 1935), excellent summaries on El Dorado and Smackover.

Kansas: L. Wallace Duncan, *History of Neosho and Wilson Counties, Kansas* (Fort Scott, 1902), containing sketch on early Kansas oil discoveries; Matthews and McMahan, *Handbook, Kansas Oil Field . . .* (n.p., *circa* 1904), 9–10; F. O. Williams, *In the Heart of the Oil Fields* (printed by the Neodesha *Register,* Neodesha, Kansas, 1904); William C. Connelley, *A Standard History of Kansas and Kansans* (5 vols., Chicago and New York, 1918), II, 1005–1007; and George F. Thompson, *Fields of Fortune: A History of the Discovery and Development of Butler County's Oil and Gas Fields* (Wichita, Kansas, 1947).

Oklahoma: T. O. Bosworth, *Geology of the Mid-Continent Oil Fields, Kansas, Oklahoma, and Northern Texas* (New York, 1906), 7–27, 62–64, 103–27, 162–222; E. R. Perry and L. L. Hutchison, *History, Geology, and Statistics of the Oklahoma Oil and Gas Fields* (n.p., *circa* 1908); D. W. Ohern and Robert E. Garrett, *Ponca City Oil and Gas Field* (Norman, 1912); L. C. Snyder, *Petroleum and Natural Gas in Oklahoma* (Oklahoma City, 1913); Rice E. Lyons, *The Oil Operator in Oklahoma* (New York, *circa* 1917); Robert Watson Clark, *Oil and Gas Developments in Okmulgee County* (Norman, 1926); Lerona Rosamond Morris (ed.), *Oklahoma Yesterday-Today-Tomorrow* (Guthrie, 1930); and *Oklahoma, the State that Oil Built* (American Petroleum Institute, New York, 1947).

Texas: Beaumont *A Guide to the City and Its Environs* (American Guide Series, Houston, n.d.); John P. ("Slim") Jones, *Borger, the Little Oklahoma* (n.p., n.d.), realistic and generally authentic; Florence Stratton, *The Story of Beaumont* (Houston, n.d.); Mrs. George Langston, *History of Eastland County* (Austin, 1904); Reid Sayers McBeth, *Pio-*

435

Oil! Titan of the Southwest

neering the *Gulf Coast, a Story of the Life and Accomplishments of Captain Anthony F. Lucas* (New York, 1918); *Ranger, Texas, and the Ranger Oil Field* (Producers Development Company, Huntington, West Va., 1919), a booklet of early-day Ranger; George R. Kelley, oil editor, Fort Worth *Star-Telegram, Oil and Gas in Texas* (Fort Worth, 1920), refineries, 13–14; *A Book of Facts. Martial Law in East Texas. What It Has Meant to the State and Nation* (East Texas Chamber of Commerce, Longview, Texas, January 9, 1932); Harry Harter, *East Texas Oil Parade* ... (San Antonio, 1934), a dependable popular narrative; *Texas Almanac* (volumes for 1925–48, Dallas); and Boyce House, *Were You in Ranger?* (Dallas, 1935), highly colored.

Donald C. Barton and George Sawtelle (eds.), *Gulf Coast Oil Fields, A Symposium on the Gulf Coast Cenozoic* (Tulsa, 1936), technical but with sketches on the "Conroe Oil Field" and "Sugarland Oil Field," 790–93, 709–11; Ruel McDaniel, *Some Ran Hot* (Dallas, 1939), an account of the "hot oil" racket; C. A. Warner, *Texas Oil and Gas Since 1543* (Houston, 1939), detailed chronology and geological discussion of Texas oil and gas fields; *Port Arthur* (*American Guide Series*, Houston, 1940); Martin W. Schwettman, *Santa Rita* (Texas State Historical Association, Austin, 1943), on Santa Rita well and West Texas; and *Texas Mineral Resources* (Bureau of Economic Geology, University of Texas Publication, *No. 4301*, January 1, 1943, Austin), 179–87.

PERIODICALS

a. Learned Society and Scientific Journals

Among the learned society and scientific journals, the publications of the American Institute of Mining and Metallurgical Engineers (New York), the bulletins of the American Association of Petroleum Geologists (Tulsa), and the Yearbooks of the National Oil Scouts Association (and mimeographed reports, Baton Rouge, Southwest Louisiana, and Southern Louisiana Oil Scouts Associations) present dependable summaries of oil development in every part of the Southwest.

Articles in other journals used in this study, grouped according to states and by subject topics, and listed chronologically, include:

Gulf Coast: Robert T. Hill, "The Beaumont Oil Field, with Notes on Other Oil Fields of the Texas Region," reprinted from *Journal of the Franklin Institute* (Philadelphia, 1902); Virginia Bradley, "The Petroleum Industry of the Gulf Coast Salt Dome Area," in *Economic Geography*, Vol. XV, No. 4 (October, 1939), 395; Gerald Forbes, "Jennings, First Louisiana Salt Dome Pool," in Louisiana *Historical Quarterly*, Vol. XXIX,

Bibliography

No. 2 (April, 1946), 496–509; Charlie Jeffries, "Reminiscences of Sour Lake," in *Southwestern Historical Quarterly,* Vol. L, No. 1 (July, 1946), 1. And in northern Louisiana, Gerald Forbes, "A History of Caddo Oil and Gas Field," in Louisiana *Historical Quarterly,* Vol. XXIX, No. 29 (January, 1946).

Oklahoma: G. E. Condra, "Opening of the Indian Territory," in American Geographic Society *Bulletin,* Vol. XLIX, No. 6 (June, 1907), 321; James H. Gardner, "The Oil Pools of Southern Oklahoma and Northern Texas," reprint from *Economic Geology,* Vol. X, No. 5 (July-August, 1915); Sidney Powers, "Healdton Oil Field," in *Economic Geology,* Vol. XII (October, 1917), 594–606; Muriel H. Wright, "First Oklahoma Oil Was Produced in 1859," in *Chronicles of Oklahoma,* Vol. IV, No. 4 (December, 1926), 320; "Northwestern Oklahoma," in *Journal of Geology,* Vol. XXXIX (February, 1931), 117–32; Gerald Forbes, "Oklahoma Oil and Indian Land Tenure," reprint from *Agricultural History* (October, 1941); Gilbert L. Robinson, "Transportation in Carter County, 1913–1914," in *Chronicles of Oklahoma,* Vol. XIX (December, 1941), 368–72; and John W. Morris, "Oklahoma Oil Fields," in *Economic Geology,* Vol. XIX (April, 1943), 129–35.

Texas: C. A. Warner, "Texas and the Oil Industry," in *Southwestern Historical Quarterly,* Vol. L, No. 1 (July, 1946), 1.

North Texas: Loy William Hartsfield, "A Brief History of Breckenridge and the Stephens County Oil Fields," in *West Texas Historical Association Year Book,* Vol. XXI (July, 1936), 100; Boyce House, "Spindletop," in *Southwestern Historical Quarterly,* Vol. L, No. 1 (July, 1946), 36; John D. Palmer, "Glimpses of the Desdemona Oil Boom," in *West Texas Historical Association Year Book,* Vol. XV (October, 1938), 48; and Abby Wheelis Cooper, "Electra, A Texas Oil Town," in *Southwestern Historical Quarterly,* Vol. L, No. 1 (July, 1946), 44.

Texas Panhandle: Charles N. Gould, "The Beginnings of the Panhandle Oil and Gas Field," in the *Panhandle-Plains Historical Review, 1935,* Vol. VIII (Canyon, 1935); Col. Ernest O. Thompson, "Summary of the Development of the Panhandle Field under Conservation Regulations", *ibid., 1939,* Vol. XII (1939), 13; N. D. Bartlett, "Discovery of the Panhandle Oil and Gas Field," *ibid.,* 48; and L. R. Hagy, "History of the Development and General Geology of the Panhandle Field of Texas," *ibid.,* 55.

West Texas: Naomi Hatton Kincaid, "Oil Development in the Abilene Area," in *West Texas Historical Association Year Book,* Vol. XXI (October, 1945), 20.

Conservation: Ely Northcutt, "The Conservation of Oil," in *Harvard*

Oil! Titan of the Southwest

Law Review, Vol. LI, No. 7 (May, 1938), 1209; Kenneth Culp Davis and York Y. Willbern, "Administrative Control of Oil Production in Texas," in *Texas Law Review*, Vol. XXII, No. 2 (February, 1944), 154–55; James P. Hart, "Oil, the Courts, and the Railroad Commission," in *Southwestern Historical Quarterly*, Vol. XLIV, No. 3 (January, 1941), 303; and Wilfred D. Webb, "The Interstate Oil Compact—Theory and Practice," in *Southwestern Social Science Quarterly*, Vol. XXI, No. 4 (March, 1941), 293.

Miscellaneous: C. Stuart Johnston, "The Origin of Petroleum," in *Panhandle-Plains Historical Review, 1939*, Vol. XII (1939), 7; and J. Edgar Pew, "Story of a Useful Life," in American Petroleum Institute *Quarterly* (April, 1947).

Trade Journals are filled with detailed daily accounts of prospecting, drilling, oil-field development, and refining. Among those I examined are *Drilling*, 1943–47; *Fuel Oil Journal* (changed later to *Oil Journal*), 1912–28; *Gulf Coast Oil News*, 1917; *Magazine of the New York Petroleum Exchange*, 1920; *National Petroleum News*, 1919–46; *Oil*, 1943–45; *Oil and Gas Journal*, 1910–48; *Oil Investors' Journal*, 1902–10; *Oil News*, 1921; *Oil Trade*, 1924–26; *Oil Weekly*, 1916–47 (*World Oil* after 1947); *Petroleum Engineer*, 1926–46; *Petroleum Age*, 1922–28; *Petroleum Reporter*, 1929–34; *Petroleum Review* (published at London, England), 1905–18; *Texas Oil*, 1946–47; *Transactions of the American Institute of Mining Engineers*, 1896–1924; *World Petroleum*, 1935–42. Company magazines from which data were taken are *Conoco Magazine* (Continental Oil Company), *Humble Way* (Humble Oil and Refining Company), *Lamp* (Standard Oil Company of New Jersey), *Link* (Carter Oil Company), *Lion Oil News* (Lion Oil Company), *Magnolia Oil News* (Magnolia Petroleum Company), *Our Sun* (Sun Oil Company), *Pure Oil News* (Pure Oil Company), *Service* (Cities Service Company), and *Texaco Star* (The Texas Company).

b. Popular Magazines

F. S. Barde, "The Oil Fields and Pipe Lines of Kansas," in *The Outlook*, Vol. LXXX (May 6 and June 17, 1905); "Black Curse of the Osages," in *Literary Digest*, Vol. LXXXIX (April 3, 1926), 42–44; Mody C. Boatright, "Oil by Hook or Crook," reprint from *Southwest Review*, Vol. XXXI (Spring, 1946); Charles E. Bowles, "Texas—Yesterday, Today, and Tomorrow," in *The Independent Monthly*, Vol. II (May, 1931), 12; Bowles, "Oklahoma's Oil Production," in *Oklahoma*, Vol. I (April, 1927); Stonewall Brown, "A Fortune in Oil—The Promoter Speaks," in *The Atlantic Monthly*, Vol. CXLI (January, 1928), 96; "Continental Oil," in

438

Bibliography

Fortune, Vol. XIX (June, 1939), 71; "Cottingham No. 1," in *Time,* Vol. XLIII (April 3, 1944), 78–80; Carrie J. Crouch, "The Oil Fields of Texas," in *National Republic,* Vol. XX (February, 1933), 6–7, 24, 28; D. T. Day, "Oil Fields of Texas and California," in *National Geographic,* Vol. XII (June, 1901), 276–78; E. DeGolyer, "Anthony F. Lucas and Spindletop," in *Southwest Review,* Vol. XXXI (Fall, 1945), 83; Joseph S. DeRamus, "Chin Deep in Mud and Oil," in *Rock Island Magazine,* Vol. XXII (April, 1927), 5; W. R. Draper, "Depression in the Osage," in *Outlook,* Vol. CLX (January 27, 1932), 113–14; Gerald Forbes, "The Passing of the Small Oil Man," in *The Southern Economic Journal,* Vol. VII (October, 1940), 204; S. W. Geiser, "Benjamin Taylor Kavanaugh, and the Discovery of East Texas Oil," reprinted from *Field and Laboratory,* Vol. XII (June, 1944).

Mrs. Dorothy (Childs) Hagner, "Oklahoma City, City of Flowing Gold," in *Travel,* Vol. LXVIII (April, 1937), 44–46; C. M. Harger, "Kansas Battles for Its Oil Interests," in *Review of Reviews,* Vol. XXI (April 1905), 471–74; G. D. Harris, "Oil in Texas," in *Science,* Vol. XIII (New Series, April 26, 1901), 666–67; Boyce House, "Rip-Roaring Days in the Oil Fields," in *Southwest Review,* Vol. XXX (Summer, 1945); Florence Howard, "Black Gold in Oklahoma," in *Review of Reviews,* Vol. LXXX (September, 1929), 142–44; L. L. Hutchison, "Mid-Continent Field for 1909," in *Sturm's Oklahoma Magazine,* Vol. IX (June, 1909), 69–73; Walter W. Liggett, "Whoopee in Oklahoma," in *Plain Talk,* Vol. XI (June, 1930), 641; "Martial-Law, Medicine for the Sick Oil Industry," in *Literary Digest,* Vol. CX (August 29, 1931), 3–4; P. J. R. McIntosh, "The Wonder Story of Texas Oil," in *Bunker's Monthly,* Vol. II (October, 1928), 490–98; "Monsieur Houdry's Invention," in *Fortune,* Vol. XIX (February, 1939), 56; G. H. Montague, "Standard Oil Co. and the Pipe Line," in *Yale Review,* Vol. XVI (August, 1907), 156–71; "Militia Bill's Latest," in *Outlook,* Vol. CLVIII (August 19, 1931), 486.

"Oil Wells Black Gold Rush," in *Popular Mechanics,* Vol. LXXXIII (March, 1945), 65–69; "Osage Oil Wealth Fading," in *Literary Digest,* Vol. CXIII (May 14, 1932), 43; Roderick Peattle, "Hunting Oil in Oklahoma," in *Atlantic Monthly,* Vol. CXXIX (May, 1922), 630–41; Charles Leroy Reed, "Oklahoma's Oil Field," in *Sturm's Oklahoma Magazine,* Vol. IX (October, 1909), 68; Edward Earl Sparling, "Oil Fields in Oklahoma," in *Outlook,* Vol. CLVII (February 11, 1931), 214–17, 236–38; "The Beaumont Oil Well," in *Scientific American,* Vol. LXXXIV (February 2, 1901), 74–75; "The Magic Knock of Fortune," in *Literary Digest,* Vol. XLVIII (March 14, 1914), 568; "Times Do Change—Especially in Laredo," in *The Rig and Reel Magazine,* Vol. LX (July, 1927), 10; Ed-

Oil! Titan of the Southwest

ward R. Treherne, "The Great Texas Oil Field," in *Cosmopolitan*, Vol. XXXI (July, 1901), 252–60; "Turning the Oil Tide with Rifles," in *Literary Digest*, Vol. CX (August 15, 1931), 6.

MISCELLANEOUS

Agricultural, Financial, Commercial, Industrial and Economic Survey of Longview and Gregg County, Texas (prepared by Longview Chamber of Commerce, July 1, 1945); *A Transcript of the Discussion Covering The East Texas Oil Field* (sponsored by the East Texas Geological Society and the Dallas Petroleum Geologists, Dallas, 1932); *Dallas—Oil Center* (published by Industrial Department, Chamber of Commerce, Dallas, *circa* 1940); Robert H. Dott, director, Oklahoma Geological Survey, "When Gushers Are Liabilities," in the files of the Oklahoma Geological Survey; *Facts About The Electra Oil Field* (Chamber of Commerce and Agriculture, Electra, 1923); Kenneth Foree, Jr., *Citizen of Luling* (booklet, Luling, 1947); George A. Hill, Jr., "The Essential Elements in the Economic and Social Development of Texas," address delivered December 8, 1939, at Austin; Houston, *A Guide and Book of Information on the Texas Metropolis* (published by *Houston Magazine*, official publication of the Chamber of Commerce, Houston, *circa* 1940); *Important Facts About Texas Oil* (prepared by The Texas Mid-Continent Oil and Gas Association, Dallas, *circa* 1937).

Kilgore, A Modern City in a Forest of Derricks (Chamber of Commerce, Kilgore, Texas, *circa* 1944); Clarel B. Mapes, "A Review of the Petroleum Industry in Oklahoma" (annual report, Mid-Continent Oil and Gas Association, Tulsa, 1929); Marcel Mitzakis, *The Oil Encyclopedia* (supplement to *Petroleum World*, August, 1912), 95; "Martial Law at Borger," in *Report of the Adjutant General of the State of Texas for the Fiscal Year, September 1,1929, to August 31, 1930; Oil and Gas in Oklahoma* (prepared and sponsored by Kansas-Oklahoma Division, Mid-Continent Oil and Gas Association, Oklahoma Stripper Well Association, and members of the Independent Petroleum Association of America, in Oklahoma, n.p., *circa* 1942); *New Mexico, A Guide to the Colorful State* (W.P.A., *American Guide Series*, New York, 1940); Glenn Patchett, "The Cushing Oil Field" (MS, Mid-Continent Oil and Gas Association, n.d.); Joseph E. Pogue, *Economics of the Petroleum Industry* (pamphlet, New York, 1939); *Post-War Planning Report, Seminole and Seminole County, Oklahoma* (Seminole Chamber of Commerce, Oklahoma State Planning and Resources Board, University of Oklahoma, March 10, 1945); Ira Rinehart, *Report on the Oil Situation in North Central Oklahoma* (Tulsa, 1922).

Bibliography

Spindletop, A Texas Titan (American Petroleum Institute, January, 1945); *Texas—From a Republic to an Economic Empire* (The Republic National Bank of Dallas, Dallas, 1945); *Texas Oil and Gas, 1947* (Texas Mid-Continent Oil and Gas Association, Dallas, August, 1947); *ibid., 1948* (Dallas, 1948); *The Petroleum Almanac* (National Industrial Conference Board, New York, 1946); *The Plan Rules and Regulations of the Committee on Conservation and Conciliation of the Kansas-Oklahoma Division of the Mid-Continent Oil and Gas Association* (Tulsa, 1921); *The Seminole Supplier*, Vol. II, No. 8 (Seminole, Oklahoma, September, 1946); *West Texas Today* (booklet issued by West Texas Chamber of Commerce, 1944–46).

Index

Abernathy, M. D.: 314

Abilene, Texas: well drilled at, 1890, 144–45; prospecting near, 1940, 331

Adger, Ellison M.: 96

Alabama Gulf Coast refineries: 385

Aldrich, R. W.: 155–56

Allen, Okla.: 390

Allen, Robert: quoted, 346

Allen County, Kan.: 33

Allowe, Ind. Terr.: 88

Almeda, Okla.: 196

Amarillo, Texas: world's major gas field by 1934, 274; Panhandle oil to, 279; oil's impact on, 401

Amarillo Oil Company: organized, 272; gas well of, 1917, 272

Amerada Petroleum Company: buys Osage lease, 201; sketch of, 201–202 (n. 28); Seminole City oil property, 239; Greater Seminole storage policy, 244; acquires Eddy County, N. M., property, 301

American Association of Petroleum Geologists: 190

American Institute of Mining Engineers: 375

American petroleum industry: production, 1914, 143; employees of, 179 (n. 24); four-fold, 182; companies, 1919, 187 (n. 7); yield, 1922, 190; rising importance of, 207–208; production, 1941, 339; in World War II, 339 ff.; daily yield, 340; production, 1945, 342–43; production, 1938, 347; effectiveness of, in World War II, 349–50; yield, 1945, 351; contribution to World War II, 367; contribution to U. S., 393–94; tax payments of, 394–95; profits of, 396 (n. 15); present practices of, 406

American Petroleum Institute: sketch of, 262 (n. 32); co-operates with F. O. C. V., 372–73; in Ft. Worth meeting, 1924, 374

American Well Works Company: 54

Anahuac oil field, Texas: discovered, 1935, 330; importance of, 400

Anderson, G. E.: 250

Anderson County, Texas: oil found in, 221; oil in, 325

Anderson-Prichard Oil Company: 267 (n. 44)

Andrews County, Tex.: University of Texas land in, 290; oil found in, 1929, 300

Anse la Butte, La.: 74

Anti-Market-Demand Act (Texas, 1931): 370

Arcadia Parish, La.: 72

Archbold, John D.: 34

Archer County, Tex.: exploration in, 114; in North Texas oil area, 1918, 163; oil in, 220

Ardmore, Okla.: 316; refinery at, 390; oil production near, 1941, 340; oil's influence on, 402

Ardmore Independent Oil Producers Organization: 130

Arkansas: oil rank of, 1922, 185; southwestern oil development, 213; oil rank, 1925, 219; development, 1937, 335–36; southwestern, exploration in, 1937, 336; oil yield, 1947, 337; 1941, 339; oil rank, 1945, 342; 1947, 382; major oil fields, 1947, 383; refineries in, 1948, 384; oil from, to Gulf Coast, 387; highway taxes, 1947–48, 395

Arkansas City, Kan.: 390

Arkansas Fuel Oil Company: 314 (n. 20)

Arkansas Gas and Fuel Corporation: 311

442

Index

Index

Caddo Lake, La.: 96

Caddo Levee Board land sales: 99

Caddo oil and gas field, La.: discovery, 1906, 96; development of, by 1908, 97; gas used at, 1908, 97; gas wells, 97–98; production of, 1907, 98; gas wasted at, 98 ff.; development, 1908, 99; The Texas Co. pipe line, 101; expansion, 102, 328

Cain, William E.: 312

Caldwell, C. M.: Ranger leases of, 148–49; Breckenridge oil operator, 166

Caldwell, J. L.: 60

Caldwell County, Tex.: 222

California: early oil fields of, *viii*; oilmen from, at Spindletop, 60; oil rank, 1924, 231; supports the Compact, 1935, 376

California Oil Company: leases, in Stephens County, 164

Calliham, Tex.: 222

Calvert, Vern: 132

Cameron Parish, La.: 338, 340

Camp Hill oil field, Tex.: 325

Campbell, W. E.: 90

Canadian River Gas Company: 279

Cap Rock Oil & Gas Corporation: 302

Capshaw, Fred: 256

Carbon-black industry: Panhandle, 279–80; in 1939, 332

Carey, W. L.: Caddo oil well, 164

Carll, John F.: 5–6 & n. 6

Carmody, Arthur R.: 399 (n. 20)

Caroll, G. W.: 52

Carpenter, Everett Z.: maps Augusta, Kansas, 192; Okla. geologist, 193; Empire geologist, 193

Carr, Nelson F.: 23

Carr City oil field, Okla.: 233

Carruth, J. W.: 159

Carson County, Tex.: leasing in, 1919, 275; oil industry of, 275; oil in, 276, 278; oil storage in, 279

Carter, Amon G.: 292 (n. 16)

Carter, Barney: North Central Texas oil operator, 148; at Ranger, 149 (n. 10); Texas wildcatter, 185

Carter County, Okla.: 340

Carter Oil Company: Standard Oil (N. J.) subsidiary, 40–41 (n. 21); growth in S.W., 137 (n. 42); buys Cushing crude oil, 1915, 137–38; buys Osage oil leases, 196; drills Burbank discovery well, 196; major Burbank oil producer, 198; Osage lease, 201; Greater

Seminole storage policy, 244; Okla.-Kansas oil storage, 1927, 245; supports Okla. City oil-field control, 257

Catalytic cracking: improvements in, 365 (n. 49); thermofor, El Dorado, Ark. 390

Cedar Lake oil field, Tex.: 403

Cement oil field, Okla.: 193, 335

Central Asphalt & Refining Company: 79

Chalk, Tex., oil pool: 291

Chalkey oil field, La.: opened, 1938, 338; importance of, 1941, 340

Chambers County, Tex.: 330

Champlin Refining Company: sketch of, 263 (n. 33); in suit, 263; at Enid, Okla., 290

Chanute, Kan.: oil boom, 36; oil and gas field, 1901, 38

Chanute Refining Company: 139, 390

Chapman, Tex.: 222

Chautuaqua County, Kans.: oil land leased in, 33; drilling in western, 33; oil activity in, 35; leasing in, 1905, 39; refinery in, 42

Chaves County, N. M.: 301, 338

Checotah, Okla.: 192

Chelsea, Ind. Terr.: oil wells near, 81; oil prospects near, 85; oil development near, 88

Chemical Process Company: 168

Cherokee County, Tex.: 221

Cherokee country, Ind. Terr.: 80

Cherokee Messenger: 249

Cherokee Oil & Gas Company: organized, 1884, 17; reorganized, 1895, 20

Cherokee Council approves Faucett contract: 17

Cherryvale, Kans.: oil boom, 36; oil and gas field, 1901, 38; refinery, 42

Chesley, Frank: 89 ff.

Chicago, Ill.: 279, 280

Chickasaw Oil Company: 14 ff.

Chiltipin oil field, Tex.: 331

Choate-Henshaw *et al.*: 291

Choctaw Oil & Refining Company: 16–17

Choctaws: in Oklahoma, 12; approve Faucett lease, 16–17

Church-Fields oil field, Tex.: Oct.-Dec., 1927, oil yield, 298; major 1926 discovery, 300

Cimarron Valley Pipe Line Company: 342

Cities Service Oil Company: growth in

445

Oil! Titan of the Southwest

Southwest, 141 (n. 48); Panhandle pipe line, 279, 342, 356, 357; refinery at Lake Charles, 386, 388
Claiborne Parish, La.: 215
Clardy, B. C.: 298–99
Clark, Cal.: 102 (n. 19)
Clay County, Tex.: reports of oil in, 10; gas field in, 170; oil discoveries in, 1939, 331
Clayco Oil & Pipe Line Company: 109
Clear Boggy, Ind. Terr.: 18
Cleveland, Okla.: oil discovery near, 1904, 88; oil-field development near, 88; boom, 89; quality of oil at, 95–96; oil profits of, prior to 1914, 119; refinery at, 390
Cleveland County, Okla.: 249
Cline, W. D.: 115, 401
Clinton, Dr. Fred S.: 83
Cochran, G. W.: 8
Coffeyville, Kans.: oil boom, 36; oil and gas field, 1901, 38; refinery at, 390
Colbert, Winchester: 14
Colcord, Charles F.: visits Red Fork, 84; interested in Red Fork, 87; Glenn Pool operator, 89; pres., I.P.A.A., 130 (n. 30)
Cole, William P., Jr.: 375–76
Coleman County, Tex.: 220
Coline Oil Company: in southern Okla., 192; at Okla. City, 251
Collins, Ray M.: 233 (n. 8); Greater Seminole umpire, 240; proration, 256
Colorado City, Tex.: oil field near, 285–86; refinery at, 304
Colorado City Record: 285
Col-Tex Refining Company: 304
Columbia County, Ark.: 336
Comanche County, Tex.: oil exploration in, 145; oil country of, 158; in North Central Texas oil area, 164; Humble's pipe line through, 279; 289
Common Purchaser Act: 1931, 280; Texas, 370
Comyn, Tex.: 279 ,289
Concho Refining Company: 304
Connelly, David P.: 93
Conroe, Tex. oil field: 339; discovery of, 1931, 329–30; importance of, 400
Conservation: Texas law, 1899, 48; in Greater Seminole, 1927, 244; early Okla. City efforts, 251–52; efforts, at Okla. City, 256 ff.; in East Texas, 318 ff.; objectives of, 368 ff.

Consolidated Gas Utilities Company: 279
Consolidated Oil Company: 357
Constantin Refining Company: 210
Continental Oil Company: growth in Southwest, 141 (n. 49); lube plant at Lake Charles, La., 388; refinery at Ponca City, Okla., 390
Cook, Captain Francis B.: 126
Cooke County, Tex.: reports of oil in, 10; oil field in, 220; oil discoveries in, 1939, 331
Cooper, S. B.: proposes Beaumont ship canal, 65
Corpus Christi, Tex.: 386, 389
Corsicana oil field, Tex.: early production, viii; Hamills spend Christmas in, 1900, 57; oil discovery mentioned, 169; Powell field near, 175–76; development of oil field near, 176–77; first Texas law controls, 370
Corsicana Deep Well Company: officers of, 176 (n. 15); No. 1 J. H. Burke well, 176
Corsicana Oil Development Company: 44
Corsicana Petroleum Company: plans Burkburnett drilling, 114; at Healdton, 129
Corsicana Sun: 176
Cosden Petroleum Company: increases Kansas-Okla. oil purchases, 142; cracking plant in Okla., 143; a major Burbank oil producer, 198; promotes Tonkawa test well, 203; at Garber, 205; refinery at Big Spring, 304
Cotton Bayou, La.: 96
Cotton Valley oil field, La.: 216
Courtney, H. P.: 296 (n. 26)
Cow Run Pool, Tex.: 169
Cowley County, Kan.: 334
Craig, George M.: 69–70
Crane County, Tex.: University of Texas land in, 290; oil in, 291; oil interests in, 1926, 300; Church-Fields oil pool in, 300
Cranfield oil field, Miss.: 383
Creek Country, Ind. Terr.: potential oil fields in, 81; oil pools in, 195
Creeks renew Red Fork lease, 1900: 82
Crescent, Okla.: 269
Crichton, La.: 101
Critchlow, James: 126
Crockett County, Tex.: leasing in, 287;

446

Index

447

Index

pany, 16–19; drilling problems, 19; death, 19

Featherston, C. H.: 116

Federal Oil Conservation Board: 372

Federal Petroleum Administrative Board: 376

Fell, H. B.: vice-pres. I.P.A.A., 373 (n. 17); letter, 406 (n. 27)

Fellows, W. J.: 88

Ferguson, Gov. Miriam: 323

Ferry Lake, La.: 101

Fertig, John: 34–35

Fisher, Frank: 196

Fitts oil field, Okla.: 269

Florence, Colo.: *viii*

Foard County, Tex.: 220

Fohs, J. Julius: leases Mexia land, 170–71; recommends Kilgore test well, 1915, 306

Fondren, W. W.: 104 (n. 25)

Foraker, Okla.: 196

Forest Oil Company: Standard Oil subsidiary, 34; oil-field policy, 35; sells holdings, 1901, 36 (n. 14); Iowa Park oil well, 115

Fort Bend County, Tex.: 224

Fort Scott, Kans.: oil discovery near, 28–29; gas piped to, 1887, 29; oil and gas field, 1901, 38

Fort Stockton, Tex.: 304

Fort Worth, Tex., *Record*: 148

Fort Worth, Tex.: uses Petrolia gas, 170; proration meeting at, 298; 313, 331; oil industries, 400

Fortuna Oil Company: 193

Fortune magazine: 188

Foster, Edwin B.: Osage lease of, 1896, 21; organizes Phoenix Oil Co., 1896, 21

Foster Petroleum Corporation: joins I.T.I.O. in drilling Okla. City discovery well, 1928, 250; controls early Okla. City oil field, 25

Fowler Farm Oil Company: 116 (n. 15)

Fowler, S. L.: 115 ff.

Fouke oil field, Ark.: opened, 1940, 337

Fox, Okla., oil field: 194

Francis, Sam: 20

Franklin County, Kans.: 39

Franklin, Wirt: at Healdton, 126 & n. 20; defines "independent," 106 (n. 27); organizes independents, 130; helps to organize I.P.A.A., 130 (n. 29); Healdton umpire, 132; as wildcatter, 185;

at Okla. City, 251; supports orderly oil-field development, 257–58; opposes federal oil control, 373 (n. 17); pres., I.P.A.A., 373 (n. 17)

Fred Hyer *et al.*: 291

Freestone County, Tex.: 180

Friendswood oil field, Tex.: 400

Frisco Railroad: 135

Fuel oil: 68 ff., 279

Fullerton oil field, Tex.: 383

Galbreath, Robert: visits Red Fork, 84; at Glenn Pool, 89 ff.; supports independent oilmen, 130 (n. 30); wildcatter, 185, 270

Galbreath and Company: 90

Galey, John: 56 ff., 68

Galey, Tom: 20 (n. 22); on Okla. oil investments, 119

Galt, Edward: 126 & n. 20

Garber oil field, Okla.: 190, 205–206, 369; discovery, 1917, 139; development, 139

Gardner, James H.: 306

Gary, Wright W.: 364

Garrity-Mills: 47

Gasoline plants in Texas Panhandle: 279

Gasoline: output, 1947, 385; federal tax, 1945, 395

Gates, John W.: at Spindletop, 60; enters The Texas Company, 70

Gay, George M.: 225

Gay Hill, Tex.: 224

Geologists: growing importance of, 1920, 186; estimate Okla. oil yield, 190; of Mid-Continent, 192; recent specialization of, 378

Geophysical prospecting: 380

Geophysical Research Corporation: 306

Geyer, "Spot": maps Tonkawa, 203

Ghost towns: Jakehamon, Tex., 162; White City, 403–404; Pershing, Okla., 403; Ragtown, Okla., 403

Gilliland Oil Company: 212

Gladewater, Tex.: 310

Gladys Bell Oil & Gas Company: 213

Gladys City Oil, Gas and Manufacturing Company: at Beaumont, 52–53; contract with Lucas, 53; with Guffey & Galey, 53

Glasscock County, Tex.: oil field of, 291; prospecting in, 1928, 300

Glenn Pool, Okla.: 185, 193, 219, 270, 328, 402; Texas pipe line to, 78; oil

Index

Index

Index

Index

O'Donnell, J. L.: 60
O'Donohoe, F.: 333 (n. 4)
Offshore drilling: 106
Ohern, D. W.: 193
Ohio: oilmen from, at Spindletop, 60; oil yield decline in, 185; refineries in, 391
Ohio Oil Company: buys Rodessa lease, 217; absorbes Trans-Continental, 295 (n. 24); Southwestern interests of, 295 (n. 25); acquires Eddy County, N. M., property, 301; at Maljamar, N. M., 302
Oil boom: Jennings, La., 73; Red Fork, Ind. Terr., 84–85; Tulsa, 88; Cleveland, Okla. Terr., 89; Petrolia, Tex., 109; Wichita Falls, Tex., 113; Burkburnett, Tex., 116 ff.; Ranger, Tex., 146 ff.; Desdemona, Tex., 161; Breckenridge, 165, 167; Mexia, Tex., 172–73; Corsicana, 1923, 176; El Dorado, Ark., 211–12; Seminole City, 246–47; Borger, Tex., 277–78; Kilgore, Tex., 312; Longview, Tex., 313–14
Oil and gas associations: 262 (n. 32); see also under individual names
Oil and Gas Journal: (n. 1)
Oil companies, major: production of, 1918–19, 185–86; oil yield of, 1920, 187; at Spindletop, 229; support conservation at Okla. City, 258; at Artesia, N. M., 301; at Longview, 314; installation investments, 1943, 394
Oil Creek, Pa.: *vii*
Oil industry: hazards of, 1918, 158; importance of, 1920, 186
Oil Investors' Journal: estimates Gulf Coast production, 77; appearance, 378 (n. 1)
Okesa, Okla.: 196
Okfuskee County, Okla.: 195
Oil market: Okla., increased, 1915, 134–35; since 1859, 181
Oil Trade Journal: 214
Oil Weekly: 379 (n. 1)
Oklahoma: Sun Oil Company enters, 1909, 70 (n. 7); competes with Louisiana oil, 96; oil investments in, prior to 1914, 119; leading oil producers, 1906, 119; oil yield, 1891–1913, 124; estimated oil yield, 1914, 125 (n. 15); refineries in, by 1915, 135–36; leads oil states, 174; oil yield, 1922, 183; high oil yield, 190; oil exploration in,

1922, 190–91; wells drilled in, 1922, 190–91; oil yield, 1916–1920, 195; oil rank, 1925, 219; oil yield, 1920–26, 231; southern, minor oil-field discoveries, 1921–26, 232 (n. 5); oil storage, 1927, 245; cumulative total, 1939, 269; oil exploration in, 269; oil discoveries in, 1930–34, 269; revived prospecting in, 1939, 335; oil fields reworked, 335; drilling in, 335; oil yield, 1941, 340; oil rank, 1945, 342; oil and gas control laws, 369–70; supports the Compact, 1935, 376; drilling in, 1946, 380; deep well in, 381; oil rank, 1947, 382; major oil fields, 1947, 383; refineries, 1948, 384; refineries, 390–91; oil- and gas-industry employees in, 1940, 399; oil taxes, 1907–43, 399; oil-industry employees, 402; eastern oilmen enter, 404; oil-county population increase, 404–405
Oklahoma capitol: 261 ff.
Oklahoma City, Okla.: oil excitement at, 84; oil exploration near, 1904, 88; early, 248; oil prospecting at, 248 ff.; oil mecca, 1928, 254; oil fire endangers, 260; Lincoln Terrace threatened, 265–66; refinery at, 390; oil's influence on, 402, 403
Oklahoma City oil field, Okla.: 318, 335, 340, 341, 369; discovery well, 250; oil zones, 251 ff.; oil-field expansion, 256; yield, 258; oil-field area, 1935, 268; gas waste in, 268–69
Oklahoma City Producers Association: promotes Okla. City oil-field control, 257
Oklahoma Corporation Commission: 258; hearings at Healdton, 130 ff.; estimates state oil returns, 1916–17, 186; regulations in Greater Seminole, 240; policy at Okla. City, 256; imposes Okla. City oil-field restrictions, 1930, 262; legislature supports, 369–70; oil production and control, 371
Oklahoma County, Okla.: 269
Oklahoma Geological Survey: lists oil and gas areas, 1923, 183; establishment of, 192–93; men of, 193; work of, 193
Oklahoma legislature: 265
Oklahoma Natural Gas, Light & Heat Company: 87
Oklahoma Natural Gas Company: 342

457

Index

Index

Oil! Titan of the Southwest

Shamrock Oil & Gas Company: 277

Sharp, Walter B.: drills Spindletop well, 52; Sour Lake well, 76

Shartel, John: 249

Shaw, S. F.: devises Seminole air lift, 240 (n. 27)

Shawnee, Ind. Terr.: 88

Shea, Edward F.: 236

Shell, John: 88

Shell Oil Company: 357; competes with independents, 189; at Van, 221, 306; supports Okla. City oil field proration, 258; pipe line to Yates, 299; Houston refinery, 386, 389

Shell Trading and Transport Company: 68

Shelton, J. H.: 311

Shephard, John A.: 170

Sherman County, Tex.: 276

Shreveport, La.: pipe line, 1908, 97; oil center, 403

Shreveport–El Dorado Pipe Line Company: 213

Shreveport Producing and Pumping Company: 213

Silica oil field, Kans.: 334

Sims-Sinclair: 106

Sinclair, Harry F.: 244

Sinclair Oil Corporation: Oklahoma pipe line, 136; growth, 136 (n. 40); at Garber, 1917, 139; buys Kans.Okla. oil, 142; pipe line to Corsicana, 177; as large independent, 189; major Burbank producer, 198; at Garber, 230; Mid-Continent–Gulf pipe line, 230; Kans.-Okla. storage, 1927, 245, 251, 256, 257; supports Okla. City oil field control, 258; Panhandle pipe line, 279; acquires Eddy County, N. M., leases, 301; Houston refinery, 386; Kansas refinery, 390; Marcus Hook refinery, 391

Skelly, William G.: 127 & n. 24

Skelly Oil Company: 198; organized, 127 (n. 24); as large independent, 189; at Burbank, 197; supports Okla. City oil-field control, 258; buys Eddy County, N. M., property, 301, at Maljamar, N. M., 302; Kansas refinery, 390

Skiatook, Okla.: 196

Skipper, B. A.: 314

Slaughter oil field, Tex.: 304

Slaughter-Dean oil field, Tex.: 339

Slick, T. B.: at Cushing, 119 ff.; Okla. wildcatter, 185; at Okla. City, 251, 255, 256

Sligo oil field, La.: 337

Smackover oil field, Ark.: 206, 207, 214–15, 403; development, 213, 214, 328, 335

Smith, Blake: 170 & n. 4

Smith, Lon A.: 316

Smith County, Tex.: East Texas oil field expands into, 314; oil wells closed in 1931, 320

Smitherman, C. B.: 215 (n. 24)

Smitherman-Anderson Company: 215

Snowden-McSweeney Company: leases in N. M., 302; plans Kilgore test well, 306

Socony Vacuum Oil Company: as independent, 188, 357; growth, 357 (n. 29)

Sohio Petroleum: pipe line to West Edmond, 342; trade name, 342 (n. 20)

"Sour Gas Law" (Tex.): 281

Sour Lake, Tex.: 76, 77, 78, 329, 330; company formed to drill at, 4; oil reported at, 1847, 8; Cochran lease, 1865, 8; oil development at, 75 ff.; pipe line, 78; decline, 103

South Bend, Tex.: 145, 164

South Pampa, Tex.: 277

South Plains Development Company: 329

South Plains Pipe Line Company: 279

Southerland oil field, Tex.: 331

Southern Crude Oil Purchasing Company: oil well on Hendricks ranch, 295; Winkler lease, 296; pipe line to Hendricks, 296

Southern Oil Corporation: formed, 73; pipe line to El Dorado, Ark., 213

Southern Pacific Railroad: 60

Southwest: population, 1900, 50; oil yield, 206; states' oil-yield rank, 219, 220; yield, 1945, 343; 1947, 379; drilling, 1947, 382–83; refineries, 1948, 384; oil yield, 1947, 392; highways and fuel taxes, 1945, 395; ghost towns, 304–404; oil's impacts, 405; county population increases, 405

Southwestern oil industry: in 1900, 50–51; importance of, 1917–41, 344; varied features, 392; future prospects, 406

Index

Index

The Texas Company: 320, 357; organized, 62; absorbs Producers Oil Company, 1915, 70; organization, 70 (n. 6); Port Arthur refinery, 70 (n. 6); success at Sour Lake, 76; Port Arthur refinery, 79; Port Arthur storage, 79; pipe line to Glenn Pool, 1908, 92; refinery at Port Arthur, receives Glenn Pool oil, 92; coastal pipe lines, 95; Port Arthur–Caddo pipe line, 101; at Electra, 111; Moran gas well, 114; pipe line to Burkburnett, 116; Okla. oil profits, 119; Kans. and Okla. refineries, 136; major Okla. pipe-line operator, 136; increase Kans.-Okla. oil purchases, 142; Breckenridge oil leases, 165; pipe line to Corsicana, 177; at Van, Tex., 221; Texas oil production, 1925, 229; at Hewitt, 231; Okla.-Kans. oil storage, 245; drills Burnett ranch oil well, 275; secures U. S. permits in Eddy County, N. M., 301; refinery at El Paso, 304; at Van, Tex., 306; refinery at Port Arthur, 386

Thompson, Col. E. O.: quoted, 282; 316–17, 318; appointed to Railroad Commission, 321; confers with President Roosevelt about conservation, 375

Thompson oil field, Tex.: 400

Thrall-Minerva, Tex.: 221

Tidal Osage Company: 198

Tide Water Oil Company: 93 (n. 24), 357; at Glenn Pool, 93; refinery at Bayonne, N. J., 391; see also Associated Producers Company

Titus County, Tex.: 325

Tonkawa oil field, Okla.: 190, 207, 232, 369; oil yield, 1922, 183; development, 203 ff.; leasing at, 204; gas wells at, 204; graveyard lease, 204; royalty interests, 204; pipe lines, 205

Torsion balance: definition, 219 (n. 2); for deep oil zone exploration, 327

Towanda, Kans.: oil field found at, 140; oil field of, 185

Trade journals: reports specialization, 378; rise of, 378–79 (n. 1)

Transcontinental Oil Company: 225

Trapp oil field, Kans.: 334

Trees, J. C.: Caddo oil properties, 99; Texas oil operator, 160, sketch of, 295 (n. 24)

Trout, L. E.: 249

Tucker, Dr. Hugh H.: 287, 288

Tulsa, Okla.: 313; Guffey & Galey hold property near, 33; oil boom at, 1901, 88; growth of, 91; West, refinery at, 136; Dorsey Hager sets up geology office in, 139; pipe-liners meet in, 355, 362; West, refineries at, 390; Mid-Continent "Oil Capital," 401–402; oil influences population, 403

Tulsa-Oklahoma City gas line, 1907: 92

Twin State Oil Company: Sun's, in Oklahoma, 1909, 70 (n. 7); leases Healdton property, 127

T-X-L oil field, Tex.: 383

Tyler, Tex.: oil interest at, 310; proration meeting in, 315; federal agents at, 322

Tyler County, Tex.: 10

Udden, Dr. John: 287, 288

Uncle Sam Refining Company: 42

Underwriters Producing Company: 285

Union County, Ark.: 335; county seat of, 208; new oil fields, 1940, 337

United Fruit Company: 69

United Gas Public Service Company: 217

United North & South Oil Company: 229

United Oil & Refining Company: 79

United States: proven oil reserves of, viii; oil production 1890–1922, 184; oil yield, 1922, 190; petroleum demand of, 1945, 379; refineries in, 1948, 384; oil refinery investments in, 388–89; petroleum's cash contribution to, 393

United States Bureau of Mines: reports Cushing oil field, 192; appraises West Edmond, 341–42

United States Geological Survey: 271; estimates Oklahoma oil potential, 190; promotes Indian Territory oil prospecting, 192; men of, 193; maps Healdton subsurface, 1915, 193 (n. 9)

United States Oil & Gas Company: 20

Unitization: proposed at Ft. Worth, 1924, 374; defined, 374–75; extensive use of, 375

University of Oklahoma: 193

University of Oklahoma Foundation: xii

University of Texas: oil revenue of, 290; West Texas land of, 290; oil income of, 1948, 405

Upshaw, A. M.: 12

Upshur County, Tex.: East Texas oil

465

Index

467

UNIVERSITY OF OKLAHOMA PRESS

NORMAN